D1032689

MODERN QUANTUM THEORY

A SERIES OF BOOKS IN PHYSICS

EDITORS: Henry M. Foley and Malvin A. Ruderman

Concepts of Classical Optics

John Strong

Thermophysics

Allen L. King

X-Ray Diffraction in Crystals, Imperfect Crystals, and Amorphous Bodies

A. Guinier

Introduction to Electromagnetic Fields and Waves

Dale Corson and Paul Lorrain

Modern Quantum Theory

Behram Kurşunoğlu

On the Interaction Between Atomic Nuclei and Electrons (*A Golden Gate Edition*)

H. B. G. Casimir

MODERN QUANTUM THEORY

Behram Kurşunoğlu UNIVERSITY OF MIAMI

W. H. FREEMAN
AND COMPANY

San Francisco and London

Library of Congress Catalog Card Number: 62-14196
Printed in the United States of America

TO SEVDA

PREFACE

This book is based on graduate-level courses which the author has taught for several years at the University of Miami. The original intention was an expansion of the author's lecture notes on "Nonrelativistic Quantum Mechanics," published in 1955 by the University of Miami Press. The present form differs considerably from the lecture notes. The level of the book is somewhat more advanced than the usual curricula followed in the graduate schools of most universities. It is believed that the trend toward higher standards of university education will continue and a book of the present scope and level will fill a definite gap between the usual "graduate course" and the needs for a thorough understanding of the foundations of quantum mechanics. Therefore the material contained in this book may form a near approximation to future teaching of quantum mechanics at the graduate level.

The theory of quantized fields, with the exception of quantization of massless free fields (Chapter XI), is not included, but an attempt has been made to give a systematic presentation of the modern aspects of quantum mechanics as it has developed, especially during the last fifteen years. The exclusion of quantum electrodynamics and the theory of weak interactions was dictated by the desire to meet the needs of graduate students and also of physicists in general on a rigorous level where most of the fundamentals, philosophies, and some important applications of quantum mechanics could be emphasized on a sounder basis.

The basic mathematics required for the formulation of quantum mechanics constitute the subject matter of Chapter I. The so-called ket and bra notation of Dirac, for the sake of clarity, is first introduced as column and row vectors, respectively, in finite-dimensional spaces. These rather obvious representations of ket and bra vectors in finite-dimensional spaces is extended, in later chapters, to the vectors of the infinite-dimensional spaces. The ket and bra notation is followed consistently. The author believes that such an approach may serve to appreciate the significance of an invariant way of formulating quantum laws, which provide such a powerful tool in attacking the problems in quantum as well as in classical physics. The column and row vector representation of quantum mechanical states should be regarded as the "natural notation" for them.

Chapter II is based on a direct use of the "correspondence principle" to introduce Schrödinger's equation. This chapter is, essentially, an outcome of the fact that Maxwell's equations for free electromagnetic field constitute the most immediate intersection of relativity and quantum theory, and that in them the two find a common origin.

A discussion on the necessity of infinite-dimensional spaces—together with the relevant mathematical machinery, quantum postulates, and the principle of uncertainty in Chapter III—is followed by a group-theoretical discussion of angular momentum and the rotation group in Chapter IV.

The derivation of Schrödinger's equation and Heisenberg's equations of motion based on the general transformation theory are included in Chapter V. This theory is applied to a discussion of symmetry principles of quantum dynamical systems in Chapter VI. In particular, symmetries pertaining to parity and time reversal operations are elaborated in some detail. The same chapter contains also an elementary discussion of isotopic spin, strangeness, and some simple applications to elementary particle reactions.

There are quite a few occasions where the simple harmonic oscillator and its formalism are needed for the formulation and understanding of some important concepts of quantum mechanics—for example, quantization of massless fields, the quantum distribution function, accidental degeneracy, specific heat of solids. In view of these facts it was found necessary to give a detailed presentation of the free harmonic oscillator theory. This is done in Chapter VII.

It is not, of course, usual practice to introduce the Lorentz group in a book that does not include field theory as its main topic. However, many qualitative aspects of elementary particle physics can be discussed without invoking the mathematical machinery of field theory; only a basic knowledge of the Lorentz group is sufficient to get some feeling of elementary particle events. For these reasons finite and infinite representations of the Lorentz group are presented in Chapter VIII. This is followed by a long discussion of the various symmetry properties of photon and neutrino in Chapter IX.

Dirac's wave equation—and its most important symmetry element, charge conjugation—the quantization of massless fields, and the relation of spin and statistics have been chosen as the main topics for Chapters X and XI.

The physical interpretation of quantum mechanics, with some thought experiments of Einstein and Bohr, Feynman's formulation of nonrelativistic quantum mechanics, and the concept of wave function in general are regarded as interesting topics, to be included in a book of this kind where fundamentals of the theory are emphasized more than its direct applications. Chapter XII has therefore been devoted entirely to the discussion of these topics.

It was felt that some important symmetry properties of simple systems, such as accidental degeneracy in the energy levels of the hydrogen atom and in the motion of a charge in a constant magnetic field, have been in the published literature for the appreciation of the expert alone. A rather detailed presentation of these symmetries, based on the four-dimensional orthogonal group (discussed in Chapter VIII), is given in Chapter XIII. The latter also contains a relativistic discussion of the hydrogen atom, a nonrelativistic account of the Zeeman effect, the Lamb shift (qualitatively), the multiplet structure of the levels, and so on.

In Chapter XIV, perturbation theory (including the Brillouin-Wigner expansion) is introduced in terms of integral equations and the unitary operator. Resonance transitions, and especially the derivation of the Breit-Wigner one-level formula, are also based on the integral equation method. Interaction with radiation and the nonrelativistic derivation of the Lamb shift are presented briefly in Chapter XV.

The recent interest in many-particle systems, accompanied by extensive research in this field, has enlarged their scope to such an extent that they can no longer be treated within a single chapter in a book on quantum mechanics. For this reason the discussion of many-particle systems in Chapter XVI is rather brief. However, besides a short discussion of the Hartree-Fock self-consistent field method, this book includes the quantum analogue of Liouville's equation and discusses some quantum statistical properties of many-particle systems in terms of a quantum distribution function. The distribution function of a harmonic oscillator, using the transformation function of a free harmonic oscillator given in Chapter V, is obtained and applied to a qualitative discussion of the specific heat of solids.

Chapters XVII and XVIII are devoted to the discussion of elementary and formal theory of scattering. In these chapters only the nonrelativistic theory is presented, but the operator formalism developed in the last chapter is also directly applicable to relativistic problems. Because of an important role played by Fredholm's method of integral equations in scattering problems, an operator technique for the Fredholm solution of any linear integral equation is developed. Chapter XVIII ends with an expansion of scattering amplitude as a Fredholm series and with some remarks on dispersion relations.

A large number of problems has been provided to help further understanding of quantum mechanics and also to supplement the textual material with additional concepts and applications. Some of these problems are trivial, but some require greater effort for their solutions than the more usual problems. There are also a few problems that, for the interested reader, might best be used as a topic for a paper (for example, problems 4, 6, and 19 of Section XI.5.C) rather than as a mere exercise on the subject.

The author is greatly indebted to Professor Charles Kittel of the University of California for his original suggestion, based on his reading of the 1955 lecture notes, to undertake the writing of this book. His encouragements were invaluable in this endeavor, although he is in no way responsible for its possible shortcomings. A critical reading of the manuscript by Professor Malvin Ruderman of the University of California and his various suggested improvements and kind remarks are gratefully acknowledged. Thanks are also due to Dr. M. A. Hakeem of the U. S. Naval Post-graduate School, Monterey, California, for the great help given in the proof stage of the book.

March 1962 Behram Kurşunoğlu

CONTENTS

CHAPTER I

BASIC ELEMENTS OF TRANSFORMATION THEORY

I.1. Introductory Considerations

A logical and comprehensive development of quantum theory requires the Hamiltonian formulation of classical mechanics. The Hamiltonian formalism is based on the possibility of obtaining complete information about the motion of a dynamical system when its total energy is expressed in terms of its coordinates and momenta, q_k and p_k, respectively. In principle, the knowledge of the Hamiltonian of a dynamical system, together with the initial conditions, is enough to predict, exactly, the future behavior of the system.*

The Hamiltonian form of the equations of motion can be obtained by the application of Hamilton's principle to the action function S, defined by

$$S = \int_{t_1}^{t_2} L(q_k, \dot{q}_k, t)\, dt, \qquad (I.1.1)$$

where the Lagrangian L of the dynamical system is related to the Hamiltonian by

$$H(q_k, p_k, t) = \sum_{k=1}^{n} (\dot{q}_k p_k) - L(q_k, \dot{q}_k, t). \qquad (I.1.2)$$

Hamilton's principle states that the path of a dynamical system between two prescribed positions at times t_1 and t_2 is one that makes the action S stationary for arbitrary variations of the configurations of the system. The time of travel is the same for all varied paths. It entails

---

* For a detailed and concise development of the Hamiltonian techniques, see H. Goldstein, *Classical Mechanics*, Addison-Wesley, Reading, Mass., 1950.

$$\delta S = \sum_{k=1}^{n} p_k \delta q_k \Big]_{t_1}^{t_2}$$

$$- \int_{t_1}^{t_2} \sum_k \left[\delta q_k \left(\dot{p}_k + \frac{\partial H}{\partial q_k} \right) - \delta p_k \left(\dot{q}_k - \frac{\partial H}{\partial p_k} \right) \right] dt = 0. \qquad (I.1.3)$$

Since the variations of all δq_k and δp_k are independent, the integral can vanish only if Hamilton's equations of motion,

$$\dot{q}_k = \frac{\partial H}{\partial p_k}, \qquad \dot{p}_k = -\frac{\partial H}{\partial q_k}, \qquad (I.1.4)$$

are satisfied. For fixed end points the first term on the right side in (*I.1.3*) vanishes.

In order to study the variations of the action along the path described by the equations (*I.1.4*), we may assume that the position of the dynamical system at time t_1 is fixed and that its position at a later time t_2 is described by Hamilton's equations of motion. In this case, from (*I.1.3*) we have

$$\delta S = \sum_{k=1}^{n} p_k \delta q_k,$$

which leads to a definition of the momenta of the dynamical system in the form

$$p_k = \frac{\partial S}{\partial q_k}. \qquad (I.1.5)$$

It should be noted that S has its extremum value on the path of the dynamical system, along which all the conservation theorems are satisfied.

A more general approach is the Lagrangian formulation of classical mechanics. The Lagrangian method of classical mechanics has the advantage of admitting a larger group of transformations than the Hamiltonian scheme. The Lagrangian of the dynamical system, however, is not an observable quantity. The Lagrangian of a dynamical system as a function of its coordinates and velocities can be used to calculate the momenta p_k by

$$p_k = \frac{\partial L}{\partial \dot{q}_k}. \qquad (I.1.6)$$

The two definitions of the momenta of a dynamical system, (*I.1.5*) and (*I.1.6*), are equivalent.

A unified presentation of the subject, containing all the advantages of the Lagrangian and Hamiltonian methods and also permitting further developments of the theory on a much wider scope, can be based on the use of the action function itself. This is the modern approach to quantum mechanics.

I.2. The Notion of Transformation

A very important formal and conceptual tool of theoretical physics is the concept of transformation. The most striking application of it was the Hamilton-Jacobi formulation of classical mechanics. Actually, with the experiences gained in relativity and quantum theory, we have come to believe that transformation theory is the most important method of theoretical physics.

The basic ideas of transformation theory can be enunciated in three types of transformations:

(a) *coordinate transformations*,
(b) *canonical transformations*,
(c) *gauge transformations*.

The laws of nature are invariant statements with respect to these three groups of transformations. Broadly speaking, these three groups of transformations taken together, when confirmed by experiment, become the laws of physics.

A few examples will serve to illustrate these formal constructions. In classical physics—that is, Newtonian physics as formulated by Hamilton, Jacobi, and others—the laws of motion of material particles, together with the potential energy, are sufficient for a complete description of the particle's dynamical behavior. The equations describing the motion of the dynamical system have some invariance properties. For example, the gravitational interaction of mass points and the electrostatic action of one charge on another are rotation-invariant. This is one way of saying that the total angular momentum of the system is conserved. The converse is also true: if a dynamical system has a constant total angular momentum, then it is rotation-invariant. As a generalization of these two facts, a dynamical system has a constant total angular momentum only when space rotations are recognized as a necessary group of coordinate transformations.

In both theories of gravitation and electrostatics, spherically symmetric solutions of the differential equation $\nabla^2\Phi = 4\pi\rho$ (with different ρ for gravitation and electrostatics) provide a potential function. Both types of forces can be calculated from the potential. The differential equation itself is, of course, invariant with respect to space rotations.

There are other groups of coordinate transformations pertaining to classical physics. For example, two observers in a uniform state of motion, with velocity v relative to one another, will reproduce the same result in the measurement of acceleration of an object in motion. The positions of these two observers must be related by means of Galilean transformations:

$$\begin{aligned} x' &= x + vt, \\ y' &= y, \\ z' &= z, \\ t' &= t. \end{aligned} \tag{I.2.1}$$

Newtonian equations of motion remain invariant under these transformations.

If we proceed in historical order we find that the first violation of the above invariance principles came with the incorporation of optics into the theory of electromagnetism. Maxwell's equations of electromagnetic field were invariant under Lorentz transformations but not under Galilean transformations.

The motion of charges creating the field must also obey Lorentz-invariant equations. Therefore, a Lorentz-invariant mechanics of mass points was needed. In this way a "partially" unified concept of mechanics and field could be realized. We used the word "partially" just to be cautious, since the equality of inertial force to electromagnetic force cannot so easily be justified.

A reinterpretation of Lorentz transformations by Einstein, as vindicated by experiment, led to the special relativistic theory of mechanics. This in turn brought about a reformulation of the electromagnetic field, treating electric and magnetic components of the field on an equal footing.

Lorentz transformations are functions of the speed of light; therefore all Lorentz-invariant equations of physics must include c, the speed of light. Newtonian physics is a special case of relativistic physics, using an infinite value for the speed of light. This feature of special relativity enables us to reinterpret the physical quantities defined by Newtonian physics. We see that the requirement of covariance with respect to coordinate transformations plays a central role in guiding us to an almost unique formulation of physical laws. Furthermore, transformations, such as space inversion and time inversion, have important bearings on the study of various interaction processes in quantum mechanics.

In classical mechanics the transformations involved in the construction of the path of a dynamical system are canonical transformations. The time development of a system is canonically invariant. Any two points on the path of a dynamical system are "connected" by a canonical transformation. Thus the path of a dynamical system corresponds to an unfolding of a canonical transformation. The Hamiltonian equations of motion are invariant under canonical transformations.

Hamilton's principle is unaffected with respect to the addition of the time derivative of an arbitrary function $W(q, p)$ to the Lagrangian. This possibility of changing the Lagrangian by adding to it in this manner induces canonical transformations on the dynamical system. The arbitrary function W plays the role of an additional action on the dynamical system.

I.3. Vectors and Operators

The formulation of the laws of nature is based on mathematical notions. The choice of a particular branch of mathematics to formulate these laws can be reached by experiment and by intuition. In this connection vectors and operators are the most immediate mathematical tools used in quantum mechanics.

Vectors and operators are basic geometrical entities in a space. An n-dimensional real linear vector space R_n consists of all the ket vectors of the form

$$|a\rangle = \begin{bmatrix} a_1 \\ a_2 \\ \cdot \\ \cdot \\ \cdot \\ \cdot \\ \cdot \\ a_n \end{bmatrix} = a_1 \begin{bmatrix} 1 \\ \cdot \\ \cdot \\ 0 \\ 0 \\ \cdot \\ \cdot \\ 0 \end{bmatrix} + \cdots + a_n \begin{bmatrix} 0 \\ \cdot \\ \cdot \\ \cdot \\ 0 \\ \cdot \\ \cdot \\ 1 \end{bmatrix} = \sum_{i=1}^{n} a_i|e_i\rangle, \qquad (I.3.1)$$

where $a_1, a_2, \cdots, a_n$ are the components of the ket vector $|a\rangle$ with respect to linearly independent orthogonal n unit vectors $|e_i\rangle$ forming a coordinate system in R_n. The totality of bra vectors

$$\langle c| = c_1[1, 0, \cdots, 0] + c_2[0, 1, \cdots, 0] + \cdots + c_n[0, \cdots, 1]$$

$$= \sum_{i=1}^{n} c_i\langle e_i| \qquad (I.3.2)$$

constitute a linear vector space of bras, called the dual space. All these vectors, for real spaces, are defined over the continuum of real numbers. The scalar product of two vectors is defined in terms of a bra and a ket vector. For example, the scalar product of $|A\rangle$ and $|B\rangle$ is

$$\langle B|A\rangle = \langle A|B\rangle = a,$$

where a is a real number. The n^2 conditions

$$\langle e_i|e_j\rangle = \delta_{ij} \qquad (I.3.3)$$

define an orthonormal coordinate system in R_n, provided the vectors $|e_i\rangle$, where $i = 1, 2, \cdots, n$, are linearly independent. (Any other vector in R_n can be expressed as a linear combination of the n unit vectors $|e_i\rangle$.) The symbol δ_{ij} is defined by

$$\delta_{ij} = \begin{cases} +1 & \text{if } i = j, \\ 0 & \text{if } i \neq j. \end{cases}$$

The ket vectors of R_n form a group. (a) If $|a\rangle$ is a member of the group, then the combination of $|a\rangle$ with another member $|b\rangle$ by "addition" gives a new member $|c\rangle = |a\rangle + |b\rangle$ of the group. (b) The zero ket is the unit member of the group. (c) We have, for any member $|a\rangle$, the rule that $|a\rangle + 0 = |a\rangle$. Multiplication by a real number α of $|a\rangle$, as $\alpha|a\rangle$, is also a member of the group. The bra vectors by themselves form a group of the same structure as the ket group. This type of group is called "commutative" or an "Abelian" group. There is a one-to-one correspondence between the bra and ket groups.

The bra corresponding to $|a\rangle + |b\rangle$ is the sum of the bras corresponding to $|a\rangle$ and $|b\rangle$. All of the above definitions for the real space R_n can be repeated for a complex linear vector space C_n by extending the continuum of real numbers to the continuum of complex numbers. We must, however, note some aspects of the complex space differing from the real one.

(a) The transposed complex conjugate of $|a\rangle$ is the bra vector $\langle a|$, or*

$$(|a\rangle)^\dagger = \langle a|. \tag{I.3.4}$$

(b) The complex conjugate of a ket $|a\rangle$, whose components consist of the complex conjugates of components of $|a\rangle$, is not equal to the bra $\langle a|$. (They belong to different spaces.)

(c) The scalar product of $|a\rangle$ and $|b\rangle$ is defined by

$$\langle b|a\rangle = (\langle a|b\rangle)^\dagger \tag{I.3.5}$$

and is a complex number.

(d) The transposed complex conjugate of $\alpha|a\rangle$ is $\alpha^* \langle a|$, where α^* is the complex conjugate of the complex number α.

In both R_n and C_n the square of the length of a vector is defined by

$$\langle a|a\rangle = \sum_{i=1}^{n} |a_i|^2 \tag{I.3.6}$$

and is a real number.

We can use definition (*I.3.3*) to define the unit operator of R_n or C_n by

$$I = \sum_i |e_i\rangle\langle e_i|, \tag{I.3.7}$$

where the unit vectors $|e_i\rangle$ are real or complex depending on the particular space we choose, R_n or C_n. All types of operations (transformations) in a linear vector space are linear operations executed by means of linear operators. A linear operator is an abstract geometrical entity characterized by the properties

(a) $A[|a\rangle + |b\rangle] = A|a\rangle + A|b\rangle$,
(b) $A(\alpha|a\rangle) = \alpha A|a\rangle$,

---

* The superscript † implies transposition and complex conjugation.

where α is a number. The unit operator I defined by (*I.3.7*) is an example of a linear operator in n-dimensional space. The operators

$$M = |a\rangle\langle a|, \qquad N = |a\rangle\langle b|$$

are also linear operators. The square of M or N is also a linear operator; for example,

$$\begin{aligned} M^2 &= |a\rangle\langle a|a\rangle\langle a| \\ &= |\boldsymbol{a}|^2|a\rangle\langle a| = |\boldsymbol{a}|^2 M. \end{aligned}$$

If $|a\rangle$ is a vector of unit magnitude, that is, $\langle a|a\rangle = |\boldsymbol{a}|^2 = 1$, then

$$M^2 = M. \tag{I.3.8}$$

In this case M is called a "projection operator." The unit operator I is also a projection operator. The operators in a R_n or C_n operate on kets or bras to produce new kets or bras:

$$|b\rangle = \alpha|a\rangle, \qquad I|a\rangle = |a\rangle, \qquad \langle b|I = \langle b|.$$

The operation of I on any ket or bra results in the same ket or bra. We may use the unit operator I to express the scalar product of two vectors in terms of their components relative to the orthonormal coordinate system:

$$\begin{aligned} \langle a|b\rangle &= \sum_i \langle a|e_i\rangle\langle e_i|b\rangle \\ &= \sum_{i=1}^{n} a_i^* b_i, \end{aligned} \tag{I.3.9}$$

where $a_i^* = \langle a|e_i\rangle$, $b_i = \langle e_i|b\rangle$ are the components of $|a\rangle$ and $|b\rangle$, respectively, and a_i^* are the complex conjugates of a_i. In R_n the components of a bra $\langle a|$ and the components of its corresponding ket $|a\rangle$ are real and equal.

Let $|I_i\rangle$ and $|f_i\rangle$ be the representative kets (or basic kets) of two orthonormal coordinate systems of the n-dimensional linear vector space. Any ket $|a\rangle$ in the two coordinate systems can be represented by

$$|a\rangle = \sum_{i=1}^{n} |I_i\rangle\langle I_i|a\rangle = \sum_{i=1}^{n} a_i|I_i\rangle \tag{I.3.10}$$

and

$$|a\rangle = \sum_{i=1}^{n} |f_i\rangle\langle f_i|a\rangle = \sum_{i=1}^{n} a_i'|f_i\rangle. \tag{I.3.11}$$

Hence

$$\sum_{i=1}^{n} a_i|I_i\rangle = \sum_{i=1}^{n} a_i'|f_i\rangle. \tag{I.3.12}$$

Multiplication of both sides of (*I.3.12*) by $\langle f_j|$ and the use of the orthogonality relations

$$\langle I_i|I_j\rangle = \langle f_i|f_j\rangle = \delta_{ij}$$

lead to

$$a'_i = \sum_{j=1}^{n} \langle f_i|I_j\rangle a_j \tag{I.3.13}$$

or

$$a'_i = \sum_{j=1}^{n} A_{ij}a_j, \tag{I.3.14}$$

where the coefficients

$$A_{ij} = \langle f_i|I_j\rangle \tag{I.3.15}$$

are the "direction cosines" of the set $\langle f_i|$ with respect to $|I_j\rangle$, and the transposed A_{ij} are the "direction cosines" of $\langle I_j|$ with respect to $|f_i\rangle$. We repeat the above procedure by multiplying both sides of (*I.3.12*) by $\langle I_j|$, giving

$$a_j = \sum_{k=1}^{n} a'_k\langle I_j|f_k\rangle. \tag{I.3.16}$$

Substituting this in (*I.3.13*) we obtain, for any vector, the relation

$$a'_i = \sum_{j,k=1}^{n} a'_k\langle f_i|I_j\rangle\langle I_jf_k\rangle,$$

valid for any vector a_i.
Hence we must have

$$\sum_{j=1}^{n} \langle f_i|I_j\rangle\langle I_j|f_k\rangle = \sum_{j} A_{ij}A^*_{jk} = \delta_{ik}.$$

The coefficients A_{ij} are called the elements of the transformation matrix (or a matrix representation of A).

The operator form of the transformation coefficients A_{ij} is

$$A = \sum_{i=1}^{n} |f_i\rangle\langle I_i|. \tag{I.3.17}$$

The adjoint of A is defined by

$$A^\dagger = \sum_{i=1}^{n} |I_i\rangle\langle f_i|, \tag{I.3.18}$$

where we assumed a one-to-one correspondence between the vectors $|I_i\rangle$ and $|f_i\rangle$, where $i = 1, 2, \cdots, n$. The operator A is a linear operator of R_n or C_n. The condition that a particular transformation operator T be linear may be expressed in the form

$$T(\alpha|a\rangle + \beta|b\rangle) = \alpha T|a\rangle + \beta T|b\rangle,$$

where $|a\rangle$ and $|b\rangle$ are any two kets of R_n or C_n and are real or complex numbers.

The transformation operator A is a linear function of two "complete orthonormal bases" of the linear vector space and its dual space. By a complete orthonormal base or representation we mean that an n-dimensional space can be spanned by n linearly independent $|I_i\rangle$ vectors and every other vector is a linear function of these vectors.

I.4. Orthogonal Transformations

I.4.A. Proper and Improper Orthogonal Transformation Operators

The measurement of distance between two points or between two events at a given time, with respect to a group of coordinate systems with the same origin, occupies an important place in physics. The orthogonal transformations are used to give an invariant meaning to the concept of distance. For this reason we shall, in this section, give a detailed discussion of orthogonal transformations.

For convenience, the ket and bra vectors in real space will be represented by the symbols $|a\supset$ and $\subset a|$, respectively. An orthogonal transformation operator in terms of two real orthonormal representations $|I_i\supset$ and $|f_i\supset$ can be represented by

$$A = \sum_{i=1}^{n} |f_i\supset\subset I_i|,$$

whose transposed form is

$$\tilde{A} = \sum_{i=1}^{n} |I_i\supset\subset f_i|. \qquad (I.4.1)$$

From the orthonormality relations

$$\subset I_i|I_j\supset = \subset f_i|f_j\supset = \delta_{ij},$$

it follows that

$$A\tilde{A} = \tilde{A}A = I, \qquad (I.4.2)$$

where the tilde ($\sim$) over the letter stands for the operation of transposition of kets and bras.

The transformation operator A has a matrix representation in any orthonormal base. The determinant corresponding to a matrix representation is, by (*I.4.2*),

$$(\det A)(\det \tilde{A}) = (\det A)^2 = 1.$$

Hence

$$\det A = \pm 1. \qquad (I.4.3)$$

We thus have two types of orthogonal transformations corresponding to $+1$ and -1 values of the determinant. All orthogonal transformation operators in n-dimensional linear vector space form an n-dimensional real orthogonal group.

(a) If A and B are, as orthogonal transformation operators, members of the group, then taking the multiplication as the rule of combination, we have AB also a member of the group. For

$$\widetilde{(AB)}(AB) = \tilde{B}\tilde{A}AB = I.$$

(b) The group contains the unit element I as the identity transformation operator.

(c) The group contains the reciprocal A^{-1} of any of its elements.

A subgroup of the real orthogonal group consists of all orthogonal transformation operators with determinant $+1$. This is a proper real orthogonal group or rotation group of dimension n. The transformation operators with determinant (-1) do not form a group by themselves, in the above sense. If A and B are two improper orthogonal rotation operators, then we have

$$\begin{aligned} \tilde{A}A &= A\tilde{A} = 1, \\ \tilde{B}B &= B\tilde{B} = 1, \\ \det A &= -1, \\ \det B &= -1, \end{aligned}$$

and

$$\begin{aligned} C &= AB, \\ \tilde{C}C &= C\tilde{C} = 1, \\ \det C &= \det A \det B = +1. \end{aligned}$$

Hence, because of the $+1$ value of the determinant, the element C, obtained as a combination by multiplication of A and B, does not belong to a class of improper rotations. This proves the nongroup character of the improper operators. The orthogonal operator can operate on a ket $|a\supset$ and change it into a ket $|a'\supset$ by

$$|a'\supset = A|a\supset$$

in such a way that

$$\subset a'|a'\supset = \subset a|a\supset,$$

that is, only the direction of a vector is affected, the square of its length remaining the same under the transformation.

The operation on the basic vector $|I_i\supset$ leads, by (*I.3.17*), to

$$|f_i\supset = A|I_i\supset. \qquad (I.4.4)$$

The inclusion of improper orthogonal transformations (reflection of coordinates) in the general group can impose a structure to a linear vector space. Reflections imply a division of vectors into two classes with respect to their transformation properties. Under reflection transformations a vector can either transform like the coordinates themselves (that is, it changes sign) or it remains the same in both the original and reflected coordinates. In the former case the particular vector does not differentiate between left and right (polar vector); in the latter case a vector can differentiate between left and right and is not affected by reflection of coordinates (axial vector).

I.4.B. Examples of Vector Transformations

(a) Let $|I_i\supset$ be the orthonormal set of basic vectors of an ordinary three-dimensional Euclidean space. We represent momentum p and position r vectors by the column vectors $|p\supset$ and $|x\supset$ and construct an operator L,

$$L = |x\supset\subset p| - |p\supset\subset x|. \tag{I.4.5}$$

The transpose of L is

$$\tilde{L} = |p\supset\subset x| - |x\supset\subset p| = -L.$$

Hence L is an antisymmetric operator. Actually L is an operator representation of the classical angular momentum vector. This can easily be seen by giving L in matrix representation in a $|I_i\supset$ system, as

$$L_{ij} = \subset I_i|L|I_j\supset = \subset I_i|x\supset\subset p|I_j\supset - \subset I_i|p\supset\subset x|I_j\supset$$

or

$$L_{ij} = x_i p_j - p_i x_j. \tag{I.4.6}$$

The matrix elements of L in another orthonormal set of basic vector $|f_i\supset$, obtained from $|I_i\supset$ by a rotation operator A, are

$$L'_{ij} = \subset f_i|L|f_j\supset = \sum_{kl} \subset f_i|I_k\supset\subset I_k|L|I_l\supset\subset I_l|f_j\supset.$$

Hence

$$L'_{ij} = \sum_{kl} A_{ik} L_{kl} A_{jl}. \tag{I.4.7}$$

This is the transformation law of an operator L under an orthogonal transformation. In operator form we write it as

$$L' = AL\tilde{A}, \tag{I.4.8}$$

where

$$A = \sum_{i=1}^{3} |f_i\supset\subset I_i| \tag{I.4.9}$$

and

$$\tilde{A} = \sum_{i=1}^{3} |I_i\supset\subset f_i|.$$

We note that the transformation (*I.4.8*) preserves the antisymmetric nature of L, since

$$\begin{aligned} \tilde{L}' &= \widetilde{(AL\tilde{A})} = \tilde{\tilde{A}}\tilde{L}\tilde{A} = A\tilde{L}\tilde{A} \\ &= -AL\tilde{A} = -L'. \end{aligned}$$

Equation (*I.4.8*), as a basic rule of operator transformation, is valid for all linear operators of R_n.

There are only three nonvanishing matrix elements of L. In matrix form we have

$$[L_{ij}] = \begin{bmatrix} 0 & L_{12} & -L_{31} \\ -L_{12} & 0 & L_{23} \\ L_{31} & -L_{23} & 0 \end{bmatrix}. \tag{I.4.10}$$

Now consider the transformation of this matrix under proper and improper transformation matrices, respectively,

$$A = \begin{bmatrix} \cos\theta & -\sin\theta & 0 \\ \sin\theta & \cos\theta & 0 \\ 0 & 0 & 1 \end{bmatrix},$$

$$A' = \begin{bmatrix} -\cos\theta & \sin\theta & 0 \\ -\sin\theta & -\cos\theta & 0 \\ 0 & 0 & -1 \end{bmatrix} = -A,$$

where

$$\det A = +1, \qquad \det A' = -1.$$

It is easy to see that

$$L' = AL\tilde{A} = A'L\tilde{A}'.$$

Thus A and A' produce the same transformation of L:

$$\begin{aligned} L'_{12} &= L_{12}, \\ L'_{31} &= L_{31}\cos\theta + L_{23}\sin\theta, \\ L'_{23} &= -L_{31}\sin\theta + L_{23}\cos\theta. \end{aligned} \tag{I.4.11}$$

But the transformation of $|x\supset$ under A' leads to

$$\begin{aligned} x'_3 &= -x_3, \\ x'_2 &= -x_2\cos\theta - x_1\sin\theta, \\ x'_1 &= x_2\sin\theta - x_1\cos\theta. \end{aligned} \tag{I.4.12}$$

If we define the vector $|L\supset$ by

$$|L\supset = \begin{bmatrix} L_{23} \\ L_{31} \\ L_{12} \end{bmatrix},$$

the results (*I.4.11*) and (*I.4.12*) are equivalent to

$$|L'\supset = A|L\supset, \tag{I.4.13}$$

$$|x'\supset = -A|x\supset, \tag{I.4.14}$$

showing that of the two vectors $|L\supset$ and $|x\supset$, $|L\supset$ did not change its sign under the improper rotation while the vector $|x\supset$ was transformed to $-|x\supset$. The vector $|L\supset$, defined by the nonvanishing components of a (3×3) antisymmetric matrix, is an axial vector.

(b) The more usual way of constructing an axial vector from the components of an antisymmetric "tensor" L_{ij} is to introduce the antisymmetric tensor ϵ_{ijk}. The tensor density ϵ_{ijk} is antisymmetric with respect to all three subscripts (ijk), its value is $+1$ or -1 if ijk is an even or odd permutation of (123), and it is zero if any two of the subscripts ijk are equal.

In tensor notation the vector L_i, defined by

$$L_i = \tfrac{1}{2}\epsilon_{ijl}L_{jl}, \qquad (I.4.15)$$

is called the "dual" of L_{ij}. The L_{ij} are related to L_k by

$$L_{ij} = \epsilon_{ijl}L_l, \qquad (I.4.16)$$

where the dummy index l implies summation over $l = 1, 2, 3$. It can easily be verified that ϵ_{ijk} satisfies the relations

$$\delta^{ij}_{kl} = \epsilon^{mij}\epsilon_{mkl} = \delta_{ik}\delta_{jl} - \delta_{il}\delta_{jk}, \qquad (I.4.17)$$

$$\delta^{ij}_{il} = \epsilon^{mij}\epsilon_{mil} = 2\delta_{jl}, \qquad (I.4.18)$$

$$\frac{1}{3!}\epsilon_{ijk}\epsilon_{mnl}A_{im}A_{jn}A_{kl} = \det A, \qquad (I.4.19)$$

$$\epsilon_{ijk}A_{im}A_{jn}A_{kl} = (\det A)\epsilon_{mnl}$$
$$= \epsilon'_{mnl}. \qquad (I.4.20)$$

The last expressions in $(I.4.20)$ are the transformation laws of the components of ϵ_{ijk}.

Replacing L_{kl} in $(I.4.7)$ by $(I.4.16)$, we get

$$L'_{ij} = \epsilon_{klr}L_rA_{ik}A_{jl}.$$

We use the relations

$$\epsilon_{klr}A_{ik}A_{jl} = (\det A)\epsilon'_{ijl}A_{lr},$$

and write

$$L_{ij} = (\det A)\epsilon'_{ijk}A_{kr}L_r.$$

Multiplying both sides by ϵ'_{ijk} and using $(I.4.18)$, we obtain

$$\tfrac{1}{2}\epsilon'_{ijk}L'_{ij} = (\det A)A_{kl}L_l.$$

Hence

$$L'_k = (\det A)A_{kl}L_l. \qquad (I.4.21)$$

This shows again that the L_i transform as an axial vector. A typical reflection of coordinates is

$$x'_i = -x_i, \qquad A_{ij} = -\delta_{ij}, \qquad \det A = -1,$$

so

$$L'_k = L_k. \qquad (I.4.22)$$

(c) Electric charges must behave as scalars under reflection of coordinates—otherwise we would have an unfamiliar situation of transition from negative to positive or from positive to negative charges just for reasons of coordinate reflections. The electric current depends on the product of charges by their velocities and it is, therefore, a polar vector.

In classical electrodynamics the nonrelativistic motion of a point charge, in the presence of a magnetic field $\mathfrak{H}$, is given by

$$\frac{d\boldsymbol{p}}{dt} = \frac{e}{mc}\boldsymbol{p} \times \mathfrak{H}, \tag{I.4.23}$$

where $\boldsymbol{p}$ is the momentum vector of the charge and $\mathfrak{H}$ is the magnetic field vector. Under a reflection, $\boldsymbol{p}$ transforms as a polar vector, that is, $\boldsymbol{p}' = -\boldsymbol{p}$.

For the equations of motion to remain invariant under a reflection of coordinates, we must have the transformation law,

$$\mathfrak{H}'(x') = \mathfrak{H}(x), \tag{I.4.24}$$

for the magnetic vector; therefore $\mathfrak{H}$ is an axial vector. In the presence of an electric field $\mathcal{E}$, the motion of the charge is given by

$$\frac{d\boldsymbol{p}}{dt} = e\mathcal{E}, \tag{I.4.25}$$

so the invariance requires $\mathcal{E}$ to transform as

$$\mathcal{E}'(x') = -\mathcal{E}(x) \tag{I.4.26}$$

under reflection.

It follows from these arguments that $\boldsymbol{p} \times \mathfrak{H}$ and $\mathcal{E} \times \mathfrak{H}$ are polar vectors. The quantity Λ, defined as the scalar product of $\mathcal{E}$ and $\mathfrak{H}$, or $\Lambda = \mathcal{E}\cdot\mathfrak{H}$, transforms under coordinate reflection as

$$\Lambda'(x') = -\Lambda(x), \tag{I.4.27}$$

so its sign changes under coordinate reflection but it remains unchanged with respect to a proper rotation of coordinates. Such a quantity is called a *pseudoscalar*. The quantity Λ^2 is a scalar.

In general, any vectors formed from the vector product of two polar vectors or two axial vectors are axial vectors.

I.4.C. Problems

1. What would be the consequences if
   (a) $\mathcal{E}$ and $\mathfrak{H}$ were both polar vectors?
   (b) $\mathfrak{H}$ was polar and $\mathcal{E}$ axial?
   (c) $\mathcal{E}$ and $\mathfrak{H}$ were both axial vectors?
2. In all three cases of problem 1, show the nature of the vector $c(\mathcal{E} \times \mathfrak{H}/4\pi)$.
3. Discuss axial and polar character of the following quantities:

$$\boldsymbol{L}\cdot\mathfrak{H},\quad \boldsymbol{L}\cdot\mathcal{E},\quad \boldsymbol{p}\cdot\mathfrak{H},\quad \boldsymbol{p}\cdot\mathcal{E},$$
$$\boldsymbol{L}\times\mathfrak{H},\quad \boldsymbol{L}\times\mathcal{E},\quad \boldsymbol{p}\times\mathfrak{H},\quad \boldsymbol{p}\times\mathcal{E}.$$

4. In analogy to Euler's representation of the rigid-body motion, discuss the properties of the operators C_1, C_2, C_3, E_1, and E_2, defined by

$$C_1 = \begin{bmatrix} 1 & 0 & 0 \\ 0 & \sin\psi & \cos\psi \\ 0 & \cos\psi & -\sin\psi \end{bmatrix}, \qquad C_2 = \begin{bmatrix} \sin\theta & 0 & \cos\theta \\ 0 & 1 & 0 \\ \cos\theta & 0 & -\sin\theta \end{bmatrix},$$

$$C_3 = \begin{bmatrix} \sin\Phi & \cos\Phi & 0 \\ \cos\Phi & -\sin\Phi & 0 \\ 0 & 0 & 1 \end{bmatrix}, \qquad E_1 = \begin{bmatrix} 0 & 0 & 1 \\ \cos\lambda & \sin\lambda & 0 \\ -\sin\lambda & \cos\lambda & 0 \end{bmatrix},$$

$$E_2 = \begin{bmatrix} 0 & \cos\tau & \sin\tau \\ 0 & -\sin\tau & \cos\tau \\ 1 & 0 & 0 \end{bmatrix}.$$

5. Show that the matrix

$$R = \begin{bmatrix} -\cos\theta & -\sin\theta & 0 \\ -\sin\theta & \cos\theta & 0 \\ 0 & 0 & -1 \end{bmatrix}$$

represents a rotation through 180° around the X_3-axis. Hence show that $-R$ is a rotation reflection about the X_3-axis.

I.5. Properties of Linear Operators

Let α be a linear operator in R_n or C_n and let M be an upper bound for the absolute values of the matrix elements $\alpha_{ij} = \langle I_i|\alpha|I_j\rangle$ of α. Then, if

$$|\alpha_{ij}| \leqq M \tag{I.5.1}$$

and if $\alpha_{ij}^{(l)}$ are the matrix elements of the linear operator α^l, we have

$$|\alpha_{ij}^{(l)}| \leqq (nM)^l. \tag{I.5.2}$$

Thus the series expansion of exp (α), with the matrix element of α satisfying (*I.5.1*), converges uniformly:

$$\exp(\alpha) = \sum_{n=0}^{\infty} \frac{\alpha^n}{n!} = I + \alpha + \frac{\alpha^2}{2!} + \cdots.$$

Theorem 1. *If V is a linear operator in C_n and if the determinant of its matrix representation in C_n does not vanish, then*

$$\exp[V\alpha V^{-1}] = V(\exp\alpha)V^{-1}. \tag{I.5.3}$$

The proof follows from observing the relation

$$\begin{aligned} V\alpha^n V^{-1} &= (V\alpha V^{-1})(V\alpha V^{-1}) \cdots (V\alpha V^{-1}) \\ &= (V\alpha V^{-1})^n, \end{aligned}$$

so

$$\exp [V\alpha V^{-1}] = \sum_0^\infty \frac{(V\alpha V^{-1})^n}{n!}$$
$$= V\left(\sum \frac{\alpha^n}{n!}\right)V^{-1} = V(\exp \alpha)V^{-1}.$$

I.5.A. Eigenvalues and Eigenvectors

A linear operator α satisfying the relation

$$\alpha^\dagger = \alpha \tag{I.5.4}$$

is called a Hermitian operator. A linear operator β with

$$\beta^\dagger = -\beta \tag{I.5.5}$$

is called an anti-Hermitian operator.

In the space R_n, (*I.5.4*) and (*I.5.5*) correspond to symmetric and anti-symmetric operators, respectively. In the real domain, symmetric and anti-symmetric operators are not closely related operators, as are the Hermitian and anti-Hermitian operators in the complex domain.

If β is an anti-Hermitian operator we can construct from it a Hermitian operator simply by multiplying it by i, so $i\beta$, satisfying

$$(i\beta)^\dagger = -i\beta^\dagger = i\beta, \tag{I.5.6}$$

is a Hermitian operator. Conversely, corresponding to the Hermitian operator α we have the anti-Hermitian operator $i\alpha$:

$$(i\alpha)^\dagger = -i\alpha^\dagger = -i\alpha. \tag{I.5.7}$$

Any linear operator can be split up into a real part and a pure imaginary part. Thus if γ is any linear operator, then

$$\gamma = \tfrac{1}{2}(\gamma + \gamma^\dagger) + \tfrac{1}{2}(\gamma - \gamma^\dagger)$$
$$= \alpha + \beta,$$

where

$$\alpha = \tfrac{1}{2}(\gamma + \gamma^\dagger), \qquad \alpha^\dagger = \alpha,$$
$$\beta = \tfrac{1}{2}(\gamma - \gamma^\dagger), \qquad \beta^\dagger = -\beta.$$

The complex conjugation and transposition operation for two operators ρ and σ follow from

$$\langle a|\rho^\dagger\sigma^\dagger|b\rangle = \langle a'|b'\rangle,$$

where

$$\langle a|\rho^\dagger = \langle a'|, \qquad \sigma^\dagger|b\rangle = |b'\rangle.$$

Thus

$$(\langle a|\rho^\dagger\sigma^\dagger|b\rangle)^\dagger = (\langle a'|b'\rangle)^\dagger$$
$$= \langle b'|a'\rangle = \langle b|\sigma\rho|a\rangle$$
$$= (\langle a|(\sigma\rho)^\dagger|b\rangle)^\dagger.$$

Since this holds for any $|a\rangle$ and $\langle b|$, we infer that

$$(\rho\sigma)^\dagger = \sigma^\dagger\rho^\dagger.$$

The study of the relations between vectors and linear operators brings about, in a natural way, the concepts of eigenvalues and eigenvectors. A rigorous discussion of the theory of eigenvalues and eigenvectors of operators in general, and of Hermitian operators in particular, requires the full machinery of highly specialized mathematics. These aspects of the properties of linear operators are discussed at great length by von Neumann.*

Theorem 2. *The eigenvalues of a linear Hermitian operator are real numbers.*

If α is a Hermitian operator in C_n, then its eigenvalues α' and corresponding eigenvectors $|\alpha'\rangle$ are related by the fundamental equation of quantum mechanics,

$$\alpha|\alpha'\rangle = \alpha'|\alpha'\rangle. \qquad (I.5.8)$$

We assume that for each eigenvalue α' there exists only one eigenvector $|\alpha'\rangle$. From (*I.5.8*), multiplying on the left by the bra $\langle\alpha'|$ corresponding to the ket $|\alpha'\rangle$, we obtain

$$\langle\alpha'|\alpha|\alpha'\rangle = \alpha'\langle\alpha'|\alpha'\rangle.$$

The Hermitian conjugate of this equation,

$$(\langle\alpha'|\alpha|\alpha'\rangle)^\dagger = \langle\alpha'|\alpha|\alpha'\rangle = \alpha^{*\prime}\langle\alpha'|\alpha'\rangle = \alpha'\langle\alpha'|\alpha'\rangle,$$

yields the result $\alpha^{*\prime} = \alpha'$, which means that the imaginary part of α' must vanish. The same result is also obtained for the degenerate case of more than one eigenvector $|\alpha', i\rangle$, where $i = 1, 2, \cdots, m$, corresponding to one eigenvalue α'.

Theorem 3. *The eigenvectors of a linear Hermitian operator corresponding to different eigenvalues are orthogonal.*

Let α_1' and α_2' be any two eigenvalues ($\alpha_1' \neq \alpha_2'$) of α, corresponding to the eigenvectors $|\alpha_1'\rangle$ and $|\alpha_2'\rangle$, respectively. Then

$$\alpha|\alpha_1'\rangle = \alpha_1'|\alpha_1'\rangle,$$
$$\alpha|\alpha_2'\rangle = \alpha_2'|\alpha_2'\rangle.$$

Multiplying both equations on the left by the bras $\langle\alpha_2'|$ and $\langle\alpha_1'|$, respectively, we get

$$\langle\alpha_2'|\alpha|\alpha_1'\rangle = \alpha_1'\langle\alpha_2'|\alpha_1'\rangle,$$
$$\langle\alpha_1'|\alpha|\alpha_2'\rangle = \alpha_2'\langle\alpha_1'|\alpha_2'\rangle.$$

---

* J. von Neumann, *Mathematical Foundations of Quantum Mechanics*, Princeton Univ. Press, Princeton, 1955.

By subtracting the Hermitian conjugate of the second equation from the first, we obtain

$$(\alpha_1' - \alpha_2')\langle\alpha_2'|\alpha_1'\rangle = 0,$$

which is possible only if $\langle\alpha_1'|\alpha_2'\rangle = 0$, proving the orthogonality of the eigenvectors.

Definition 1. *A Hermitian operator α with eigenvalues $\alpha' \geqq 0$ is called a positive semidefinite Hermitian operator. If $\alpha' > 0$, then it is called a positive definite Hermitian operator.*

If M is a positive semidefinite operator, then the operator $\exp(M)$ is a positive definite Hermitian operator.

Definition 2. *The eigenvectors (eigenkets or eigenbras) of a Hermitian operator α of C_n are said to constitute a complete orthonormal set if any vector whatever can be expressed as a sum of such eigenvectors.*

A rigorous proof of this theorem (especially for infinite-dimensional spaces) can be found in von Neumann's book. Here we shall only point out some important features of the theorem. The eigenvectors of a Hermitian operator can span a C_n; that is, there exists no linear relation of the form

$$\sum_{i=1}^{n} a_i|\alpha^{(i)}\rangle = 0, \tag{I.5.9}$$

among the n eigenkets $|\alpha^{(i)}\rangle$ of α. If the relation (*I.5.9*) exists, then multiplication by any bra $\langle\alpha^{(j)}|$ belonging to the bras of α leads to $a_j = 0$, for $j = 1, 2, \cdots, n$. Consequently the set of eigenvectors $|\alpha^{(i)}\rangle$ cannot have $n + 1$ linearly independent eigenvectors; that is, any vector in C_n can be expressed as a linear combination of the n eigenvectors of α.

If any ket $|b\rangle$ of C_n can be expressed in terms of the orthonormal set $|\alpha^{(i)}\rangle$, that is, if we can write

$$|b\rangle = \sum_{i=1}^{n} |\alpha^{(i)}\rangle\langle\alpha^{(i)}|b\rangle = \sum_{i=1}^{n} b_i|\alpha^{(i)}\rangle,$$

then we say that the $|\alpha^{(i)}\rangle$ constitute a complete set and that this set can span a C_n.

Definition 3. *The trace of an operator is the sum of the diagonal elements of its matrix representation.*

The trace of the operator γ with matrix representation $\gamma_{ij} = \langle I_i|\gamma|I_j\rangle$ is given by

$$\mathrm{tr}\,(\gamma) = \sum_{i=1}^{n} \langle I_i|\gamma|I_i\rangle = \sum_{i=1}^{n} \gamma_{ii}.$$

Theorem 4. *The trace of a linear operator γ is independent of the choice of orthonormal set in C_n (or R_n).*

Consider two orthonormal sets $|I_i\rangle$ and $|f_i\rangle$. The matrix elements of γ in the two coordinate systems are related by

$$\langle I_i|\gamma|I_j\rangle = \gamma_{ij} = \sum_{kl} \langle I_i|f_k\rangle\langle f_k|\gamma|f_l\rangle\langle f_l|I_j\rangle.$$

Hence

$$\begin{aligned}\text{tr}\,(\gamma) &= \sum_{i=1}^{n} \langle I_i|\gamma|I_i\rangle \\ &= \sum_{ikl} A_{ik}A_{il}\langle f_k|\gamma|f_l\rangle \\ &= \sum_{kl} \delta_{kl}\langle f_k|\gamma|f_l\rangle \\ &= \sum_{l} \langle f_l|\gamma|f_l\rangle = \sum_{l} \gamma_{ll}.\end{aligned}$$

Corollary 1. *The trace of γ remains invariant under a similarity transformation:*

$$V^{-1}\gamma V = \gamma'.$$

Corollary 2. *The dimension number of a linear space is defined by the trace of its unit operator:*

$$I = \sum_{i} |I_i\rangle\langle I_i|, \qquad \text{tr}\,(I) = n.$$

Theorem 5. *If $\gamma_1, \gamma_2, \cdots, \gamma_m$ are the eigenvalues of any linear operator γ, with any multiplicity of its eigenvalues, then the eigenvalues of $\exp(\gamma)$ are given by $\exp(\gamma_1), \cdots, \exp(\gamma_m)$, respectively.*

Theorem 6. *The determinant of the matrix representation of a linear operator γ' is $\exp(\text{tr}\,\gamma)$, where $\gamma' = \exp(\gamma)$.*

Let V be an operator both linear and nonsingular (that is, the matrix of V has a unique inverse V^{-1}), such that

$$V\gamma V^{-1} = \Gamma,$$

where Γ is a diagonal matrix. Then

$$\det \Gamma = \det V \det \gamma \det V^{-1} = \det \gamma.$$

Hence, if $\exp(\gamma_1), \cdots, \exp(\gamma_m)$ are eigenvalues of the operator $\exp(\gamma)$, then

$$\begin{aligned}\det(\exp \gamma) &= \exp(\gamma_1)\exp(\gamma_2)\cdot\cdots\cdot\exp(\gamma_m) \\ &= \exp(\text{tr}\,\gamma).\end{aligned}$$

I.5.B. Examples

(a) The projection operator M satisfies the algebraic equation

$$M^2 - M = 0.$$

The eigenvalue equation

$$M|M'\rangle = M'|M'\rangle$$

yields the eigenvalues $M' = 0$ and $M' = 1$, with the corresponding eigenvectors $|0\rangle$ and $|1\rangle$. The two eigenvectors satisfy the orthogonality condition

$$\langle 0|1\rangle = 0.$$

The two eigenvectors can span a two-dimensional C_2. The corresponding unit operator is

$$I = |0\rangle\langle 0| + |1\rangle\langle 1|.$$

The matrix representation of M in its own orthonormal base has the form

$$(M_{ij}) = \begin{bmatrix} 1 & 0 \\ 0 & 0 \end{bmatrix},$$

whose eigenvectors can be represented by

$$|0\rangle = \begin{bmatrix} 0 \\ 1 \end{bmatrix}, \qquad |1\rangle = \begin{bmatrix} 1 \\ 0 \end{bmatrix}.$$

The operator form of M in its own orthonormal base can be expressed (by multiplying the unit operator with M) as

$$M = |1\rangle\langle 1|. \tag{I.5.10}$$

Any two-dimensional ket $|b\rangle$ can be expanded according* to

$$\begin{aligned}|b\rangle &= |0\rangle\langle 0|b\rangle + |1\rangle\langle 1|b\rangle \\ &= b_1|0\rangle + b_2|1\rangle\end{aligned}$$

or

$$|b\rangle = b_1|0\rangle + M|b\rangle.$$

(b) The positive definite operator $Q = \exp(\lambda M)$ can be expressed in terms of M as

$$Q = I - M + \exp(\lambda)M.$$

The eigenvalues of Q corresponding to the eigenvectors $|0\rangle$ and $|1\rangle$ are 1 and $\exp(\lambda)$, respectively. The operator representation of Q in its own orthonormal base is

$$Q = |0\rangle\langle 0| + \exp(\lambda)|1\rangle\langle 1|. \tag{I.5.11}$$

The operator $M' = 1 - M$ is also a projection operator.

---

* The projection operator M can find important applications in describing mass and massless states of a dynamical system.

(c) An operator α satisfying the equation $\alpha^2 - 1 = 0$ has the eigenvalues $+1$ and -1. The unit operator

$$I = |1\rangle\langle 1| + |-1\rangle\langle -1|$$

can be used to record α as

$$\alpha = |1\rangle\langle 1| - |-1\rangle\langle -1|. \qquad (I.5.12)$$

For any ket $|b\rangle$ we can write

$$|b\rangle = |1\rangle\langle 1|b\rangle + |-1\rangle\langle -1|b\rangle$$

and

$$\alpha|b\rangle = |1\rangle\langle 1|b\rangle - |-1\rangle\langle -1|b\rangle.$$

Solving for $\langle 1|b\rangle$ and $\langle -1|b\rangle$ and substituting in the expression of $|b\rangle$, we get

$$|b\rangle = \tfrac{1}{2}(1 + \alpha)|b\rangle + \tfrac{1}{2}(1 - \alpha)|b\rangle, \qquad (I.5.13)$$

where each term on the right is an eigenket of α.

In general, any linear operator satisfies its corresponding eigenvalue equation. The polynomial obtained by taking the determinant of the matrix $(\alpha - \alpha' I)$,

$$\det(\alpha - \alpha' I) = \alpha'^n + a_1\alpha'^{n-1} + a_2\alpha'^{n-2} + \cdots + a_{n-1}\alpha' + a_n,$$

leads to an algebraic equation for $\alpha' = \alpha$:

$$\alpha^n + a_1\alpha^{n-1} + a_2\alpha^{n-2} + \cdots + a_n = 0,$$

where $a_1 = \mathrm{tr}\,(\alpha)$, a_2, a_3, $\cdots$, a_{n-1} = the sum of (2×2), (3×3), $\cdots$, $(n-1) \times (n-1)$ minors of the determinant a_n, respectively, and

$$a_n = \det \alpha.$$

I.5.C. Antilinear Operators

The scalar product of two vectors in C_n, defined by (*I.3.5*), is a linear operation. We may also define a simple scalar product of two vectors $|a\rangle$ and $|b\rangle$ by

$$\subset a|b\supset = \subset b|a\supset, \qquad (I.5.14)$$

where the components of the bra vector $\langle a|$ are equal to the components of the corresponding ket vector $|a\rangle$. In row-vector notation we have

$$\langle a| = (a_1^*, a_2^*, \cdots, a_n^*),$$
$$\subset a| = (a_1, a_2, \cdots, a_n).$$

Thus the simple scalar product of $|a\rangle$ and $|b\rangle$ is defined by

$$\subset a|b\supset = \sum_{i=1}^{n} \subset a|I_i\supset\subset I_i|b\supset = \sum_{i=1}^{n} a_i b_i, \qquad (I.5.15)$$

which is not equal to the scalar product defined by (*I.3.5*), as

$$\langle a|b\rangle = \sum_{i=1}^{n} a_i^* b_i. \qquad (I.5.16)$$

If we take $|a\rangle = |b\rangle$, then the two scalar products (*I.5.15*) and (*I.5.16*) lead respectively to

$$\subset a|a\supset = \sum_{i=1}^{n} (a_i)^2$$

and

$$\langle a|a\rangle = |\boldsymbol{a}|^2 = \sum_{i=1}^{n} |a_i|^2.$$

The former is in general a complex number. If λ is a number, then the two scalar products of two vectors $|a\rangle$ and $\lambda|b\rangle$ are given by

$$\subset a|\lambda|b\supset = \lambda\subset a|b\supset$$

and

$$\langle a|\lambda|b\rangle = \lambda\langle a|b\rangle,$$

while the scalar products of $\lambda|a\rangle$ and $|b\rangle$ are

$$\subset a|\lambda|b\supset = \lambda\subset a|b\supset$$

and

$$\langle a|\lambda^*|b\rangle = \lambda^*\langle a|b\rangle.$$

In particular, we may define an operator of complex conjugation. If $\overline{C}$ is such an operator, then

$$\overline{C}|a\rangle = |a^*\rangle,$$
$$\overline{C}(\lambda|a\rangle) = \lambda^*\overline{C}|a\rangle = \lambda^*|a^*\rangle,$$

and

$$\overline{C}[\lambda|a\rangle + \mu|b\rangle] = \lambda^*\overline{C}|a\rangle + \mu^*\overline{C}|b\rangle. \qquad (I.5.17)$$

An operator satisfying (*I.5.17*) is called an *antilinear operator.*

The scalar product of $\overline{C}|a\rangle$ and $\overline{C}|b\rangle$ is given by

$$\langle a|\overline{C}^\dagger\overline{C}|b\rangle = \langle a^*|b^*\rangle = (\langle a|b\rangle)^*. \qquad (I.5.18)$$

The operator $\overline{C}$ satisfying (*I.5.17*) and (*I.5.18*) is an example of an *antiunitary operator.* Furthermore, for any ket $|a\rangle$ we have

$$\overline{C}^2|a\rangle = \overline{C}|a^*\rangle = |a\rangle.$$

Hence

$$\overline{C}^2 = 1. \qquad (I.5.19)$$

The absolute value of the scalar product of $\overline{C}|a\rangle$ and $\overline{C}|b\rangle$ is

$$|\langle a|\overline{C}^\dagger\overline{C}|b\rangle|^2 = |\langle a^*|b^*\rangle|^2 = |\langle a|b\rangle|^2.$$

Hence we infer that $\overline{C}^\dagger C$ is a unitary operator.* Thus in general the product

---

* Unitary operators will be discussed in more detail in later sections.

of two antiunitary operators $\overline{C}$ and D, or $\overline{C}D = U$, satisfies the condition of unitarity, $U^\dagger U = UU^\dagger = 1$. It follows that every antiunitary operator $\mathfrak{J}$ can be written as the product of a unitary operator U and an operator $\overline{C}$ of complex conjugation:*

$$\mathfrak{J} = U\overline{C}. \tag{I.5.20}$$

I.5.D. Order of Magnitude of an Operator

Every observation of a dynamical variable is represented by a number with appropriate units of measurement. In quantum mechanics linear Hermitian operators represent dynamical variables. It is, therefore, necessary to define the concept of order of magnitude of a linear operator. It will be given here for the special case of finite-dimensional spaces and it will be extended to real physical situations in later chapters.

In a space C_n, matrix representation of an operator depends on n^2 complex numbers or $2n^2$ real numbers. In $2n^2$-dimensional rectangular Cartesian space, the α matrix is just a point, whose elements are the coordinates of the point. The square of the distance of the point from the origin of the coordinates can be represented by the sum of the absolute squares of the matrix elements of α. Such a number is called the square of the norm of α. Therefore, the norm of an operator can be defined by

$$[N(\alpha)]^2 = \operatorname{tr}(\alpha^\dagger\alpha) = \sum_{i,j=1}^{n} |\alpha_{ij}|^2. \tag{I.5.21}$$

If the points (that is, the matrices) all lie within a "sphere" with center at the origin (*zero matrix*), then we say that all linear operators of type α are bounded. The necessary condition is the existence of a number M such that

$$N(\alpha) \leqq M. \tag{I.5.22}$$

If α happens to be a function of a parameter t, then (*I.5.22*) must be satisfied for every t.

Remark. *The norms of α and $A\alpha$, αA are the same, where A satisfies $AA^\dagger = A^\dagger A = I$.*

This is true because $\operatorname{tr}[(A\alpha)(A\alpha)^\dagger] = \operatorname{tr}(\alpha\alpha^\dagger) = \operatorname{tr}(\alpha^\dagger\alpha)$. Inequalities related to the norm of matrices can be derived by using Schwartz's inequality,

$$\left|\sum_{i=1}^{n} a_i b_i\right|^2 \leqq \left(\sum_{i=1}^{n} |a_i|^2\right)\left(\sum_{j=1}^{n} |b_j|^2\right).$$

---

* The concept of the antiunitary operator was first introduced by Wigner. The time-reversal operation as an element of symmetry of a dynamical system is represented by an antiunitary operator. See E. P. Wigner, *Group Theory and Its Applications to the Quantum Mechanics of Atomic Spectra*, Academic Press, New York, 1959.

For any two matrices B and C, this gives

$$N(B + C) \leqq N(B) + N(C). \tag{I.5.23}$$

A second inequality for the norm follows from applying Schwartz's inequality to the element

$$d_{ij} = \sum_{k=1}^{n} b_{ik}c_{jk}$$

of $D = BC$.

Thus

$$|d_{ij}|^2 \leqq \left(\sum_k |b_{ik}|^2\right)\left(\sum_k |c_{kj}|^2\right).$$

Summing over i and j, we get

$$N(BC) \leqq N(B)N(C). \tag{I.5.24}$$

We can also apply these results to the integral of an operator $B(t)$. If $B(t)$ is a continuous function of time in a finite interval of time—(t_0, t), say—then

$$N\left[\int_{t_0}^{t} B(t)\, dt\right] \leqq \int_{t_0}^{t} N[B(t)]\, dt. \tag{I.5.25}$$

I.6. Time-Dependent Orthogonal Transformations

I.6.A. Differential Equations for Orthogonal Transformations

If A of (*I.3.17*) is a function of time, we can introduce a continuously rotating coordinate system. We differentiate the orthogonality conditions $\tilde{A}A = A\tilde{A} = I$ to obtain

$$\tilde{A}\frac{dA}{dt} = -\frac{d\tilde{A}}{dt}A$$

and

$$A\frac{d\tilde{A}}{dt} = -\frac{dA}{dt}\tilde{A}.$$

From

$$\widetilde{\tilde{A}\frac{dA}{dt}} = -\tilde{A}\frac{dA}{dt},$$

we infer that $\tilde{A}(dA/dt)$ and $A(d\tilde{A}/dt)$ are antisymmetric operators. Let $(dA/dt)\tilde{A} = \Omega$, where $\tilde{\Omega} = -\Omega$. Hence

$$\frac{dA}{dt} = \Omega A, \tag{I.6.1}$$

where Ω is an antisymmetric operator.

A more suitable form of the equation is obtained by the use of a Hermitian operator, $S = i\Omega$, so the differential equation becomes

$$i\frac{dA}{dt} = SA, \tag{I.6.2}$$

where $S^\dagger = S$, and the transpose operation (sign $\sim$) can be replaced by the Hermitian conjugate operation (sign †). The solutions of (*I.6.2*), with appropriate boundary conditions, can constitute a subgroup of the full orthogonal group.

The operator representation of A as a function of the initial time t_0 and later time t can be given as

$$A(t, t_0) = \sum_{i=1}^{n} |e_i(t)\rangle\langle e_i(t_0)|, \tag{I.6.3}$$

where the basic vectors are subject to the orthonormality conditions

$$\langle e_i(t_0)|e_j(t_0)\rangle = \delta_{ij},$$
$$\langle e_i(t)|e_j(t)\rangle = \delta_{ij},$$

so the definition (*I.6.3*) contains the orthogonality conditions. The interchange of t and t_0 is equivalent to the Hermitian conjugation

$$A(t_0, t) = A^\dagger(t, t_0) = \sum_{i=1}^{n} |e_i(t_0)\rangle\langle e_i(t)|. \tag{I.6.4}$$

The matrix elements of A in the initial configuration of coordinate axes are

$$\langle e_i(t_0)|A|e_j(t_0)\rangle = \langle e_i(t_0)|e_j(t)\rangle. \tag{I.6.5}$$

At $t = t_0$ the matrix elements become δ_{ij}, the matrix representation of the unit operator. Hence our definition of A by (*I.6.3*) does not include reflections and is valid only for proper orthogonal transformations. All proper orthogonal transformations can be looked upon as generated by infinitesimal steps from the initial identity transformation,

$$A(t_0, t_0) = I. \tag{I.6.6}$$

The generator of the transformation is the Hermitian operator S.

From (*I.6.3*) we see that the operation of $A(t, t_0)$ on the initial basic vector $|e_i(t_0)\rangle$ produces the basic vector $|e_i(t)\rangle$ at time t. Thus

$$|e_i(t)\rangle = A(t, t_0)|e_i(t_0)\rangle. \tag{I.6.7}$$

The time rate of change of $|e_i(t)\rangle$, from (*I.6.7*) and (*I.6.2*), is

$$i\frac{d|e_i(t)\rangle}{dt} = S|e_i(t)\rangle. \tag{I.6.8}$$

From (*I.6.3*) and (*I.6.7*) one easily obtains the group property of the transformation operators:

$$A(\tau, t)A(t, t_0) = A(\tau, t_0). \tag{I.6.9}$$

Because of the continuous variation of t we say that the rotation group in R_n is a connected group.

I.6.B. Infinitesimal Rotations

We assume that

(a) the generator S is independent of time,
(b) the norm of $S(t - t_0)$ is very small compared to unity.

Assumption (a) leads to the solutions

$$|e_i(t)\rangle = e^{-iS(t-t_0)}|e_i(t_0)\rangle \tag{I.6.10}$$

and

$$A(t, t_0) = e^{-i(t-t_0)S} \tag{I.6.11}$$

of equations (*I.6.8*) and (*I.6.2*), respectively. Assumption (b) contains the statement that

$$N[(t - t_0)S] = (t - t_0)\omega < 1, \tag{I.6.12}$$

where

$$\omega = \sqrt{\left[\sum_{ij} |S_{ij}|^2\right]}.$$

Thus the changes in A and $|e_i(t)\rangle$, due to an infinitesimal rotation generated by S satisfying (*I.6.12*), are

$$\delta|e_i(t)\rangle = |e_i(t)\rangle - |e_i(t_0)\rangle = -\Delta t S|e_i(t_0)\rangle \tag{I.6.13}$$

and

$$\delta A = A(t, t_0) - I = -i\Delta t S, \tag{I.6.14}$$

where $\Delta t = t - t_0$.
Replacing $(-i\Delta t S)$ by an antisymmetric operator ϵ, the change in any vector $|a\rangle$ can be written as

$$\delta a_i = \langle a|e_i(t)\rangle - \langle a|e_i(t_0)\rangle = -\langle a|\epsilon|e_i(t_0)\rangle$$

or

$$a_i(t) = a_i(t_0) + \sum_j a_j(t_0)\epsilon_{ij}, \tag{I.6.15}$$

where

$$\epsilon_{ij} = \langle e_i(t_0)|\epsilon|e_j(t_0)\rangle$$

and ϵ_{ij} is antisymmetric—that is,

$$\epsilon_{ij} = -\epsilon_{ji}. \tag{I.6.16}$$

I.6.C. Examples of Infinitesimal Rotations

(a) Infinitesimal rotation of coordinates in R_3 is given by

$$x_i' = x_i + \epsilon_{ij}x_j, \tag{I.6.17}$$

summed for the dummy index $j = 1, 2, 3$.

(b) The change caused in a scalar function of position is

$$F(x') = F(x_i + \epsilon_{ij}x_j)$$
$$\cong F(x_i) + \epsilon_{ij}x_j \frac{\partial F}{\partial x_i}.$$

We may introduce the dual vector ϵ_i (axial vector) of the tensor ϵ_{ij} by $\epsilon_{ij} = \epsilon_{ijk}\epsilon_k$ and write

$$F(x_i') = F(x_i) + \epsilon_{ijk}\epsilon_k x_j \frac{\partial F}{\partial x_i}.$$

In ordinary vector notation this becomes

$$\delta_\epsilon F = F(\boldsymbol{r}') - F(\boldsymbol{r}) = -\boldsymbol{\epsilon}\cdot\boldsymbol{r} \times \nabla F, \tag{I.6.18}$$

where ∇F = gradient of F (a polar vector). The vector $\boldsymbol{r} \times \nabla F$ is axial, so the change δF is a scalar. If we take F to be the action function S of a dynamical system, then from (*I.1.5*) and (*I.6.18*) we can write

$$\delta_\epsilon S = -\boldsymbol{\epsilon}\cdot\boldsymbol{L}, \tag{I.6.19}$$

where $\boldsymbol{L} = \boldsymbol{r} \times \nabla S = \boldsymbol{r} \times \boldsymbol{p}$.

(c) We may choose a special generator $\boldsymbol{\epsilon}$, defined by

$$\boldsymbol{\epsilon} = \frac{e}{mc}\mathfrak{H}\delta t. \tag{I.6.20}$$

This follows from the Lorentz equation of motion,

$$d\boldsymbol{p} = \frac{e}{mc}\delta t\boldsymbol{p} \times \mathfrak{H}.$$

The change in S from (*I.6.19*) becomes

$$\delta_\epsilon S = -\frac{e\delta t}{mc}\mathfrak{H}\cdot\boldsymbol{L}. \tag{I.6.21}$$

Hence

$$-\frac{\delta_\epsilon S}{\delta t} = \frac{e}{mc}\mathfrak{H}\cdot\boldsymbol{L} \tag{I.6.22}$$

would be the additional energy required in our dynamical system to maintain invariance under the infinitesimal transformation generated by (*I.6.20*).

The change in the momentum vector caused by the particular ϵ characterized by (*I.6.20*), as follows from (*I.6.15*), yields the Lorentz equation of motion,

$$\delta\boldsymbol{p} = \frac{e\delta t}{mc}\boldsymbol{p} \times \mathfrak{H},$$

as would be expected.

(d) Taking F to be the Hamiltonian of a dynamical system, we obtain

$$\delta_\epsilon H = -\boldsymbol{\epsilon}\cdot\boldsymbol{r} \times \nabla H = \boldsymbol{\epsilon}\cdot\boldsymbol{r} \times \dot{\boldsymbol{p}} = \boldsymbol{\epsilon}\cdot\dot{\boldsymbol{L}}.$$

Thus the Hamiltonian will be invariant under an infinitesimal rotation of coordinates if $\dot{\boldsymbol{L}} = 0$; that is, if the angular momentum vector is conserved. But, if the angular momentum of a dynamical system is conserved, then the Hamiltonian is invariant with respect to infinitesimal rotations of coordinates.

I.6.D. Problems

1. With $\lambda\boldsymbol{L}$ as the generator of an infinitesimal transformation, show that the change in a scalar function F is given by

$$\delta F = -\lambda \boldsymbol{L}\cdot\boldsymbol{r} \times \nabla F, \tag{I.6.23}$$

where λ is a small constant and $\boldsymbol{L}$ is an angular momentum vector. What is the general nature of a system unaffected by such transformations?

2. Prove that a spherically symmetric function F does not change under an infinitesimal transformation of coordinates, regardless of the nature of the generator of the transformation. Conversely, any function remaining unchanged under any infinitesimal change of coordinates is a spherically symmetric function of coordinates.

3. If the function F in (*I.6.23*) is taken to be the Lagrangian of a dynamical system, then the Lagrangian does not change if the total angular momentum is conserved and the angular momentum vector can be a function of time.

I.7. The Integral Equation for the Time-Dependent Rotation Operator

I.7.A. Derivation and Solution of the Integral Equation

The material to be discussed in this section will be found very useful in connection with the formulation of scattering processes and, in particular, for the integral equation formulation of quantum mechanics.

The differential equation $i(dA/dt) = SA$, with the initial condition $A(t_0, t_0) = I$, can be replaced by an integral equation. We integrate both sides of the differential equation in the time interval (t_0, t), where the flow of time is characterized by

$$t \geqq t_0. \tag{I.7.1}$$

The integration gives

$$i[A(t, t_0) - A(t_0, t_0)] = \int_{t_0}^{t} S(t')A(t', t_0)\, dt'.$$

The condition $t \geqq t_0$ can be formulated in terms of discontinuous function of time, $\epsilon_+(t, t_0)$, defined by

$$\epsilon_+(t, t_0) = \begin{cases} 1 & \text{if } t \geqq t_0, \\ 0 & \text{if } t < t_0. \end{cases} \tag{I.7.2}$$

This condition can be incorporated into the integral equation in the form

$$A(t, t_0) = I - i \int_{t_0}^{t} \epsilon_+(t, t_1) S(t_1) A(t_1, t_0)\, dt_1, \tag{I.7.3}$$

where S now plays the role of a "kernel" of a linear integral equation. The solution of (*I.7.3*) is a rotation operator operating on vectors at time t_0 to produce vectors at a later time t. The operator $A(t, t_0)$ varies with time t and its determinant remains $+1$ at all times.

Without the knowledge of the Hermitian generator $S(t_1)$ the solutions of (*I.7.3*) are only of formal interest. It is, actually, this formal aspect of the problem that will interest us most, since in quantum mechanics A will be replaced by a unitary operator in a Hilbert space and S by the quantum Hamiltonian of a dynamical system.

The more usual method of solving the differential equation is to assume an infinite series expansion of A in powers of small generator S.

The series for A is

$$A(t, t_0) = I + \sum_{n=1}^{\infty} A_n, \tag{I.7.4}$$

where A_n is of order n in S. Substitution of the infinite series (*I.7.4*) in the differential equation, and equating on both sides terms of the same order, leads to an infinite number of coupled sets of differential equations. In principle the solution of these equations would define each A_n in terms of A_{n-1}, ad infinitum.

However, the modern approach to the problem requires the use of the integral equation. Its advantages, in the absence of exact solutions of the differential equation, and its superiority over the former method will be understood better when we have more occasions to apply it to other problems.

There are, in general, various methods available for solving integral equations. For the present problem we shall use Neumann-Liouville's "method of successive substitutions," the iteration method.

We substitute in the second member of (*I.7.3*), in place of $A(t_1, t_0)$, its value as given by the equation itself, and we find

$$A(t, t_0) = I + (-i) \int_{t_0}^{t} \epsilon_+(t, t_1) S(t_1)\, dt_1 + (-i)^2 \int_{t_0}^{t} \int_{t_0}^{t} \epsilon_+(t, t_1) \epsilon_+(t_1, t_2) S(t_1) S(t_2) A(t_2, t_0)\, dt_1\, dt_2,$$

where the limits of the integrals are, because of ϵ_+ function, the same. Continuing the process of substitution we obtain

$$\begin{aligned} A(t, t_0) = I &+ (-i) \int_{t_0}^{t} \epsilon_+(t, t_1) S(t_1)\, dt_1 \\ &+ (-i)^2 \int_{t_0}^{t} \int_{t_0}^{t} dt_1\, dt_2\, \epsilon_+(t, t_1) \epsilon_+(t_1, t_2) S(t_1) S(t_2) \\ &+ \cdots + (-i)^n \int_{t_0}^{t} \cdots \int_{t_0}^{t} dt_1 \cdots dt_n\, \epsilon_+(t, t_1) \cdots \epsilon_+(t_{n-1}, t_n) \\ &\times S(t_1) \cdots S(t_n) + R_{n+1}. \end{aligned} \tag{I.7.5}$$

The solution is an infinite series,

$$A(t, t_0) = I + \sum_{n=1}^{\infty} A_n(t, t_0),$$

differing from the former method in the definition of A_n.

The process of substitution requires justification. We assume that our kernel S is a continuous function of time in (t_0, t). Therefore each term of the series is a continuous function of time. The generator S must, because of its continuity, have a maximum in (t_0, t). The orthogonality condition $A^\dagger A = AA^\dagger = I$ must be satisfied during (t_0, t). From tr $(A^\dagger A) =$ tr $I = n$, we get

$$N(A) = \sqrt{n}. \tag{I.7.6}$$

This condition of the norm can be incorporated into the proof of convergence of the series. We have tr $(A^\dagger A_l^\dagger A_l A) =$ tr $A_l^\dagger A_l$. Hence

$$N(A_l) = N(A_l A) = N(AA_l), \tag{I.7.7}$$

so the use of the inequality (*I.5.24*) yields the result*

$$N(A_l) \leqq N(A) \int_{t_0}^{t} \cdots \int_{t_0}^{t} dt_1 \cdots dt_l\, \epsilon_+(t, t_1) \cdots \epsilon_+(t_{l-1}, t_l)[N(S)]^l.$$

If we assume that

$$N(S) \leqq \omega, \tag{I.7.6}$$

we find that

$$N(A_l) \leqq \sqrt{n} \int_{t_0}^{t} \int_{t_0}^{t} \epsilon_+(t, t_1) \cdots \epsilon_+(t_{l-1}, t_l)\, dt_1 \cdots dt_l.$$

The integral is easily evaluated:

$$\int_{t_0}^{t} \cdots \int_{t_0}^{t} \epsilon_+(t, t_1)\epsilon_+(t_1, t_2) \cdots \epsilon_+(t_{l-1}, t_l)\, dt_1 \cdots dt_l = \frac{(t - t_0)^l}{l!}.$$

Hence the condition for absolute convergence becomes

$$N(A_l) \leqq \sqrt{n}\, \frac{\omega^l (t - t_0)^l}{l!}. \tag{I.7.7}$$

The sum over l from 1 to ∞ leads to

$$\left[\sqrt{n} + \sum_{l=1}^{\infty} N(A_l)\right] \leqq \sqrt{n} e^{\omega(t-t_0)}. \tag{I.7.8}$$

I.7.B. Symbolic Expression for a General Time-Dependent Rotation Operator

Consider the term A_2 of the series

$$A_2 = (-i)^2 \int_{t_0}^{t} \int_{t_0}^{t} \epsilon_+(t, t_1)\epsilon_+(t_1, t_2) S(t_1) S(t_2)\, dt_1\, dt_2.$$

---

* See H. Weyl, *Theory of Groups and Quantum Mechanics*, Dover, New York, 1931, p. 30.

We can interchange the variables t_1 and t_2 and write

$$A_2 = (-i)^2 \int_{t_0}^{t} \int_{t_0}^{t} \epsilon_+(t, t_2)\epsilon_+(t_2, t_1)S(t_2)S(t_1)\, dt_1\, dt_2.$$

The two integrals are identical. In both of them the time labels, by means of ϵ_+ functions, are rearranged in such a way that the operator with the latest time label occurs first in the product of operators.

We may, therefore, introduce an operator P to rearrange the time labels of a product of operators, reading from right to left—that is, from earlier to the later time.* For the product of two operators there are only two possible permutations of the time labels (because of integration over the same time intervals), so

$$A_2 = \frac{1}{2!}(-i)^2 \int_{t_0}^{t} \int_{t_0}^{t} P[S(t_1)S(t_2)]\, dt_1\, dt_2.$$

For the kth term, because of k integrations over k variables, we have $k!$ possible permutations of the time labels to symmetrize the integrand. Thus

$$A_k = \frac{1}{k!}(-i)^k \int_{t_0}^{t} \cdots \int_{t_0}^{t} P[S(t_1) \cdots S(t_k)]\, dt_1 \cdots dt_k.$$

In this way the role of the ϵ_+ functions under the integral sign is replaced by the P operator. The infinite series, then, becomes

$$A(t, t_0) = P \exp\left[-i \int_{t_0}^{t} S(t_1)\, dt_1\right]. \qquad (I.7.9)$$

This result will be found very useful in the discussion of scattering theory.

I.7.C. Problems

1. Show that all proper rotation operators can be expressed by

$$A = \frac{I - iK}{I + iK}, \qquad (I.7.10)$$

where $K^\dagger = K$.

2. Assume the initial condition

$$A(t_0, t_0) = -I$$

in the integral equation and discuss the solutions for even- and odd-dimensional spaces.

3. Prove that for an orthogonal matrix with determinant -1, $\det(I + A) = 0$. Prove also that for odd-dimensional spaces, $-A$ is the transformation operator with determinant -1. What is the meaning of

$$\det(I - A) = 0?$$

---

* F. J. Dyson, *Phys. Rev.*, **75** (1949), 486.

4. Prove that a time-dependent operator $V(t)$, given by

$$V(t) = A(t)V(O)\tilde{A}(t), \tag{I.7.11}$$

satisfies the equation

$$i\frac{dV}{dt} = [S, V], \tag{I.7.12}$$

where $[S, V] = SV - VS$.

5. The proper orthogonal transformations can be obtained from the infinitesimal rotations by integration. Prove that the improper orthogonal transformations (determinant -1) cannot be obtained from the infinitesimal transformations.

I.8. Finite Rotations

The motion of a rigid body in Euclidean space with one point fixed is described by the group of rotations in three-dimensional space. Finite rotations of the body can be thought of as built up from the integration of successive infinitesimal rotations. At any moment the operator for rotation has the form

$$A = e^{iS}, \tag{I.8.1}$$

where S can be expressed in terms of the three parameters of the group or the three rotational degrees of freedom of body as

$$S = S_i K_i, \tag{I.8.2}$$

where the matrices K_i, where $i = 1, 2, 3$, are given by

$$K_j = \begin{bmatrix} 0 & -i\delta_{j3} & i\delta_{j2} \\ i\delta_{j3} & 0 & -i\delta_{j1} \\ -i\delta_{j2} & i\delta_{j1} & 0 \end{bmatrix}. \tag{I.8.3}$$

The generator matrices K_l of the rotation satisfy the commutation relations

$$\begin{aligned} K_iK_j - K_jK_i &= i\epsilon_{ijl}K_l, \\ K_i^\dagger &= K_i, \qquad i = 1, 2, 3. \end{aligned} \tag{I.8.4}$$

A very useful (to be seen later) relation is

$$K^2 = K_1^2 + K_2^2 + K_3^2 = 2\mathrm{I}.$$

The parameters S_k are independent of space and time coordinates. We may regard each set of values of the group parameters or the generator S itself as a point in the group manifold. The values $S_k = 0$ (that is, $S = 0$) being the identity (I) element of the group. All other members of the group being generated by at least one nonvanishing S_k. With two of the parameters S_k taken to be zero, the remaining nonzero element generates an element of orthogonal transformation of the rotation group. In order to bring about a clear understanding of the group-theoretical discussion of orthogonal transformations, we shall work out an especially simple case in some detail.

A K_i matrix is the generator of a rotation (with parameter S_i) around the ith coordinate axis. For example, a rotation around the z-axis with $S_3 = \phi$ is affected by the operator

$$A(\phi) = e^{i\phi K_3}. \tag{I.8.5}$$

The eigenvalue equation,

$$K_3|K_3'\rangle = K_3'|K_3'\rangle, \tag{I.8.6}$$

provides an orthonormal basis in S space with the (normalized) eigenkets

$$|1\rangle = \sqrt{(\tfrac{1}{2})}\begin{bmatrix}1\\ i\\ 0\end{bmatrix}, \qquad |-1\rangle = \sqrt{(\tfrac{1}{2})}\begin{bmatrix}1\\ -i\\ 0\end{bmatrix}, \qquad |0\rangle = \begin{bmatrix}0\\ 0\\ 1\end{bmatrix}, \tag{I.8.7}$$

which belong to the eigenvalues $+1$, -1, and 0, respectively. Every eigenket in S-space can be expressed in terms of $|1\rangle$, $|-1\rangle$, $|0\rangle$. In particular, the operator representation for unit operator I is

$$I = |1\rangle\langle 1| + |-1\rangle\langle -1| + |0\rangle\langle 0|. \tag{I.8.8}$$

Hence, operating with K_3, we get the operator representation of K_3 by

$$K_3 = |1\rangle\langle 1| - |-1\rangle\langle -1|. \tag{I.8.9}$$

From (*I.8.5*), (*I.8.6*), and (*I.8.7*) we have

$$\begin{aligned} e^{i\phi K_3}|1\rangle &= e^{i\phi}|1\rangle, \\ e^{i\phi K_3}|-1\rangle &= e^{-i\phi}|-1\rangle, \\ e^{i\phi K_3}|0\rangle &= |0\rangle. \end{aligned} \tag{I.8.10}$$

The rotation operator $e^{i\phi K_3}$, operating on the vector $|x\rangle$, gives another vector $|x'\rangle$,

$$|x'\rangle = e^{iK_3\phi}|x\rangle, \tag{I.8.11}$$

the Hermitian conjugate of which is

$$\langle x'| = \langle x|e^{-i\phi K_3}. \tag{I.8.12}$$

The Hermitian conjugates of (*I.8.10*) are

$$\begin{aligned} \langle 1|e^{-i\phi K_3} &= \langle 1|e^{-i\phi}, \\ \langle -1|e^{-i\phi K_3} &= \langle -1|e^{i\phi}, \\ \langle 0|e^{-i\phi K_3} &= \langle 0|, \end{aligned} \tag{I.8.13}$$

where

$$\langle 1| = \frac{1}{\sqrt{2}}[1, -i, 0],$$

$$\langle -1| = \frac{1}{\sqrt{2}}[1, i, 0],$$

$$\langle 0| = [0, 0, 1].$$

If we multiply $(I.8.13)$ scalarly on the right by the ket $|x'\rangle$—that is, take the projection of $|x'\rangle$ into S space—we obtain

$$\begin{aligned} \langle 1|x'\rangle &= e^{i\phi}\langle 1|x\rangle, \\ \langle -1|x'\rangle &= e^{-i\phi}\langle -1|x\rangle, \\ \langle 0|x'\rangle &= \langle 0|x\rangle. \end{aligned}$$

Hence, with

$$|x\rangle = \begin{bmatrix} x_1 \\ x_2 \\ x_3 \end{bmatrix},$$

the transformations lead to

$$\begin{aligned} x_+ &= e^{i\phi}x'_+, \\ x_- &= e^{-i\phi}x'_-, \\ x_3 &= x'_3, \end{aligned} \qquad (I.8.14)$$

where $x_+ = (x_1 + ix_2)$, $x_- = (x_1 - ix_2)$, and $e^{i\phi}$, $e^{-i\phi}$, $+1$ are the eigenvalues of $A(\phi)$. The matrix representation of the operator $A(\phi)$ in S space reduces to a diagonal form:

$$\begin{aligned} \langle 1|A|1\rangle &= e^{i\phi}, \\ \langle -1|A|-1\rangle &= e^{-i\phi}, \\ \langle 0|A|0\rangle &= 1. \end{aligned}$$

All other elements are zero. Thus

$$|x_c\rangle = \Lambda|x'_c\rangle, \qquad (I.8.15)$$

where

$$\Lambda = \begin{bmatrix} e^{i\phi} & 0 & 0 \\ 0 & e^{-i\phi} & 0 \\ 0 & 0 & 1 \end{bmatrix}, \qquad (I.8.16)$$

$$|x_c\rangle = \begin{bmatrix} x_+ \\ x_- \\ x_3 \end{bmatrix}, \qquad \Lambda^\dagger\Lambda = I. \qquad (I.8.17)$$

The transformation equation $(I.8.11)$ in real space is replaced by the transformation equation $(I.8.15)$ in complex space with unitary diagonal rotation operator Λ. In both cases,

$$\langle x'_c|x'_c\rangle = \langle x_c|x_c\rangle = \langle x'|x'\rangle = \langle x|x\rangle.$$

Thus a one-parameter real orthogonal transformation can be represented by a one-parameter unitary diagonal transformation. There is a one-to-one correspondence between the group of one-parameter orthogonal transformations and the one-parameter commutative (Abelian) group of unitary transformations. Both groups have a common parameter.

In general, any real vector

$$|\pi\rangle = \begin{bmatrix} \pi_1 \\ \pi_2 \\ \pi_3 \end{bmatrix},$$

which transforms according to $|\pi'\rangle = e^{i\phi K_3}|\pi\rangle$ in three-dimensional Euclidean space, can be projected into the S space by (*I.8.8*), as

$$|\pi\rangle = |1\rangle\langle 1|\pi\rangle + |-1\rangle\langle -1|\pi\rangle + |0\rangle\langle 0|\pi\rangle.$$

The projections form a new vector

$$|\pi_c\rangle = \begin{bmatrix} \pi_+ \\ \pi_- \\ \pi_3 \end{bmatrix} = \begin{bmatrix} \pi_1 + i\pi_2 \\ \pi_1 - i\pi_2 \\ \pi_3 \end{bmatrix},$$

which transforms in the unitary space according to

$$|\pi_c'\rangle = \Lambda|\pi_c\rangle.$$

Written explicitly, the transformations are

$$\begin{aligned} \pi_+' &= e^{i\phi}\pi_+, \\ \pi_-' &= e^{-i\phi}\pi_-, \\ \pi_3' &= \pi_3, \end{aligned} \tag{I.8.18}$$

where $|\pi_c'\rangle$ is the complex vector resulting from a rotation in C_3 around the $|0\rangle$ eigenvector of S space. Here again we have

$$\langle\pi_c'|\pi_c'\rangle = \langle\pi_c|\pi_c\rangle. \tag{I.8.19}$$

These results will find an important application in the field of gauge transformations. The representation of K_3 in S space, in terms of a unitary matrix U, is

$$K_0 = U^\dagger K_3 U = \begin{bmatrix} 1 & 0 & 0 \\ 0 & -1 & 0 \\ 0 & 0 & 0 \end{bmatrix},$$

where

$$U = i\begin{bmatrix} \frac{1}{\sqrt{2}} & \frac{1}{\sqrt{2}} & 0 \\ \frac{i}{\sqrt{2}} & -\frac{i}{\sqrt{2}} & 0 \\ 0 & 0 & 1 \end{bmatrix}, \qquad \det U = 1,$$

is formed from the eigenvectors of K_3 and multiplied by a phase factor i to make $\det U = +1$. Thus

$$\Lambda = e^{i\phi K_0}, \qquad A(\phi) = e^{i\phi K_3},$$

and

$$U^\dagger A U = \Lambda = e^{iU^\dagger K_3 U\phi}. \tag{I.8.20}$$

A member of the three-dimensional proper rotation group can be represented as an orthogonal transformation operator expressed in terms of the product of three one-parameter rotation operators:

$$A = \exp(i\psi K_1)\exp(i\theta K_2)\exp(i\phi K_3). \tag{I.8.21}$$

This is equivalent to classical Euler factorization of any three-dimensional rotation into three plane rotations.

The parameters S_i of the orthogonal group may be thought of as functions of some other continuous parameter or parameters. For example, if the S_i are functions of time t, then a finite rotation can be regarded as built up from infinitesimal rotations executed during small time intervals. In this way every element of the rotation group is reached from the identity element I of the group by a continuous unfolding of infinitesimal steps of rotations. When we think in terms of the infinitesimal elements of a continuous group, the mathematical scheme involved is called "Lie algebra." For example, the K-matrices of the rotation group are typical elements of a Lie algebra, since each K_i is the generator of an infinitesimal rotation.

I.9. Unitary Transformations and the Orthogonal Group

I.9.A. Properties and Operator Representation of Unitary Transformations

The invariance requirements of quantum mechanics are formulated over the continuum of complex numbers. In this connection unitary transformations are found to be the most relevant complex operators used in the formulation of the theory.

The simplest unitary transformations arise from the requirement of invariance of the Hermitian form

$$\begin{aligned} L &= x_1^* x_1 + \cdots + x_n^* x_n \\ &= \langle x|x\rangle, \end{aligned} \tag{I.9.1}$$

under a rotation of coordinates in complex space C_n. The expression (*I.9.1*) is the general concept of length in C_n. The coefficients of a Hermitian form are the diagonal elements of a unit matrix (the metric of a linear unitary space),

$$L = \langle x|I|x\rangle.$$

A vector $|x\rangle$ in unitary space transforms according to

$$|x'\rangle = U|x\rangle, \tag{I.9.2}$$

so

$$\langle x'|x'\rangle = \langle x|U^\dagger U|x\rangle = \langle x|x\rangle,$$

and hence

$$U^\dagger U = I. \tag{I.9.3}$$

The transformation must be reversible; that is, we must also require the existence of the same transformation operator for going from $|x'\rangle$ to $|x\rangle$, namely

$$U^{-1}|x'\rangle = U^\dagger|x'\rangle = |x\rangle.$$

Hence

$$\langle x|x\rangle = \langle x'|UU^\dagger|x'\rangle = \langle x'|x'\rangle$$

and

$$UU^\dagger = I. \tag{I.9.4}$$

Therefore, a necessary and sufficient condition for the unitary character of a transformation operator in C_n is

$$U^\dagger U = UU^\dagger = I. \tag{I.9.5}$$

If we set up (with the same origin) two orthonormal basic sets $|c_i\rangle$ and $|c_i'\rangle$ in C_n, then the corresponding operator representation of the unitary transformation operator is

$$U = \sum_{i=1}^{n} |c_i'\rangle\langle c_i|, \tag{I.9.6}$$

where

$$\langle c_i|c_j\rangle = \langle c_i'|c_j'\rangle = \delta_{ij}. \tag{I.9.7}$$

Under unitary transformations, an operator O transforms according to

$$O' = U^\dagger O U.$$

The definition (*I.9.6*) satisfies the condition of unitarity (*I.9.5*). The basic sets $|c_i'\rangle$ and $|c_i\rangle$ are related by

$$|c_i'\rangle = U|c_i\rangle. \tag{I.9.8}$$

For any vector $|a\rangle$ in a $|c_i\rangle$-coordinate system we have

$$|a'\rangle = U|a\rangle = \sum_i |c_i'\rangle\langle c_i|a\rangle$$

$$= \sum_{i=1}^{n} a_i|c_i'\rangle$$

in the $|c_n'\rangle$-coordinate system.

The matrix representation of $U^\dagger$ in any coordinate system is the transposed complex conjugate of the matrix representation of U.

Condition (*I.9.5*) implies that a unitary operator in C_n requires the specification of

$$(2n^2) - n - 2\,\frac{n(n-1)}{2} = n^2$$

parameters. The determinant of U is

$$|\det U| = \pm 1.$$

Hence

$$\det U = e^{i\gamma} \tag{I.9.9}$$

is a complex number of unit magnitude. The unitary character of the transformation allows an extra degree of freedom through its invariance with respect to an arbitrary phase transformation. Thus

$$U' = e^{i\delta} U \tag{I.9.10}$$

is also a unitary operator satisfying the same condition of unitarity as U. The determinant of U' is

$$\det U' = \det (e^{i\delta} U) = e^{i\gamma + in\delta}.$$

We can choose the phase δ in such a way that det U' becomes $+1$. The particular phase factors satisfying this requirement are

$$\delta_N = \frac{2N\pi}{n} - \frac{\gamma}{n}, \tag{I.9.11}$$

where $N = 1, 2, \cdots$.

The use of the phase invariance of the unitarity condition enables us to reduce the number of parameters required for the specification of a unitary transformation from n^2 to $n^2 - 1$. Let D_U and D_R be the dimensionalities of any complex and real spaces, respectively. The number of parameters required for a complete specification of unitary and of real orthogonal transformations is the same only for those cases where

$$D_U^2 - 1 = \tfrac{1}{2} D_R (D_R - 1). \tag{I.9.12}$$

The examples

(a) $D_U = 2, D_R = 3$,
(b) $D_U = 4, D_R = 6$,

are of special importance in quantum mechanics.

The number of parameters for (a) is 3 and for (b) is 15.

The collection of unitary operators in C_n possesses the group property. If U_1 and U_2 are two unitary operators in C_n, then

$$U_1^\dagger U_1 = U_1 U_1^\dagger = I,$$
$$U_2^\dagger U_2 = U_2 U_2^\dagger = I,$$

and

$$(U_1 U_2)^\dagger (U_1 U_2) = (U_1 U_2)(U_1 U_2)^\dagger = I.$$

The collection contains I and the reciprocal $U^\dagger$ of any of its members. Thus the collection of all $n \times n$ unitary operators in C_n constitutes a group. This is called an n-dimensional unitary group.

A subgroup of the n-dimensional unitary group is a collection of n-dimensional unitary operators with determinant $+1$. This is called an n-dimensional unimodular unitary group.

I.9.B. Generators of a Two-Dimensional Unitary Transformation

A finite unitary transformation operator in C_2 can be represented by

$$U = e^{iS}, \tag{I.9.13}$$

where S is a 2×2 Hermitian operator

$$S^\dagger = S, \tag{I.9.14}$$

with trace $S = 0$.

Where $n = 2$, the phase factor δ_N, defined in (*I.9.11*), becomes

$$\delta_N = N\pi - \frac{\gamma}{2}.$$

Thus for a given γ there are two unitary transformation operators with its determinant having the value $+1$:

(a) N even, $U' = e^{-i\gamma/2}U$,
(b) N odd, $U' = -e^{-i\gamma/2}U$.

The even dimensionality of C_2 allows the multiplication of the unitary transformation operators by -1 without changing the $+1$ value of its determinant. Both U and $-U$ are members of the unitary group.

Because of the condition det $U = 1$, the generators of U must be Hermitian 2×2 matrices with zero trace. The most general form of such a generator is

$$S = \begin{bmatrix} a & c^* \\ c & -a \end{bmatrix}, \tag{I.9.15}$$

where a is real and c is a complex number. There are, actually, four possible generators of the type (*I.9.15*) which can be taken. They are

$$S_1 = \begin{bmatrix} a_3 & a_1 - ia_2 \\ a_1 + ia_2 & -a_3 \end{bmatrix}, \qquad S_2 = \begin{bmatrix} a_3 & a_1 + ia_2 \\ a_1 - ia_2 & -a_3 \end{bmatrix},$$

$$S_3 = \begin{bmatrix} -a_3 & a_1 - ia_2 \\ a_1 + ia_2 & a_3 \end{bmatrix}, \qquad S_4 = \begin{bmatrix} -a_3 & a_1 + ia_2 \\ a_1 - ia_2 & a_3 \end{bmatrix},$$

where a_1, a_2, a_3 are arbitrary real numbers. The generators S_1 and S_2 can be written as

$$S_1 = \sum_{i=1}^{3} a_i \sigma_i, \tag{I.9.16}$$

$$S_2 = \sum_{i=1}^{3} a_i \sigma_i^L, \tag{I.9.17}$$

where

$$\sigma_1 = \begin{bmatrix} 0 & 1 \\ 1 & 0 \end{bmatrix}, \qquad \sigma_2 = \begin{bmatrix} 0 & -i \\ i & 0 \end{bmatrix}, \qquad \sigma_3 = \begin{bmatrix} 1 & 0 \\ 0 & -1 \end{bmatrix}, \tag{I.9.18}$$

are Pauli's spin matrices and

$$\sigma_1^L = \sigma_1, \qquad \sigma_2^L = -\sigma_2, \qquad \sigma_3^L = \sigma_3, \tag{I.9.19}$$

usually called left-handed Pauli matrices, differ from the σ only in the sign of σ_2^L. Because of the antilinear relation

$$\sigma_2^L = \overline{C}\sigma_2\overline{C} = -\sigma_2, \tag{I.9.20}$$

it is not possible to transform σ_i^L into σ_i by means of a canonical or unitary transformation. The remaining alternatives, S_3 and S_4, give rise to the sets

$$\sigma_1, \qquad \sigma_2, \quad -\sigma_3, \tag{I.9.21}$$

and

$$\sigma_1, \quad -\sigma_2, \quad -\sigma_3. \tag{I.9.22}$$

By applying a unitary transformation with

$$U = \begin{bmatrix} 0 & 1 \\ 1 & 0 \end{bmatrix} = \sigma_1$$

to the sets (*I.9.21*) and (*I.9.22*), we obtain the original sets (*I.9.18*) and (*I.9.19*). Thus there are only two possible sets of spin matrices.

The Pauli spin matrices satisfy the anticommutation relations

$$\sigma_i\sigma_j + \sigma_j\sigma_i = 2\delta_{ij}, \tag{I.9.23}$$

and the commutation relations

$$\sigma_i\sigma_j - \sigma_j\sigma_i = 2i\epsilon_{ijk}\sigma_k, \tag{I.9.24}$$

and that they are Hermitian matrices:

$$\sigma_i^\dagger = \sigma_i.$$

We now discuss in some detail a particular unitary transformation generated by σ_3:

$$U(a_3) = e^{ia_3\sigma_3}.$$

The eigenvalues of σ_3 are $+1$ and -1 and the corresponding eigenvalues of U are e^{ia_3} and e^{-ia_3}. The eigenvectors of σ_3 are

$$|1\rangle = \begin{bmatrix} 1 \\ 0 \end{bmatrix}, \qquad |-1\rangle = \begin{bmatrix} 0 \\ 1 \end{bmatrix}. \tag{I.9.25}$$

The unit operator is

$$I = |1\rangle\langle 1| + |-1\rangle\langle -1|. \tag{I.9.26}$$

Hence any "vector" $|u\rangle$ in C_2 can be expanded as

$$\begin{aligned} |u\rangle &= |1\rangle\langle 1|u\rangle + |-1\rangle\langle -1|u\rangle \\ &= u_1|1\rangle + u_2|-1\rangle. \end{aligned} \tag{I.9.27}$$

The operator form of σ_3 follows from operating by σ_3 onto I, as

$$\sigma_3 = |1\rangle\langle 1| - |-1\rangle\langle -1|, \tag{I.9.28}$$

and for U we obtain

$$U = e^{ia_3}|1\rangle\langle 1| + e^{-ia_3}|-1\rangle\langle -1|.$$

The matrix representation of U in the system $|1\rangle$ and $|-1\rangle$ is

$$U = \begin{bmatrix} e^{ia_3} & 0 \\ 0 & e^{-ia_3} \end{bmatrix}. \tag{I.9.29}$$

We can set up a homomorphism (one-to-two correspondence) of the two-dimensional unitary group onto the rotation group. We first observe that the particular unitary transformation (*I.8.14*), which leaves $x_1^2 + x_2^2 + x_3^2$ unchanged, can be cast in a two-dimensional complex space as

$$T = \begin{bmatrix} x_3 & x_- \\ x_+ & -x_3 \end{bmatrix} = \begin{bmatrix} x_3' & e^{-i\phi}x_-' \\ e^{+i\phi}x_+' & -x_3' \end{bmatrix}, \tag{I.9.30}$$

where both matrices are Hermitian, with the determinantal connection

$$-(x_1'^2 + x_2'^2 + x_3'^2) = -(x_1^2 + x_2^2 + x_3^2).$$

We may consider T as arising from a two-dimensional unitary transformation given by (*I.9.30*).

Thus

$$T = e^{ia_3\sigma_3}\begin{bmatrix} x_3 & x_- \\ x_+ & -x_3 \end{bmatrix} e^{-ia_3\sigma_3} = \begin{bmatrix} x_3' & x_-'e^{-i\phi} \\ x_+'e^{+i\phi} & -x_3' \end{bmatrix}.$$

Hence

$$\begin{bmatrix} x_3' & x_-'e^{2ia_3} \\ x_+'e^{-2ia_3} & -x_3' \end{bmatrix} = \begin{bmatrix} x_3' & x_-'e^{-i\phi} \\ x_+'e^{+i\phi} & -x_3' \end{bmatrix}.$$

The unitary transformation $U(a_3)$ will induce the same transformation on coordinates as the orthogonal transformation,

$$|x'\rangle = e^{+i\phi K_3}|x\rangle,$$

provided we choose a_3 to be $2a_3 = \phi$. Hence

$$U(\tfrac{1}{2}\phi) = e^{(i\phi/2)\sigma_3}, \tag{I.9.31}$$

and the required homomorphism is

$$A(\phi) \to \pm U(\tfrac{1}{2}\phi). \tag{I.9.32}$$

Result (*I.9.32*) applies also for rotations around x_1 and x_2 directions and for

$$A = e^{i\Psi K_1}e^{i\theta K_2}e^{i\phi K_3} \to \pm e^{(i\Psi/2)\sigma_1}e^{(i\theta/2)\sigma_2}e^{(i\phi/2)\sigma_3}. \tag{I.9.33}$$

We have, thus, seen that in general the transformation $|x'\rangle = A|x\rangle$ in R_3 is induced in C_2 by replacing $|x\rangle$ by a Hermitian matrix T and transforming it according to

$$T' = U^\dagger T U, \tag{I.9.34}$$

where U is a member of the two-dimensional unitary group.

Consider two successive transformations,

$$|x''\rangle = B|x'\rangle,$$
$$|x'\rangle = A|x\rangle,$$

so

$$|x''\rangle = BA|x\rangle.$$

The corresponding unitary transformations are

$$\begin{aligned} T'' &= V^{\dagger}T'V, \\ T' &= U^{\dagger}TU, \end{aligned}$$

so

$$\begin{aligned} T'' &= V^{\dagger}U^{\dagger}TUV = (UV)^{\dagger}T(UV) \\ &= Q^{\dagger}TQ, \end{aligned}$$

where $Q = UV$, or $= e^{i\delta}UV$.

We may, therefore, represent the correspondence of orthogonal and unitary transformation operators by

$$O(Q) = O(U)O(V) = O(UV).$$

If U and V are members of the unitary group, so is $Q = UV$, the unit element being 2×2 unit operator I_2 (or $-I_2$). In R_3, if A and B or $O(U)$ and $O(V)$ are members of the proper orthogonal group, so is $O(UV) = O(U)O(V)$, the unit element being $O(\pm I_2) = I_3$. The correspondence is not one-to-one since $O(U)$ and $O(-U)$ refer to the same transformation in R_3.

We see that the collection of 3×3 real orthogonal matrices $O(U)$ or $O(-U)$, obtained by letting U vary over the 2×2 unitary group, constitutes a representation of this group. We may also regard the 2×2 unimodular unitary group as a representation $O(U) \to \pm U$ of the three-dimensional rotation group, the representation being two-valued. For example, when ϕ varies from 0 to 2π the corresponding $U(\phi/2)$ begins at I_2 and ends at $-I_2$.

Such two-valued representations are called "spin representations." Accordingly, the vectors of C_2 are called "spinors." The two eigenvectors $|1\rangle$ and $|-1\rangle$ spanning C_2 are unit spinors.

I.9.C. Definitions on Group Representations

Definition. *A group G whose representation consists of square matrices is said to be irreducible if the only matrices which commute with its elements are square matrices of the type λI, where λ is a complex number.*

Criterion for Irreducibility. If the matrices $M_1, M_2, \cdots, M_n$ form a group of order n, then the group $G \equiv (M_1, M_2, \cdots, M_n)$ is said to be irreducible if and only if

$$\frac{1}{n}\sum_{i=1}^{n} |C(M_i)|^2 = 1,$$

where $C(M_i)$, which equals trace M_i, is the "character" of the group.*

* J. S. Lomont, *Applications of Finite Groups*, Academic Press, New York, 1959.

The matrices $\pm I_2$, $\pm iI_2$, $\pm \sigma_1$, $\pm \sigma_2$, $\pm \sigma_3$, $\pm i\sigma_1$, $\pm i\sigma_2$, $\pm i\sigma_3$ form an irreducible group of the sixteenth order. It satisfies the criterion for irreducibility. Furthermore the group $G_\sigma \equiv (\pm I_2, \pm iI_2, \pm \sigma_i, \pm i\sigma_i)$ possesses also the property

$$\sum_{i=1}^{16} M_i = 0$$

of an irreducible group, where the M_i, for $i = 1, \cdots, 16$, refer to the elements of the group G_σ.

I.9.D. Examples of Finite Groups

(a) The special proper and improper orthogonal matrices I_3 and $-I_3$, respectively, form a finite group of the second order. The corresponding group multiplication table is

	I_3	$-I_3$
I_3	I_3	$-I_3$
$-I_3$	$-I_3$	I_3

In the same way, I_2 and $-I_2$ form a finite group of the second order; these groups are subgroups of the full orthogonal and unitary groups, respectively.

(b) By substituting $\Psi = \theta = \phi = 2\pi$ in the matrices defined in problem 4 of section I.4, we obtain the matrices belonging to the representation of the rotation-reflection group given by

$$C_1 = \begin{bmatrix} 1 & 0 & 0 \\ 0 & 0 & 1 \\ 0 & 1 & 0 \end{bmatrix}, \qquad C_2 = \begin{bmatrix} 0 & 0 & 1 \\ 0 & 1 & 0 \\ 1 & 0 & 0 \end{bmatrix}, \qquad C_3 = \begin{bmatrix} 0 & 1 & 0 \\ 1 & 0 & 0 \\ 0 & 0 & 1 \end{bmatrix},$$

and

$$E_1 = \begin{bmatrix} 0 & 0 & 1 \\ 1 & 0 & 0 \\ 0 & 1 & 0 \end{bmatrix}, \qquad E_2 = \begin{bmatrix} 0 & 1 & 0 \\ 0 & 0 & 1 \\ 1 & 0 & 0 \end{bmatrix}, \tag{I.9.35}$$

where E_1 and E_2 can be expressed as

$$\begin{aligned} E_1 &= C_2C_3 = C_3C_1 = C_1C_2, \\ E_2 &= C_3C_2 = C_1C_3 = C_2C_1. \end{aligned} \tag{I.9.36}$$

The matrices defined by (*I.9.35*) have the following properties.

(i) They belong to the rotation-reflection group, since

$$\tilde{C}_1C_1 = \tilde{C}_2C_2 = \tilde{C}_3C_3 = \tilde{E}_1E_1 = \tilde{E}_2E_2 = I_3.$$

(ii) The determinants of C_1, C_2, C_3 are

$$\det C_1 = \det C_2 = \det C_3 = -1$$

and

$$\det E_1 = \det E_2 = 1.$$

(iii) The matrices C_1, C_2, and C_3 induce reflection transformations of the generator K_i of the proper rotation group:

$$\begin{aligned} C_iK_iC_i &= -K_i & &\text{for } i = 1, 2, 3, \\ C_iK_jC_i &= -K_k & &\text{for } i, j, k = 1, 2, 3 \text{ (in cyclic order).} \end{aligned} \tag{I.9.37}$$

(iv) The matrices E_1 and E_2 can induce exchange transformation of K_i, as

$$\tilde{E}_1K_1E_1 = K_3, \qquad \tilde{E}_2K_1E_2 = K_2, \cdots,$$

where $\tilde{E}_1 = E_2$, $\tilde{E}_2 = E_1$.

(v) The operators C_1, C_2, C_3, E_1, E_2, together with I_3, form a group of the sixth order; the multiplication table can easily be constructed as

	I_3	C_1	C_2	C_3	E_1	E_2
I_3	I_3	C_1	C_2	C_3	E_1	E_2
C_1	C_1	I_3	E_1	E_2	C_2	C_3
C_2	C_2	E_2	I_3	E_1	C_3	C_1
C_3	C_3	E_1	E_2	I_3	C_1	C_2
E_1	E_1	C_3	C_1	C_2	E_2	I_3
E_2	E_2	C_2	C_3	C_1	I_3	E_1

This is the multiplication table of a finite group. The existence of unique inverses for the members of the group is equivalent to the fact that each group member occurs exactly once in every row and column. The matrices C_1, C_2, C_3 and E_1, E_2, together with I_3, constitute a representation of a subgroup of the rotation-reflection group.

I.10. Lorentz Transformations

A complete description of a dynamical system cannot be based on the principles of quantum mechanics alone; relativistic behavior of nature must be reconciled with its quantum behavior and vice versa. Such a unified point of view is essentially the subject matter of quantum electrodynamics, which is touched on rather briefly in this book. However, the inclusion of special relativity in the discussion of quantum phenomena is of great importance also for ordinary quantum mechanics that does not use the machinery of second quantization in its formulation. For example, the spin coordinate of elementary particles can only be obtained, in a natural way, from the relativistic formulation of quantum mechanics. Furthermore, the logical foundations of quantum mechanics cannot completely be apprehended without relativity, since the former borrows the concept of field from the latter via the electromagnetic field. For these reasons we shall give a preliminary discussion of the Lorentz group in this chapter. A brief explanation of special relativity will be followed by a nonabstract discussion of the Lorentz group.

Experiments prove (a) the constancy of the velocity of light with respect to reference frames in uniform motion relative to one another (inertial frames), and (b) the independence of the laws of physics (in particular the law of the constancy of the light velocity) of the choice of the inertial system.

The observational facts (a) and (b) imply that, from the point of view of measurement of space and time intervals, it is not possible to maintain simultaneity of two events with respect to arbitrary inertial frames in relative motion. Hence the statements (a) and (b) are compatible only when we postulate some new rules of transformations for the conversion of coordinates and times of events. The new transformation rules are called "Lorentz transformations" and are, directly, derivable from experiment.

The constancy of the velocity of light with respect to any two inertial reference frames S and S', moving relative to one another with a constant velocity, finds its mathematical expression in the statement

$$\Delta x_1^2 + \Delta x_2^2 + \Delta x_3^2 - c^2\Delta t^2 = \Delta x_1'^2 + \Delta x_2'^2 + \Delta x_3'^2 - c^2\Delta t'^2 = 0, \qquad (I.10.1)$$

where Δx_i and $\Delta x_i'$ for $i = 1, 2, 3$, together with $c\Delta t$ and $c\Delta t'$, specify space and time intervals of two events in S and S', respectively. We have assumed that light propagates rectilinearly and isotropically in free space with constant speed c. Observers in S and S' can measure space and time intervals with rods and clocks having identical physical constitution for both S and S'. The measuring processes of space and time are carried out with completely independent devices, but the measured results are related to one another by Lorentz transformations.

If the observer in S assigns four coordinates* x^μ to an event, where $\mu = 1, 2, 3, 4$, then he may also define in S the metric

$$-ds^2 = dx_1^2 + dx_2^2 + dx_3^2 - c^2\,dt^2. \qquad (I.10.2)$$

With the aid of this metric the observer can

(a) measure time intervals $dt = (1/c)\,ds$ at any fixed point x_i for $i = 1, 2, 3$;
(b) measure space intervals $dr^2 = -ds^2$ at any fixed time t;
(c) relate all space-time events causally with respect to a light cone $ds^2 = 0$, with a particular event E as its vertex.

In special relativity the time coordinate is treated on an equal footing with the space coordinates, so we describe physical phenomena in a single four-

---

* Greek indices run through 1 to 4 and Latin indices through 1 to 3.

dimensional world instead of in the usual (3 + 1)-dimensional world. The four-dimensionality of the physical continuum in special relativity comes as a necessity, since it creates a formal dependence between the way in which the spatial coordinates, on the one hand, and the temporal coordinates, on the other, have to enter into the laws of physics. This equivalent treatment of space and time has had far reaching consequences in physics; besides its many classical results in relativistic quantum mechanics, the existence of the magnetic moment (and hence of intrinsic spin of elementary particles) is entirely a relativistic effect.

Because of these considerations we have to introduce four-dimensional scalars, vectors, tensors, and so on, representing physical entities, and also their transformation rules relating the components of these quantities in different coordinate systems.

The only and important difference between a four-dimensional Euclidean interval $dx_1^2 + dx_2^2 + dx_3^2 + dx_4^2$ and the interval defined by (*I.10.2*) comes from the negative sign of the $c^2\,dt^2$ term in (*I.10.2*). This fundamental aspect of the theory (as imposed by the law of propagation of light in free space) can best be studied in terms of a group-theoretical approach.

I.10.A. Discussion of the Lorentz Group

In this book it will not be necessary to invoke the mathematical theory of groups. We shall, as in previous sections, use the words of group theory somewhat freely; for example, the usual group terminology includes, among others, "representation," "irreducibility," "correspondence," and so on. We believe that it is possible to discuss essential features of the Lorentz group without further mathematical elaboration of group theory.

We first define a metric tensor $a_{\mu\nu}$ by

$$a_{ij} = -\delta_{ij}, \qquad a_{i4} = a_{4i} = 0, \qquad a_{44} = 1, \tag{I.10.3}$$

which has the matrix representation

$$F = [a_{\mu\nu}] = \begin{bmatrix} -1 & 0 & 0 & 0 \\ 0 & -1 & 0 & 0 \\ 0 & 0 & -1 & 0 \\ 0 & 0 & 0 & 1 \end{bmatrix}. \tag{I.10.4}$$

The metric tensor $a_{\mu\nu}$ and its reciprocal $a^{\mu\nu}$ can be used to introduce covariant and contravariant components of tensorial quantities. Thus, if the A_μ are the components of a covariant vector, then the components of the corresponding contravariant vector are $A^\mu = a^{\mu\nu}A_\nu$, where the dummy index ν implies a summation convention and the contravariant metric tensor is related to the covariant metric tensor by $a^{\alpha\rho}a_{\beta\rho} = \delta_\beta^\alpha$.

The scalar product of two vectors A_μ and B_μ is given by

$$a^{\mu\nu}A_\mu B_\nu = a_{\mu\nu}A^\mu B^\nu = A_4B_4 - \boldsymbol{A}\cdot\boldsymbol{B},$$

where $\boldsymbol{A}\cdot\boldsymbol{B}$ is the ordinary scalar product of two three-dimensional vectors $\boldsymbol{A}$ and $\boldsymbol{B}$. The square of a vector A_μ is, therefore, defined by $A_\mu A^\mu = A_4^2 - \boldsymbol{A}^2$.

We shall find it more convenient to give the above definitions in terms of row and column vector notation, as in previous sections. We can represent a four-dimensional covariant vector a_μ as the ket vector $|a\supset$ and its contravariant components a^μ as a bra vector $\subset a|F$. In this case the scalar product of two vectors a_μ and b_μ is

$$a^\mu b_\mu = \subset a|F|b\supset, \qquad (I.10.5)$$

where

$$\subset a|F = [-a_1, -a_2, -a_3, a_4]$$

and

$$|b\supset = \begin{bmatrix} b_1 \\ b_2 \\ b_3 \\ b_4 \end{bmatrix},$$

$$F^2 = I.$$

The four-dimensional space-time interval can be written as

$$ds^2 = \subset dx|F|dx\supset. \qquad (I.10.6)$$

Let us stipulate a four-dimensional transformation from the coordinates x^μ to another set of coordinates x'^μ affected by means of a 4×4 transformation matrix L,

$$|x'\supset = L|x\supset. \qquad (I.10.7)$$

A matrix L satisfying the invariance condition

$$\subset x|F|x\supset = \subset x'|F|x'\supset \qquad (I.10.8)$$

is called a "Lorentz matrix." The transformations of four-dimensional quantities (scalars, vectors, tensors, and so on) effected by a Lorentz matrix are called Lorentz transformations. The forms of the matrix elements of L are defined by experiment.

The invariance condition (*I.10.8*) together with the transformation rule (*I.10.7*) of any vector $|x\supset$ leads, for any Lorentz matrix L, to the matrix equation

$$\tilde{L}FL = F. \qquad (I.10.9)$$

This restriction on L implies that any Lorentz matrix is completely determined by six parameters.

The reverse transformation, from $|x'\supset$ to $|x\supset$, is effected by the transpose of L, $\tilde{L}$. Transformation from the S' frame to the S frame is

$$|x\supset = F\tilde{L}F|x'\supset, \qquad (I.10.10)$$

where $F\tilde{L}F = L^{-1}$. Thus the reciprocal of a Lorentz transformation is again such a transformation. Two successive Lorentz transformations,

$$|x'\supset = L_1|x\supset,$$
$$|x''\supset = L_2|x'\supset,$$

can be replaced by a single Lorentz transformation,

$$|x''\supset = L|x\supset,$$

where

$$L = L_2L_1,$$
$$\tilde{L}_2FL_2 = F,$$
$$\tilde{L}_1FL_1 = F,$$

so $L = L_2L_1$ is a Lorentz matrix. The Lorentz transformations defined by (*I.10.7*) and (*I.10.9*) are called "homogeneous Lorentz transformations" and they form an infinite group. We may also introduce "inhomogeneous Lorentz transformations." The latter differ from the homogeneous Lorentz transformations by a translation of coordinates,

$$|x'\supset = |a\supset + L|x\supset. \tag{I.10.11}$$

The inhomogeneous group is a group of ten parameters.

The determinant of a Lorentz matrix can be calculated from (*I.10.9*), as

$$\det L = \pm 1. \tag{I.10.12}$$

The matrices F and $-F$ are Lorentz matrices* of determinant -1. If L is a Lorentz matrix of determinant -1, then FL and LF are Lorentz matrices of determinant $+1$. The collection of Lorentz matrices of determinant $+1$ constitute a subgroup of the full Lorentz group and it is called the "proper Lorentz group."

If it was not for the $+1$ value of the F_{44} element (that is, if F_{44} was also -1) of the special Lorentz matrix F, condition (*I.10.9*) of the Lorentz group would be replaced by the orthogonality condition of the four-dimensional orthogonal group (Euclidean group).

The fourth diagonal element of (*I.10.9*) gives

$$(L_{44})^2 - (L_{14})^2 - (L_{24})^2 - (L_{34})^2 = 1. \tag{I.10.13}$$

Hence we see that

$$(L_{44})^2 \geqq 1 \tag{I.10.14}$$

[or equivalently, $|L_{44}| \geqq 1$, where $L_{44} \geqq 1$ and $L_{44} \leqq -1$] must be satisfied by members of the Lorentz group. For the proper group the condition $L_{44} \geqq 1$ is satisfied.

---

* The Lorentz matrices I_4, $-I_4$, F, $-F$ form a subgroup of the Lorentz group, where I_4 is a 4×4 unit matrix.

Because of the non-Euclidean nature of four-dimensional physical space we have to distinguish among various directions of space-time. We define three types of vectors.

(a) A timelike vector $|a\supset$ satisfies the condition

$$\subset a|F|a\supset\ > 0; \qquad (I.10.15)$$

it lies in the positive light cone if $a_4 > 0$, and it lies in the negative light cone if $a_4 < 0$.

(b) A null vector $|b\supset$ lies along the light cone

$$\subset b|F|b\supset\ = 0 \qquad (I.10.16)$$

(c) A vector satisfying the condition

$$\subset C|F|C\supset\ < 0 \qquad (I.10.17)$$

is called a spacelike vector.

Two vectors $|a\supset$ and $|b\supset$ are orthogonal if

$$\subset a|F|b\supset\ = 0. \qquad (I.10.18)$$

If $\subset a|F|b\supset\ > 0$, then both $|a\supset$ and $|b\supset$ lie either in the positive or in the negative light cone. The scalar product is negative if one lies in the positive and the other in the negative light cone.

For transformations of the class $L_{44} \geqq 1$, the timelike or spacelike nature of a vector does not change.*

I.10.B. Generators of the Proper Lorentz Group (The Homogeneous Group)

The connection of a member L of the proper Lorentz group to unit element I_4 of the group can be obtained by assuming that L is a function of an invariant parameter τ. In this case the differentiation of the Lorentz condition $(I.10.9)$ with respect to τ leads to a differential equation for L,

$$i\frac{dL}{d\tau} = \Omega F L, \qquad (I.10.19)$$

where Ω is a 4×4 Hermitian matrix and $i\Omega$ is a real antisymmetric matrix. The operator

$$M = \Omega F \qquad (I.10.20)$$

* The sign of the scalar product of two vectors is fixed by the sign of the product of their time components.

is the generator of the proper Lorentz matrix L and its matrix representation is

$$M = \begin{bmatrix} 0 & -i\Omega_{12} & i\Omega_{31} & -i\Omega_{14} \\ i\Omega_{12} & 0 & -i\Omega_{23} & -i\Omega_{24} \\ -i\Omega_{31} & i\Omega_{23} & 0 & -i\Omega_{34} \\ -i\Omega_{14} & -i\Omega_{24} & -i\Omega_{34} & 0 \end{bmatrix}, \qquad (I.10.21)$$

which can be written as

$$M = \Omega_{\mu\nu} M_{(\mu\nu)}, \qquad (I.10.22)$$

where the $\Omega_{\mu\nu}$ are the six parameters of the group. The six generator matrices $M_{(\mu\nu)}$, corresponding to the six possible plane Lorentz transformations, are given by

$$M_{(23)} = \begin{bmatrix} 0 & 0 & 0 & 0 \\ 0 & 0 & -i & 0 \\ 0 & i & 0 & 0 \\ 0 & 0 & 0 & 0 \end{bmatrix}, \quad M_{(14)} = \begin{bmatrix} 0 & 0 & 0 & -i \\ 0 & 0 & 0 & 0 \\ 0 & 0 & 0 & 0 \\ -i & 0 & 0 & 0 \end{bmatrix},$$

$$M_{(31)} = \begin{bmatrix} 0 & 0 & i & 0 \\ 0 & 0 & 0 & 0 \\ -i & 0 & 0 & 0 \\ 0 & 0 & 0 & 0 \end{bmatrix}, \quad M_{(24)} = \begin{bmatrix} 0 & 0 & 0 & 0 \\ 0 & 0 & 0 & -i \\ 0 & 0 & 0 & 0 \\ 0 & -i & 0 & 0 \end{bmatrix}, \qquad (I.10.23)$$

$$M_{(12)} = \begin{bmatrix} 0 & -i & 0 & 0 \\ i & 0 & 0 & 0 \\ 0 & 0 & 0 & 0 \\ 0 & 0 & 0 & 0 \end{bmatrix}, \quad M_{(34)} = \begin{bmatrix} 0 & 0 & 0 & 0 \\ 0 & 0 & 0 & 0 \\ 0 & 0 & 0 & -i \\ 0 & 0 & -i & 0 \end{bmatrix}.$$

The matrices ($M_{(23)}$, $M_{(31)}$, $M_{(12)}$) and ($M_{(14)}$, $M_{(24)}$, $M_{(34)}$) are, respectively, Hermitian and anti-Hermitian generators of Lorentz transformations.

In order to see the types of transformations generated by the M matrices, we consider, for a time-independent generator, the solutions of equation (*I.10.19*).

The equation is satisfied by

$$L(\tau) = e^{-\tau\Omega F i}, \qquad (I.10.24)$$

and is connected to the identity element I_4 of the group by $\tau = 0$. The operator $L(\tau)$ satisfies the conditions

(a) $\det [L(\tau)] = \exp [-i\tau \operatorname{tr} (\Omega F)] = 1$, and
(b) $\tilde{L}(\tau) F L(\tau) = F$,

where in (b) we used the commutation property

$$F e^{-i\tau\Omega F} = e^{-i\tau F\Omega} F. \qquad (I.10.25)$$

We may now use (*I.10.24*) and the matrix equations

$$\begin{array}{lll} [M_{(23)}]^3 = M_{(23)}, & [M_{(31)}]^3 = M_{(31)}, & [M_{(12)}]^3 = M_{(12)}, \\ [M_{(14)}]^3 = -M_{(14)}, & [M_{(24)}]^3 = -M_{(24)}, & [M_{(34)}]^3 = -M_{(34)} \end{array} \tag{I.10.26}$$

to record the corresponding Lorentz matrices:

$$L_{(23)} = R_1(\psi) = \begin{bmatrix} 1 & 0 & 0 & 0 \\ 0 & \cos\psi & \sin\psi & 0 \\ 0 & -\sin\psi & \cos\psi & 0 \\ 0 & 0 & 0 & 1 \end{bmatrix},$$

$$L_{(31)} = R_2(\phi) = \begin{bmatrix} \cos\phi & 0 & -\sin\phi & 0 \\ 0 & 1 & 0 & 0 \\ \sin\phi & 0 & \cos\phi & 0 \\ 0 & 0 & 0 & 1 \end{bmatrix}, \tag{I.10.27}$$

$$L_{(12)} = R_3(\theta) = \begin{bmatrix} \cos\theta & \sin\theta & 0 & 0 \\ -\sin\theta & \cos\theta & 0 & 0 \\ 0 & 0 & 1 & 0 \\ 0 & 0 & 0 & 1 \end{bmatrix}$$

and

$$L_{(14)} = L_1(\lambda) = \begin{bmatrix} \cosh\lambda & 0 & 0 & -\sinh\lambda \\ 0 & 1 & 0 & 0 \\ 0 & 0 & 1 & 0 \\ -\sinh\lambda & 0 & 0 & \cosh\lambda \end{bmatrix}$$

$$L_{(24)} = L_2(\epsilon) = \begin{bmatrix} 1 & 0 & 0 & 0 \\ 0 & \cosh\epsilon & 0 & -\sinh\epsilon \\ 0 & 0 & 1 & 0 \\ 0 & -\sinh\epsilon & 0 & \cosh\epsilon \end{bmatrix}, \tag{I.10.28}$$

$$L_{(34)} = L_3(\rho) = \begin{bmatrix} 1 & 0 & 0 & 0 \\ 0 & 1 & 0 & 0 \\ 0 & 0 & \cosh\rho & -\sinh\rho \\ 0 & 0 & -\sinh\rho & \cosh\rho \end{bmatrix}.$$

Here we assume that

$$\tanh\lambda_i = \frac{v_i}{c}, \qquad i = 1, 2, 3,$$

$$\lambda_1 = \lambda, \qquad \lambda_2 = \epsilon, \qquad \lambda_3 = \rho,$$

and that the v_i are the components of the velocity of a Lorentz frame.

The above Lorentz matrices have these properties.

(a) All six of them belong to the class of Lorentz matrices with $L_{44} \geqq 1$.

(b) The matrices $R_1(\psi)$, $R_2(\phi)$, $R_3(\theta)$ generated by the Hermitian generators $M_{(23)}$, $M_{(31)}$, $M_{(12)}$, respectively, are plane rotation matrices corresponding to rotations around the spatial axes x_1, x_2, x_3 at a fixed time. These rotation matrices with $L_{44} = 1$ constitute a subgroup of the proper Lorentz group.

(c) The matrices $L_1(\lambda)$, $L_2(\epsilon)$, $L_3(\rho)$ generated by the anti-Hermitian generators $M_{(14)}$, $M_{(24)}$, $M_{(34)}$ give rise to Lorentz transformations in which the transformed coordinate systems are moving with velocities v_i, for $i = 1, 2, 3$, in the directions x_i, for $i = 1, 2, 3$, respectively. These matrices with $L_{44} > 1$ constitute a subgroup of the proper Lorentz group.

(d) The most general representation of the six-parameter proper Lorentz matrix can be given as

$$L = A_1 L(v_3) A_2, \tag{I.10.29}$$

where A_1 and A_2 are pure rotations and $L(v_3)$ is an acceleration in the direction of the x_3-axis.

I.10.C. Examples

Properties of Lorentz Transformations.

(a) Let us choose an arbitrary but fixed Lorentz frame of reference S and assume that a particle with mass m is at rest in S. A particle moving with a velocity v in the x_3 direction can be represented by looking at it from another coordinate system S_I moving with the velocity v in the $-x_3$ direction. We call m the rest mass of the particle and mc^2 its rest energy (S reference). The state of the particle in the S frame can be represented by a four-dimensional vector $P_{0\mu}$ with components $(0, 0, 0, mc)$. The state of the moving particle (as seen from the S_I frame) can be obtained by a Lorentz transformation of $P_{0\mu}$. Thus, since S_I is moving in the $-x_3$ direction, the required Lorentz transformation is one obtained by replacing ρ in $L(\rho)$ by $-\rho$—that is, $L(-\rho)$ is the relevant Lorentz matrix. The state $|P\rangle$ in S_I is

$$|P\supset = L(-\rho)|P_0\supset$$

or

$$|P\supset = \begin{bmatrix} 0 \\ 0 \\ \dfrac{mv}{\left(1 - \dfrac{v^2}{c^2}\right)^{1/2}} \\ \dfrac{mc}{\left(1 - \dfrac{v^2}{c^2}\right)^{1/2}} \end{bmatrix}.$$

Hence the energy and momentum of the particle are

$$E = \frac{mc^2}{\left(1 - \frac{v^2}{c^2}\right)^{1/2}}$$

and

$$P = \frac{mv}{\left(1 - \frac{v^2}{c^2}\right)^{1/2}},$$

so for $v = 0$ the particle can be transformed to rest in S. However, the existence of the factor

$$\left(1 - \frac{v^2}{c^2}\right)^{-1/2}$$

in the Lorentz transformation implies certain restriction on the transformation properties of the particles.

(i) *All particles with nonzero mass can be transformed to rest.*

(ii) *If a particle cannot be transformed to rest, then its velocity must always be equal to the velocity of light; in this case its rest mass must be zero. A nonzero rest mass for a particle moving with the velocity of light would entail infinite energy.**

(b) A further comparison of the state of a particle in different coordinate systems can be envisaged in terms of two vectors describing the state of the system. We choose one of these vectors as the velocity of the particle. The second vector of the system may refer to an intrinsic property such that it is not a property of a Lorentz transformation, but the vector also exists in the system's rest frame S. Spin and polarization of particles are such internal degrees of freedom. In this example we wish to study the Lorentz transformation properties of a mass particle moving with a velocity $\boldsymbol{v}$ and having an intrinsic property represented by a vector $\mathbf{s}$.

As in example (a), we may represent a moving particle by a Lorentz transformation of the coordinates effected, say, by $L(-\rho)$. We now inquire: under which class of Lorentz transformations can the velocity $\boldsymbol{v}$ and spin $\boldsymbol{s}$ of the particle remain parallel to one another?

Let us suppose that in the frame S the spin $\mathbf{s}$ points in the x_3 direction. A particle moving in the x_3 direction with a velocity $\boldsymbol{v}$ will have its spin and velocity parallel in the moving frame S_I, obtained from S by the transforma-

---

* We thus see that relativistic transformation properties of particles draws a sharp line of demarcation between mass and massless particles.

tion $L(-\rho)$. We can find another Lorentz frame where the vectors $\boldsymbol{s}$ and $\boldsymbol{v}$ still remain parallel to one another. We choose a new rest frame S_0', obtained from S_0 by a Lorentz transformation effected by $R_1(\psi)$, corresponding to a rotation around the x_1-axis by an angle ψ; the particle is at rest in S_0' and its spin includes an angle ψ with the x_3 direction of S_0'. We impart a motion to S_0' in the ψ direction with a velocity $-\boldsymbol{v}$ to obtain a new coordinate system representing a particle moving with a velocity $\boldsymbol{v}$, which includes an angle ψ with its spin. The latter operation is equivalent to a transformation of the $L(-\rho)$ by $R_1(\psi)$. Therefore, in accordance with the rule of transformation of operators [see (*I.4.8*)], we write

$$L(\psi, \rho) = R_1(\psi)L_3(-\rho)\tilde{R}_1(\psi) = R_1(\psi)L_3(-\rho)R_1(-\psi)$$

A further counterclockwise rotation by an angle ψ will represent a particle moving in the direction ψ with a velocity $\boldsymbol{v}$ with respect to S_0'. Hence the required transformation is

$$L_f = L(\psi, \rho)R_1(\psi) = R_1(\psi)L_3(-\rho),$$

or

$$L_f = \begin{bmatrix} 1 & 0 & 0 & 0 \\ 0 & \cos\psi & \sin\psi\ \cosh\rho & \sin\psi\ \sinh\rho \\ 0 & -\sin\psi & \cos\psi\ \cosh\rho & \cos\psi\ \sinh\rho \\ 0 & 0 & \sinh\rho & \cosh\rho \end{bmatrix}. \qquad (I.10.30)$$

Hence, the parallelism of spin and velocity is an invariant statement under rotations. We could also choose another moving frame, obtained from S_I by a Lorentz transformation effected by $L(u)$, where u is the velocity of the new reference frame moving in the x_3 direction; the corresponding transformation is $L(u, -v) = L_3(u)L_3(-v)$.

In this case the velocity of the particle in the x_3 direction is

$$V = \frac{v - u}{1 - \dfrac{uv}{c^2}}.$$

Thus, if $u < v$, the particle will still appear to move in the x_3 direction and its spin will remain parallel to its velocity. But if $u > v$, the direction of spin and velocity will become antiparallel; such transformations do not belong to the class of Lorentz transformations, where the parallelism of the velocity and spin remain unchanged. However, the spin and velocity will not appear parallel when viewed from coordinate systems moving in directions not parallel to the x_3 direction. This unisotropic behavior disappears if the particle moves with the speed of light, with respect to which all Lorentz frames are equivalent in every respect. In the latter case the parallel state of spin and velocity is maintained in all Lorentz transformations. Examples of such invariant parallelism of spin and velocity are photon and neutrino; this statement can further be qualified by using the relation between energy, momentum, and mass of a particle:

$$P_\mu P^\mu = P_4^2 - P_1^2 - P_2^2 - P_3^2 = M^2c^2, \qquad (I.10.31)$$

where $P_4 = (1/c)E$. Thus, for a photon or for a neutrino we have

$$P_\mu P^\mu = 0, \qquad (I.10.32)$$

a null-vector.

Wigner* has shown in great detail that the subgroup of the Lorentz group which leaves a null-vector invariant is different from the subgroup which leaves a timelike vector ($P^\mu P_\mu > 0$) invariant.

I.10.D. Problems

1. Prove that the velocity of a particle, with nonzero mass, with respect to its rest frame is given by

$$v_i = -c\frac{L_{i4}}{L_{44}}, \qquad \text{for } i = 1, 2, 3, \qquad (I.10.33)$$

where L_{i4} and L_{44} are the elements of the Lorentz matrix L. Hence calculate the final particle velocity arising from two successive Lorentz transformations effected by Lorentz matrices L and L'.

2. Prove that the Lorentz transformations FL and $-FL$, where the L refer to matrices defined by (*I.10.27*) and (*I.10.28*), are related to space and time reflection transformations. Discuss the group properties of the transformations and classify the subgroups with respect to the matrix element L_{44}.

3. If the state of a particle, discussed in example (a), as viewed from a coordinate system moving with velocity $-v$ in the x_3 direction is obtained from the rest frame by the transformation $L_{(34)}(-\rho)$, where $v = c \tanh \rho$, show that the same state when viewed from a coordinate system moving in the $-x_2$ direction with velocity v' can be obtained from the rest system by the transformation

$$L = L_{(24)}(-\epsilon)L_{(34)}(-\rho) = [L_{(34)}(\rho)L_{(24)}(\epsilon)]^{-1}.$$

Hence prove that the angle α between the spin of the particle and its velocity is given by

$$\tan \alpha = \frac{\tanh \epsilon}{\sinh \rho} = \frac{v'}{v}\left(1 - \frac{v^2}{c^2}\right)^{1/2}.$$

4. If for two vectors $|a\supset$ and $|b\supset$, (a) $\subset a|F|b\supset = 0$ and (b) $\subset a|F|a\supset > 0$, then

$$\subset b|F|b\supset < 0.$$

---

* E. P. Wigner, *Rev. Mod. Phys.*, **29**, No. 3 (1957), 255.

5. From problem 4 show that if $\subset a|F|b\supset = 0$ and $\subset a|F|a\supset = 0$, then we have

$$\subset b|F|b\supset < 0,$$
$$|b\supset = \lambda|a\supset,$$

where λ is any real constant.*

6. Use the results of problems 4 and 5 to show that if the vectors $|e_\mu\supset$, for $\mu = 1, 2, 3, 4$, are mutually orthogonal and linearly independent, then one of them is timelike and three are spacelike.

7. Find the class of vectors $|u_\alpha\supset$ which do not change direction under Lorentz transformations. In what way do the transformed vectors differ from one another for Lorentz matrices belonging to the classes $L_{44} > 1$ and $L_{44} < -1$, respectively.

8. Both the homogeneous Lorentz group and the four-dimensional Euclidean group are six-parameter groups. In what way do the generators of the two groups differ?

9. Show that the tensor form of the matrix equation $\tilde{L}FL = F$ is given by

$$L^\mu_\alpha L_{\mu\beta} = a_{\alpha\beta}$$

or

$$L^{\mu\alpha} L_{\mu\beta} = a^\alpha_\beta, \qquad (I.10.34)$$

where μ in $L^{\mu\alpha}$ is to be regarded as the matrix index specifying the rows of L, and a^α_β is defined by

$$a^4_4 = 1, \qquad a^i_j = -\delta^i_j, \qquad a^i_4 = a^4_i = 0. \qquad (I.10.35)$$

10. The relativistic form of the equations of motion for a charged point particle in an electromagnetic field is given by

$$\frac{dp_\mu}{ds} = \frac{e}{mc^2} f_{\mu\nu} p^\nu, \qquad f_{4i} = \mathcal{E}_i, \qquad f_{ij} = \epsilon_{ijl}\mathcal{H}_l, \qquad (I.10.36)$$

where p_u is the 4-momentum of the particle. Show that the operator form of $(I.10.36)$ is given by

$$\frac{d}{ds}|p\rangle = -\frac{e}{mc^2} fF|p\rangle, \qquad |p\rangle = \begin{bmatrix} p_1 \\ p_2 \\ p_3 \\ p_4 \end{bmatrix}, \qquad (I.10.37)$$

and f is the matrix of $f_{\mu\nu}$. Show also that the most general formal solution of $(I.10.37)$ is given by

$$|p\rangle = P \exp\left[-\frac{e}{mc^2}\int_0^s fF\,ds\right]|p_0\rangle, \qquad (I.10.38)$$

where $|p_0\rangle$ is the initial momentum and the operator P is defined by $(I.7.9)$.

---

* Many other interesting aspects of Lorentz transformations can be found in Wigner's article, *Ann. Math.*, **40** (1939), 149.

CHAPTER II

DYNAMICS OF THE PHOTON AND FOUNDATIONS OF QUANTUM MECHANICS

II.1. Energy of an Electromagnetic Wave

Experiments on thermal radiation, with their gross disagreement with classical theories, gave birth to quantum theory. The equilibrium distribution of electromagnetic radiation (that is, emission and absorption of radiation at constant temperature) in a hollow cavity could not be explained on the basis of classical electrodynamics (Maxwell's equations plus the laws of motion of particles). Thermal radiation is a certain function of the temperature (T) of the emitting body. When dispersed by a prism, thermal radiation forms a continuous spectrum. It was found that the energy distribution of the radiation had a regular dependence on its wavelength. Furthermore the energy E_ν as a function of the temperature of the material did not depend upon the structure of the cavity or its shape. On these bases it was shown that the energy E_ν ought to have a dependence upon frequency ν, at temperature T, in the form

$$E_\nu = \nu^3 F\left(\frac{cT}{\nu}\right).$$

All attempts to find the correct form of F on the basis of classical theory failed. The classical theory led to the now well-known "ultra-violet difficulty," since the contribution of high frequencies caused the energy to assume infinite value. The difficulty was removed by a hypothesis of Planck, according to which the energy of a monochromatic wave with frequency ν can only assume those values which are integral multiples of energy $h\nu$; that is, $E_n = nh\nu$, where n is an integer referring to the number of "photons." Thus the energy of a single photon of frequency ν is

$$E = h\nu. \tag{II.1.1}$$

The finiteness of Planck's constant h and its resulting implications laid the foundations of quantum theory. Quantum theory, like the special theory of relativity, was discovered through the experiments on electromagnetic phenomena and their theoretical interpretations.

The fundamental equation (*II.1.1*) of quantum mechanics implies, on the one hand, that energy of radiation stays concentrated in limited regions of space in amounts of $h\nu$ and therefore behaves like the energy of particles; on the other hand, it establishes a definite relationship between the frequency ν and the energy E of an electromagnetic wave. This dual behavior of light corresponds, in one way, to experimental situations of the interference properties of radiation, for the description of which one uses the wave theory of light; in another way it corresponds to the properties of exchange of energy and momentum between radiation and matter, which require for their explanation the particle picture of light. Thus the dual behavior of light has necessitated the quantum description (quantization) of the electromagnetic field. A unified point of view was formulated quantitatively by de Broglie, according to which all forms of energy and momentum related to matter will manifest a dual behavior of belonging to a wave or particle description of the physical system, depending on the type of experiment performed.

The most interesting example of a quantum mechanical object is the photon itself. By using the relativistic and quantum mechanical definition of the photon energy we can obtain a quantitative formulation of the above ideas. The relativistic form of the total energy of a particle with rest mass m and momentum p is

$$E = c\sqrt{(p^2 + m^2c^2)}. \tag{II.1.2}$$

We set $m = 0$ and obtain the relativistic definition of the energy of a photon:

$$E = cp. \tag{II.1.3}$$

Hence the first unification of relativity and quantum theory originated from the combination of (*II.1.1*) and (*II.1.3*) in the form

$$cp = h\nu. \tag{II.1.4}$$

By using $\nu\lambda = c$ for the plane electromagnetic wave we obtain the fundamental statement of quantum mechanics,

$$\lambda\!\!\!^{-} p = \hbar, \tag{II.1.5}$$

valid for all particles with or without mass, where

$$\lambdabar = \frac{\lambda}{2\pi}, \qquad \hbar = \frac{h}{2\pi}.$$

If we define the wave number and frequency of a wave by $|k| = 1/\lambdabar$ and $k_4 = \omega/c = (2\pi/c)\nu$, respectively, and its momentum and energy by p_μ, then we have

$$p_\mu = \hbar k_\mu. \tag{II.1.6}$$

The validity of (*II.1.6*), relating wave and particle properties of matter and fields, is now completely established by experiments on nuclear, atomic, and molecular systems.

II.1.A. Photon Gas

Rutherford's scattering experiments, which resulted in the discovery of the atomic nucleus, were followed by Bohr's atomic theory. In the light of these new developments Einstein was the first to show that Planck's formula can also be derived, for all atomic systems obeying general statistical laws, for the spontaneous and induced emission processes and the inverse process of absorption. He further proved that for every elementary process of radiation an amount $h\nu/c$ of momentum is emitted in a random direction and that the emitting atomic system suffers a corresponding recoil in the opposite direction. These processes do, of course, take place in a black-body radiation process. If we assume that the photons do not interact with one another, then the black-body radiation may be regarded as a "photon gas." If the energy spectrum of the gas does not contain many frequencies coinciding with the absorption range of its container, then the interaction of the photon gas with the container can be neglected. However, in order to maintain a thermal equilibrium, enough absorption and emission of radiation is necessary.

One of the most important properties of a photon gas has to do with the nonconservation of the total number of particles in the gas. The variation of the photon number depends entirely on the conditions of thermal equilibrium—mass of the container, its atomic structure, its temperature, and so on. According to Planck's law the distribution of the photons over different energies $E = h\nu$ is given by

$$f = \frac{1}{e^{(h\nu/\varkappa T)} - 1}. \tag{II.1.7}$$

If V is the volume of the gas, then the number of photons in the wave-number range k, $k + dk$ is given by

$$N = 2f\Delta n, \tag{II.1.8}$$

where the factor 2 corresponds to two possible directions of photon polarizations and where

$$\Delta n = \frac{1}{(2\pi)^3} V d^3k = \frac{V}{(2\pi\hbar)^3} p^2\, dp\, d\Omega_p, \qquad (II.1.9)$$

with $d\Omega_p = \sin\theta\, d\theta\, d\phi$. For an isotropic distribution of momentum, definition (*II.1.9*) can be replaced by

$$\Delta n = \frac{4\pi V}{(2\pi\hbar)^3} p^2\, dp = \frac{4\pi V}{h^3} p^2\, dp. \qquad (II.1.10)$$

Hence the number of photons in momentum range p, $p + dp$ in a volume V are

$$N_\nu = \frac{8\pi V}{c^3} \frac{\nu^2\, d\nu}{e^{(h\nu/\kappa T)} - 1}, \qquad (II.1.11)$$

which, for a given volume, is a function of temperature and frequency. Thus, radiation energy in the frequency range ν, $\nu + d\nu$ is

$$\Delta E_\nu = \frac{8\pi V h}{c^3} \frac{\nu^3\, d\nu}{e^{(h\nu/\kappa T)} - 1}. \qquad (II.1.12)$$

II.1.B. Electromagnetic Waves and the Wave Equation of the Photon

We need to develop a dynamical theory to describe the wave character of material particles. We shall base our approach on the idea that the concept of photon must play a fundamental role in building a quantum theory of matter. To this end a preliminary understanding of free photons in quantum theory will provide a first orientation, and it will set a clear path for further generalizations of the subject matter.

In the case of particles with mass, one has the possibility of comparing their kinetic energies with their rest masses. If the kinetic energy is small compared to rest energy then we can formulate a nonrelativistic theory. However, with the photon there exists no possibility for the formulation of a nonrelativistic theory. The theory of a free photon will have to be a relativistic one; it is a relativistic particle. There are important advantages in entering quantum mechanics via the photon.

(a) The energy of a photon is a quantum mechanical quantity, $E = h\nu$.

(b) It has provided a natural basis to postulate the wave-particle relation, $\lambda = h/p$.

(c) The wave aspects of the photon are completely described by charge-free Maxwell equations. Therefore it is natural to try to reconcile Planck's hypothesis with the wave theory of light.

A reinterpretation of Maxwell's equations in conjunction with the quantum relations $E = h\nu$ and $\lambda = h/p$ will, in a natural way, lead us to a wave equation for the photon.

We begin with the free-field Maxwell equations

$$\frac{1}{c}\frac{\partial \mathcal{E}}{\partial t} - \nabla \times \mathcal{H} = 0, \qquad \frac{1}{c}\frac{\partial \mathcal{H}}{\partial t} + \nabla \times \mathcal{E} = 0, \tag{II.1.13}$$

$$\nabla \cdot \mathcal{E} = 0, \qquad \nabla \cdot \mathcal{H} = 0. \tag{II.1.14}$$

Now consider the complex three-dimensional vector

$$\chi = \mathcal{E} + i\mathcal{H}. \tag{II.1.15}$$

It has the following interesting properties.

(a) For a plane electromagnetic wave, whose electric and magnetic vectors are perpendicular and equal (in magnitude), the Lorentz-invariant square of χ vanishes; that is,

$$\chi^{*2} = \langle \chi | \overline{C} | \chi \rangle = (\mathcal{E} - i\mathcal{H})^2 = \mathcal{E}^2 - \mathcal{H}^2 - 2i\mathcal{E}\cdot\mathcal{H} = 0 \tag{II.1.16}$$

or

$$|\mathcal{E}| = |\mathcal{H}|, \qquad \mathcal{E}\cdot\mathcal{H} = 0,$$

where

$$|\chi\rangle = \begin{bmatrix} \chi_1 \\ \chi_2 \\ \chi_3 \end{bmatrix}.$$

The latter two are the two Lorentz-invariant properties of a plane electromagnetic wave.

(b) The energy density of the field can be expressed in terms of the rotation-invariant square of χ as

$$cP_4 = \frac{1}{8\pi}|\chi|^2 = \frac{1}{8\pi}\langle \chi | \chi \rangle = \frac{\mathcal{E}^2 + \mathcal{H}^2}{8\pi}. \tag{II.1.17}$$

(c) The momentum density of the field has the form

$$P_i = \frac{1}{8\pi c}\langle \chi | K_i | \chi \rangle, \tag{II.1.18}$$

where the Hermitian 3×3 matrices K_i were defined by (*I.8.3*).

The two expressions (*II.1.17*) and (*II.1.18*) for energy and momentum densities, respectively, can be combined into a single equation,

$$cP_\mu = \frac{1}{8\pi}\langle \chi | K_\mu | \chi \rangle, \tag{II.1.19}$$

where K_4, corresponding to $\mu = 4$, is a 3×3 unit matrix. In order to illustrate the meaning of (*II.1.19*) we shall, as an example, work out the third component of (*II.1.19*). It is given by

$$cP_3 = \frac{1}{8\pi}[\chi_1^*, \chi_2^*, \chi_3^*]\begin{bmatrix} 0 & -i & 0 \\ i & 0 & 0 \\ 0 & 0 & 0 \end{bmatrix}\begin{bmatrix} \chi_1 \\ \chi_2 \\ \chi_3 \end{bmatrix}$$

$$= \frac{i}{8\pi}(\chi_1\chi_2^* - \chi_1^*\chi_2) = \frac{1}{4\pi}(\mathcal{E}_1\mathcal{H}_2 - \mathcal{E}_2\mathcal{H}_1) = \frac{1}{4\pi}(\boldsymbol{\mathcal{E}} \times \boldsymbol{\mathcal{H}})_3,$$

which verifies the statement in (c) above.

(d) The momentum and energy density of the field is conserved; that is,

$$\frac{\partial cP_\mu}{\partial x_\mu} = \frac{\partial P_4}{\partial t} + c\boldsymbol{\nabla}\cdot\boldsymbol{P} = 0, \qquad (II.1.20)$$

provided the complex vector $|\chi\rangle$ satisfies the equation

$$K_\mu \frac{\partial}{\partial x_\mu}|\chi\rangle = 0. \qquad (II.1.21)$$

The Hermitian conjugate of (*II.1.21*) is

$$K_\mu \frac{\partial}{\partial x_\mu}\langle\chi| = 0, \qquad (II.1.22)$$

where the coordinates x_μ and x^μ are related by

$$x_\mu = a_{\mu\nu}x^\nu. \qquad (II.1.23)$$

Equation (*II.1.21*) can also be written as

$$i\frac{\partial}{\partial t}|\chi\rangle = -ic\boldsymbol{K}\cdot\boldsymbol{\nabla}|\chi\rangle, \qquad (II.1.24)$$

where, it is easy to see,

$$-i\boldsymbol{K}\cdot\boldsymbol{\nabla}|\chi\rangle = \boldsymbol{\nabla}\times\boldsymbol{\chi}. \qquad (II.1.25)$$

Hence (*II.1.24*) is equivalent to Maxwell's equations (*II.1.13*). Therefore the conservation of energy and momentum density of the field is a consequence of Maxwell's equations or, conversely, if Maxwell's equations are satisfied, the vector P_μ is conserved.*

To introduce Planck's constant into electromagnetic field theory we multiply both sides of (*II.1.24*) by $\hbar$ and obtain Maxwell's equations in the form

$$i\hbar\frac{\partial}{\partial t}|\chi\rangle = H|\chi\rangle, \qquad (II.1.26)$$

where

$$\boldsymbol{\nabla}\cdot\boldsymbol{\chi} = 0, \qquad (II.1.27)$$

$$H = -ic\hbar\boldsymbol{K}\cdot\boldsymbol{\nabla} = c\boldsymbol{K}\cdot\boldsymbol{p} \qquad (II.1.28)$$

has the dimensions of energy. The momentum operator $\boldsymbol{p}$ is defined as

$$\boldsymbol{p} = -i\hbar\boldsymbol{\nabla}.$$

---

* A group-theoretical motivation in introducing the complex vector $\boldsymbol{\chi}$ is discussed in Chapter VIII.

The complex vector $|\chi\rangle$ has the physical dimensions of the square root of energy density. It will be more convenient to work with a complex vector $|\eta\rangle$, having the dimensions of the square root of $(\text{volume})^{-1}$, defined by

$$|\chi\rangle = \sqrt{(8\pi E)}\,|\eta\rangle \qquad (II.1.29)$$

and satisfying the condition of normalization,

$$\int \langle\eta|\eta\rangle\, d^3x = 1, \qquad (II.1.30)$$

where E is the energy of the photon. With these premises the wave equation (or Schrödinger's equation) of the photon becomes

$$i\hbar \frac{\partial}{\partial t}|\eta\rangle = H|\eta\rangle, \qquad (II.1.31)$$

$$\nabla \cdot \boldsymbol{\eta} = 0. \qquad (II.1.32)$$

The formalism contained in (*II.1.31*) and (*II.1.32*),* with the definitions of H by (*II.1.28*), will be shown to be consistent and compatible with the observed facts $E = h\nu$ and $\lambda = h/p$ of the photon. This will be shown, first, by defining the physical meanings of $|\eta\rangle$, and H, and $\boldsymbol{p}$ in later sections. The extension of the qualitative implications of this theory to systems with mass can be carried through in a heuristic way.

A monochromatic wave can be described by a function of the form

$$\psi = Ae^{i\boldsymbol{k}\cdot\boldsymbol{r}}e^{-i\omega t},$$

where $\boldsymbol{k}$ is the wave number vector and ω is the frequency of the wave. The function ψ as defined in the above cannot distinguish between different points in space and time; that is, the intensity $\psi^*\psi = A^*A = |A|^2$ of the wave is everywhere the same. But experiments on the interference of waves require a certain superposition of plane waves. In this way we can construct waves having different intensities (as in interference phenomena) at different space-time points. We can represent the most general form of an electromagnetic wave—or rather, of the wave function $|\eta\rangle$—in the form of a Fourier series where each wave number k of a particular wave has a correspondence with the set of positive integral numbers. We shall restrict the space part of the Fourier expansion by a periodicity condition extended over the periodicity domain of a cube with dimension L, or with volume $V = L^3$. The wave-number vector k in the plane wave exp $(i\boldsymbol{k}\cdot\boldsymbol{r})$ is characterized according to

$$k_1 = \frac{2\pi}{L}n_1, \qquad k_2 = \frac{2\pi}{L}n_2, \qquad k_3 = \frac{2\pi}{L}n_3, \qquad (II.1.33)$$

---

* An approach similar to the one discussed here has also been considered by R. J. Oppenheimer, *Phys. Rev.*, **38** (1931), 725, and more recently by W. J. Archibald, *Can. J. Phys.*, **33** (1955), 565 and R. H. Good, *Phys. Rev.*, **105** (1957), 1914.

where n_1, n_2, n_3 are integers ranging from 1 to infinity. The k defined in this manner will describe a cubical point lattice with lattice constant $2\pi/L$ and a cell volume $(2\pi/L)^3$.

The Fourier series expansion can now be given as

$$|\eta\rangle = \frac{1}{\sqrt{V}} \sum_{\boldsymbol{k}} e^{i\boldsymbol{k}\cdot\boldsymbol{r}} |\phi_k\rangle, \tag{II.1.34}$$

where summation refers to all three components of the $\boldsymbol{k}$ vector and over all the $\boldsymbol{k}$ defined according to (*II.1.33*). The complex vectors $|\phi_k(t)\rangle$ are functions of the wave number and of time t. By substituting the function $|\eta\rangle$ given by (*II.1.34*) in equations (*II.1.31*) and (*II.1.32*), we obtain

$$\begin{aligned} i\hbar \frac{\partial}{\partial t} |\phi_k\rangle &= H|\phi_k\rangle, \\ \boldsymbol{k}\cdot\boldsymbol{\phi}_k &= 0, \end{aligned} \tag{II.1.35}$$

where

$$H = \hbar c \boldsymbol{k}\cdot\boldsymbol{K},$$

so the operator p acts on $|\phi_k\rangle$ according to

$$\boldsymbol{p}|\phi_k\rangle = \hbar\boldsymbol{k}|\phi_k\rangle. \tag{II.1.36}$$

Thus the vector $\hbar\boldsymbol{k}$ can be interpreted as the eigenvalue of the operator $\boldsymbol{p}$ corresponding to the eigenvector $|\phi_k\rangle$.

Multiplication of (*II.1.35*) scalarly by $\boldsymbol{k}$ leads to

$$\frac{\partial}{\partial t} (\boldsymbol{k}\cdot\boldsymbol{\phi}_k) = 0, \tag{II.1.37}$$

so the scalar $\boldsymbol{k}\cdot\boldsymbol{\phi}_k$ does not have an explicit time dependence. In deriving result (*II.1.37*) we used the property

$$\langle k|H = \hbar c\langle k|(\boldsymbol{k}\cdot\mathbf{K}) = \hbar c[k_1, k_2, k_3] \begin{bmatrix} 0 & -ik_3 & ik_2 \\ ik_3 & 0 & -ik_1 \\ -ik_2 & ik_1 & 0 \end{bmatrix} \equiv 0.$$

For free fields the scalar $\boldsymbol{k}\cdot\boldsymbol{\phi}_k$ vanishes, because of Maxwell's equations.

In order to find the eigenvalues of the operator H we may look for the stationary-state solutions of equations (*II.1.35*). We assume that the vector $|\phi_k(t)\rangle$ is periodic in time and that in accordance with the relation $E = h\nu$ we write

$$|\phi_k(t)\rangle = |a_k\rangle e^{-(i/\hbar)Et}. \tag{II.1.38}$$

This form of the wave refers to a stationary state. The first of equations (*II.1.35*) now becomes

$$E|a_k\rangle = H|a_k\rangle. \tag{II.1.39}$$

In matrix form it can be written as

$$\begin{bmatrix} E & icp_3 & -icp_2 \\ -icp_3 & E & icp_1 \\ icp_2 & -icp_1 & E \end{bmatrix} \begin{bmatrix} a_{k1} \\ a_{k2} \\ a_{k3} \end{bmatrix} = 0. \qquad (II.1.40)$$

Solutions for (*II.1.40*) require the vanishing of the determinant of $(E - H)$. In (*II.1.40*) the vector $\boldsymbol{a}_k$ is, of course, subject to the condition

$$\boldsymbol{k} \cdot \boldsymbol{a}_k = 0.$$

By taking the determinant of $(E - H)$ we obtain

$$E(E^2 - c^2p^2) = 0.$$

The eigenvalue $E = 0$ implies [as seen from (*II.1.40*)] that the vectors $\boldsymbol{a}$ and $\boldsymbol{p}$ are parallel, which is not consistent with $\boldsymbol{p} \cdot \boldsymbol{a} = 0$. Hence the solution $E = 0$ must be discarded by the condition of transversality of the wave. The remaining two solutions are

$$E = cp = c\hbar k = h\nu,$$
$$E = -cp = -c\hbar k = -h\nu.$$

The negative sign in the second case is not to be understood as referring to a negative energy state. It has to do with the spin degree of freedom of the photon. This can be seen from writing the wave equation for negative energy,

$$(c\boldsymbol{p} \cdot \boldsymbol{K})|\eta\rangle = -E|\eta\rangle,$$

in the form

$$c\boldsymbol{p} \cdot (-\boldsymbol{K})|\eta\rangle = E|\eta\rangle.$$

Thus both energy states are positive and they refer respectively to the energy of a right circularly or left circularly polarized photon, with spin parallel or antiparallel to $\boldsymbol{k}$.

The two solutions $E = \pm h\nu$ obtained above can be incorporated into (*II.1.38*) in an operator form,

$$|\phi_k\rangle = e^{-i\omega t \mathfrak{m}}|a_k\rangle, \qquad (II.1.41)$$

where the operator $\mathfrak{m}$ is defined by

$$\mathfrak{m} = \frac{H}{E} \qquad (II.1.42)$$

and satisfies an operator algebraic equation of the form

$$\mathfrak{m}^3 = \mathfrak{m}. \qquad (II.1.43)$$

In obtaining (*II.1.43*) we used the properties of H:

$$H^3 = E^2 H, \qquad \tilde{H} = -H. \qquad (II.1.44)$$

The operator H is Hermitian and therefore the roots of (*II.1.43*) are real and are given as $+1$, -1, and 0. The root $\mathfrak{m}' = 0$ is excluded by the transversality condition. If $|1\rangle$, $|-1\rangle$ and $|0\rangle$ are the normalized eigenvectors of $\mathfrak{m}$ corresponding to its eigenvalues $+1$, -1, and 0, respectively, then the unit operator of the space spanned by the orthogonal vectors $|1\rangle$, $|-1\rangle$, and $|0\rangle$ is given by

$$I = |1\rangle\langle 1| + |-1\rangle\langle -1| + |0\rangle\langle 0|,$$

where the vector $|0\rangle$ is in the direction of propagation of the wave and is, therefore, orthogonal to $|a_k\rangle$. By using the unit operator I together with (*II.1.41*) we can express the state $|\phi_k(t)\rangle$ of the wave with wave number $\boldsymbol{k}$ in the form

$$|\phi_k\rangle = b_k^{(+)} e^{-i\omega t}|1\rangle + b_k^{(-)} e^{i\omega t}|-1\rangle, \qquad (II.1.45)$$

where the complex numbers $b_k^{(+)}$ and $b_k^{(-)}$ are given by

$$b_k^{(+)} = \langle 1|\alpha_k\rangle,$$

$$b_k^{(-)} = \langle -1|a_k\rangle,$$

and

$$\omega = \frac{E}{\hbar}.$$

For a better understanding of the last relations let us consider a wave moving in the p_3 direction. On setting $p_1 = p_2 = 0$ in $\mathfrak{m}$, we obtain

$$\mathfrak{m} = K_3.$$

In this case the eigenvectors of $\mathfrak{m}$ are defined by (*I.8.7*). Hence

$$|\phi_k\rangle = \frac{1}{\sqrt{2}}(a_{k1} + ia_{k2})e^{-i\omega t}|1\rangle + \frac{1}{\sqrt{2}}(a_{k1} - ia_{k2})e^{i\omega t}|-1\rangle, \qquad (II.1.46)$$

so

$$b_k^{(+)} = \frac{1}{\sqrt{2}}(a_{1k} + ia_{2k})e^{-i\omega t},$$

$$b_k^{(-)} = \frac{1}{\sqrt{2}}(a_{1k} - ia_{2k})e^{i\omega t}$$

correspond to right circularly and left circularly polarized waves, respectively. In this way we see that the stationary state $|\phi_k\rangle$ is a superposition of two oppositely polarized waves. The above results also show that the "complexity" of the quantities used in the description of the waves is a necessity for internal consistency and also for the logical simplicity of the theory. For example, a real $|\phi_k\rangle$ could not describe the two possible directions of polarization. The latter is an internal degree of freedom of a wave.

For the sake of the following argument on the properties of waves we shall, provisionally, call the vector $|\eta\rangle$ the wave function of the photon. We have seen that at a given time the value of the wave function can be obtained by a certain superposition of plane waves. In analogy to the classical definition of the intensity of a wave we shall look upon the real quantity

$$P = \langle \eta|\eta\rangle$$

as a probability density in the sense that EP is the energy density over a region that is large compared to the wavelength of the photon. The probability depends, of course, on the value of the wave function at the particular point. We can choose $|\eta\rangle$ in such a way that it differs from zero only over a region Ω of the dimensions of the wavelength of the photon. It shall be composed of monochromatic plane waves that interfere destructively outside the region Ω; the frequencies and wave numbers of these waves differ very little from each other inside the region Ω. In this particular region the waves interfere constructively and the wave function $|\eta\rangle$ assumes large values there. This is equivalent to a localization of the photon. If this localization process is described in accordance with uncertainty relations (see Chapter III, Section IV.A) between the dynamical variables of the photon, then the region in question is a wave packet. These arguments are, of course, valid also for mass particles.

The amplitudes of the waves that constitute a packet are different from zero only in the packet. These wave amplitudes constitute a wave group and have a group velocity that differs from the velocity of a single plane wave ("phase velocity").

A wave packet involves many frequencies; therefore its velocity will depend on the frequency and energy of the waves in a continuous fashion. Such a description of the velocity can be related to a dispersion law of the type

$$v_g = \frac{\partial\omega}{\partial k}, \qquad (II.1.47)$$

valid for all types of waves with or without mass. Relation (*II.1.47*) is a consequence of

$$\boldsymbol{p}\cdot\boldsymbol{k} = p_4 k_4, \qquad (II.1.48)$$

which follows from

$$\boldsymbol{p} = \hbar\boldsymbol{k}, \qquad p_4 = \hbar k_4, \qquad ck_4 = \omega,$$

and (for the photon)

$$\boldsymbol{k}^2 - k_4^2 = 0.$$

Differentiation of (*II.1.48*) with respect to $\boldsymbol{k}$ leads to

$$c\frac{\boldsymbol{p}}{p} = \boldsymbol{v} = \frac{\partial\omega}{\partial\boldsymbol{k}}.$$

The classical form of (*II.1.47*) for a mass point follows from Hamilton's equations of motion:

$$v_g = \frac{\partial E}{\partial p}. \qquad (II.1.49)$$

This is an example of a correspondence between classical and quantum mechanical descriptions.

II.1.C. Problem

(1) By use of (*II.1.40*), show that the normalized eigenvectors $|a_k, cp\rangle$, $|a_k, -cp\rangle$, and $|a_k, 0\rangle$, corresponding to energy eigenvalues cp, $-cp$, and 0, respectively, are given by

$$|a_k, cp\rangle = N\begin{bmatrix} ipp_2 - p_1p_3 \\ -ipp_1 - p_2p_3 \\ p_1^2 + p_2^2 \end{bmatrix},$$

$$|a_k, -cp\rangle = N\begin{bmatrix} -ipp_2 - p_1p_3 \\ ipp_1 - p_2p_3 \\ p_1^2 + p_2^2 \end{bmatrix},$$

$$|a_k, 0\rangle = \frac{1}{p}\begin{bmatrix} p_1 \\ p_2 \\ p_3 \end{bmatrix},$$

where $N = [2p^2(p_1^2 + p_2^2)]^{1/2}$.

II.2. Wave Function of the Photon and Schrödinger's Representation

An observable in quantum mechanics is usually a function of position and momentum variables. The possible values of an observable are calculated according to probability laws. The basic tool for calculating probabilities is the wave function whose time development is described by the Schrödinger equation, which in our case is given by (*II.1.31*). For example, the quantity

$$\langle\eta|\eta\rangle\, d^3\mathbf{r}$$

is the probability of finding a photon within the volume element $d^3\mathbf{r}$. Actually, because of the massless character of the photon, the concept of probability density for a localized photon does not exist. The observation of a photon must be based on its interaction with electric charges, which requires the knowledge of the wave function over all space. Therefore, for massless particles described by free fields we shall be interested in calculating average values of energy, momentum, spin, and so on. The formalism developed in the above is most suitable for the derivation of "Schrödinger's representation" in quantum mechanics. The results obtained for the photon are, of course, valid for all other physical systems.

(a) *Average Energy*: From the classical definition of energy,

$$E_c = \frac{1}{8\pi}\int \langle\chi|\chi\rangle\, d^3\mathbf{r}, \qquad (II.2.1)$$

and from (*II.1.29*) we get

$$E_c = \int \langle\eta|E|\eta\rangle\, d^3\mathbf{r}. \tag{II.2.2}$$

By using (*II.1.31*) and (*II.1.32*), the expression for E_c can be transformed into

$$\begin{aligned} E_c &= \int \langle\eta|H|\eta\rangle\, d^3\mathbf{r} \\ &= \int \langle\eta|i\hbar\frac{\partial}{\partial t}|\eta\rangle\, d^3\mathbf{r}. \end{aligned} \tag{II.2.3}$$

This result will be interpreted as an *expectation value* of the operator $i\hbar(\partial/\partial t)$. Hence we infer that *Schrödinger's representation of energy in quantum mechanics is given by*

$$E \longrightarrow i\hbar\frac{\partial}{\partial t}. \tag{II.2.4}$$

The operational statement (*II.2.4*) *holds for all quantum mechanical systems.*

(b) *Average Momentum:* The classical definition of the momentum of electromagnetic field is

$$\begin{aligned} P_{ci} &= \frac{1}{8\pi c}\int \langle\chi|K_i|\chi\rangle\, d^3\mathbf{r} \\ &= \frac{1}{c}\int \langle\eta|EK_i|\eta\rangle\, d^3\mathbf{r}. \end{aligned} \tag{II.2.5}$$

By using the procedure followed in the definition of energy we can write

$$\begin{aligned} P_{ci} &= \frac{1}{c}\int \langle\eta|HK_i|\eta\rangle\, d^3\mathbf{r} \\ &= \frac{1}{c}\int \langle\eta|K_iH|\eta\rangle\, d^3\mathbf{r}. \end{aligned} \tag{II.2.6}$$

Carrying out the implied matrix multiplication for each component and using equations (*II.1.31*), including the transverse condition $\nabla\cdot\boldsymbol{\eta} = 0$, we find that

$$P_{ci} = \int \langle\eta|-i\hbar\frac{\partial}{\partial x_i}|\eta\rangle\, d^3\mathbf{r}. \tag{II.2.7}$$

As before, this result can be interpreted as the expectation value of the operator $-i\hbar(\partial/\partial x_i)$. Hence *Schrödinger's representation of momentum in quantum mechanics is given by the Hermitian operator*

$$\boldsymbol{p} \longrightarrow -i\hbar\,\nabla. \tag{II.2.8}$$

The Hermitian character of $\boldsymbol{p}$ (that is, $\boldsymbol{p}^\dagger = \boldsymbol{p}$) follows from the reality of P_c, the classical momentum. *The operational statement* (*II.2.8*) *also is valid for all quantum mechanical systems.*

(c) *Average Angular Momentum:* The classical expression for the total angular momentum of the electromagnetic field can be written as

$$\boldsymbol{J}_c = \frac{1}{8\pi c}\int \langle\chi|(\boldsymbol{r}\times\boldsymbol{K})|\chi\rangle\, d^3\boldsymbol{r}$$

$$= \frac{1}{4\pi c}\int \boldsymbol{r}\times(\mathcal{E}\times\mathcal{H})\, d^3\boldsymbol{r}. \tag{II.2.9}$$

In terms of the wave function $|\eta\rangle$ we have

$$\boldsymbol{J}_c = \frac{1}{c}\int \langle\eta|H(\boldsymbol{r}\times\boldsymbol{K})|\eta\rangle\, d^3\boldsymbol{r}$$

$$= \frac{1}{c}\int \langle\eta|(\boldsymbol{r}\times\boldsymbol{K})H|\eta\rangle\, d^3\boldsymbol{r}. \tag{II.2.10}$$

The first component of $\boldsymbol{J}_c$ is

$$J_{c1} = \frac{1}{c}\int \langle\eta|H(x_2K_3 - x_3K_2)|\eta\rangle\, d^3\boldsymbol{r}.$$

The matrix form of the operator $H(x_2K_3 - x_3K_2)$ is given by

$$H(x_2K_3 - x_3K_2) = c\begin{bmatrix} L_1 & 0 & 0 \\ x_3p_1 & L_1 + x_3p_2 & p_3x_3 \\ -x_2p_1 & -p_2x_2 & L_1 - x_2p_3 \end{bmatrix},$$

where $L_1 = x_2p_3 - x_3p_2$ and $p_i = -i\hbar(\partial/\partial x^i)$ for $i = 1, 2, 3$. In order to include the role of the transversality condition (*II.1.32*), we may, further, write the above as

$$\frac{1}{c}H(x_2K_3 - x_3K_2) = L_1 + \hbar K_1 + x_3\begin{bmatrix} 0 & 0 & 0 \\ p_1 & p_2 & p_3 \\ 0 & 0 & 0 \end{bmatrix} - x_2\begin{bmatrix} 0 & 0 & 0 \\ 0 & 0 & 0 \\ p_1 & p_2 & p_3 \end{bmatrix}$$

$$+\begin{bmatrix} 0 & 0 & 0 \\ 0 & 0 & p_3x_3 - x_3p_3 + i\hbar \\ 0 & -p_2x_2 + x_2p_2 - i\hbar & 0 \end{bmatrix}.$$

Hence we see that the third and fourth terms, because of (*II.1.32*), will not contribute to J_{c1} and we obtain

$$J_{c1} = \int \langle\eta|(L_1 + \hbar K_1)|\eta\rangle\, d^3\boldsymbol{r}. \tag{II.2.11}$$

This result follows only if the operator relations

$$x_3p_3 - p_3x_3 = i\hbar,$$
$$x_2p_2 - p_2x_2 = i\hbar$$

are satisfied.

If we carry out the same procedure above for the components J_{c2} and J_{c3} we find that

$$J_{ci} = \int \langle\eta|J_i|\eta\rangle\, d^3\boldsymbol{r}, \tag{II.2.12}$$

with $x_ip_i - p_ix_i = i\hbar$, where $i = 1, 2, 3$ (not summed) and $J_i = L_i + \hbar K_i$.

Actually, we shall see in later chapters that the operator relations

$$x_i p_j - p_j x_i = i\hbar\, \delta_{ij} \qquad (II.2.13)$$

are postulated as "quantum conditions." The latter, as obtained from the present formalism of photon theory, are also valid for particles with mass. The statements contained in (*II.2.13*), usually called commutation relations, are uniquely determined and the form of the total angular momentum,

$$\boldsymbol{J} = \boldsymbol{L} + \hbar\boldsymbol{K}, \qquad (II.2.14)$$

is a consequence of these commutation relations. The operator $\boldsymbol{L}$ represents the orbital angular momentum,

$$\boldsymbol{L} = \boldsymbol{r} \times \boldsymbol{p}, \qquad (II.2.15)$$

and it, also, is valid for particles with mass. *The definition (II.2.15) is Schrödinger's representation of the angular momentum operator*. Thus, classical angular momentum of the field is just the expectation value of quantum angular momentum $\boldsymbol{J}$.

The operational statement (*II.2.14*) is of purely relativistic origin and it means that all quantum mechanical systems have total angular momentum $\boldsymbol{J}$ consisting of the sum of orbital and spin angular momenta. We see also that the spin term $\hbar\boldsymbol{K}$ in $\boldsymbol{J}$ arises from the relativistic transformation property of the electromagnetic field and also from its reinterpretation in terms of a wave function. Therefore spin is a quantum mechanical concept and could not be obtained on the basis of relativity alone. Spin is a natural by-product of relativity and quantum mechanics. It is a new degree of freedom and is independent of the coordinates. We shall see later that spin degree of freedom is not the same for all systems. Actually the transformation properties of a particle (or its wave function) is intimately related to the transformation properties of its spin.

The spin $\boldsymbol{S} = \hbar\boldsymbol{K}$ of the photon satisfies the angular momentum eigenvalue relation [see (*I.8.4*) and Chapter IV],

$$S(S + \hbar) = S_1^2 + S_2^2 + S_3^2 = 2\hbar^2, \qquad (II.2.16)$$

where $\boldsymbol{S} = \hbar\boldsymbol{K}$, so the photon is a particle of spin 1 ($S = \hbar$).
The wave function $|\eta\rangle$ of the photon is a complex vector and for this reason it is a vector particle. In general, all vector particles have spin 1 and, conversely, all particles of spin 1 are vector particles. *The spin of the photon is not defined for a photon at rest.* The latter does not apply for particles with mass, since in this case one can define a rest frame and hence the spin of the particle at rest is also defined.

The total angular momentum operator $\boldsymbol{J}$, as can easily be shown by using (*II.2.13*), commutes with the operator H:

$$J_i H - H J_i = [L_i + \hbar K_i, H] = 0. \qquad (II.2.17)$$

If we regard H as the Hamiltonian of the transverse photon field, then result (*II.2.17*) can be interpreted as the conservation law of the total angular momentum of the photon. The reasons for this fact will be discussed in later chapters.

II.2.A. Problem

1. Prove that the expectation value of the spin $\boldsymbol{S} = \hbar \boldsymbol{K}$ in right and left circular polarization states are $\hbar \hat{\boldsymbol{p}}$ and $-\hbar \hat{\boldsymbol{p}}$, respectively, where $\hat{\boldsymbol{p}}$ is a unit vector in the direction of the propagation of the wave.

CHAPTER III

GENERAL FORMALISM OF QUANTUM MECHANICS

III.1. Canonical Transformations

Both in classical and quantum physics the coordinates and momenta are dynamical variables of a system. In classical physics, the time development of these and other relevant dynamical variables is determined by the Hamiltonian equations of motion, given by (*I.1.4*). The corresponding equations in quantum mechanics are "Heisenberg's equations of motion." The transformations of dynamical variables which leave equations of motion unchanged are called canonical transformations.

If $\xi(q_i, p_i, t)$ is, as a function of coordinates and momenta, a dynamical variable, then its change with respect to time is given by

$$\frac{d\xi}{dt} = \frac{\partial \xi}{\partial t} + \sum_i \left(\frac{\partial \xi}{\partial q_i} \dot{q}_i + \frac{\partial \xi}{\partial p_i} \dot{p}_i\right).$$

A more general expression for $d\xi/dt$ in terms of the Hamiltonian of the dynamical system is obtained by using Hamilton's equations of motion (*I.1.4*):

$$\frac{d\xi}{dt} = \frac{\partial \xi}{\partial t} + [\xi, H]_c, \tag{III.1.1}$$

where the Poisson bracket $[\xi, H]_c$ for any two dynamical systems is defined by

$$[\xi, \eta]_c = \sum_i \left[\frac{\partial \xi}{\partial q_i}\frac{\partial \eta}{\partial p_i} - \frac{\partial \eta}{\partial q_i}\frac{\partial \xi}{\partial p_i}\right]. \tag{III.1.2}$$

The form (*III.1.1*) is one that is used in the formulation of quantum mechanics. Some of the most frequently used Poisson bracket relations for any three dynamical variables ξ, η, ζ are

$$[\xi, \eta]_c = -[\eta, \xi]_c, \tag{III.1.3}$$

$$[\xi, \eta + \zeta]_c = [\xi, \eta]_c + [\xi, \zeta]_c, \tag{III.1.4}$$

$$[\xi, \eta\zeta]_c = [\xi, \eta]_c\zeta + \eta[\xi, \zeta]_c, \tag{III.1.5}$$

$$[[\xi, \eta]_c, \zeta]_c + [[\eta, \zeta]_c, \xi]_c + [[\zeta, \xi]_c, \eta]_c = 0. \tag{III.1.6}$$

Poisson brackets of dynamical variables are canonical invariants. The Hamiltonian forms of the equations of motion in terms of Poisson brackets are

$$\frac{dq_i}{dt} = [q_i, H]_c, \tag{III.1.7}$$

$$\frac{dp_i}{dt} = [p_i, H]_c. \tag{III.1.8}$$

The Poisson brackets of q_i and p_i are

$$\begin{aligned} [q_i, q_j]_c &= 0, \\ [p_i, p_j]_c &= 0, \\ [q_i, p_j]_c &= \delta_{ij}. \end{aligned} \tag{III.1.9}$$

The coordinates q_i and the momenta p_i are canonically conjugate variables.

The time development of q_i and p_i (or any other dynamical variable) can also be expressed in terms of Poisson brackets:

$$\begin{aligned} q(t) &= q_0 + t[q, H]_c + \frac{1}{2!}t^2 [[q, H]_c, H]_c + \cdots, \\ p(t) &= p_0 + t[p, H]_c + \frac{1}{2!}t^2 [[p, H]_c, H]_c + \cdots, \end{aligned} \tag{III.1.10}$$

where the Poisson brackets are evaluated at time $t = 0$.

The Poisson brackets of a dynamical variable ξ, with coordinates q_i and momenta p_i, can be calculated from (*III.1.2*):

$$[\xi, q_i]_c = -\frac{\partial\xi}{\partial p_i}, \tag{III.1.11}$$

$$[\xi, p_i]_c = \frac{\partial\xi}{\partial q_i}. \tag{III.1.12}$$

In the same way one can easily show that the Poisson bracket of the angular momentum vector with itself is

$$[L_i, L_j]_c = \epsilon_{ijk}L_k, \tag{III.1.13}$$

where

$$\boldsymbol{L} = \boldsymbol{r} \times \boldsymbol{p}. \tag{III.1.14}$$

We may, further, generalize Poisson bracket relations to relativistic systems. If ξ and η are functions of p_μ and x^μ, for $\mu = 1, 2, 3, 4$, we define relativistic Poisson bracket relations by

$$[\xi, \eta]_R = \left(\frac{\partial\xi}{\partial x^\mu}\frac{\partial\eta}{\partial p_\mu} - \frac{\partial\eta}{\partial x^\mu}\frac{\partial\xi}{\partial p_\mu}\right), \tag{III.1.15}$$

where

$$p_\mu = a_{\mu\nu}p^\nu.$$

In particular, for $\xi = x^\alpha$ and $\eta = p^\beta$, we obtain

$$[x_\mu, p_\nu]_R = a_{\mu\nu}. \tag{III.1.16}$$

The relativistic equations of motion of a single particle in an external electromagnetic field can be written as

$$\frac{dx^\alpha}{d\tau} = [x^\alpha, H']_R, \tag{III.1.17}$$

$$\frac{dp^\alpha}{d\tau} = [p^\alpha, H']_R, \tag{III.1.18}$$

where τ is the proper time of the particle, H' is given by

$$H' = \frac{1}{2m}\left(p_\alpha - \frac{e}{c}A_\alpha\right)\left(p^\alpha - \frac{e}{c}A^\alpha\right), \tag{III.1.19}$$

and the A_α are the potentials of the electromagnetic field.

Thus

$$mV^\alpha = m\frac{dx^\alpha}{d\tau} = p^\alpha - \frac{e}{c}A^\alpha \tag{III.1.20}$$

and

$$\frac{dp^\alpha}{d\tau} = \frac{e}{c}\frac{\partial A_\rho}{\partial x_\alpha}V^\rho. \tag{III.1.21}$$

By differentiating (*III.1.20*) and eliminating $dp^\alpha/d\tau$ from (*III.1.21*) we obtain the equations of motion of a point electric charge in an external electromagnetic field:

$$\frac{d}{d\tau}(mV^\alpha) = \frac{e}{c}f^\alpha_{\cdot\rho}V^\rho, \tag{III.1.22}$$

where the electromagnetic field tensor $f_{\mu\nu}$ is defined by

$$f_{\mu\nu} = \frac{\partial A_\nu}{\partial x^\mu} - \frac{\partial A_\mu}{\partial x^\nu}. \tag{III.1.23}$$

The quantities p_μ represent the total momentum of the particles in the presence of fields.

By using (*III.1.15*) we can record the relativistic Poisson bracket relations

$$[Q_{\mu\nu}, p_\rho]_R = a_{\rho\nu}p_\mu - a_{\mu\rho}p_\nu \tag{III.1.24}$$

and

$$[Q_{\mu\nu}, Q_{\rho\sigma}]_R = -a_{\mu\rho}Q_{\nu\sigma} + a_{\nu\rho}Q_{\mu\sigma} - a_{\mu\sigma}Q_{\rho\nu} + a_{\nu\sigma}Q_{\rho\mu}, \tag{III.1.25}$$

where the

$$Q_{\mu\nu} = x_\mu p_\nu - x_\nu p_\mu \tag{III.1.26}$$

are relativistic generalizations of angular momentum. The orbital angular momentum is

$$L_i = \tfrac{1}{2}\epsilon_{ijk}Q_{jk}. \tag{III.1.27}$$

Furthermore, the relativistic generalizations of (*III.1.11*) and (*III.1.12*) are

$$[\![\xi, x^\mu]\!]_R = \frac{\partial \xi}{\partial p_\mu}, \tag{III.1.28}$$

$$[\![\xi, p_\mu]\!]_R = \frac{\partial \xi}{\partial x^\mu}. \tag{III.1.29}$$

The more usual form of the Hamiltonian of a particle in an electromagnetic field can be obtained from

$$\left(p_\mu - \frac{e}{c}A_\mu\right)\left(p^\mu - \frac{e}{c}A^\mu\right) = m^2c^2, \tag{III.1.30}$$

as

$$H = cp_4 = e\phi + c\sqrt{\left[m^2c^2 + \left(\mathbf{p} - \frac{e}{c}\mathbf{A}\right)^2\right]}, \tag{III.1.31}$$

where $\phi = A_4$. The use of this Hamiltonian in (*III.1.7*) and (*III.1.8*) leads to (*III.1.21*).

III.1.A. Examples of Canonical Transformations

(*a*) A one-dimensional harmonic oscillator can be represented by the canonical transformation

$$\begin{bmatrix} m\omega q \\ p \end{bmatrix} = \begin{bmatrix} \cos\omega t & \sin\omega t \\ -\sin\omega t & \cos\omega t \end{bmatrix} \begin{bmatrix} m\omega q_0 \\ p_0 \end{bmatrix}. \tag{III.1.32}$$

The Hamiltonian of the harmonic oscillator is

$$H = \frac{p^2}{2m} + \frac{1}{2}m\omega^2q^2. \tag{III.1.33}$$

The equations of motion,

$$\dot{q} = [\![q, H]\!]_c = \frac{p}{m},$$

$$\dot{p} = [\![p, H]\!]_c = -m\omega^2 q,$$

are left unchanged under the canonical transformation (*III.1.32*).

(b) The Poisson brackets of the q and p at different, and equal, times are

$$[\![q(0), p(0)]\!]_c = [\![q(t), p(t)]\!]_c = 1,$$

$$[\![q(0), q(t)]\!]_c = \frac{1}{m\omega}\sin\omega t, \tag{III.1.34}$$

$$[\![p(0), p(t)]\!]_c = m\omega \sin\omega t.$$

(c) A complex representation of the harmonic oscillator is

$$a = a_0 e^{i\omega t}, \tag{III.1.35}$$

where

$$a = \frac{1}{\sqrt{(2m)}} (p + im\omega q),$$

$$a_0 = \frac{1}{\sqrt{(2m)}} (p_0 + im\omega q_0),$$

so the Hamiltonian can be written as

$$H = a^*a = a_0^*a_0. \qquad (III.1.36)$$

The Poisson bracket of a^* and a is

$$[a^*, a] = -i\omega. \qquad (III.1.37)$$

The above representation of the one-dimensional harmonic oscillator can be extended to a three-dimensional oscillator. The atoms of a crystal behave like three-dimensional harmonic oscillators. They can execute simple harmonic motions about their equilibrium position. The oscillations for an anisotropic crystal can take place along the three principal axes of the oscillator. The potential energy is given by

$$V = \tfrac{1}{2}m(\omega_1^2x_1^2 + \omega_2^2x_2^2 + \omega_3^2x_3^2). \qquad (III.1.38)$$

The Hamiltonian can be written as

$$H = \langle a|a\rangle = \langle a_0|a_0\rangle, \qquad (III.1.39)$$

where

$$|a\rangle = \frac{1}{\sqrt{(2m)}} [|p\rangle + im\Omega|x\rangle],$$

$$|p\rangle = \begin{bmatrix} p_1 \\ p_2 \\ p_3 \end{bmatrix},$$

$$\Omega = \begin{bmatrix} \omega_1 & 0 & 0 \\ 0 & \omega_2 & 0 \\ 0 & 0 & \omega_3 \end{bmatrix};$$

thus

$$\langle a|a\rangle = \frac{\boldsymbol{p}^2}{2m} + \frac{1}{2} m(\omega_1^2x_1^2 + \omega_2^2x_2^2 + \omega_3^2x_3^2).$$

It is easily seen from (*III.1.39*) that the solution of the three-dimensional harmonic oscillator is a canonical transformation expressible as a unitary transformation by

$$|a\rangle = U|a_0\rangle, \qquad (III.1.40)$$

where U is a 3×3 unitary matrix.

On writing the Hamiltonian in the form

$$H = \sum_{i=1}^{3} a_i^*a_i, \qquad (III.1.41)$$

and noting that

$$[a_i^*, a_j]_c = -i\Omega_{ij},$$

we obtain the equations of motion.

$$-i\frac{d}{dt}|a\rangle = \Omega|a\rangle. \tag{III.1.42}$$

The unitary matrix U satisfies

$$-i\frac{dU}{dt} = \Omega|U\rangle. \tag{III.1.43}$$

Hence

$$U = e^{i\delta}e^{i\Omega t}, \tag{III.1.44}$$

where δ is an arbitrary phase.

III.1.B. Problems

1. Show that if any two components of the angular momentum L_i are constants of the motion—that is, if their Poisson brackets with the Hamiltonian of the system vanish—then the total angular momentum $\boldsymbol{L}^2$ is also a constant of the motion. Compare the conservation of a particular component of angular momentum to that of a linear momentum.

2. Show that the Poisson bracket of the position vectors $x_i(t)$ and $x_i(t_0)$, at times t and $t_0(< t)$, is given by

$$[x_i(t), x_j(t_0)]_c = -\frac{\partial}{\partial p_j}\int_{t_0}^{t}\frac{\partial H}{\partial p_i}\,dt. \tag{III.1.45}$$

Then prove that for a harmonic oscillator of angular frequency ω and mass m, and also for a free particle of mass m, the corresponding Poisson bracket relations are respectively

$$[q(t), q(t_0)]_c = \frac{\sin\omega(t - t_0)}{m\omega} \tag{III.1.46}$$

and

$$[x_i(t), x_j(t_0)]_c = \frac{t - t_0}{m}\,\delta_{ij}. \tag{III.1.47}$$

III.2. The Hamilton-Jacobi Equation

Because of the important role played by the concept of "action function" in the formulation of quantum mechanics, we shall discuss some of its properties in detail.

We begin by considering the simplest case of a free nonrelativistic particle. The action function is

$$S = \int_{t_0}^{t} \tfrac{1}{2} m \boldsymbol{v}^2 \, dt \tag{III.2.1}$$

The corresponding equations of motion are

$$\frac{d\boldsymbol{v}}{dt} = 0,$$

so the classical path of the particle is described by

$$\boldsymbol{r} = \boldsymbol{r}_0 + \boldsymbol{v}_0(t - t_0),$$
$$\boldsymbol{v} = \boldsymbol{v}_0.$$

Hence

$$\boldsymbol{v} = \boldsymbol{v}_0 = \frac{\boldsymbol{r} - \boldsymbol{r}_0}{t - t_0}.$$

We use the path equations to calculate the "extremum value" of the action as

$$S = \frac{1}{2} m \boldsymbol{v}_0^2 (t - t_0)^2 = \frac{m(\boldsymbol{r} - \boldsymbol{r}_0)^2}{2(t - t_0)}, \tag{III.2.2}$$

along the actual path of the particle. By differentiating the extremum action S defined by (*III.2.2*) we can easily see that it satisfies the differential equation

$$\frac{\partial S}{\partial t} + \frac{1}{2m} (\boldsymbol{\nabla} S)^2 = 0, \tag{III.2.3}$$

which is the Hamilton-Jacobi equation for a free particle. From (*I.1.5*) it follows that

$$-\frac{\partial S}{\partial t} = \frac{\boldsymbol{p}^2}{2m} = H_0,$$

$$\frac{\partial S}{\partial \boldsymbol{r}} = \frac{m(\boldsymbol{r} - \boldsymbol{r}_0)}{t - t_0} = m\boldsymbol{v}_0 = \boldsymbol{p},$$

where H_0 is the Hamiltonian of a free particle. In general, the Hamilton-Jacobi equation of a nonrelativistic particle in the presence of external forces is of the form

$$\frac{\partial S}{\partial t} + H\left(q_i, \frac{\partial S}{\partial q_i}, t\right) = 0, \tag{III.2.4}$$

where H is the total classical Hamiltonian of the dynamical system.

The extremum action function S is the generator of a canonical transformation from the coordinates and momenta at any time t to the coordinates and momenta at the initial time t_0. Thus a solution of Hamilton-Jacobi equation provides, automatically, a solution of the dynamical problem.

For a relativistic free particle the action function

$$S = -mc^2 \int_{t_0}^{t} \sqrt{\left(1 - \frac{\boldsymbol{v}^2}{c^2}\right)} \, dt. \tag{III.2.5}$$

The extremum value of the action function in this case is obtained as

$$S = -mcR, \tag{III.2.6}$$

where

$$R^2 = c^2(t - t_0) - (\boldsymbol{r} - \boldsymbol{r}_0)^2, \tag{III.2.7}$$

and it satisfies the relativistic Hamilton-Jacobi equation

$$\frac{\partial S}{\partial x^\mu}\frac{\partial S}{\partial x_\mu} - m^2c^2 = 0, \tag{III.2.8}$$

where

$$\frac{\partial S}{\partial x^\mu} = p_\mu, \qquad \frac{\partial S}{\partial x_\mu} = p^\mu. \tag{III.2.9}$$

If we use (*III.2.6*), we find that

$$E = -\frac{\partial S}{\partial t} = \frac{mc^2}{\sqrt{1 - \dfrac{\boldsymbol{v}^2}{c^2}}}$$

$$\boldsymbol{p} = \nabla S = \frac{m\boldsymbol{v}}{\sqrt{1 - \dfrac{\boldsymbol{v}^2}{c^2}}}$$

In the presence of an external electromagnetic field represented by the potentials A_μ, the corresponding Hamilton-Jacobi equation is

$$\left(\frac{\partial S}{\partial x^\mu} - \frac{e}{c}A_\mu\right)\left(\frac{\partial S}{\partial x_\mu} - \frac{e}{c}A^\mu\right) - m^2c^2 = 0. \tag{III.2.10}$$

This is a gauge-invariant equation. If G is an arbitrary scalar function of x^μ, then equation (*III.2.10*) remains unchanged under the transformations

$$S' = S + \frac{e}{c}G, \qquad A'_\mu = A_\mu + \frac{\partial G}{\partial x^\mu}. \tag{III.2.11}$$

Hence the action S and potentials A_μ are arbitrary up to a gauge transformation generated by G.

III.2.A. A Simple Derivation of the Hamilton-Jacobi Equation

The classical path of a particle acted on by external forces can be constructed as an unfolding of a canonical transformation in a time interval (t_0, t).

Because of its simplicity we shall discuss the nonrelativistic theory only. Let $L[x_i(t), \dot{x}_i(t), t]$ be the Lagrangian of a one-particle system. Its action function in a time interval (t_0, t) is given by

$$S = \int_{t_0}^{t} L[x_i(t), \dot{x}_i(t), t]\, dt, \tag{III.2.12}$$

where the classical Lagrangian L is of the form

$$L = \frac{\mathbf{p}^2}{2m} - V(\mathbf{r}, t), \tag{III.2.13}$$

in which V is the potential energy.

The entire path of the particle can be built up as a sum of paths generated during small time intervals arising from division of the interval (t_0, t) into n equal parts. The number n can be made as large as we wish and the corresponding time intervals $t_{i+1} - t_i = \epsilon$ for $i = 0, 1, 2, \cdots, n$ and hence the paths can assume small values.

Thus, if the particle strikes the potential V at time $t_{i+1} = t_i + \epsilon$, it will deviate from its original free path and its action will decrease by an amount

$$\epsilon V[\mathbf{r}(t_i + \epsilon)] = \epsilon V[\mathbf{r}(t_{i+1})].$$

The classical path is one for which the action assumes its extremum value. Thus, from

$$S[\mathbf{r}(t_{i+1}), \mathbf{r}(t_i)] = \text{ext} \int_{t_i}^{t_{i+1}} L[\mathbf{r}(t), \dot{\mathbf{r}}(t)]\, dt$$

and from (*III.2.2*), we obtain

$$S[\mathbf{r}(t_{i+1}), \mathbf{r}(t_i)] = \frac{1}{2} m\epsilon \left[\frac{\mathbf{r}(t_{i+1}) - \mathbf{r}(t_i)}{\epsilon}\right]^2 - \epsilon V[\mathbf{r}(t_{i+1})]. \tag{III.2.14}$$

Each $S[\mathbf{r}(t_{i+1}), \mathbf{r}(t_i)]$, where $i = 1, 2, \cdots$, generates a canonical transformation from the variables $\mathbf{r}(t_{i+1})$, $\mathbf{p}(t_{i+1})$ at time t_{i+1} to the variables $\mathbf{r}(t_i)$, $\mathbf{p}(t_i)$ of the path at time t_i.

The total extremum action along the path generated during the time $t - t_0$ is

$$\begin{aligned} S &= \sum_{l=0}^{n} S[\mathbf{r}(t_{i+1}), \mathbf{r}(t_i)] \\ &= \sum_{i=0}^{n} \left[\text{ext} \int_{t_i}^{t_{i+1}} L\, dt\right]. \end{aligned} \tag{III.2.15}$$

Because of the finite extent of time, the sum in (*III.2.15*) is finite, for any value of n. The function $\mathbf{r}(t)$ in the interval between t_i and t_{i+1} is the path followed by a classical particle, with the Lagrangian L. We choose a particular time t_n and record the sum (*III.2.15*):

$$S - \sum_{i=0}^{n-1} S[\mathbf{r}(t_i + \epsilon), \mathbf{r}(t_i)] = S[\mathbf{r}(t_{n+1}), \mathbf{r}(t_n)].$$

Then, using (*III.2.14*), we write

$$\frac{S - \sum_{i=0}^{n-1} S[\mathbf{r}(t_i + \epsilon), \mathbf{r}(t_i)]}{\epsilon} = \frac{1}{2} m \left[\frac{\mathbf{r}(t_{n+1}) - \mathbf{r}(t_n)}{\epsilon}\right]^2 - V[\mathbf{r}(t_{n+1})].$$

As ϵ tends to zero, the left side becomes

$$\frac{\partial S}{\partial t}\,dt + \frac{d\boldsymbol{r}}{dt}\cdot \nabla S\,dt,$$

where $dt = \epsilon$; the right side tends to

$$\frac{\boldsymbol{p}^2}{2m} - V[\boldsymbol{r}(t)].$$

By using the definitions

$$\boldsymbol{p} = \nabla S, \qquad \frac{d\boldsymbol{r}}{dt} = \frac{\boldsymbol{p}}{m},$$

we obtain

$$\frac{\partial S}{\partial t} + \frac{1}{2m}(\nabla S)^2 + V = 0 \tag{III.2.16}$$

as the nonrelativistic Hamilton-Jacobi equation for a particle in a potential V.

The Langrangian formulation of classical or quantum mechanics has some advantages over the Hamiltonian formulation. First, the Lagrangian formulation (the use of the S function) allows direct application of Hamilton's principle of stationary action. There is no such principle in terms of the Hamiltonian of the dynamical system. Second, the Lagrangian formulation, in particular, admits a larger group of coordinate and gauge transformations.

We shall see an explicit demonstration of these points in connection with the Dirac-Feynman formulation of quantum mechanics.

III.3. Infinite-Dimensional Spaces in Quantum Mechanics

There are many reasons for introducing infinite-dimensional spaces into the quantum mechanical description of natural phenomena. Heisenberg's uncertainty principle (to be discussed later) is needed in dealing with micro phenomena, where Planck's constant h cannot be ignored. In quantum mechanics we have also to use a wave function ψ for predicting all possible behaviors of a physical system. The knowledge of ψ enables us to calculate probabilities of dynamical variables. The concept of probability, as used in quantum mechanics, together with the uncertainty principle, constitute a "complete" description for physical phenomena. The latter replaces the "classical path" by a "quantum path" which—because of the finiteness of Planck's constant h—cannot be predicted exactly as a "single path." *All paths in space-time have a certain probability of occurrence. Such a description necessitates the introduction of infinite-dimensional spaces.**

---

* However, despite the above facts, the use of infinite-dimensional spaces is not necessarily a requirement of quantum mechanics alone. We can use an infinite-dimensional (statistical) description for the classical scattering processes where $\hbar = 0$.

The infinite-dimensional spaces in quantum mechanics are either discretely infinite or continuously infinite-dimensional spaces. For example, a unitary space consists of the set of all vectors $|\xi\rangle$, whose components ξ constitute an infinite sequence of numbers for which

$$\langle\xi|\xi\rangle = \sum_{i=1}^{\infty} |\xi_i|^2 \tag{III.3.1}$$

converges. If the components ξ_i of $|\xi\rangle$ are of finite length, they are said to constitute a "Hilbert space."

The case of a continuously infinite dimensionality can best be understood by considering all continuous complex functions $F(u)$ of a real variable u.

The various values of u in a given interval (a, b) constitute the components of the vector F with vector index u. The variable u can cover the entire domain of real or complex numbers. The totality of such functions F makes up what mathematicians call a "function space" of continuously infinite dimensionality. The rules of vector addition and multiplication discussed in Chapter I are also applicable in this case.

A function space need not depend on a single parameter. Sometimes it is necessary to generalize to more complicated cases where each vector depends on more than one index parameter; this is usually the case in quantum mechanics. However, not all the vectors (states) of quantum mechanics are representable in a Hilbert space; exceptions exist but they will not be discussed in this section.

Most of the theorems for finite-dimensional spaces—except the convergence discussed for the series (*I.7.4*) can be carried over to infinite-dimensional spaces. For example, all unitary transformations which leave unchanged the quadratic form

$$\langle\xi|\xi\rangle$$

form an infinite unitary group in an infinite-dimensional space.

All the definitions of the linear operators defined in Chapter I are also applicable in this case. If K is a linear Hermitian operator in a Hilbert space, then from it we can construct a unitary operator U:

$$U = \frac{1 + iK}{1 - iK}, \qquad U^\dagger = \frac{1 - iK}{1 + iK}. \tag{III.3.2}$$

Hence

$$U^\dagger U = UU^\dagger = 1. \tag{III.3.3}$$

A more general representation of the unitary operator U can be obtained by expressing it in terms of α, defined by

$$\alpha = 2 \tan^{-1} K. \tag{III.3.4}$$

Hence

$$U = e^{-i\alpha}. \tag{III.3.5}$$

III.3.A. Vectors and Linear Operators in Infinite-Dimensional Spaces

The mathematical formulation of quantum mechanics is based on the use and transformation properties of linear Hermitian and linear unitary and (antiunitary) operators defined over a linear vector space (Hilbert space or a more general space). The eigenvectors of a set of commuting linear Hermitian operators are used to set up an orthonormal representation, where all eigenvectors are independent and any two of them are orthogonal. If any vector can be expressed over the orthonormal base, then it is said that the eigenvectors form a complete set.

Let α be a linear Hermitian operator whose eigenvectors $|\alpha'\rangle$ form a complete set. The most general case refers to the possibilities of the eigenvalues consisting of all real numbers lying in an interval (a, b) or of the eigenvalues consisting of a finite or infinite discrete set of real numbers or, alternatively, both discrete and continuous numbers. Assuming that all eigenvectors are normalized, then in the case of discrete eigenvalues we may define the unit operator by

$$I = \sum_{n=1}^{\infty} |\alpha_n\rangle\langle\alpha_n|, \qquad (III.3.6)$$

where $\langle\alpha_n|\alpha_m\rangle = \delta_{nm}$ for $n, m = 1, 2, 3, \cdots$. Any vector $|V\rangle$ of Hilbert space can be expressed as

$$|V\rangle = \sum_{n=1}^{\infty} |\alpha_n\rangle\langle\alpha_n|V\rangle, \qquad (III.3.7)$$

$$= \sum_{n=1}^{\infty} V_n|\alpha_n\rangle.$$

In the case of a continuous set of eigenvalues and eigenvectors the unit operator is

$$I = \int |\alpha'\rangle\, d\alpha'\, \langle\alpha'|, \qquad (III.3.8)$$

and the vector $|V\rangle$ can be expressed as

$$|V\rangle = \int |\alpha'\rangle\, d\alpha'\, \langle\alpha'|V\rangle. \qquad (III.3.9)$$

Any member $|\alpha''\rangle$ of the set of eigenkets $|\alpha'\rangle$ is independent of all other eigenkets. Thus from (*III.3.8*) we have

$$|\alpha''\rangle = \int |\alpha'\rangle\, d\alpha'\, \langle\alpha'|\alpha''\rangle. \qquad (III.3.10)$$

From the assumption of orthogonality of the eigenkets $|\alpha'\rangle$ and $|\alpha''\rangle$, it follows that the integrand in (*III.3.10*) must vanish over the whole range of integration except at the one point $\alpha' = \alpha''$. The integration at the point

$\alpha' = \alpha''$ will of course be zero, unless the integrand of (*III.3.10*) at the point $\alpha' = \alpha''$ assumes an arbitrarily large value. The latter requires the introduction of a special function $\delta(x - a)$ such that

$$\int_{-\infty}^{\infty} f(x)\delta(x - a)\, dx = f(a), \qquad (III.3.11)$$

where $f(x)$ is any continuous function of x. Thus the function $\delta(x - a)$ vanishes over an arbitrarily small neighborhood of the point a. Hence the choice of

$$\langle\alpha'|\alpha''\rangle = \delta(\alpha' - \alpha'') \qquad (III.3.12)$$

for the normalization of continuous eigenkets will lead to

$$|\alpha''\rangle = \int |\alpha'\rangle\, d\alpha'\, \delta(\alpha' - \alpha'') = |\alpha''\rangle.$$

III.3.B. Properties of the Dirac δ Function

Dirac's δ function is an important mathematical tool in quantum mechanics. There are many definitions of it. It is meaningful only when it appears under an integral; otherwise it must be treated as an operational symbol.

(a) We define it as

$$\begin{aligned}\delta(x) &= \frac{1}{2\pi} \lim_{\lambda\to\infty} \int_{-\lambda}^{\lambda} e^{i\tau x}\, d\tau \qquad (III.3.13)\\ &= \frac{1}{\pi} \lim_{\lambda\to\infty} \frac{\sin \lambda x}{x}.\end{aligned}$$

Hence

$$\int_{-a}^{b} \delta(x)f(x)\, dx = \frac{1}{\pi} \lim_{\lambda\to\infty} \int_{-\lambda a}^{\lambda b} f\left(\frac{y}{\lambda}\right) \frac{\sin y}{y}\, dy = f(0).$$

(b) The differential coefficient of a function $\eta(x)$, defined by

$$\eta(x) = \begin{cases} 0 & \text{if } x < 0, \\ 1 & \text{if } x > 0, \end{cases} \qquad (III.3.14)$$

is a δ *function*. For if $a > 0$, $b > 0$, we have

$$\int_{-a}^{b} f(x)\eta'(x)\, dx = f(b) - \int_0^b f'(x)\, dx = f(0).$$

(c) The function $\epsilon(x)$, defined by

$$\epsilon(x) = \begin{cases} 1 & \text{if } x > 0, \\ -1 & \text{if } x < 0, \end{cases} \qquad (III.3.15)$$

can be used to define a δ function.

(d) Consider the function

$$\frac{1}{x - i\epsilon} = \frac{x + i\epsilon}{x^2 + \epsilon^2} = \frac{x}{x^2 + \epsilon^2} + \frac{i\epsilon}{x^2 + \epsilon^2}$$

If we let ϵ tend to zero, then

$$\lim_{\epsilon\to 0} \frac{x}{x^2+\epsilon^2} \longrightarrow P\frac{1}{x}$$

and

$$\lim_{\epsilon\to 0} \frac{i\epsilon}{x^2+\epsilon^2} \longrightarrow i\pi\delta(x).$$

Hence

$$\lim_{\epsilon\to 0} \frac{1}{x \pm i\epsilon} = \delta_{\pm}(x) = P\frac{1}{x} \mp i\pi\delta(x), \tag{III.3.16}$$

where

$$\delta_{-}^{*}(x) = \delta_{+}(x).$$

An integral representation of $P(1/x)$—principal part of $1/x$—which is zero for $x = 0$ and $1/x$ for $x \neq 0$, can be given as

$$P\frac{1}{x} = \frac{1}{2\pi}\int_{-\infty}^{\infty} e^{ix\tau} f(\tau)\, d\tau,$$

where

$$f(\tau) = P\int e^{-ix\tau}\frac{1}{x}\, dx.$$

A contour integration of $e^{-i\tau x}/x$ above the real axis with a semicircle indented at the origin, with $\tau < 0$, will give

$$f(\tau) = -i\pi.$$

If we choose as the contour of integration the reflection of the previous contour with respect to the real axis, with $\tau > 0$, we get

$$f(\tau) = i\pi.$$

Hence we can write

$$f(\tau) = -i\pi\frac{\tau}{|\tau|}$$

and obtain the representation

$$P\frac{1}{x} = -\frac{i}{2}\int_{-\infty}^{\infty} e^{ix\tau}\frac{\tau}{|\tau|}\, d\tau. \tag{III.3.17}$$

Furthermore, frequently used integral representations of the functions $1/(x \pm i\epsilon)$ are

$$\frac{1}{x - i\epsilon} = i\int_0^{\infty} e^{-i\tau(x-i\epsilon)}\, d\tau \tag{III.3.18}$$

and

$$\frac{1}{x + i\epsilon} = -i\int_0^{\infty} e^{i\tau(x+i\epsilon)}\, d\tau. \tag{III.3.19}$$

(e) From the equation

$$\lim_{\epsilon\to 0}\int_1^x \frac{d\tau}{\tau + i\epsilon} = \log x, \tag{III.3.20}$$

we obtain

$$\frac{d}{dx}(\log x) = \lim_{\epsilon \to 0} \frac{1}{x + i\epsilon} = P\frac{1}{x} - i\pi\delta(x). \qquad (III.3.21)$$

The derivative of the δ function follows from

$$\delta'(x) = -\frac{2}{\pi}\lim_{\epsilon \to 0} \frac{\epsilon x}{(\epsilon^2 + x^2)^2} = -\frac{2}{\pi}\lim_{\substack{\epsilon \to 0 \\ \epsilon' \to 0}} \left(\frac{\epsilon}{\epsilon^2 + x^2}\right)\left(\frac{x}{\epsilon'^2 + x^2}\right).$$

The limit depends on which of the limits $\epsilon \longrightarrow 0$ and $\epsilon' \longrightarrow 0$ is dealt with first, and is ambiguous. If, however, we add the condition that both limits are to be taken simultaneously, with $\epsilon = \epsilon'$, we obtain

$$\delta'(x) = -2\left(P\frac{1}{x}\right)\delta(x). \qquad (III.3.22)$$

(f) A δ function can also be defined by a contour integration in the complex plane. Let c be a closed path containing the point $x = 0$ and where the function $f(x)$ is finite; then

$$\int_{-\infty}^{\infty} f(x)\delta(x)\, dx = f(0) = \frac{1}{2\pi i}\oint_c \frac{f(x)}{x}\, dx.$$

Hence

$$\delta(x) = \frac{1}{2\pi i}\frac{1}{x}\Big]_c, \qquad (III.3.23)$$

where the symbol c means that the subsequent integration over x should be carried out along c. The contour c may be taken as a very small circle enclosing the origin. Thus, putting $x = \epsilon e^{i\theta}$, we obtain

$$\frac{1}{2\pi i}\int_0^{2\pi} if(\epsilon e^{i\theta})e^{i\theta}\, d\theta = f(0).$$

Similarly, for the function $P(1/x)$ the contour is to be taken along the real axis from $-\infty$ to $+\infty$,

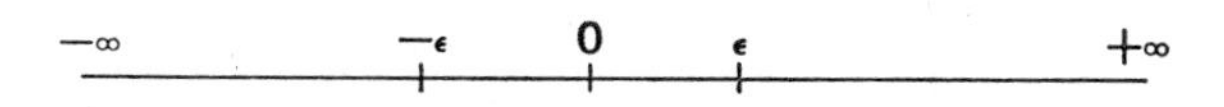

Thus, for $\epsilon \longrightarrow 0$,

$$P\frac{1}{x} = \frac{1}{2\pi i}\frac{1}{x}\Big]_c \text{ gives}$$

$$\int_{-\infty}^{\infty} f(x)P\frac{1}{x}\, dx = \int_{-\infty}^{-\epsilon} \frac{f(x)}{x}\, dx + \int_0^{\infty} \frac{f(x)}{x}\, dx.$$

For a $\delta_+(x)$ function the contour is

and for $\delta_-(x)$ the contour is

(g) If we have $A = B$ then A/x is not equal to B/x. The correct equation is

$$\frac{A}{x} = \frac{B}{x} + c\delta(x), \qquad (III.3.24)$$

where c is unknown.

(h) Another representation of the δ function is

$$\delta(x) = \frac{1}{\pi} \lim_{\lambda\to\infty} \frac{1}{\lambda} \frac{1 - \cos x\lambda}{x^2},$$

since

$$\int_{-\infty}^{\infty} \frac{1 - \cos y}{y^2}\, dy = \pi.$$

(i) Other properties of the δ function are

$$\begin{aligned}
&\text{(i)} && \delta(x) = \delta(-x) \text{ (an even function)},\\
&\text{(ii)} && \delta(\mathbf{r}) = \delta(x_1)\delta(x_2)\delta(x_3),\\
&\text{(iii)} && x\delta(x) = 0,\\
&\text{(iv)} && \delta(\lambda x) = \frac{1}{\lambda}\delta(x) \quad \text{for } \lambda > 0, \qquad (III.3.25)\\
&\text{(v)} && \delta(\lambda^2 - x^2) = \frac{1}{2\lambda}[\delta(x - \lambda) + \delta(x + \lambda)] \quad \text{for } \lambda > 0,\\
&\text{(vi)} && \delta(x - \lambda)f(x) = f(x - \lambda + \lambda)\delta(x - \lambda) = f(\lambda)\delta(x - \lambda).
\end{aligned}$$

III.3.C. Further Discussion of Linear Operators

If the linear Hermitian operator α has both discrete and continuous eigenvalues α_n and α', respectively, then we have the set of equations

$$\begin{aligned}
\langle\alpha_n|\alpha_m\rangle &= \delta_{mn},\\
\langle\alpha_n|\alpha'\rangle &= 0, \qquad (III.3.26)\\
\langle\alpha'|\alpha''\rangle &= \delta(\alpha' - \alpha'').
\end{aligned}$$

The unit operator for a space spanned by discrete and continuous eigenvectors is

$$I = \sum_{n=1}^{\infty} |\alpha_n\rangle\langle\alpha_n| + \int |\alpha'\rangle\, d\alpha'\, \langle\alpha'|. \qquad (III.3.27)$$

Hence for any ket $|V\rangle$ we have

$$|V\rangle = \sum_{n=1}^{\infty} |\alpha_n\rangle\langle\alpha_n|V\rangle + \int |\alpha'\rangle\, d\alpha'\, \langle\alpha'|V\rangle$$

and the scalar product of $|V\rangle$ and $|Q\rangle$ is

$$\langle Q|V\rangle = \sum_{n=1}^{\infty} \langle Q|\alpha_n\rangle\langle\alpha_n|V\rangle + \int \langle Q|\alpha'\rangle\, d\alpha'\, \langle\alpha'|V\rangle. \qquad (III.3.28)$$

There are infinite ways of setting up a coordinate system in an infinite-dimensional linear vector space. Correspondingly all linear operators will have certain matrix representations in the respective spaces. The transition from one space into another is affected by a transformation. Each coordinate system provides a representation for all the vectors and linear operators representing a physical state. The normalized basic vectors of a coordinate system may be specified by several parameters. Thus, if $|a_1a_2 \cdots a_n\rangle$ is a basic vector, then the corresponding component of any vector $|V\rangle$ is given by

$$\langle a_1a_2 \cdots a_n|V\rangle. \qquad (III.3.29)$$

All other components of $|V\rangle$ are specified according to the numerical values of the parameters $a_1 \cdots a_n$.

By using the parameters a_i for $i = 1, 2, \cdots, n$, we can form various sets of numbers of the form

$$a_i\langle a_1a_2 \cdots a_n|V\rangle. \qquad (III.3.30)$$

For example, for $i = 1$ we can take $a_1\langle a_1 \cdots a_n|V\rangle$ to be, for various values of $a_1 \cdots a_n$, the components of a new vector $|Q\rangle$, since all the numbers obtained in this way are independent. Thus we can write

$$\langle a_1a_2 \cdots a_n|Q\rangle = a_1\langle a_1 \cdots a_n|V\rangle,$$

which shows that the vector $|Q\rangle$ is a linear function of the vector $|V\rangle$. We may, therefore, regard $|Q\rangle$ as resulting from a linear operation on $|V\rangle$ by $|Q\rangle = A_1|V\rangle$, so

$$\langle a_1 \cdots a_n|A_1|V\rangle = a_1\langle a_1 \cdots a_n|V\rangle.$$

Since $|V\rangle$ is an arbitrary vector, we obtain

$$\langle a_1 \cdots a_n|A_1 = a_1\langle a_1 \cdots a_n|, \qquad (III.3.31)$$

which defines completely the linear operator A_1. Hence each basic vector is an eigenvector of A_1 with eigenvalue a_1.

From (*III.3.31*) we can easily infer the equations

$$\langle a_1' \cdots a_n'|A_1|a_1'' \cdots a_n''\rangle = a_1'\langle a_1' \cdots a_n'|a_1'' \cdots a_n''\rangle$$

and

$$\langle a_1'' \cdots a_n''|A_1|a_1' \cdots a_n'\rangle = a_1''\langle a_1'' \cdots a_n''|a_1' \cdots a_n'\rangle,$$

where $(a_1' \cdots a_n')$ and $(a_1'' \cdots a_n'')$ are any set of values for the parameters $a_1a_2 \cdots a_n$. Because of the orthogonality of the basic vectors, from the above equations we can write (for $a_i' = a_i''$)

$$\langle a_1' \cdots a_n'|A_1|a_1'' \cdots a_n''\rangle = [\langle a_1' \cdots a_n'|A_1|a_1'' \cdots a_n''\rangle]^{\dagger}.$$

Since the vectors $|a_1 \cdots a_n\rangle$ form a complete set of vectors, we infer that $A_1 = A_1^\dagger$ and that all the vectors $|a_1 \cdots a_n\rangle$ are eigenvectors of A_1.

We can continue the above procedure by taking $i = 2, 3, \cdots, n$ in (*III.3.30*) and introduce the linear operators $A_2, A_3, \cdots, A_n$. In this way we can deduce that all the eigenvectors $|a_1 \cdots a_n\rangle$ are simultaneous eigenvectors of the set of linear operators*

$$A_1, A_2, \cdots, A_n.$$

The fact that the vectors $|a_1 \cdots a_n\rangle$ form a complete set can be used to prove that all the A commute with one another. Let us take a simple case where the two linear Hermitian operators α and β have the same eigenket $|\lambda\rangle$,

$$\alpha|\lambda\rangle = \alpha'|\lambda\rangle,$$
$$\beta|\lambda\rangle = \beta'|\lambda\rangle.$$

Hence

$$\alpha\beta|\lambda\rangle = \beta'\alpha'|\lambda\rangle,$$
$$\beta\alpha|\lambda\rangle = \alpha'\beta'|\lambda\rangle,$$

and

$$(\alpha\beta - \beta\alpha)|\lambda\rangle = 0. \qquad (III.3.32)$$

There are now two possibilities:

(a) The eigenket $|\lambda\rangle$ may belong to the zero eigenvalue (if it exists) of the linear operator $A = i(\alpha\beta - \beta\alpha)$. This is a special case and does not occur frequently.

(b) The linear operator A may vanish, in which case the linear Hermitian operators α and β commute and there exist so many simultaneous eigenvectors that they form a complete set. We have, of course, assumed that α and β by themselves alone can span a space through their eigenstates. Thus, the unit operator for the space spanned by the eigenvectors of β is

$$I = \sum_{n=1}^{\infty} |\beta_n\rangle\langle\beta_n| + \int |\beta'\rangle\, d\beta'\, \langle\beta'|.$$

We can, therefore, expand an eigenvector of α as

$$|\alpha'\rangle = \sum_{n=1}^{\infty} \alpha_n'|\beta_n\rangle + \int f(\alpha'\beta')|\beta'\rangle\, d\beta'$$
$$= \sum_{n=1}^{\infty} |\beta_n\alpha'\rangle + \int |\beta'\alpha'\rangle\, d\beta',$$

where α_n' and $f(\alpha'\beta')$ refer to discrete and continuous components of $|\alpha'\rangle$, respectively. From

* P. A. M. Dirac, *Principles of Quantum Mechanics*, Oxford Univ. Press, Oxford, 1947, p. 54.

$$(\alpha - \alpha')|\alpha'\rangle = 0 = \int (\alpha - \alpha')|\beta'\alpha'\rangle\, d\beta' + \sum_n (\alpha - \alpha')|\beta_n\alpha'\rangle$$

and

$$\beta(\alpha - \alpha')|\beta_n\alpha'\rangle = (\alpha - \alpha')\beta|\beta_n\alpha'\rangle = \beta_n(\alpha - \alpha')|\beta_n\alpha'\rangle.$$

we see that α and β have the same eigenvectors and from

$$(\alpha - \alpha')|\beta_n\alpha'\rangle = 0, \qquad (\alpha - \alpha')|\beta'\alpha'\rangle = 0,$$

we infer that all vectors $|\beta_n\alpha'\rangle$ and $|\beta'\alpha'\rangle$ are eigenvectors of α as well as of β. Hence the simultaneous eigenvectors form a complete set. Conversely, if α and β are two linear Hermitian operators having a complete set of eigenvectors, then α and β commute.

A set A_i, where $i = 1, 2, \cdots, n$, of commuting linear Hermitian operators having a simultaneous set of eigenvectors which form a complete set, is called a "complete set of commuting linear Hermitian operators." *The basic vectors of an orthonormal representation are simultaneous eigenvectors of a certain complete set of commuting linear Hermitian operators.*

III.4. Quantum Postulates

The dynamical variables of classical mechanics are replaced in quantum mechanics by linear Hermitian operators of a Hilbert or more general space or by finite-dimensional spaces. The construction of quantum mechanics can be guided by the classical theory. The value of the classical theory lies in the fact that it provides a valid description of dynamical systems under certain conditions. We shall see in the discussion of Heisenberg's uncertainty principle that for some physical systems the disturbance accompanying an act of observation can be neglected. We can make some use of this fact by noting that for such systems the finite value of Planck's constant h is ineffective and that it can be taken to be zero. The latter means that a physical law formulated in terms of linear Hermitian operators must be such that, for $h = 0$, it must reduce to the classical description. This is the basis of Bohr's "correspondence principle."

The classical description is formulated in terms of Hamilton's equations of motion and the related Poisson brackets for the canonical coordinates and momenta, q_i and p_i, respectively. It is therefore natural to use the same dynamical variables in going from the classical to the quantum description. The transition from classical to quantum mechanics can be based on two fundamental assumptions.

(a) The quantities q_i and p_i are still canonical coordinates and momenta, but they are to be regarded as linear Hermitian operators.

(b) A quantum Poisson bracket is defined as a commutator for the operators representing measurable quantities.*

According to Dirac's formulation of quantum mechanics, the "quantum Poisson brackets" of two quantum dynamical observables α and β are defined by

$$[\alpha, \beta] = i\hbar[\alpha, \beta]_c, \qquad (III.4.1)$$

where $[\alpha, \beta]_c$ is the classical Poisson bracket of α and β and $[\alpha, \beta] = \alpha\beta - \beta\alpha$.

Planck's constant h is introduced in the form $\hbar = h/2\pi$ to obtain correct definition of energy, frequency, and so on. Equation (*III.4.1*) shows that for $h = 0$ the operators α and β will commute at all times. In this case the two canonically conjugate variables α and β can be measured simultaneously with unlimited accuracy (see Section III.4.A), which is the classical description. However, equation (*III.4.1*) does not imply the existence of a classical analogue for every quantum mechanical description.

The classical relations (*III.1.9*) are to be replaced in quantum mechanics by

$$\begin{aligned} [q_i, q_j] &= 0, \\ [p_i, p_j] &= 0, \\ [q_i, p_j] &= i\hbar\delta_{ij}, \end{aligned} \qquad (III.4.2)$$

where, as in classical mechanics, q_i and p_i are called canonically conjugate dynamical variables. The third equation of (*III.4.2*) has the dimensions of an action on both sides. Both sides of the latter are anti-Hermitian, which is required for mathematical compatibility. The coordinates and momenta corresponding to different degrees of freedom commute, like q_1 and p_2, for example. Both the coordinates q_i and momenta p_i are now linear Hermitian operators. The Poisson bracket relations (*III.1.11*) and (*III.1.12*) correspond to

$$[\xi, q_i] = -i\hbar \frac{\partial \xi}{\partial p_i}, \qquad (III.4.3)$$

$$[\xi, p_i] = i\hbar \frac{\partial \xi}{\partial q_i}. \qquad (III.4.4)$$

From (*III.1.13*) and (*III.4.1*) it follows that quantum mechanical definitions of angular momentum are given by

$$[J_i, J_j] = i\hbar\epsilon_{ijk}J_k. \qquad (III.4.5)$$

The relativistic Poisson bracket relations (*III.1.16*) and (*III.1.29*) are replaced by the operator relations

---

* A less axiomatic but more direct approach to quantum mechanics was discussed in Chapter II.

$$[x_\mu, p_\nu] = i\hbar a_{\mu\nu},$$
$$[\xi, p_\mu] = i\hbar \frac{\partial \xi}{\partial x^\mu}, \qquad (III.4.6)$$

where the time coordinate is not to be regarded as an operator.

III.4.A. The Observables of Quantum Mechanics, and the Principle of Uncertainty

In classical mechanics the specification of positions and velocities of a dynamical system at each time is sufficient for a complete determination of its state. The basic concepts of classical theory (*mechanics*) consist of the material point, the force of interaction between material points (*potential energy*), and the inertial system (= the Cartesian coordinate system + the time coordinate). When the electromagnetic field is included, classical physics gains the concept of field. Special relativity brings into the structure of the inertial system the constancy of the velocity of light. In this theory one cannot preserve the concepts of action at a distance and potential energy and, as pointed out before, this in turn implies that the concept of the material point can be discarded and replaced by the field concept.

A more profound change in our concepts of space and time came with the discovery of general relativity (*the principle of general covariance*). According to this theory, inertial systems need not be qualified as the only group of systems for the formulation of physical laws. The "space" represented by the inertial group (the Lorentz group), and considered as a part of the physical reality, can only have a limited meaning. The inertial group is used to determine the behavior of mass points in space and time, without itself being influenced by mass points. Therefore, according to special relativity, the inertial group occupies an absolute position in the description of physical phenomena.

In general relativity, however, the inertial group does not have this privileged position; in general relativity it has been integrated into the field and has, therefore, been deprived of its "absoluteness." It is the field which has an independent meaning, and it depends on four parameters (the coordinates). The space aspect of matter or matter itself is described by the field. The inertial character of real things must be derivable from a field; we do not try to fit a field to a given inertial group or to a mechanical system without considering that it will not change or influence the inertial system. In short, the mechanics of a system should be derivable from a field.

In quantum theory we retain the inertial frame and the action-at-a-distance concepts, but it is no longer true that a state is completely defined by the initial conditions of the dynamical system.

According to quantum theory a "small system"—that is, a system that can change its state (energy, momentum, position, angular momentum, and so on) by an act of observation—cannot be observed with the greatest possible amount of detail. The behavior of nature in the micro system is such that there exists a limitation or a lower limit to the power of observation. This limitation on the observability of a dynamical system implies a restriction on the data that can be assigned to the state of the physical system. Both classical and relativistic mechanics permit a definite distinction between observer and observed. This is essentially a complete fulfillment of the principle of causality in a deterministic sense. Accordingly, the interaction between observed and observer, arising in the act of observation, can be made infinitely small. For this reason it is meaningful, in classical mechanics, to say that the state of a dynamical system can be defined in its entirety with no limitation on the detail of the data. The continuous nature of things—for example the absorption of a wave by an electron—will allow enough time to measure its position and momentum rapidly before it absorbs sufficient energy from the incident wave to change its state abruptly.

The quantum mechanical point of view, at the expense of some loss of exact information on the dynamical system, recognized the impossibility of controlling the interaction between observer and observed. In the act of observation large changes in the state of the system being observed must be taking place. It is, therefore, not possible to assign simultaneous "initial values" to canonically conjugate variables referring to the same degree of freedom of the dynamical system—for example x and p_x. This proposal of quantum mechanics can only be reconciled with a statistical or probabilistic approach to the description of physical reality. The complete determinism of classical theory is replaced by an indeterministic description, the extent of indeterminism being determined by the size of the universal constant h. In classical mechanics a cause causes another definite cause. In quantum mechanics a cause can only produce a statistical trend to a given cause. This in turn can be regarded as a tendency towards some effect. The mode of the statistical tendency can be incorporated into a fundamental principle of nature, first enunciated by Heisenberg as the "principle of uncertainty" in the origination of physical events.*

According to the principle of uncertainty, the position of an electron can be defined within a certain accuracy Δx at the time t, where Δx is a possible spread in the location of the electron; that is, the electron can be seen within

---

* W. Heisenberg, *The Physical Principles of the Quantum Theory*, Dover, New York, 1930.

a region of the dimensions of Δx. The size of this region will depend on the spread of its momentum caused by the act of observation. In modern theory it is believed that the only description consistent with the principle of uncertainty is to represent the spread Δx as a "wave packet," the particle under observation being the wave itself. A wave packet has the properties of waves whose amplitudes are different from zero only in a limited region of space-time.

A dynamical system, having a well-defined single path in classical mechanics, is described in quantum mechanics by a wave-packet containing coordinates and momenta with approximate numerical values that are restricted by the uncertainty principle. The size of the packet will increase with time; that is, a wave packet can spread out and decay. If we succeed in obtaining, during our act of observation, a wave packet that can be located in a region smaller than Δx, then the location of the electron is sharper than ever. The latter result can only be approached as a result of large interaction between the electron and observer, resulting in a spread of the momentum of the wave packet much larger than the spread in its position. This uncertainty must be regarded as a fundamental property of a small object (electron) and, indeed, as its definition. The mathematical statement of the principle of uncertainty is contained in the relation

$$\Delta x \Delta p_x \geqq \hbar. \qquad (III.4.7)$$

The same kind of uncertainties will, of course, prevail for all other canonically conjugate dynamical variables of the wave packet—for example the spread in its energy—and the corresponding spread in the time will satisfy the uncertainty relation

$$\Delta t \Delta E \geqq \hbar. \qquad (III.4.8)$$

In general, the uncertainty relations (*III.4.7*) and (*III.4.8*) can be combined into

$$\Delta(x_\mu)\Delta(p_\nu) \geqq \hbar a_{\mu\nu}, \qquad (III.4.9)$$

with the convention that the coordinates x^μ and momenta p_μ are always measured as contravariant and covariant vectors, respectively.

The question now arises: what is it that the act of observation does to a dynamical system? What kind of a statement is the observer going to make following the observation of the dynamical system? An observable in quantum mechanics—such as energy, momentum, and so on—is, first of all, represented by a linear Hermitian operator. Let α be such an operator, with eigenstates $|\alpha'\rangle$ corresponding to its eigenvalue α'. If the state of the dynamical system during the act of measurement happens to be the eigenstate α, then the eigenvalue α' is the result of the measurement. Whatever the state of the system prior to measurement was, the act of observation has caused it to jump to its eigenstate $|\alpha'\rangle$. A second measurement carried out in the state represented by $|\alpha'\rangle$ must give the same result. Therefore, any result of a measurement of an observable is one of its eigenvalues. The eigenvalues of a dynamical variable come into existence as a result of acts of measurement. Without the act of observation we cannot talk of any state and consequently there exists no wave functions prior to the process of measurement. Quantum mechanics is not concerned with the state and the corresponding possible values of a dynamical variable prior to observation. Quantum mechanics predicts the future from the present data in accordance with the principle of uncertainty. In general, every experiment aimed at a determination of some numerical quantity causes a loss of information in some other quantity, related to the former by uncertainty relations. The uncontrollable perturbation of the observed systems alters the value of the previously determined quantities, except when the corresponding linear Hermitian operators commute with one another.

The fact that an act of observation can bring the dynamical system from an arbitrary state to one of its eigenstates implies that an arbitrary state represented by a vector $|V\rangle$ must be expressible as a linear combination of the eigenstates of the dynamical variable. An observable, therefore, besides being a Hermitian operator, must have enough eigenvectors to span a space.

The act of observation carried out at any state $|V\rangle$ can be regarded as a rotation of $|V\rangle$ (or of Hilbert space itself) to one of the eigenstates $|\alpha\rangle$ of the observable α. Two observables can be measured simultaneously provided they form a complete commuting set of observables as defined in Section 3.C. If two observables do not commute, they generally cannot be measured simultaneously.

Recapitulation: an observable in quantum mechanics is represented by a linear Hermitian operator α whose eigenvectors by themselves (or by additional linear Hermitian operators having the same eigenvectors with α) form a complete set of states.

CHAPTER IV

ANGULAR MOMENTUM

IV.1. Representation of the Rotation Group

The most important quantum data—such as angular momentum, isotopic spin, and possibly other discrete states—on the behavior of a dynamical variable are usually obtainable from some kind of quantum Poisson bracket relations satisfied by the Hermitian linear operators which represent the observables of the system. Orbital angular momentum, spin angular momentum, and isotopic spin are important examples of such observables. The concept of angular momentum in quantum mechanics is, therefore, a symbolic name for different types of quantum degrees of freedom, with transformation properties similar to that of angular momentum (in the ordinary sense). Furthermore, the fact that the angular momentum operator satisfies an algebraic type of Poisson bracket relation makes it a more fundamental concept than a classical angular momentum. The latter satisfies a classical Poisson bracket relation defined with respect to canonically conjugate coordinates and momenta. Actually, the classical Poisson bracket relations for angular momentum are only differential identities, and therefore are not important statements on angular momentum.

For the above reasons it is necessary to study the concept of quantum mechanical angular momentum in some detail. From the point of view of transformation theory it is more convenient to approach our discussion from a group-theoretical formulation. We shall discuss the most general case—the linear inhomogeneous transformation group. Such a group consists of the linear transformations on a three-dimensional space which leave the form

$$(x_1 - a_1)^2 + (x_2 - a_2)^2 + (x_3 - a_3)^2$$

invariant. A linear inhomogeneous transformation in three-dimensional space is of the form

$$|x'\rangle = |a\rangle + A|x\rangle, \qquad (IV.1.1)$$

where all the vectors are real and three-dimensional and A is a rotation operator. In accordance with the discussion of orthogonal transformations of

Chapter I, we observe that the generators K_i of infinitesimal rotations around x_1, x_2, x_3 satisfy the commutation relations

$$K_iK_j - K_jK_i = i\epsilon_{ijl}K_l. \tag{IV.1.2}$$

The spin $\frac{1}{2}$ representation generated by Pauli matrices σ_i also satisfies the same commutation relations. In general, linear Hermitian operators G_i satisfying the commutation relations

$$G_iG_j - G_jG_i = i\epsilon_{ijk}G_k \tag{IV.1.3}$$

can generate representations of the rotation group. The commutation relations (*IV.1.3*) are invariant with respect to the transformation

$$G'_i = S^{-1}G_iS. \tag{IV.1.4}$$

The orbital angular momentum operator $\boldsymbol{L}$, given by

$$\boldsymbol{L} = \boldsymbol{r} \times \boldsymbol{p}, \tag{IV.1.5}$$

also satisfies the same type of commutation relations as in (*IV.1.3*), where $\boldsymbol{p}$ is a linear operator represented by $\boldsymbol{p} = -i\hbar\boldsymbol{\nabla}$ (see Chapter II).

The first term in (*IV.1.1*) corresponds to a translation of coordinates. On writing (*IV.1.1*) in the form

$$x'_i = \left(a_j \frac{\partial}{\partial x_j} + A_{ij}\right) x_j, \tag{IV.1.6}$$

we see that the operator $\partial/\partial x_j$ can be regarded as the generator of infinitesimal translations. Hence the inhomogeneous linear transformations constitute a six-parameter group—for example a_1, a_2, a_3 for translations and ψ, θ, ϕ for rotations. As in the case of rotations, we shall use Hermitian operators to represent the generators of translations. The momentum operator $\boldsymbol{p}$ is the generator of infinitesimal translations. For the following discussion we shall need the linear combinations

$$p_+ = p_1 + ip_2, \qquad p_- = p_1 - ip_2.$$

Now let J_i be the components of a vector linear Hermitian operator satisfying the commutation rules (*III.4.5*). We wish to find eigenvalues and eigenvectors of J_i and all other possible operators obtained from J_i—for example $\boldsymbol{J}^2 = J_1^2 + J_2^2 + J_3^2$ and others. For this purpose we need to form with J_i a complete set of commuting observables to set up an orthonormal coordinate system. If we take the symbol Γ to represent a set of commuting Hermitian operators which together with $\boldsymbol{J}^2$ and J_3, say, form a complete commuting set of observables, then we can set up a representation where the eigenvectors are simultaneous eigenvectors of Γ, $\boldsymbol{J}^2$, and J_3. The construction of the required representation can be simplified if we work with the operators J_+ and J_-, defined by

$$J_+ = J_1 + iJ_2, \qquad J_- = J_1 - iJ_2. \tag{IV.1.7}$$

From the commutation relations (*III.4.2*) and (*III.4.5*) it follows that J_+, J_-, and p_+, p_- satisfy the operator relations

$$[\boldsymbol{J}^2, J_-] = 0, \qquad [p_+, J_-] = 2\hbar p_3, \qquad (IV.1.8)$$
$$[\boldsymbol{J}^2, J_+] = 0, \qquad [p_-, J_+] = -2\hbar p_3, \qquad (IV.1.9)$$
$$[J_3, J_+] = \hbar J_+ \qquad [J_3, p_+] = \hbar p_+ \qquad (IV.1.10)$$
$$[J_3, J_-] = -\hbar J_-, \qquad [J_3, p_-] = -\hbar p_-, \qquad (IV.1.11)$$
$$[J_+, J_-] = 2\hbar J_3, \qquad [J_\mp, p_3] = \mp\hbar p_\pm, \qquad (IV.1.12)$$
$$[\boldsymbol{J}^2, J_i] = 0 \qquad \text{for } i = 1, 2, 3, \qquad (IV.1.13)$$

where we note that p_+ and p_- commute with the spin term of the total angular momentum operators J_i.

The quantities which commute with all six operators (p_i and J_i) are called invariants of the group. The invariants can be constructed as follows:

$$\boldsymbol{p}^2 = p_1^2 + p_2^2 + p_3^2 \qquad (IV.1.14)$$

and

$$\boldsymbol{p}\cdot\boldsymbol{J} = \boldsymbol{J}\cdot\boldsymbol{p} = p_1J_1 + p_2J_2 + p_3J_3. \qquad (IV.1.15)$$

We observe that $\boldsymbol{J}^2 = J_1^2 + J_2^2 + J_3^2$ commutes with J_i for $i = 1, 2, 3$, but not with p_i for $i = 1, 2, 3$, and for the latter reason it is not an invariant of the inhomogeneous group. The operator $\boldsymbol{J}^2$ is related to p_i by the commutation relations

$$[\boldsymbol{J}^2, p_j] = [J_iJ_i, p_j] = J_i[J_i, p_j] + [J_i, p_j]J_i.$$

Hence

$$[\boldsymbol{J}^2, p_1] = 2i\hbar(p_2J_3 - J_2p_3),$$
$$[\boldsymbol{J}^2, p_2] = 2i\hbar(p_3J_1 - J_3p_1), \qquad (IV.1.16)$$
$$[J_1^2, p_3] = 2i\hbar(p_1J_2 - J_1p_2),$$

and

$$[\boldsymbol{J}^2, [\boldsymbol{J}^2, p_i]] = 2\hbar^2(\boldsymbol{J}^2p_i + p_i\boldsymbol{J}^2) - 4\hbar^2(\boldsymbol{J}\cdot\boldsymbol{p})J_i. \qquad (IV.1.17)$$

The simultaneous eigenvectors of the complete commuting set Γ, $\boldsymbol{J}^2$, J_3 will be labeled with the eigenvalues γ, j (total angular momentum eigenvalue), and m, respectively, as $|\gamma jm\rangle$. The eigenvectors $|\gamma jm\rangle$ for a given set γ of eigenvalues of Γ are normalized according to

$$\langle\gamma jm|\gamma j'm'\rangle = \delta_{jj'}\delta_{mm'}. \qquad (IV.1.18)$$

For a representation where J_3 is diagonal the eigenvalue equations are

$$J_3|\gamma jm\rangle = \hbar m|\gamma jm\rangle, \qquad (IV.1.19)$$
$$\boldsymbol{J}^2J_i|\gamma jm\rangle = J_i\boldsymbol{J}^2|\gamma jm\rangle = \lambda_jJ_i|\gamma jm\rangle, \qquad (IV.1.20)$$

where λ_j is the eigenvalue of $\boldsymbol{J}^2$, a certain function of j. Thus if $|\gamma jm\rangle$ is an eigenvector of $\boldsymbol{J}^2$ belonging to eigenvalue λ_j, so are the vectors $J_i|\gamma jm\rangle$ for $i = 1, 2, 3$.

Furthermore, from (*IV.1.10*) we get

$$(m' - m)\langle \gamma j m' | J_+ | \gamma j m \rangle = \langle \gamma j m' | J_+ | \gamma j m \rangle. \qquad (IV.1.21)$$

Hence the only nonvanishing matrix elements of J_+ are those arising from taking $m' = m + 1$, so various m values differ by integers. We may, therefore, write

$$J_+ | \gamma j m \rangle = \hbar a_m | \gamma j m + 1 \rangle, \qquad (IV.1.22)$$

where a_m is a number, a function of j and m. In a similar way the commutation relation (*IV.1.11*) yields

$$J_- | \gamma j m \rangle = \hbar a'_m | \gamma j m - 1 \rangle. \qquad (IV.1.23)$$

We use the relation $J_+ = J_-^\dagger$ and (*IV.1.23*), with m replaced by $m + 1$, to obtain

$$\langle \gamma j m + 1 | J_+ = \hbar a'^*_{m+1} \langle \gamma j m |.$$

If we multiply scalarly from the right by $|\gamma j m\rangle$ and use (*IV.1.22*), we get

$$a'^*_{m+1} = a_m.$$

We can now find the matrix representation of (*IV.1.12*):

$$\langle \gamma j m | J_+ J_- | \gamma j m \rangle - \langle \gamma j m | J_- J_+ | \gamma j m \rangle = 2\hbar^2 \langle \gamma j m | J_3 | \gamma j m \rangle = 2\hbar^2 m. \qquad (IV.1.24)$$

From (*IV.1.21*) and (*IV.1.22*) we infer that the matrix representations of J_+J_- and J_-J_+ do not require all the vectors of the space spanned by $|\gamma j m\rangle$; that is, we do not need to introduce the unit operator of the space into (*IV.1.24*). Thus the only nonvanishing matrix elements of J_+J_- and J_-J_+ are

$$\begin{aligned} F(m) &= \langle \gamma j m | J_+ J_- | \gamma j m \rangle \\ &= \langle \gamma j m | J_+ | \gamma j m - 1 \rangle \langle \gamma j m - 1 | J_- | \gamma j m \rangle, \qquad (IV.1.25) \\ F(m+1) &= \langle \gamma j m | J_- J_+ | \gamma j m \rangle \\ &= \langle \gamma j m | J_- | \gamma j m + 1 \rangle \langle \gamma j m + 1 | J_+ | \gamma j m \rangle, \qquad (IV.1.26) \end{aligned}$$

so (*IV.1.24*) yields the equation

$$F(m) - F(m+1) = 2\hbar^2 m, \qquad (IV.1.27)$$

which can be solved by

$$F(m) = \hbar^2 \mu - \hbar^2 m(m-1). \qquad (IV.1.28)$$

It is important to notice that $F(m)$ as defined above is just the square of the vector $J_-|\gamma j m\rangle$ and therefore $F(m)$ is a nonnegative number.

The square of the total angular momentum can be written as

$$\boldsymbol{J}^2 = \tfrac{1}{2}(J_+J_- + J_-J_+) + J_3^2. \qquad (IV.1.29)$$

The diagonal element $\langle \gamma j m | \boldsymbol{J}^2 | \gamma j m \rangle$ can be written as $\langle \gamma j m | J_i J_i | \gamma j m \rangle$, so it is, essentially, the square of the vector $J_i|\gamma j m\rangle$ and hence also a nonnegative number:

$$\langle\gamma jm|\boldsymbol{J}^2|\gamma jm\rangle = \tfrac{1}{2}\langle\gamma jm|J_+J_-|\gamma jm\rangle + \tfrac{1}{2}\langle\gamma jm|J_-J_+|\gamma jm\rangle + \langle\gamma jm|J_3^2|\gamma jm\rangle$$
$$= \tfrac{1}{2}[F(m) + F(m+1)] + m^2 = \mu\hbar^2, \qquad (IV.1.30)$$

where $\mu \geqq 0$, the equality occurring for $\boldsymbol{J}|\gamma jm\rangle = 0$. From

$$F(m) = \langle\gamma jm|J_+J_-|\gamma jm\rangle = \hbar^2(\mu - m^2 + m),$$

we infer that

$$\mu - m^2 + m \geqq 0, \qquad (IV.1.31)$$

where the equality holds for $J_-|\gamma jm\rangle = 0$. The inequality (*IV.1.31*) can be written as

$$\mu + \tfrac{1}{4} \geqq (m - \tfrac{1}{2})^2. \qquad (IV.1.32)$$

In order to prove finiteness of the representation, we introduce a number j by

$$j + \tfrac{1}{2} = \sqrt{(\mu + \tfrac{1}{4})}, \qquad (IV.1.33)$$

so from (*IV.1.32*) we can write

$$j + \tfrac{1}{2} \geqq |m - \tfrac{1}{2}|$$

or

$$-j \leqq m \leqq j + 1, \qquad (IV.1.34)$$

where equality occurs for

$$j_-|\gamma jm\rangle = 0.$$

By carrying out a similar calculation with $F(m+1)$, or the matrix elements of J_-J_+, we obtain the inequality

$$-j - 1 \leqq m \leqq j, \qquad (IV.1.35)$$

where the equality holds for $J_+|\gamma jm\rangle = 0$. Comparing (*IV.1.34*) and (*IV.1.35*), we obtain

$$j \geqq 0 \quad \text{and} \quad -j \leqq m \leqq j, \qquad (IV.1.36)$$

with $m = j$ if $j_+|\gamma jm\rangle = 0$ and $m = -j$ if $J_-|\gamma jm\rangle = 0$.

By using the commutation relation between J_3 and J_- we get

$$J_3J_-|\gamma jm\rangle = (J_-J_3 - \hbar J_-)|\gamma jm\rangle = \hbar(m-1)J_-|\gamma jm\rangle.$$

If $m \neq -j$, then $J_-|\gamma jm\rangle$ does not vanish and is then an eigenvector of J_3 belonging to the eigenvalue $(m-1)$. A second operation by J_- yields

$$J_3J_-^2|\gamma jm\rangle = \hbar(m-2)J_-^2|\gamma jm\rangle,$$

so $J_-^2|\gamma jm\rangle$ is an eigenvector of J_3 with eigenvalue $m - 2$. Continuation of this process leads to a series of eigenvalues

$$m,\ m-1,\ m-2,\ \cdots,$$

which, because of (*IV.1.36*), must terminate with the value $m = -j$.

A similar argument on the commutation relation between J_3 and J_+ leads to a series of eigenvalues $m, m+1, m+2, \cdots$, which, because of (*IV.1.36*), must terminate with the value $m = j$. Hence $2j$ is an integral number and the eigenvalues of J_3 are

$$\hbar m = \hbar j,\ \hbar(j-1),\ \hbar(j-2),\ \cdots,\ \hbar(-j+1),\ -\hbar j, \qquad (IV.1.37)$$

so for a given j number, J_3 has $2j+1$ eigenvalues. These eigenvalues are all integral or half-integral multiples of $\hbar$, as $2j$ is an even or an odd number. The corresponding eigenvectors are

$$|\gamma jj\rangle,\ J_-|\gamma jj\rangle,\ J_-^2|\gamma jj\rangle,\ \cdots,\ J_-^{2j}|\gamma jj\rangle, \qquad (IV.1.38)$$

where

$$J_+|\gamma jj\rangle = 0.$$

Operation on the $2j+1$ vectors $(IV.1.38)$ with J_- and also with J_+ produces new vectors dependent on these $2j+1$ vectors. Thus the representation is irreducible; in other words, the set of vectors $(IV.1.38)$ is a complete set. We see that in this case J_3 forms a complete commuting set by itself.

Since the J_i are generators of the rotation group, then the corresponding rotation matrices will have their determinants equal to $+1$ only if the trace of J_i vanish (see Theorem 7 of Chapter I). The latter is strictly valid for finite-dimensional representations. Therefore the trace of J_3 is zero and hence

$$\mathrm{tr}\,[J_+, J_-] = 2\hbar\ \mathrm{tr}\,J_3 = 0, \qquad (IV.1.39)$$

or

$$\Sigma m = 0. \qquad (IV.1.40)$$

This means that m values are either integer or half odd integer. Therefore the m values, as defined by $(IV.1.37)$, show that j is a positive quantity which can assume the values $0, \frac{1}{2}, 1, \frac{3}{2}, \cdots$. Using $(IV.1.27)$ and $(IV.1.39)$ we obtain $F(-j) = F(j+1) = 0$, so $\mu = j(j+1) =$ eigenvalue of $\boldsymbol{J}^2$.

IV.1.A. Problems

1. By using matrices K_1, K_2, K_3 of spin 1, show [by $(IV.1.38)$] that the eigenvectors $|1\rangle$, $|-1\rangle$, and $|0\rangle$ of K_3 can be represented, with $j = 1$, in the form $(IV.1.38)$ and that they form a complete set—that is, the representation is irreducible.
2. Repeat problem 1 for Pauli's spin matrices σ_1, σ_2, σ_3.

IV.1.B. Matrix Representation of Angular Momentum Operators

We write $F(m+1)$ in the form

$$F(m+1) = j(j+1) - m(m+1) = (j-m)(J+m+1) = |a_m|^2$$

and obtain a_m defined by $(IV.1.22)$, as

$$a_m = e^{i\delta}[(j - m)(j + m + 1)]^{1/2}, \qquad (IV.1.41)$$

where the arbitrary phase factor $e^{i\delta}$ will be taken equal to $+1$. We can now calculate the matrix elements for a fixed j:

$$\begin{aligned} \langle \gamma jm'|J_+|\gamma jm\rangle &= \hbar[(j - m)(j + m + 1)]^{1/2}\delta_{m',m+1}, \\ \langle \gamma jm'|J_-|\gamma jm\rangle &= \hbar[(j + m)(j - m + 1)]^{1/2}\delta_{m',m-1}. \end{aligned} \qquad (IV.1.42)$$

Hence

$$\langle \gamma jm'|J_1|\gamma jm\rangle = \tfrac{1}{2}\hbar[(j - m)(j + m + 1)]^{1/2}\delta_{m',m+1} + \tfrac{1}{2}\hbar[(j + m)(j - m + 1)]^{1/2}\delta_{m',m-1} \qquad (IV.1.43)$$

and

$$\langle \gamma jm'|J_2|\gamma jm\rangle = -\tfrac{1}{2}i\hbar[(j - m)(j + m + 1)]^{1/2}\delta_{m',m+1} + \tfrac{1}{2}i\hbar[(j + m)(j - m + 1)]^{1/2}\delta_{m',m-1}, \qquad (IV.1.44)$$

$$\langle \gamma jm'|J_3|\gamma jm\rangle = \hbar m\delta_{m,m'}. \qquad (IV.1.45)$$

If $j = \frac{1}{2}$, then m takes on the values $m = -\frac{1}{2}$, $m = \frac{1}{2}$. From the above we easily obtain

$$J_1(\tfrac{1}{2}) = \tfrac{1}{2}\hbar\sigma_1, \qquad J_2(\tfrac{1}{2}) = \tfrac{1}{2}\hbar\sigma_2, \qquad J_3(\tfrac{1}{2}) = \tfrac{1}{2}\hbar\sigma_3. \qquad (IV.1.46)$$

If $j = 1$, then m takes on $2j + 1 = 3$ values, $m = -1, 0, 1$, and the corresponding matrices are

$$J_1(1) = \frac{\hbar}{\sqrt{2}}\begin{bmatrix} 0 & 1 & 0 \\ 1 & 0 & 1 \\ 0 & 1 & 0 \end{bmatrix},$$

$$J_2(1) = \frac{\hbar}{\sqrt{2}}\begin{bmatrix} 0 & -i & 0 \\ i & 0 & -i \\ 0 & i & 0 \end{bmatrix}, \qquad (IV.1.47)$$

$$J_3(1) = \hbar\begin{bmatrix} 1 & 0 & 1 \\ 0 & 0 & 0 \\ 0 & 0 & -1 \end{bmatrix},$$

and $\boldsymbol{J}^2 = 2\hbar^2$.

IV.2. Rotation of the Eigenvectors of Angular Momentum

The most general form of any element A of the three-dimensional rotation group is of the form (*I.8.21*). Let us consider its representation with respect to the complete set $|1\rangle$, $|-1\rangle$, $|0\rangle$ [see (*I.8.7*)] of the eigenvectors of K_3. Using the unit operator (*I.8.8*) we may write

$$A = \sum_{s=-1}^{1} e^{iK_1\psi}e^{iK_2\theta}e^{is\phi}|s\rangle\langle s|, \qquad (IV.2.1)$$

where we use the eigenvalue equation

$$K_3|s\rangle = s|s\rangle.$$

By using once more the unit operator of the space of spin 1, we can rewrite (*IV.2.1*) in the form

$$A = \sum_{s'=-1}^{1} \sum_{s=-1}^{1} \langle s'|e^{i\psi K_1}e^{i\theta K_2}|s\rangle e^{is\phi}|s'\rangle\langle s|$$

$$= \sum_{s'=-1}^{1} \sum_{s=-1}^{1} D^{(1)}_{s's}(\psi\theta\phi)|s'\rangle\langle s|, \qquad (IV.2.2)$$

where the coefficients $D^{(1)}_{s's}(\psi\theta\phi)$ are defined by

$$D^{(1)}_{s's}(\psi\theta\phi) = \langle s'|e^{i\psi K_1}e^{i\theta K_2}|s\rangle e^{is\phi}. \qquad (IV.2.3)$$

The superscript 1 in $D^{(1)}_{s's}$ represents the j value corresponding to

$$\boldsymbol{S}^2 = \hbar^2 s(s+1) = \hbar^2 j(j+1),$$

where $\boldsymbol{S} = \hbar\boldsymbol{K}$ is the vector operator of spin 1.

In the more general case the representative coefficients are given by

$$D^{(j)}_{m'm}(\psi\theta\phi) = \langle\gamma jm'|e^{(i\psi/\hbar)J_1}e^{(i\theta/\hbar)J_2}|\gamma jm\rangle e^{im\phi}, \qquad (IV.2.4)$$

so the $(2j+1)$-dimensional rotation operator can be expressed as

$$D(\psi\theta\phi) = \sum_{m'=-j}^{j} \sum_{m=-j}^{j} D^{(j)}_{m'm}(\psi\theta\phi)|\gamma jm'\rangle\langle\gamma jm|. \qquad (IV.2.5)$$

For the special case of $j = 1$ and $\psi = 0$, we easily obtain from (*IV.2.3*) the representation

$$[D^{(1)}_{s's}] = \begin{bmatrix} \frac{1}{2}(1+\cos\theta)e^{-i\phi} & -\frac{1}{\sqrt{2}}\sin\theta & -\frac{1}{2}(1-\cos\theta)e^{i\phi} \\ \frac{1}{\sqrt{2}}e^{-i\phi}\sin\theta & \cos\theta & \frac{\sin\theta}{\sqrt{2}}e^{i\phi} \\ -\frac{1}{2}(1-\cos\theta)e^{-i\phi} & -\frac{\sin\theta}{\sqrt{2}} & \frac{1}{2}(1+\cos\theta)e^{i\phi} \end{bmatrix}. \qquad (IV.2.6)$$

For $j = \frac{1}{2}$ we use the unit operator (*I.9.26*) and the unitary operator (*I.9.33*), corresponding to A in (*IV.2.2*), to record $D^{(1/2)}_{\alpha'\alpha}(\alpha', \alpha = \frac{1}{2}, \frac{1}{2})$ as

$$[D^{(1/2)}_{\alpha'\alpha}] = \begin{bmatrix} \cos\frac{\theta}{2}\,e^{(i/2)\phi} & \sin\frac{\theta}{2}\,e^{-(i/2)\phi} \\ -\sin\frac{\theta}{2}\,e^{(i/2)\phi} & \cos\frac{\theta}{2}\,e^{-(i/2)\phi} \end{bmatrix}. \qquad (IV.2.7)$$

We thus see that under a rotation of the state by a unitary matrix $D^{(j)}(\psi\theta\phi)$, the eigenvalue j will not change.

The general expression (*I.8.21*) for an orthogonal transformation operator can be extended to the generators $(1/\hbar)J_i$ and we can write for the most general unitary transformation operator in a space spanned by the eigenvectors $|\gamma jm\rangle$, the expression

$$D(\psi\theta\phi) = \exp\left(\frac{i\psi}{\hbar}J_1\right)\exp\left(\frac{i\theta}{\hbar}J_2\right)\exp\left(\frac{i\phi}{\hbar}J_3\right), \qquad (IV.2.8)$$

A $(2j+1)$-dimensional rotation matrix $D(\psi\theta\phi)$ is orthogonal (or unitary) and of determinant $+1$.

For $\psi = \theta = 0$, as follows from (*IV.2.4*), the representation is

$$D^{(j)}_{m'm}(00\phi) = e^{im\phi}\delta_{mm'}, \qquad (IV.2.9)$$

which is a diagonal matrix where m and m' range from $-j$ to j. From (*IV.2.4*) we see that $D^{(j)}_{m'm}(\psi\theta\phi)$ can also be written as

$$D^{(j)}_{m'm}(\psi\theta\phi) = \sum_{m''=-j}^{j} \langle\gamma jm'|e^{(i\psi/\hbar)J_1}|\gamma jm''\rangle\langle\gamma jm''|e^{(i\theta/\hbar)J_2}|\gamma jm\rangle e^{im\phi}$$

$$= e^{im\phi}\sum_{m''=-j}^{j} D^{(j)}_{m'm''}(\psi)D^{(j)}_{m''m}(\theta), \qquad (IV.2.10)$$

where we used $(2j+1)$-dimensional unit operator

$$I = \sum_{m=-j}^{j} |\gamma jm\rangle\langle\gamma jm| \qquad (IV.2.11)$$

and the notation

$$D^{(j)}_{m'm''}(\psi) = D^{(j)}_{m'm''}(\psi, 0, 0),$$
$$D^{(j)}_{m''m}(\theta) = D^{(j)}_{m''m}(0, \theta, 0).$$

The expression (*IV.2.10*) is related to the group property of the representation.

IV.2.A. Matrix Elements of Finite Rotations and Spherical Harmonics

We first observe that the orbital angular momentum $\boldsymbol{L} = \boldsymbol{r} \times \boldsymbol{p}$ can be represented by

$$L_i = i\langle x|K_i|p\rangle, \qquad (IV.2.12)$$

where

$$|x\rangle = \begin{bmatrix} x_1 \\ x_2 \\ x_3 \end{bmatrix}, \qquad |p\rangle = \begin{bmatrix} p_1 \\ p_2 \\ p_3 \end{bmatrix}, \qquad \boldsymbol{p} = -i\hbar\boldsymbol{\nabla},$$

and

$$[x_i, p_j] = i\hbar\delta_{ij}. \qquad (IV.2.13)$$

The eigenvectors $|1\rangle$ and $|-1\rangle$ of σ_3 define a linear unitary space of two dimensions; it is called spin space. In analogy to the representations (*IV.2.12*) and (*IV.2.13*), we can introduce the concept of "spin coordinates," represented by s_1 and s_2 instead of by $|1\rangle$ and $|-1\rangle$, and also the concept of "spin momenta" q_1, q_2 satisfying the commutation relations

$$[s_\alpha, q_\beta] = i\hbar\delta_{\alpha\beta}, \qquad (IV.2.14)$$

where $\alpha, \beta = 1, 2$. Hence the corresponding representation for the total angular momentum is

$$J_i = i\langle s|\tfrac{1}{2}\sigma_i|q\rangle, \qquad (IV.2.15)$$

where

$$|s\rangle = \begin{bmatrix} s_1 \\ s_2 \end{bmatrix}, \qquad |q\rangle = \begin{bmatrix} q_1 \\ q_2 \end{bmatrix}.$$

From the commutation relations (*IV.2.14*) it follows that the operator q_2 can be represented by

$$q_\alpha = -i\hbar\frac{\partial}{\partial s_\alpha}. \qquad (IV.2.16)$$

A simple calculation* gives

$$\boldsymbol{J}^2 = \hbar^2\mathfrak{m}(\mathfrak{m} + 1), \qquad (IV.2.17)$$

where

$$\mathfrak{m} = \frac{i}{2\hbar}s_\alpha q_\alpha. \qquad (IV.2.18)$$

For the calculation of eigenvalues and eigenvectors we shall use, in addition to $\boldsymbol{J}^2$ and J_3, the operators

$$J_+ = is_1q_2, \qquad J_- = is_2q_1. \qquad (IV.2.19)$$

If we assume eigenvectors (as a product of two spinors) of the form $s_1^a s_2^b$, then the corresponding eigenvalues of J_3 and $\boldsymbol{J}^2$, respectively, are obtained:

$$\frac{1}{2}\hbar(a - b), \qquad \hbar^2\left(\frac{a+b}{2}\right)\left(\frac{a+b}{2} + 1\right).$$

Operations with J_+ and J_- yield

$$J_+(s_1^a s_2^b) = \hbar b s_1^{a+1} s_2^{b-1},$$
$$J_-(s_1^a s_2^b) = \hbar a s_1^{a-1} s_2^{b+1},$$

so the degree $a + b$ of the eigenfunction does not change. The $2j + 1$ complete set of eigenvectors

$$|\gamma jm\rangle = A_{jm}s_1^{j+m}s_2^{j-m},$$

with $m = -j, -j + 1, \cdots, j$, can form the basis for the $D(j)$ representation of the angular momentum operators. The constants A_{jm} are defined in such a

---

* A. R. Edmonds, *Angular Momentum in Quantum Mechanics*, Princeton Univ. Press, Princeton, 1957.

way that operation on $|\gamma jm\rangle$ by J_3 and $\boldsymbol{J}^2$ will result in expressions similar to (*IV.1.19*). The eigenvectors are, therefore, given by

$$|\gamma jm\rangle = \frac{s_1^{j+m} s_2^{j-m}}{[(j+m)!(j-m)!]^{1/2}}. \tag{IV.2.20}$$

The representation is $(2j+1)$-dimensional. Every representation $D(j)$ of the two-dimensional unitary group is also a representation (single or double valued) of the rotation group. Hence operation by the orthogonal $(2j+1)$-dimensional operator $D(\psi\theta\phi)$ onto the eigenvectors (*IV.2.20*) is equivalent to unitary transformations of the spinor s_α. We choose for the unitary transformation operator U the expression

$$U = e^{(i/2)\theta\sigma_2} = \begin{bmatrix} \cos\frac{\theta}{2} & \sin\frac{\theta}{2} \\ -\sin\frac{\theta}{2} & \cos\frac{\theta}{2} \end{bmatrix}.$$

Hence, using (*IV.2.4*) and (*IV.2.20*), we can write

$$D(\psi\theta\phi)|\gamma jm\rangle = \sum_{m'=-j}^{j} D_{m'm}^{(j)}(\psi\theta\phi)|\gamma jm'\rangle$$
$$= \frac{(s_1')^{j+m}(s_2')^{j-m}}{[(j+m)!(j-m)!]^{1/2}},$$

where $|s'\rangle = U\,|s\rangle$. For the special case $\psi = \phi = 0$, we have

$$D(0,\theta,0)|\gamma jm\rangle = \sum_{m'=-j}^{j} D_{m'm}^{(j)}(0,\theta,0)|\gamma jm\rangle$$
$$= \frac{\left(s_1\cos\frac{\theta}{2} - s_2\sin\frac{\theta}{2}\right)^{j+m}\left(s_1\sin\frac{\theta}{2} + s_2\cos\frac{\theta}{2}\right)^{j-m}}{[(j+m)!(j-m)!]^{1/2}}$$
$$= A_{jm}(s_1')^{j+m}(s_2')^{j-m}.$$

Since the eigenvectors defined by (*IV.2.20*) form a complete set, we can expand according to

$$A_{jm}(s_1')^{j+m}(s_2')^{j-m} = \sum_{m'=-j}^{j} A_{jm'} s_1^{j+m'} s_2^{j-m'} D_{m'm}^{(j)}(\theta),$$

where

$$D_{m'm}^{(j)}(\theta) = \left[\frac{(j+m')!(j-m')!}{(j+m)!(j-m)!}\right]^{1/2} \times \sum_n \begin{bmatrix} j+m \\ j-m'-n \end{bmatrix}\begin{bmatrix} j-m \\ n \end{bmatrix}(-1)^{j-m-n}$$
$$\left(\cos\frac{\theta}{2}\right)^{2n+m'+m}\left(\sin\frac{\theta}{2}\right)^{2j-2n-m'-m}, \tag{IV.2.21}$$

where

$$\begin{bmatrix} a \\ b \end{bmatrix} = \frac{a!}{(a-b)!b!}.$$

The matrix elements of finite rotations are related to Jacobi polynomials by

$$D^{(j)}_{m'm}(\theta) = \left[\frac{(j+m')!(j-m')!}{(j+m)!(j-m)!}\right]^{1/2} \times \left(\cos\frac{\theta}{2}\right)^{m'+m}\left(\sin\frac{\theta}{2}\right)^{m'-m} P^{(m'-m,m'+m)}_{j-m'}(\cos\theta), \qquad (IV.2.22)$$

where $m' - m$ and $m' + m$ are not restricted to nonnegative values alone. The function $P^{(a,b)}(x)$ satisfies the differential equation*

$$(1-x^2)\frac{d^2f}{dx^2} + [b - a - (a+b+2)x]\frac{df}{dx} + n(n+a+b+1)f = 0. \qquad (IV.2.23)$$

A Jacobi polynomial is normalized in such a way that

$$P^{(a,b)}_n(1) = \begin{bmatrix} n+a \\ n \end{bmatrix} \qquad (IV.2.24)$$

The most general form of a normalized Jacobi polynomial is given by

$$P_n{}^{(a,b)}(x) = \frac{(-1)^n}{2^n n!}(1-x)^{-a}(1+x)^{-b}\frac{d^n}{dx^n}[(1-x)^{a+n}(1+x)^{b+n}]. \qquad (IV.2.25)$$

For $a = b = 0$ it yields Legendre polynomials

$$P_n(x) = \frac{1}{2^n n!}\frac{d^n}{dx^n}(x^2-1)^n, \qquad (IV.2.26)$$

which are normalized according to

$$\int_{-1}^{1} P_n(x)P_l(x)\,dx = \frac{2\delta_{nl}}{2n+1}. \qquad (IV.2.27)$$

We also define associated Legendre polynomials by

$$P^m_l(x) = (x^2-1)^{(1/2)m}\frac{d^m}{dx^m}P_l(x). \qquad (IV.2.28)$$

The properties of Jacobi polynomials discussed in Szegö's book yield the values of $D^{(l)}_{m0}(\theta)$, for orbital angular momentum, as

$$D^{(l)}_{m0}(\theta) = \left[\frac{(l-m)!}{(l+m)!}\right]^{1/2} P^m_l(\cos\theta),$$

$$D^{(l)}_{0m}(0,\theta,\phi) = e^{im\phi}\sum_{m''=-l}^{l} D^{(l)}_{0m''}(0)D^{(l)}_{m''m}(\theta) = e^{im\phi}D^{(l)}_{0m}(\theta). \qquad (IV.2.29)$$

Hence

$$D^{(l)}_{0m}(0,\theta,\phi) = \sqrt{\left(\frac{4\pi}{2l+1}\right)}\,Y_{lm}(\theta,\phi) \qquad (IV.2.30)$$

---

* G. Szegö, *Orthogonal Polynomials*, American Mathematical Society, Providence, 1939.

and

$$D^{(l)}_{00}(0, \theta, \phi) = P_l(\cos\theta). \qquad (IV.2.31)$$

We have thus shown that the spherical harmonics $Y_{lm}(\theta, \phi)$ are matrix elements of the rotation operators in a representation where L_3 is diagonal. The spherical harmonics $Y_{lm}(\theta, \phi)$ are defined by

$$Y_{lm}(\theta, \phi) = (-1)^m \left[\frac{(2l+1)(l-m)!}{4\pi(l+m)!}\right]^{1/2} P_l^m(\cos\theta)e^{im\phi}, \qquad (IV.2.32)$$

where

$$Y_{l0}(\theta, \phi) = \sqrt{\left(\frac{2l+1}{4\pi}\right)} P_l(\cos\theta). \qquad (IV.2.33)$$

In polar coordinates

$$x_1 = r \sin\theta \cos\phi,$$
$$x_2 = r \sin\theta \sin\phi,$$
$$x_3 = r \cos\theta,$$

the orbital angular momenta L_i can be expressed as

$$L_+ = L_1 + iL_2 = \hbar e^{i\phi}\left(\frac{\partial}{\partial\theta} + i\cot\theta\frac{\partial}{\partial\phi}\right),$$

$$L_- = L_1 - iL_2 = \hbar e^{-i\phi}\left(-\frac{\partial}{\partial\theta} + i\cot\theta\frac{\partial}{\partial\phi}\right), \qquad (IV.2.34)$$

$$L_3 = -i\hbar\frac{\partial}{\partial\phi}.$$

Hence

$$\boldsymbol{L}^2 = L_1^2 + L_2^2 + L_3^2 = -\hbar^2\left[\frac{1}{\sin\theta}\frac{\partial}{\partial\theta}\left(\sin\theta\frac{\partial}{\partial\theta}\right) + \frac{1}{\sin^2\theta}\frac{\partial^2}{\partial\phi^2}\right]. \qquad (IV.2.35)$$

From

$$\boldsymbol{L}^2 f = \hbar^2 l(l+1)f$$

and $x = \cos\theta$ we obtain the differential equation

$$(1-x^2)\frac{d^2f}{dx^2} - 2x\frac{df}{dx} + l(l+1)f + \frac{1}{1-x^2}\frac{\partial^2 f}{\partial\phi^2} = 0, \qquad (IV.2.36)$$

which is satisfied by the spherical harmonics defined by (*IV.2.32*). Thus the spherical harmonics Y_{lm} are simultaneous eigenfunctions of $\boldsymbol{L}^2$ and L_3, corresponding to their respective eigenvalues $\hbar^2 l(l+1)$ and $\hbar m$. The normalized form (*IV.2.32*) of Y_{lm} is imposed by the relations

$$\int_{-1}^{1} P_l^m(x)P_{l'}^m(x)\,dx = \frac{2\delta_{ll'}(l'+m)!}{(2l'+1)(l'-m)!}, \qquad (IV.2.37)$$

$$\int_{-1}^{1} P_l^m(x)P_l^{m'}(x)\frac{dx}{1-x^2} = \frac{\delta_{mm'}(l+m)!}{m(l-m)!}. \qquad (IV.2.38)$$

IV.3. Addition of Angular Momenta

Angular momentum is an observable vector operator and therefore addition of two different angular momenta must be discussed in accordance with the rules developed for angular momentum in the previous sections. The simplest examples of addition of angular momenta are the sum of orbital and spin angular momenta of an elementary particle, the addition of different isotopic spins, and so on. There are many occasions, especially in the study of atomic and nuclear spectra, where it is necessary to calculate interactions involving the coupling of two angular momenta; spin-orbit coupling and hyperfine structure of atomic levels are simple examples.

Let J_1 and J_2 be any two commuting angular momenta,

$$[J_{1i}, J_{2j}] = 0, \qquad i, j = 1, 2, 3,$$

and let $\boldsymbol{J} = \boldsymbol{J}_1 + \boldsymbol{J}_2$ be the sum of the two.

We may choose a set of complete commuting set in two ways: (a) the observables

$$\Gamma,\ \boldsymbol{J}_1^2,\ \boldsymbol{J}_2^2,\ J_{1z},\ J_{2z},$$

where the set Γ commutes with all the angular momenta and constitutes a complete set with them, is one set; (b) the observables

$$\Gamma,\ \boldsymbol{J}_1^2,\ \boldsymbol{J}_2^2,\ \boldsymbol{J}^2,\ J_z$$

constitute the second alternative.

We shall indicate the simultaneous orthogonal and normalized eigenvectors corresponding respectively to the first and second set by

$$|\gamma j_1 j_2 m_1 m_2\rangle \qquad (IV.3.1)$$

and

$$|\gamma j_1 j_2 j M\rangle, \qquad (IV.3.2)$$

where j_1, j_2, j, m_1, m_2, and M are eigenvalues of $\boldsymbol{J}_1^2$, $\boldsymbol{J}_2^2$, $\boldsymbol{J}^2$, J_{1z}, J_{2z}, and J_z, respectively.*†

The two representations (*IV.3.1*) and (*IV.3.2*) will be connected by a unitary transformation.

For a given set of values of γ the subspace characterized by the eigenvalues j_1 and j_2 is a $(2j_1 + 1)(2j_2 + 1)$-dimensional space and the corresponding unit operator is

$$I_{j_1j_2} = \sum_{\substack{m_1=-j_1 \\ m_2=-j_2}}^{j_1,j_2} |\gamma j_1 j_2 m_1 m_2\rangle\langle\gamma j_1 j_2 m_1 m_2|. \qquad (IV.3.3)$$

---

* E. U. Condon and G. H. Shortley, *The Theory of Atomic Spectra*, 2nd ed., Cambridge Univ. Press, Cambridge, 1951.

† M. E. Rose, *Multipole Fields*, Wiley, New York, 1955.

By using the unit operator we can, for the same γ, expand the eigenvector (*IV.3.2*) in the form

$$|\gamma j_1 j_2 j M\rangle = \sum_{\substack{m_1=-j_1\\ m_2=-j_2}}^{j_1,j_2} C(j_1 j_2 j;\, m_1 m_2 M)|\gamma j_1 j_2 m_1 m_2\rangle, \qquad (IV.3.4)$$

where the expansion coefficients are defined by

$$C(j_1 j_2 j;\, m_1 m_2 M) = \langle\gamma j_1 j_2 m_1 m_2|\gamma j_1 j_2 j M\rangle; \qquad (IV.3.5)$$

they are called "Clebsch-Gordon coefficients." The quantum number M is given by

$$M = m_1 + m_2. \qquad (IV.3.6)$$

The largest M which can occur in $|\gamma j_1 j_2 m_1 m_2\rangle$ is $M = j_1 + j_2$, when $m_1 = j_1$ and $m_2 = j_2$. The same largest M occurs also in $|\gamma j_1 j_2 j M\rangle$. Because of the dimension number of the subspace under consideration the largest j is $j_1 + j_2$. The value of M next to its maximum is

$$M = j_1 + j_2 - 1.$$

It is easy to see from

$$\begin{aligned} m_1 &= -j_1,\ -j_1 + 1,\ -j_2 + 2,\ \cdots,\ j_1 - 1,\ j_1,\\ m_2 &= -j_2,\ -j_2 + 1,\ -j_2 + 2,\ \cdots,\ j_2 - 1,\ j_2, \end{aligned}$$

that there exist two $|\gamma j_1 j_2 m_1 m_2\rangle$, with $M = j_1 + j_2 - 1$ given by $m_1 = j_1$, $m_2 = j_2 - 1$ and $m_1 = j_1 - 1$, $m_2 = j_2$. In the same way there are, of course, two $|\gamma j_1 j_2 j M\rangle$ with the same value of M, one of which has for j the value $j_1 + j_2$ and the other the value $j_1 + j_2 - 1$. This argument can be continued for other angular momentum states. Hence one finds that in adding two angular momenta j_1 and j_2, the resultant j assume the values

$$j = j_1 + j_2,\ j_1 + j_2 - 1,\ \cdots,\ |j_1 - j_2|, \qquad (IV.3.7)$$

where $|j_1 - j_2|$ is the least value of j. The eigenvalues of $\boldsymbol{J}^2$ are to be obtained from $j(j + 1)$ with the j given by (*IV.3.7*). To each value of j corresponds $2j + 1$ states with

$$M = -j,\ -j + 1,\ \cdots,\ j - 1,\ j. \qquad (IV.3.8)$$

Thus the number of states in the two representations is the same and is given by

$$\sum_{j=|j_1-j_2|}^{j_1+j_2} (2j + 1) = (2j_1 + 1)(2j_2 + 1). \qquad (IV.3.9)$$

A more general formulation of the addition theory for angular momenta can be based on the generalization of the orthogonal transformation operators of Chapter I [see (*I.3.17*)]. The normalized eigenvectors $|\gamma j_1 j_2 m_1 m_2\rangle$ and

$|\gamma j_1 j_2 jM\rangle$ of the two representations can be used to define a rotation operator

$$C = \sum_{\substack{m_1=-j_1\\m_2=-j_2}}^{j_1,j_2} |\gamma j_1 j_2 jM\rangle\langle\gamma j_1 j_2 m_1 m_2|, \qquad (IV.3.10)$$

where

$$M = m_1 + m_2, \qquad \tilde{C}C = I. \qquad (IV.3.11)$$

The matrix elements of the orthogonal transformation operator C in the coordinate system $|\gamma j_1 j_2 m_1 m_2\rangle$ yield the Clebsh-Gordon coefficients

$$\begin{aligned}\langle\gamma j_1 j_2 m_1' m_2'|C|\gamma j_1 j_2 m_1' m_2'\rangle &= \sum_{\substack{m_1=-j_1\\m_2=-j_2}}^{j_1,j_2} \langle\gamma j_1 j_2 m_1' m_2'|\gamma j_1 j_2 jM\rangle\langle\gamma j_1 j_2 m_1 m_2|\gamma j_1 j_2 m_1' m_2'\rangle \\ &= \sum_{\substack{m_1=-j_1\\m_2=-j_2}}^{j_1,j_2} \langle\gamma j_1 j_2 m_1' m_2'|\gamma j_1 j_2 jM\rangle\delta_{m'_1 m_1}\delta_{m'_2 m_2} \\ &= \langle\gamma j_1 j_2 m_1 m_2|\gamma j_1 j_2 jM\rangle = C(j_1 j_2 j;\, m_1 m_2 M). \qquad (IV.3.12)\end{aligned}$$

Further, by taking the matrix elements of the orthogonality condition $(IV.3.11)$, we get the orthogonality relations between the Clebsh-Gordon coefficients:

$$\sum_{\substack{m_1=-j_1\\m_2=-j_2}}^{j_1,j_2} C(j_1 j_2 j;\, m_1 m_2 M)C(j_1 j_2 j';\, m_1 m_2 M') = \delta_{jj'}\delta_{MM'} \qquad (IV.3.13)$$

and

$$\sum_{jm} C(j_1 j_2 j;\, m_1 m_2 M)C(j_1 j_2 j;\, m_1' m_2' M) = \delta_{m_1 m'_1}\delta_{m_2 m'_2} \qquad (IV.3.14)$$

It is to be understood that the right side of $(IV.3.13)$, for j values outside the numbers $(IV.3.7)$, will vanish regardless of M and M'.

We may also express the normalized eigenvectors $|\gamma j_1 j_2 m_1 m_2\rangle$ in terms of the normalized vectors $|\gamma j_1 j_2 jM\rangle$. We use the unit operator

$$I_{j_1 j_2} = \sum_{j=|j_1-j_2|}^{j_1+j_2} \sum_{m=-j}^{j} |\gamma j_1 j_2 jM\rangle\langle\gamma j_1 j_2 jM| \qquad (IV.3.15)$$

and expand $|\gamma j_1 j_2 m_1 m_2\rangle$ as

$$|\gamma j_1 j_2 m_1 m_2\rangle = \sum_{j=|j_1-j_2|}^{j_1+j_2} \sum_{M=-j}^{j} C(j_1 j_2 j;\, m_1 m_2 M)|\gamma j_1 j_2 jM\rangle. \qquad (IV.3.16)$$

Only the most general formal aspects of C coefficients have been discussed. The method of calculation of these coefficients will not be carried out, and in this book only the cases $j_2 = 1$ and $j_2 = \frac{1}{2}$ will be considered. The corresponding Clebsh-Gordon coefficients are given in the following tables.

TABLE IV.1. Clebsh-Gordon Coefficients for $j_2 = 1$, $C(j_1 1 j;\, m_1 m_2 M)$

	$m_2 = 1$	$m_2 = 0$	$m_2 = -1$
$j = j_1 + 1$	$\left[\frac{(j_1+M)(j_1+M+1)}{(2j_1+1)(2j_1+2)}\right]^{1/2}$	$\left[\frac{(j_1-M+1)(j_1+M+1)}{(2j_1+1)(j_1+1)}\right]^{1/2}$	$\left[\frac{(j_1-M)(j_1-M+1)}{(2j_1+1)(2j_1+2)}\right]^{1/2}$
$j = j_1$	$-\left[\frac{(j_1+M)(j_1-M+1)}{2j_1(j_1+1)}\right]^{1/2}$	$\left[\frac{M^2}{[j_1(j_1+1)]}\right]^{1/2}$	$\left[\frac{(j_1-M)(j_1+M+1)}{2j_1(j_1+1)}\right]^{1/2}$
$j = j_1 - 1$	$\left[\frac{(j_1-M)(j_1-M+1)}{2j_1(2j_1+1)}\right]^{1/2}$	$-\left[\frac{(j_1-M)(j_1+M)}{j_1(2j_1+1)}\right]^{1/2}$	$\left[\frac{(j_1+M+1)(j_1+M)}{2j_1(2j_1+1)}\right]^{1/2}$

TABLE IV.2. Clebsh-Gordon Coefficients for $j_2 = \frac{1}{2}$, $C(j_1 \tfrac{1}{2} j;\, m_1 m_2 M)$

	$m_2 = \frac{1}{2}$	$m_2 = -\frac{1}{2}$
$j = j_1 + \frac{1}{2}$	$\left[\frac{j_1+M+\frac{1}{2}}{2j_1+1}\right]^{1/2}$	$\left[\frac{j_1-M+\frac{1}{2}}{2j_1+1}\right]^{1/2}$
$j = j_1 - \frac{1}{2}$	$-\left[\frac{j_1-M+\frac{1}{2}}{2j_1+1}\right]^{1/2}$	$\left[\frac{j_1+M+\frac{1}{2}}{2j_1+1}\right]^{1/2}$

IV.3.A. Expansion of a Plane Wave

A plane wave of the form $e^{i\boldsymbol{k}\cdot\boldsymbol{r}}$ is a solution of the wave equation

$$(\boldsymbol{\nabla}^2 + \boldsymbol{k}^2)\psi = 0.$$

From the definition of orbital angular momentum we have

$$\boldsymbol{L}^2 = (\boldsymbol{r} \times \boldsymbol{p})^2 = \boldsymbol{r}^2\boldsymbol{p}^2 + 2i\hbar r p_r - x_j(\boldsymbol{r}\cdot\boldsymbol{p})p_j,$$

where

$$p_r = \frac{1}{r}\,\boldsymbol{r}\cdot\boldsymbol{p} = -i\hbar\,\frac{\partial}{\partial r}.$$

By using the commutation relations $[x_j, \boldsymbol{r}\cdot\boldsymbol{p}] = i\hbar x_j$ and $[r, p_r] = i\hbar$, we obtain

$$x_j(\boldsymbol{r}\cdot\boldsymbol{p})p_j = rp_r^2 r + 2i\hbar r p_r.$$

Hence

$$\boldsymbol{L}^2 = \boldsymbol{r}^2\boldsymbol{p}^2 - rp_r^2 r, \tag{IV.3.17}$$

and therefore

$$\boldsymbol{p}^2 = \frac{1}{r^2}\,\boldsymbol{L}^2 + \frac{1}{r}\,p_r^2 r.$$

Thus, from

$$(\boldsymbol{\nabla}^2 + \boldsymbol{k}^2)\psi = \left(-\frac{1}{\hbar^2}\,\boldsymbol{p}^2 + \boldsymbol{k}^2\right)\psi = 0,$$

we obtain

$$\left(-\frac{1}{\hbar^2 r^2}\,\boldsymbol{L}^2 - \frac{1}{\hbar^2}\,\frac{1}{r}\,p_r^2 r + \boldsymbol{k}^2\right)\psi = 0. \tag{IV.3.18}$$

This result suggests that we can express a plane wave as a superposition of spherical harmonics by

$$\psi = \sum_{l=0}^{\infty} A_l f_l(r) P_l(\cos\theta), \qquad (IV.3.19)$$

where we chose the k vector in the z direction, so the angle between $\boldsymbol{k}$ and $\boldsymbol{r}$ is θ. By using definition (*IV.3.19*) we obtain

$$\left[\frac{1}{r}\frac{\partial^2}{\partial r^2} r - \frac{l(l+1)}{r^2} + \boldsymbol{k}^2\right] f_l(r) = 0, \qquad (IV.3.20)$$

where

$$P_l(\cos\theta) = \sqrt{\left(\frac{4\pi}{2l+1}\right)}\, Y_{l,0}(\theta)$$

and

$$\mathbf{L}^2 Y_{lm} = \hbar^2 l(l+1) Y_{lm}.$$

Equation (*IV.3.20*) has two series solutions beginning with r^l and r^{-l-1} and both are expressible in terms of Bessel functions. Because of the regularity of a plane wave we must choose the solution that is finite at $r = 0$. On multiplying both sides of the series (*IV.3.19*) by $P_{l'}(\cos\theta)\sin\theta$, integrating from 0 to π, and using the orthogonality property

$$\int_0^{2\pi}\int_0^{\pi} Y^*_{lm}(\theta,\phi) Y_{l'm'}(\theta,\phi)\sin\theta\, d\theta\, d\phi = \delta_{ll'}\delta_{mm'} \qquad (IV.3.21)$$

of spherical harmonics, we get

$$\frac{2}{2l+1} A_l f_l = \int_{-1}^{1} e^{ikrx} P_l(x)\, dx = \frac{1}{ikr}\left[e^{ikrx}P_l(x)\right]_{-1}^{1} - \frac{1}{ikr}\int_{-1}^{1} e^{ikrx} P_l'(x)\, dx.$$

For large r we have

$$\frac{2}{2l+1} A_l f_l \cong \frac{1}{ikr}\left[e^{ikrx}P_l(x)\right]_{-1}^{1} = 2i^l \frac{1}{kr}\sin\left(kr - \frac{1}{2}l\pi\right).$$

Hence it follows that the constants A_l are to be defined as

$$A_l = (2l+1)i^l.$$

The final form of the expansion is, therefore, given by

$$e^{ikr\cos\theta} = \sum_{l=0}^{\infty}(2l+1)i^l j_l(kr) P_l(\cos\theta), \qquad (IV.3.22)$$

where $j_l(kr)$ are spherical Bessel functions related to Bessel functions of the first kind* by

$$j_l(x) = \sqrt{\left(\frac{\pi}{2x}\right)}\, J_{l+1/2}(x).$$

---

* E. Jahnke and F. Emde, *Tables of Functions with Formulae and Curves*, 4th ed., Dover, New York, 1945.

For a plane wave with a wave vector $\boldsymbol{k}$ in the direction Θ, Φ we have

$$e^{i\boldsymbol{k}\cdot\boldsymbol{r}} = e^{ikr\cos\alpha} = \sum_{l=0}^{\infty} (2l+1) i^l j_l(kr) P_l(\cos\alpha),$$

where $\cos\alpha = \cos\theta\cos\Theta + \sin\theta\sin\Theta\cos(\Phi - \phi)$ and α is the angle subtended by any two points on the unit sphere, at the center of the sphere. According to the addition theorem of spherical harmonics we have

$$Y_{l,0}(\alpha)Y_{l,0}(0) = \sqrt{\left(\frac{2l+1}{4\pi}\right)}\, Y_{l,0}(\alpha) = \sum_{m=-l}^{l} Y^*_{lm}(\theta, \phi) Y_{lm}(\Theta, \Phi). \qquad (IV.3.23)$$

Hence

$$e^{i\boldsymbol{k}\cdot\boldsymbol{r}} = 4\pi \sum_{l=0}^{\infty} \sum_{m=-l}^{l} i^l j_l(kr) Y^*_{lm}(\Theta, \Phi) Y_{lm}(\theta, \phi). \qquad (IV.3.24)$$

This method of expansion of a plane wave was first applied by Lord Rayleigh to the scattering of sound waves and by Faxen and Holtsmark to the scattering of Schrödinger waves.

For $l = 0$ we have an S-wave given by

$$\psi_0 = \frac{\sin kr}{kr} = \frac{1}{2ikr}(e^{ikr} - e^{-ikr}).$$

Thus an S-wave is the sum of outgoing and ingoing spherical waves, each moving in the radial direction. It corresponds to a situation where the waves are made to converge at the origin, after which they diverge away.

According to expansion ($IV.3.22$), each partial wave is a solution of the wave equation and each therefore describes particles with particular angular momentum. A "complete" sum or superposition of waves of all angular momenta gives a plane wave. Thus such a plane wave containing all possible angular momenta describes an infinite number of angular momentum states for particles. Each angular momentum state is associated with a wave function of the appropriate angular dependence $P_l(\cos\theta)$.

IV.3.B. Problems

1. Consider the addition of two angular momenta $\frac{1}{2}\hbar\boldsymbol{\sigma}_a$ and $\frac{1}{2}\hbar\boldsymbol{\sigma}_b$ of two dynamical systems a and b. By writing the states $|\gamma j_1 j_2 m_1 m_2\rangle$ in the form

$$|\gamma j_1 j_2 m_1 m_2\rangle = |a j_1 m_1\rangle |b j_2 m_2\rangle$$

and using Table IV.2, with $j_1 = \frac{1}{2}$, $j_2 = \frac{1}{2}$, $j = 1, 0$ and $M(j=1) = -1, 0, 1$ and $M(j=0) = 0$, show that there exist three symmetric states (in particles a and b) and one antisymmetric state, corresponding to $j = 1$ and $j = 0$, respectively. Use expansion ($IV.3.4$) and note that the Clebsh-Gordon coefficients vanish for $M \neq m_1 + m_2$. The states with $j = 1$ and $j = 0$ constitute a triplet and a singlet state; for the triplet symmetric states,

$$|\gamma\tfrac{1}{2}\tfrac{1}{2}1, -1\rangle = |a\tfrac{1}{2}, -\tfrac{1}{2}\rangle|b, \tfrac{1}{2}, -\tfrac{1}{2}\rangle,$$

$$|\gamma\tfrac{1}{2}\tfrac{1}{2}1, 0\rangle = \frac{1}{\sqrt{2}}\,[|a1\tfrac{1}{2}, \tfrac{1}{2}\rangle|b\tfrac{1}{2}, -\tfrac{1}{2}\rangle + |a\tfrac{1}{2}, -\tfrac{1}{2}\rangle|b\tfrac{1}{2}, \tfrac{1}{2}\rangle],$$

$$|\gamma\tfrac{1}{2}\tfrac{1}{2}1, 1\rangle = |a\tfrac{1}{2}, \tfrac{1}{2}\rangle|b\tfrac{1}{2}, \tfrac{1}{2}\rangle, \qquad (IV.3.25)$$

and for the singlet antisymmetric state,

$$|\gamma\tfrac{1}{2}\tfrac{1}{2}0, 0\rangle = \frac{1}{\sqrt{2}}\,[|a\tfrac{1}{2}, \tfrac{1}{2}\rangle|b\tfrac{1}{2}, -\tfrac{1}{2}\rangle - |a\tfrac{1}{2}, -\tfrac{1}{2}\rangle|b\tfrac{1}{2}, \tfrac{1}{2}\rangle], \qquad (IV.3.26)$$

Note that in the triplet and singlet states the spins are parallel and antiparallel, respectively.

2. Repeat the previous problem for the addition of angular momenta $\hbar\boldsymbol{K}$ and $\frac{1}{2}\hbar\boldsymbol{\sigma}$ and show that the states $|\gamma j_1 j_2 j M\rangle$ are given by

$$|\gamma\tfrac{1}{2}\tfrac{3}{2}, -\tfrac{3}{2}\rangle = |a1, -1\rangle|b\tfrac{1}{2}, -\tfrac{1}{2}\rangle,$$

$$|\gamma1\tfrac{1}{2}\tfrac{3}{2}, -\tfrac{1}{2}\rangle = \frac{1}{\sqrt{3}}\,|a1, -1\rangle|b\tfrac{1}{2}, \tfrac{1}{2}\rangle + \sqrt{(\tfrac{2}{3})}|a1, 0\rangle|b\tfrac{1}{2}, -\tfrac{1}{2}\rangle,$$

$$|\gamma1\tfrac{1}{2}\tfrac{3}{2}, \tfrac{1}{2}\rangle = \frac{1}{\sqrt{3}}\,|a1, 1\rangle|b\tfrac{1}{2}, -\tfrac{1}{2}\rangle + \sqrt{(\tfrac{2}{3})}|a1, 0\rangle|b\tfrac{1}{2}, \tfrac{1}{2}\rangle,$$

$$|\gamma1\tfrac{1}{2}\tfrac{3}{2}, \tfrac{3}{2}\rangle = |a1, 1\rangle|b\tfrac{1}{2}, \tfrac{1}{2}\rangle, \qquad (IV.3.27)$$

for $j = \frac{3}{2}$ and $M(j = \frac{3}{2}) = -\frac{3}{2}, -\frac{1}{2}, \frac{1}{2}, \frac{3}{2}$ states, and

$$|\gamma\tfrac{1}{2}\tfrac{1}{2}, -\tfrac{1}{2}\rangle = \frac{1}{\sqrt{3}}\,|a1, 0\rangle|b\tfrac{1}{2}, -\tfrac{1}{2}\rangle - \sqrt{(\tfrac{2}{3})}|a1, -1\rangle|b\tfrac{1}{2}, \tfrac{1}{2}\rangle,$$

$$|\gamma\tfrac{1}{2}\tfrac{1}{2}, \tfrac{1}{2}\rangle = -\frac{1}{\sqrt{3}}\,|a1, 0\rangle|b\tfrac{1}{2}, \tfrac{1}{2}\rangle + \sqrt{\tfrac{2}{3}}|a1, 1\rangle|b\tfrac{1}{2}, -\tfrac{1}{2}\rangle \qquad (IV.3.28)$$

for $j = \frac{1}{2}$ and $M(j = \frac{1}{2}) = -\frac{1}{2}, \frac{1}{2}$ states.

3. By using the operator properties of the $\boldsymbol{\sigma}$ and the $\boldsymbol{K}$, calculate total angular momentum values of $\boldsymbol{S} = \frac{1}{2}\boldsymbol{\sigma}_a + \frac{1}{2}\boldsymbol{\sigma}_b$ and $\boldsymbol{S} = \boldsymbol{K} + \frac{1}{2}\boldsymbol{\sigma}$ without using the general rules of addition of angular momentum given in the text.

4. Use the Table IV.1 and record the nine angular momentum states corresponding to $\boldsymbol{S} = \boldsymbol{K}_a + \boldsymbol{K}_b$, in the form

$$|\gamma110, 0\rangle = \frac{1}{\sqrt{3}}\,[|a1, 1\rangle|b1, -1\rangle + |a1, -1\rangle|b1, 1\rangle - |a1, 0\rangle|b1, 0\rangle] \qquad (IV.3.29)$$

for the state $j = 0$ and $M(j = 0) = 0$; in the form

$$|\gamma111, -1\rangle = \frac{1}{\sqrt{2}}\,[|a1, 0\rangle|b1, -1\rangle - |a1, -1\rangle|b1, 0\rangle],$$

$$|\gamma 11 1, 0\rangle = \frac{1}{\sqrt{2}} [|a1, 1\rangle |b1, -1\rangle - |a1, -1\rangle |b1, 1\rangle],$$

$$|\gamma 11 1, 1\rangle = \frac{1}{\sqrt{2}} [|a1, 1\rangle |b1, 0\rangle - |a1, 0\rangle |b1, 1\rangle] \qquad (IV.3.30)$$

for the states $j = 1$ and $M(j = 1) = -1, 0, 1$; and in the form

$$|\gamma 11 2, -2\rangle = |a1, -1\rangle |b1, -1\rangle,$$

$$|\gamma 11 2, -1\rangle = \frac{1}{\sqrt{2}} [|a1, 0\rangle |b1, -1\rangle + |a1, -1\rangle |b1, 0\rangle],$$

$$|\gamma 11 2, 0\rangle = \frac{1}{\sqrt{6}} [|a1, 1\rangle |b1, -1\rangle + |a1, -1\rangle |b1, 1\rangle + 2|a1, 0\rangle |b1, 0\rangle], \qquad (IV.3.31)$$

$$|\gamma 11 2, 1\rangle = \frac{1}{\sqrt{2}} [|a1, 1\rangle |b1, 0\rangle + |a1, 0\rangle |b1, 1\rangle],$$

$$|\gamma 11 2, 2\rangle = |a1, 1\rangle |b1, 1\rangle$$

for states $j = 2$ and $M(j = 2) = -2, -1, 0, 1, 2$. Discuss the symmetries of the angular momentum states.

5. Show that the matrices K_i of spin 1, for $i = 1, 2, 3$, can be transformed by a unitary transformation into the representation of $j = 1$ matrices (*IV.1.47*), where the unitary matrix U is given by

$$U = \frac{1}{\sqrt{2}} \begin{bmatrix} -1 & 0 & 1 \\ -i & 0 & -i \\ 0 & 2 & 0 \end{bmatrix}. \qquad (IV.3.32)$$

6. The spaces spanned by the eigenvectors of total angular momenta $\boldsymbol{J} = \boldsymbol{J}_a + \boldsymbol{J}_b$ where $\boldsymbol{J}_a$ and $\boldsymbol{J}_b$ commute, are called "product spaces." For example, the eigenvectors defined by (*IV.3.25*) for $j = 1$ can span together with the singlet ($j = 0$) eigenvector a four-dimensional product space of two spaces of spin $\frac{1}{2}$. If $|\lambda\rangle$ is any vector belonging to the product space $P_{1/2,1/2}$ then it can be expanded with respect to that product space. Use definition (*IV.3.15*) and write down the expansion of $|\lambda\rangle$, where λ is a symbol representing the two respective degrees of freedom of two spaces of spin $\frac{1}{2}$.

IV.4. Selection Rules on *j* and the Matrix Representation of Vector Operators

A large class of observables in quantum mechanics are related to the angular momentum operator by a commutation relation of the type

$$[J_i, \kappa_j] = i\hbar \epsilon_{ijs} \kappa_s, \qquad (IV.4.1)$$

where $\boldsymbol{\kappa}$ is a vector operator. Examples of such operators are x_i, p_i and their various vector combinations. We can obtain matrix representations of κ_i in a coordinate system determined by a complete commuting set of observables, for example Γ, $\boldsymbol{J}^2$, J_3. The most general form for the matrix representation is based on a relation between any two j and j' as conditions for the nonvanishing matrix elements.

We begin with the operator relation

$$[\boldsymbol{J}^2, \kappa_i] = -2i\hbar\epsilon_{ijl}J_j\kappa_l - 2\hbar^2\kappa_i. \qquad (IV.4.2)$$

This can be obtained by writing

$$[\boldsymbol{J}^2, \kappa_i] = [J_lJ_l, \kappa_i] = J_l[J_l, \kappa_i] + [J_l, \kappa_i]J_l.$$

In a similar way we can obtain the double commutator

$$[\boldsymbol{J}^2, [\boldsymbol{J}^2, \kappa_i]] = 2\hbar^2(\boldsymbol{J}^2\kappa_i + \kappa_i\boldsymbol{J}^2) - 4\hbar^2J_i(\boldsymbol{J}\cdot\boldsymbol{\kappa}). \qquad (IV.4.3)$$

Hence, expanding the commutator on the left, we get

$$\boldsymbol{J}^4\kappa_i - 2\boldsymbol{J}^2\kappa_i\boldsymbol{J}^2 + \kappa_i\boldsymbol{J}^4 = 2\hbar^2(\boldsymbol{J}^2\kappa_i + \kappa_i\boldsymbol{J}^2) - 4\hbar^2J_i(\boldsymbol{J}\cdot\boldsymbol{\kappa}). \qquad (IV.4.4)$$

From the commutation relations ($IV.4.1$), setting $i = j$ and summing over i, we find that

$$\boldsymbol{J}\cdot\boldsymbol{\kappa} = \boldsymbol{\kappa}\cdot\boldsymbol{J}. \qquad (IV.4.5)$$

Multiplication of both sides of ($IV.4.1$) by ϵ_{ijl} yields

$$\boldsymbol{J}\times\boldsymbol{\kappa} + \boldsymbol{\kappa}\times\boldsymbol{J} = 2i\hbar\boldsymbol{\kappa}. \qquad (IV.4.6)$$

Furthermore, we have

$$[J_i, \boldsymbol{J}\cdot\boldsymbol{\kappa}] = [J_i, J_s\kappa_s] = J_s[J_i, \kappa_s] + [J_i, J_s]\kappa_s$$
$$= i\hbar\epsilon_{isl}J_s\kappa_l + i\hbar\epsilon_{isl}J_l\kappa_s,$$

so the result

$$[\boldsymbol{J}, \boldsymbol{J}\cdot\boldsymbol{\kappa}] = i\hbar(\boldsymbol{J}\times\boldsymbol{\kappa} - \boldsymbol{J}\times\boldsymbol{\kappa}) = 0 \qquad (IV.4.7)$$

implies that the matrix elements of the last term in ($IV.4.4$) vanish. The remaining term, having only terms in $\boldsymbol{J}^2$ and $\boldsymbol{J}^4$, makes it most convenient to obtain a relation between j and j' of different angular momentum states, for the existence of non-vanishing matrix elements of κ_i. Thus taking the matrix representation referring to the states $|\gamma jm\rangle$ and $|\gamma' j' m'\rangle$, equation ($IV.4.4$) yields the result

$$[j^2(j+1)^2 - 2j(j+1)j'(j'+1) + j'^2(j'+1)^2]\langle\gamma jm|\kappa_i|\gamma' j' m'\rangle$$
$$= 2[j(j+1) + j'(j'+1)]\langle\gamma jm|\kappa_i|\gamma' j' m'\rangle,$$

which can be combined into

$$[(j+j'+1)^2 - 1][(j-j')^2 - 1]\langle\gamma jm|\kappa_i|\gamma' j' m'\rangle = 0, \qquad (IV.4.8)$$

where $j \neq j'$.

The nonvanishing matrix elements of κ_i can only arise from either $(j+j'+1)^2 = 1$ or $(j'-j)^2 = 1$. Because $j, j' \geqq 0$, the first cannot hold; the second yields the conditions $j' = j \pm 1$. However, since κ_3 commutes with J_3, its matrix elements can only exist for $j = j'$. Thus the "selection rules"

$$j' - j = 0, \pm 1 \qquad (IV.4.9)$$

are the necessary conditions for the existence of the nonvanishing matrix elements of κ_i.

In order to find the dependence on m of the matrix representation of κ_i, we observe from (*IV.4.1*) that

$$[\![J_+, \kappa_+]\!] = [\![J_-, \kappa_-]\!] = 0 \qquad (IV.4.10)$$

and

$$[\![J_3, \kappa_-]\!] = -\hbar\kappa_-, \qquad (IV.4.11)$$

$$[\![J_3, \kappa_+]\!] = \hbar\kappa_+, \qquad (IV.4.12)$$

where $\kappa_\pm = \kappa_1 \pm i\kappa_2$. Taking the matrix representation of (*IV.4.11*) we find

$$\langle\gamma jm|J_3\kappa_-|\gamma' j' m'\rangle - \langle\gamma jm|\kappa_- J_3|\gamma' j' m'\rangle = -\hbar\langle\gamma jm|\kappa_-|\gamma' j' m'\rangle.$$

Hence the equations

$$(m - m' + 1)\langle\gamma jm|\kappa_-|\gamma' j' m'\rangle = 0,$$

$$(m - m' - 1)\langle\gamma' j' m'|\kappa_+|\gamma jm\rangle = 0$$

yield the selection rules

$$m' - m = \pm 1, \qquad (IV.4.13)$$

and from $[\![J_3, \kappa_3]\!] = 0$, a further selection rule,

$$m' - m = 0, \qquad (IV.4.14)$$

for the existence of nonvanishing matrix elements.

From (*IV.4.10*) we have the diagonal element

$$\langle\gamma jm|J_-\kappa_-|\gamma jm\rangle = \langle\gamma jm|\kappa_- J_-|\gamma jm\rangle,$$

or

$$\langle\gamma jm|J_-|\gamma jm + 1\rangle\langle\gamma jm + 1|\kappa_-|\gamma jm\rangle = \langle\gamma jm|\kappa_-|\gamma jm - 1\rangle\langle\gamma jm - 1|J_-|\gamma jm\rangle.$$

Using the matrix elements of J_- defined in (*IV.1.42*), we get

$$[(j - m)(j + m + 1)]^{1/2}\langle\gamma jm + 1|\kappa_-|\gamma jm\rangle = [(j + m)(j - m + 1)]^{1/2}\langle\gamma jm|\kappa_-|\gamma jm - 1\rangle$$

or

$$\frac{\langle\gamma jm + 1|\kappa_-|\gamma jm\rangle}{[(j + m)(j - m + 1)]^{1/2}} = \frac{\langle\gamma jm|\kappa_-|\gamma jm - 1\rangle}{[(j - m)(j + m + 1)]^{1/2}}. \qquad (IV.4.15)$$

This holds for any value of m; for example, if we replace m on the left by $m - 1$, we get the right side. Therefore each ratio is independent of m. Let this ratio be represented by $\langle\gamma j|\kappa_-|\gamma j\rangle$ and write the matrix element in the form

$$\langle\gamma jm + 1|\kappa_-|\gamma jm\rangle = \langle\gamma j|\kappa_-|\gamma j\rangle[(j + m)(j - m + 1)]^{1/2}. \qquad (IV.4.16)$$

For a more general case we take matrix elements with respect to states $|\gamma jm-1\rangle$ and $|\gamma' j' m+1\rangle$ and obtain

$$\langle\gamma jm-1|J_-\kappa_-|\gamma'j'm+1\rangle = \langle\gamma jm-1|\kappa_-J_-|\gamma'j'm+1\rangle$$

or

$$\langle\gamma jm-1|J_-|\gamma jm\rangle\langle\gamma jm|\kappa_-|\gamma'j'm+1\rangle = \langle\gamma jm-1|\kappa_-|\gamma'j'm\rangle\langle\gamma'j'm|J_-|\gamma'j'm+1\rangle,$$

where $j'-j=0, \pm 1$. Hence

$$\frac{\langle\gamma jm|\kappa_-|\gamma'j'm+1\rangle}{[(j'-m)(j'+m+1)]^{1/2}} = \frac{\langle\gamma jm-1|\kappa_-|\gamma'j'm\rangle}{[(j+m)(j-m+1)]^{1/2}}. \quad (IV.4.17)$$

If we put $j'=j-1$, equation (*IV.4.17*) can be written as

$$\frac{\langle\gamma jm|\kappa_-|\gamma'j-1, m+1\rangle}{[(j-m)(j-m-1)]^{1/2}} = \frac{\langle\gamma jm-1|\kappa_-|\gamma'j-1, m\rangle}{[(j-m)(j-m+1)]^{1/2}}, \quad (IV.4.18)$$

where we multiplied through by the factor $(j-m)^{1/2}(j+m)^{-1/2}$ to make each ratio independent of m. Thus we may write

$$\langle\gamma jm|\kappa_-|\gamma'j-1, m+1\rangle = \langle\gamma j|\kappa_-|\gamma'j-1\rangle [(j-m)(j-m-1)]^{1/2}. \quad (IV.4.19)$$

Many other relations of the above forms can be found in Condon and Shortley.*

IV.5. Representation of Momentum Operators and the Rotation Group

By using the methods of the previous section we can find the only non-vanishing matrix elements of $\kappa_+ = p_+$, $\kappa_- = p_-$ and $\kappa_3 = p_3$:

$$\begin{aligned}
\langle\gamma jm|p_3|\gamma jm\rangle &= m\langle\gamma j|p|\gamma j\rangle,\\
\langle\gamma jm|p_+|\gamma jm-1\rangle &= \langle\gamma j|p|\gamma j\rangle[(j+m)(j-m+1)]^{1/2},\\
\langle\gamma jm|p_-|\gamma jm+1\rangle &= \langle\gamma j|p|\gamma j\rangle[(j-m)(j+m+1)]^{1/2},\\
\langle\gamma jm|p_3|\gamma j+1, m\rangle &= \langle\gamma j|p|\gamma j+1\rangle[(j+m+1)(j-m+1)]^{1/2},\\
\langle\gamma jm|p_+|\gamma j+1, m-1\rangle &= \langle\gamma j|p|\gamma j+1\rangle[(j-m+2)(j-m+1)]^{1/2},\\
\langle\gamma jm|p_-|\gamma j+1, m+1\rangle &= -\langle\gamma j|p|\gamma j+1\rangle[(j+m+1)(j+m+2)]^{1/2},\\
\langle\gamma jm|p_3|\gamma j-1, m\rangle &= \langle\gamma j|p|\gamma j-1\rangle[(j+m)(j-m)]^{1/2},\\
\langle\gamma jm|p_+|\gamma j-1, m-1\rangle &= -\langle\gamma j|p|\gamma j-1\rangle[(j+m)(j+m-1)]^{1/2},\\
\langle\gamma jm|p_-|\gamma j-1, m+1\rangle &= \langle\gamma j|p|\gamma j-1\rangle[(j-m)(j-m-1)]^{1/2}.
\end{aligned} \quad (IV.5.1)$$

It is to be observed that the last three elements do not exist for $j = 0, 1/2$, so in these cases $\langle\gamma j|p|\gamma j-1\rangle = 0$.

---

* E. U. Condon and G. H. Shortley, *The Theory of Atomic Spectra*, Cambridge Univ. Press, Cambridge, 1951, p. 63.

For the present let us ignore the fact that p_+ and p_- commute with one another. Thus the diagonal matrix element of $p_+p_- - p_-p_+$ is

$$
\begin{aligned}
\langle\gamma jm|(p_+p_- - p_-p_+)|\gamma jm\rangle = {} & [\langle\gamma jm|p_+|\gamma j, m-1\rangle\langle\gamma j, m-1|p_-|\gamma jm\rangle \\
& + \langle\gamma jm|p_+|\gamma j+1, m-1\rangle\langle\gamma j+1, m-1|p_-|\gamma jm\rangle \\
& + \langle\gamma jm|p_+|\gamma j-1, m-1\rangle\langle\gamma j-1, m-1|p_-|\gamma jm\rangle] \\
& - [\langle\gamma jm|p_-|\gamma j, m+1\rangle\langle\gamma j, m+1|p_+|\gamma jm\rangle \\
& + \langle\gamma jm|p_-|\gamma j+1, m+1\rangle\langle\gamma j+1, m+1|p_+|\gamma jm\rangle \\
& + \langle\gamma jm|p_-|\gamma j-1, m+1\rangle\langle\gamma j-1, m+1|p_+|\gamma jm\rangle] \\
= {} & [|\langle\gamma j|p|\gamma j\rangle|^2(j+m)(j-m+1) \\
& + |\langle\gamma j|p|\gamma j+1\rangle|^2(j-m+2)(j-m+1) \\
& + |\langle\gamma j|p|\gamma j-1\rangle|^2(j+m)(j+m-1)] \\
& - [|\langle\gamma j|p|\gamma j\rangle|^2(j-m)(j+m+1) \\
& + |\langle\gamma j|p|\gamma j+1\rangle|^2(j+m+1)(j+m+2) \\
& + |\langle\gamma j|p|\gamma j-1\rangle|^2(j-m)(j-m-1)] \\
= {} & 2m[|\langle\gamma j|p|\gamma j\rangle|^2 - (2j+3)|\langle\gamma j|p|\gamma j+1\rangle|^2 \\
& + (2j-1)|\langle\gamma j|p|\gamma j-1\rangle|^2]. \qquad (IV.5.2)
\end{aligned}
$$

Hence we may write

$$\langle\gamma jm|p_+p_- - p_-p_+)|\gamma jm\rangle = 2m\left[|\langle\gamma|pj|\gamma j\rangle|^2 + \frac{\phi(j+1) - \phi(j)}{2j+1}\right], \qquad (IV.5.3)$$

where

$$
\begin{aligned}
\phi(j) &= \langle\gamma j|p|\gamma j+1\rangle\langle\gamma j+1|p|\gamma j\rangle(2j+1)(2j+3), \\
\phi(j-1) &= \langle\gamma j|p|\gamma j-1\rangle\langle\gamma j-1|p|\gamma j\rangle(2j-1)(2j+1), \\
\phi(-1) &= 0.
\end{aligned}
$$

The quantity $\boldsymbol{p}^2 = \frac{1}{2}(p_+p_- + p_-p_+) + p_3^2$ is rotation-invariant and has the eigenvalue

$$\boldsymbol{p}'^2 = \left[\phi(j)\frac{j+1}{2j+1} + \phi(j-1)\frac{j}{2j+1} + |\langle\gamma j|p|\gamma j\rangle|^2 j(j+1)\right], \qquad (IV.5.4)$$

which is independent of m.

Another rotation-invariant quantity is

$$\boldsymbol{p}\cdot\boldsymbol{J} = \boldsymbol{J}\cdot\boldsymbol{p} \qquad (IV.5.5)$$

and has the eigenvalue

$$
\begin{aligned}
\lambda &= \langle\gamma jm|\boldsymbol{p}\cdot\boldsymbol{J}|\gamma jm\rangle \\
&= \tfrac{1}{2}\langle\gamma jm|(p_+J_- + p_-J_+)|\gamma jm\rangle + \langle\gamma jm|p_3J_3|\gamma jm\rangle \\
&= j(j+1)\langle\gamma j|p|\gamma j\rangle. \qquad (IV.5.6)
\end{aligned}
$$

The quantities defined by $(IV.5.4)$ and $(IV.5.6)$ as eigenvalues of the group invariants $\boldsymbol{p}^2$ and $\boldsymbol{p}\cdot\boldsymbol{J} = \boldsymbol{J}\cdot\boldsymbol{p}$, respectively, are constants for a given representation.*

---

* W. Pauli, *Continuous Groups in Quantum Mechanics, CERN* 56–31, 1956.

So far we have not used the commutation property of the $\boldsymbol{p}$. We take the latter fact into account and distinguish two cases.

(a) $\lambda = 0$. In this case the matrix element of $[p_+, p_-] = 0$ gives

$$\phi(j) = \phi(j-1) = \text{constant} = \boldsymbol{p}'^2.$$

From the definition of $\phi(j)$ and from (*IV.5.3*) we get

$$|\langle\gamma j|p|\gamma j+1\rangle|^2 = \frac{\boldsymbol{p}'^2}{(2j+1)(2j+3)}. \qquad (IV.5.7)$$

Also, $\lambda = 0$ with (*IV.5.6*) and (*IV.5.3*) gives

$$2m\left[\frac{\phi(j-1) - \phi(j)}{2j+1}\right] = 0. \qquad (IV.5.8)$$

This is not possible for $\boldsymbol{p}'^2 \neq 0$ unless the lowest possible value of j is zero, in which case $m = 0$ and (*IV.5.8*) is then satisfied. This situation corresponds to an infinite representation with j taking all values starting from zero.

(b) $\lambda \neq 0$. In this case the matrix element of $p_+p_- - p_-p_+$ gives

$$\frac{\phi(j-1) - \phi(j)}{2j+1} + \frac{\lambda^2}{j^2(j+1)^2} = 0.$$

Hence

$$\phi(j) - \phi(j-1) = \lambda^2\left[\frac{1}{j^2} - \frac{1}{(j+1)^2}\right],$$

so

$$\phi(j) + \frac{\lambda^2}{(j+1)^2} = \text{constant}. \qquad (IV.5.9)$$

If we use this in the expression of $\boldsymbol{p}'^2$, the value of the constant in (*IV.5.9*) is just equal to $\boldsymbol{p}'^2$. Since $\phi(-1) = 0$, the minimum value of j, j_0 is to be determined from

$$\phi(J_0 - 1) = 0, \qquad (IV.5.10)$$

as

$$\lambda^2 = j_0^2\boldsymbol{p}'^2,$$

so

$$\lambda = \pm\sqrt{\boldsymbol{p}'^2}j_0. \qquad (IV.5.11)$$

Thus we obtain two nonequivalent representations corresponding to $\sqrt{\boldsymbol{p}'^2}j_0$ and $-\sqrt{\boldsymbol{p}'^2}j_0$ values of the eigenvalue λ of group-invariant $\boldsymbol{J}\cdot\boldsymbol{p}$. The quantity j_0, being the component of $\boldsymbol{J}$ parallel to $\boldsymbol{p}$, can be represented by

$$\pm j_0 = \frac{\boldsymbol{J}\cdot\boldsymbol{p}}{\sqrt{\boldsymbol{p}^2}}, \qquad (IV.5.12)$$

which can be an integer or half-odd-integer. For the rotation-reflection group, the representation includes both signs of λ. This is equivalent to the reversal of sign of $\boldsymbol{J}\cdot\boldsymbol{p}$ under reflection. Hence λ is a pseudoscalar.

IV.5.A. Problems

1. Let $\psi(1, 2)$ be a function of the coordinates of two particles, where the numbers of 1 and 2 are used to label the coordinates $x_i^{(1)}$ and $x_i^{(2)}$ of the particles with $i = 1, 2, 3$. We define a parity operator $\mathcal{P}$ by its operator properties:

$$\mathcal{P}\psi(1, 2) = \psi(2, 1), \tag{IV.5.13}$$

$$\mathcal{P}[a\psi + b\phi] = a\mathcal{P}\psi + b\mathcal{P}\phi. \tag{IV.5.14}$$

Prove that the linear operator $\mathcal{P}$ is a member of the orthogonal group.

2. Show that in spherical polar coordinates, reflection of coordinates corresponds to the transformations

$$\theta' = \pi - \theta, \qquad \phi' = \phi + \pi.$$

3. If the function $\psi(1, 2)$ is a solution of a differential equation of the form

$$(\nabla_1^2 + \nabla_2^2)\psi(1, 2) + \lambda^2 V(1, 2)\psi(1, 2) = \mu E\psi,$$

satisfying the boundary conditions

$$\psi(\pm\infty, 2) = \psi(1, \pm\infty) = 0,$$

then show that $\mathcal{P}\psi$ is also a solution and that it is a constant multiple of ψ

$$\mathcal{P}\psi = a\psi.$$

Hence prove that

$$a^2 = 1, \qquad a = \pm 1,$$

so

$$\mathcal{P}\psi = \pm\psi, \tag{IV.5.15}$$

where

$$V(1, 2) = V(2, 1).$$

In particular, if we choose the origin of the coordinates at the location of one of the particles, we have

$$\mathcal{P}\phi(x_1, x_2, x_3) = \phi(-x_1, -x_2, -x_3),$$

so

$$\phi(x_1, x_2, x_3) = \pm\phi(-x_1, -x_2, -x_3).$$

4. Let the linear operator $\mathcal{P}_A$ have the effect of producing the value of a function $\psi(1)$ at another point $1'$, the points 1 and $1'$ being related by an orthogonal transformation,

$$|x'\rangle = A|x\rangle.$$

Thus

$$\mathcal{P}_A\psi(1') = \psi(1), \tag{IV.5.16}$$

where the dimensionality of the space is not in any way restricted.

Prove that for two linear operators $\mathcal{P}_A$ and $\mathcal{P}_B$ we have

$$\mathcal{P}_A\mathcal{P}_B = \mathcal{P}_{AB},$$

where A and B are orthogonal transformation operators and

$$|x'\rangle = A|x\rangle,$$
$$|x''\rangle = B|x'\rangle,$$
$$\mathcal{P}_A\mathcal{P}_B\psi(1'') = \mathcal{P}_B\psi(1') = \psi(1),$$

and

$$\mathcal{P}_{AB}\psi(1'') = \psi(1).$$

For an arbitrary function ψ, it follows that

$$\mathcal{P}_{AB} = \mathcal{P}_A\mathcal{P}_B.$$

Thus the group $\mathcal{P}_A$ is isomorphic to the group of A.

5. Consider an eigenvalue equation of the form

$$H\psi_i = E\psi_i, \tag{IV.5.17}$$

where $i = 1, 2, \cdots, l$, so there are l linearly independent eigenfunctions corresponding to an eigenvalue E, and where

$$H = -\frac{\hbar^2}{2m}\nabla^2 + V(r),$$

$$r = (x_1^2 + x_2^2 + x_3^2)^{1/2}.$$

We can regard ψ_i as the components of a "vector" in l-dimensional space and define $\mathcal{P}_A\psi_i$ by

$$\mathcal{P}_A\psi_i = \sum_{j=1}^{l} D(A)_{ji}\psi_j. \tag{IV.5.18}$$

By considering the operations $\mathcal{P}_A$ and $\mathcal{P}_B$, show that the l dimensional matrices $D(A)$ and $D(B)$ satisfy

$$D(AB)_{ij} = \sum_{l=1}^{l} D(A)_{il}D(B)_{lj}, \tag{IV.5.19}$$

and prove that the matrices $D(A)$ form a representation of the group under which the eigenvalue equation (*IV.5.17*) remains invariant.

6. If $A(\alpha\beta\gamma)$ is any rotation matrix, show that the corresponding irreducible representation of the three-dimensional orthogonal group is $(2l + 1)$-dimensional and that

$$\mathcal{P}_A(\alpha\beta\gamma)r^lY_{lm}(\theta, \phi) = \sum_{m'=-l}^{l} D^{(l)}(\alpha\beta\gamma)_{m'm}r^lY_{lm'}(\theta, \phi).$$

7. Prove that under $\mathcal{P}$ operation the functions $Y_{lm}(\theta, \phi)$ transform according to

$$\mathcal{P}Y_{lm}(\theta, \phi) = Y_{lm}(\pi - \theta, \pi + \phi) = (-1)^lY_{lm}(\theta, \phi). \tag{IV.5.20}$$

CHAPTER V

TRANSFORMATION THEORY AND THE EQUATIONS OF MOTION

V.1. Measurement of Position and Momentum

The uncertainty relations impose certain restrictions on the measurements of position and momentum. A sharp localization of an electron cannot be achieved without a very large spread in its momentum, which can also mean a high momentum for the electron, on the average. For this reason it takes large energies to localize an electron. This fact is represented in terms of wave packets. The wave packet representing a localization of the electron will eventually decay because of the indefiniteness of the momentum, and therefore any initial localization will be destroyed.

Position and momentum can be represented by linear Hermitian operators in infinitely continuous spaces and each operator by itself can form a complete commuting set of observables. The latter assumption is, of course, based on the measurabilities of position and momentum. In principle, the position or momentum of a dynamical system, by observing it, can be made to assume any value, since space and time is a continuum.

If we represent the position in one dimensional continuum by an operator q, then its value x at a time t corresponding to an eigenstate $|x, t\rangle$ is to be calculated from the eigenvalue equation

$$q|x, t\rangle = x|x, t\rangle. \qquad (V.1.1)$$

A similar eigenvalue equation holds for the momentum operator p:

$$p|p, t\rangle = p|p, t\rangle. \qquad (V.1.2)$$

If x is the position of the particle at time t and if we do not carry out a second measurement on it, then its position at a later time t' is the "same" as in the first measurement. Its state at time t' can be obtained from its state at time t by a "rotation in time"—that is, by a unitary transformation

$$|x, t'\rangle = U(t't)|x, t\rangle, \tag{V.1.3}$$

where the unitary operator $U(t't)$, by analogy with the definition of an orthogonal operator [like (*I.4.1*)], can be defined by

$$U(t't) = \int_{-\infty}^{\infty} |x, t'\rangle\, dx\, \langle x, t| \tag{V.1.4}$$

provided it fulfills the unitarity condition

$$U^\dagger U = UU^\dagger = I. \tag{V.1.5}$$

Thus

$$U^\dagger U = \int |x, t\rangle\, dx\, \langle x, t'|x', t'\rangle\, dx'\, \langle x', t|$$

will yield (*V.1.5*) only if the state vectors $|x, t\rangle$ are normalized according to

$$\langle x, t|x', t\rangle = \delta(x - x'), \tag{V.1.6}$$

in which case we have

$$U^\dagger U = \int |x, t\rangle\, dx\, \delta(x - x')\, dx'\, \langle x', t|$$

$$= \int |x, t\rangle\, dx\, \langle x, t| = 1, \tag{V.1.7}$$

where the last integral is the unit operator of the continuously infinite-dimensional space spanned by the vectors $|x, t\rangle$.

In deriving the above results we have used some important properties of unitary transformations.

(a) *Under a unitary transformation the eigenvalue spectrum (discrete or continuous) of a dynamical variable does not change.*

(b) *A unitary transformation transforms real linear operators into real linear operators and it leaves unchanged any algebraic equation between linear operators.*

Let α represent a complete commuting set of linear Hermitian operators and $|\alpha'\rangle$ an eigenstate belonging to the eigenvalues α':

$$\alpha|\alpha'\rangle = \alpha'|\alpha'\rangle.$$

Applying a unitary transformation

$$U\alpha|\alpha'\rangle = \alpha' U|\alpha'\rangle$$

or

$$U\alpha U^\dagger\, U|\alpha'\rangle = \alpha' U|\alpha'\rangle,$$

we obtain

$$\alpha_u|\alpha_u'\rangle = \alpha'|\alpha_u'\rangle,$$

where

$$\alpha_u = U\alpha U^\dagger \tag{V.1.8}$$

and

$$|\alpha'_u\rangle = U|\alpha'\rangle. \tag{V.1.9}$$

Thus the rotated state vector $|\alpha'_u\rangle$ is also an eigenstate of α belonging to the same eigenvalue α'.

If p is the momentum of the particle at time t and if we do not carry out a second measurement on it, then its momentum at a later time t' is the "same" as in the first measurement. The two states $|p, t\rangle$ and $|p, t'\rangle$ are related by a unitary transformation of the same type as (*V.1.4*):

$$U(t't) = \int_{-\infty}^{\infty} |p, t'\rangle \, dp \, \langle p, t|. \tag{V.1.10}$$

As before, the unitarity condition requires the normalization of the momentum eigenstate $|p, t\rangle$ by

$$\langle p, t|p', t\rangle = \delta(p - p'). \tag{V.1.11}$$

The normalization rules (*V.1.6*) and (*V.1.7*) show clearly that eigenvectors $|x, t\rangle$ and $|p, t\rangle$ are of infinite length.

The unitary operators defined by (*V.1.4*) and (*V.1.10*) can be related. First we note the following facts.

(a) They differ in the labeling of the eigenvectors and they span different spaces. In both cases an integration over a continuous domain is performed, from $-\infty$ to ∞.

(b) Both $|x, t\rangle$ and $|p', t\rangle$ form by themselves complete sets in continuously infinite-dimensional spaces.

A connection between the two unitary operators (*V.1.4*) and (*V.1.10*) can be established by means of a certain relationship between the eigenstates of position and the momentum operators. We multiply the Hermitian conjugate of the unitary operator (*V.1.4*) with the unitary operator (*V.1.10*), and impose the unitarity condition (*V.1.5*) to obtain

$$\iint |x, t\rangle \, dx \, \langle x, t'|p, t'\rangle \, dp \, \langle p, t| = I, \tag{V.1.12}$$

where the function $\langle x, t'|p, t'\rangle$ is called a "transformation function" from position to momentum space.

Requirement (*V.1.12*), relating the two unitary operators, can be fulfilled provided the integration over x or over p leads to $|p, t\rangle$ or to $\langle x, t|$, respectively. In the latter case we obtain a unit operator. The part that refers to p integration in (*V.1.12*) is

$$\int \langle x, t'|p, t'\rangle \, dp \, \langle p, t|,$$

which must be equal to $\langle x, t|$ in order to get the required unit operator. Thus we write

$$\int_{-\infty}^{\infty} \langle x, t'|p, t'\rangle \, dp \, \langle p, t| = \langle x, t|. \qquad (V.1.13)$$

From the theory of Fourier integral transformation it follows that the transformation function must be given by

$$\langle x, t'|p, t'\rangle = ae^{ikx}, \qquad (V.1.14)$$

where a is a constant to be defined. The Fourier transform of $\langle x, t|$ is given by

$$\langle x, t| = \frac{1}{2\pi} \int e^{ikx} \langle k, t| \, dk, \qquad (V.1.15)$$

where $\langle k, t|$ is the bra vector in k space corresponding to the vector $|x, t\rangle$ in q space. We shall assume that the momentum p and the wave number k are related by the de Broglie relation

$$p = \hbar k.$$

The constant a will be determined from the commutation relation

$$qp - pq = i\hbar$$

by taking its representation in the $|x, t\rangle$ coordinate system. Hence, suppressing the label t in $|x, t\rangle$, we have

$$\langle x|(qp - pq)|x'\rangle = i\hbar\delta(x - x').$$

Using the eigenvalue equation ($V.1.1$) we obtain

$$(x - x')\langle x|p|x'\rangle = i\hbar\delta(x - x')$$

or, inserting the unit operator $\int |p\rangle \, dp \, \langle p|$ on the left side, we get

$$(x - x') \int \langle x|p\rangle \, dp \, \langle p|p|x'\rangle = i\hbar\delta(x - x').$$

Hence, from ($V.1.14$) we have

$$|a|^2(x - x') \int pe^{(i/\hbar)p(x-x')} \, dp = i\hbar\delta(x - x')$$

or

$$|a|^2(x - x') \frac{\hbar}{i} \frac{\partial}{\partial x} \int e^{(i/\hbar)p(x-x')} \, dp = i\hbar\delta(x - x').$$

From the definition of the δ function,

$$\delta(x - x') = \frac{1}{2\pi} \int e^{ik(x-x')} \, dk,$$

the last relation reduces to

$$2\pi|a|^2\hbar(x - x') \frac{\partial}{\partial x} \delta(x - x') = -\delta(x - x').$$

The left side can be written as

$$2\pi|a|^2\hbar(x - x')\frac{\partial}{\partial x}\delta(x - x') = |a|^2 2\pi\hbar\frac{\partial}{\partial x}[(x - x')\delta(x - x')]$$
$$- |a|^2 2\pi\hbar\delta(x - x')\frac{\partial}{\partial x}(x - x'),$$

where $(x - x')\delta(x - x') = 0$ and we have

$$-2\pi\hbar|a|^2\delta(x - x') = -\delta(x - x').$$

Hence the equality can only hold if we choose $|a|^2 = 1/h$. For a special choice of phase the constant a is given by $a = h^{-1/2}$. The Fourier transformation function (*V.1.14*) is, therefore, obtained as

$$\langle x, t|p, t\rangle = \frac{1}{\sqrt{h}}e^{(i/\hbar)xp}. \qquad (V.1.16)$$

The quantity

$$|\langle xt|pt\rangle|^2\,dx = \frac{1}{h}\,dx \qquad (V.1.17)$$

is proportional to the probability of x having a value in the range $x, x + dx$ for the state for which p certainly has the value p. So if p certainly has a definite value p, then all values of x are equally probable. This argument can be reversed for p and q. In the latter situation we use the expression

$$|\langle xt|pt\rangle|^2\,dp = \frac{1}{h}\,dp \qquad (V.1.18)$$

as the quantity proportional to the probability of p having a value in the range $p, p + dp$ for the state for which q certainly has the value x.

The above results can easily be extended to three-dimensional representations. In this case the relevant unitary operator is

$$U = \int |\boldsymbol{r}, t'\rangle\,d^3x\,\langle\boldsymbol{r}, t|, \qquad (V.1.19)$$

where $d^3x = dx_1dx_2dx_3$ is the volume element and

$$|\boldsymbol{r}, t\rangle = |x_1, t\rangle|x_2, t\rangle|x_3, t\rangle. \qquad (V.1.20)$$

The three-dimensional transformation function is then given by

$$\langle\boldsymbol{r}, t|\boldsymbol{p}, t\rangle = h^{-3/2}e^{(i/\hbar)\boldsymbol{r}\cdot\boldsymbol{p}}. \qquad (V.1.21)$$

In the same way we may write the four-dimensional transformation function,

$$\langle x_\mu, \tau|p_\mu, \tau\rangle = \frac{1}{h^2}e^{(i/\hbar)x^\mu p_\mu}, \qquad (V.1.22)$$

where τ is proper time or any other parameter. The eigenvectors $|\boldsymbol{r}, t\rangle$, $|\boldsymbol{p}, t\rangle$, $|x_\mu, \tau\rangle$, $|p_\mu, \tau\rangle$ are normalized according to

$$\langle\boldsymbol{r}, t|\boldsymbol{r}', t\rangle = \delta(\boldsymbol{r} - \boldsymbol{r}'),$$
$$\langle\boldsymbol{p}, t|\boldsymbol{p}', t\rangle = \delta(\boldsymbol{p} - \boldsymbol{p}'),$$
$$\langle x_\mu, \tau|x_\mu', \tau\rangle = \delta(x_\mu - x_\mu'),$$

where the δ functions on the right are three- and four-dimensional δ functions, respectively.

V.1.A. The Schrödinger Representation

The state of a dynamical system is represented by a vector $|\boldsymbol{\Psi}\rangle$. A complete definition of this vector requires the use of a certain quantum mechanical coördinate system—for example a Hilbert space or a space spanned by the eigenvectors of the position or momentum operators. The components of $|\boldsymbol{\Psi}\rangle$ in the q representation, as defined in previous sections, are just the scalar products of $|\boldsymbol{\Psi}\rangle$ with the eigenvectors $|\boldsymbol{r}, t\rangle$ of the $\boldsymbol{q}$ representation; that is,

$$\langle \boldsymbol{r}, t|\boldsymbol{\Psi}\rangle = \psi(\boldsymbol{r}, t), \qquad (V.1.23)$$

where $\psi(\boldsymbol{r}, t)$ is an ordinary function of space and time. The scalar product of two state vectors $|\boldsymbol{\Psi}\rangle$ and $|\boldsymbol{\Phi}\rangle$ is

$$\langle \boldsymbol{\Phi}|\boldsymbol{\Psi}\rangle = \int \langle \boldsymbol{\Phi}|\boldsymbol{r}, t\rangle\, d^3x\, \langle \boldsymbol{r}, t|\boldsymbol{\Psi}\rangle = \int \phi^*(\boldsymbol{r}, t)\psi(\boldsymbol{r}, t)\, d^3x, \qquad (V.1.24)$$

where $\phi^*(\boldsymbol{r}, t)$ is the complex conjugate of the function $\langle \boldsymbol{r}, t|\boldsymbol{\Phi}\rangle$.

The momentum operator $\boldsymbol{p}$ in the $\boldsymbol{q}$ representation is

$$\begin{aligned}\langle \boldsymbol{r}, t|\boldsymbol{p}|\boldsymbol{r}', t\rangle &= \int \langle \boldsymbol{r}, t|\boldsymbol{p}|\boldsymbol{p}, t\rangle\, d^3\boldsymbol{p}\, \langle \boldsymbol{p}, t|\boldsymbol{r}', t\rangle \\ &= \frac{1}{h^3}\int \boldsymbol{p}e^{(i/\hbar)(\boldsymbol{r}-\boldsymbol{r}')\cdot\boldsymbol{p}}\, d^3\boldsymbol{p} \\ &= \frac{\hbar}{i}\frac{1}{h^3}\boldsymbol{\nabla}\int e^{(i/\hbar)(\boldsymbol{r}-\boldsymbol{r}')\cdot\boldsymbol{p}}\, d^3\boldsymbol{p} \\ &= \frac{\hbar}{i}\boldsymbol{\nabla}[\delta(\boldsymbol{r}-\boldsymbol{r}')],\end{aligned} \qquad (V.1.25)$$

where we use the formula

$$\delta(\boldsymbol{r}-\boldsymbol{r}') = \left(\frac{1}{2\pi}\right)^3 \int e^{(i/\hbar)(\boldsymbol{r}-\boldsymbol{r}')\cdot\boldsymbol{p}}\, d^3\boldsymbol{k}, \qquad (V.1.26)$$

with $\boldsymbol{p} = \hbar\boldsymbol{k}$.

The momentum operator $\boldsymbol{p}$ can operate on a vector $|\boldsymbol{\Psi}\rangle$ to produce another vector $\boldsymbol{p}|\boldsymbol{\Psi}\rangle$. The vector $\boldsymbol{p}|\boldsymbol{\Psi}\rangle$ can be represented by

$$\begin{aligned}\langle \boldsymbol{r}, t|\boldsymbol{p}|\boldsymbol{\Psi}\rangle &= \int \langle \boldsymbol{r}, t|\boldsymbol{p}|\boldsymbol{r}', t\rangle\, d^3x'\, \langle \boldsymbol{r}', t|\boldsymbol{\Psi}\rangle \\ &= \frac{\hbar}{i}\int \boldsymbol{\nabla}[\delta(\boldsymbol{r}-\boldsymbol{r}')]\, d^3x'\, \psi(\boldsymbol{r}', t),\end{aligned}$$

where the gradient operator $\boldsymbol{\nabla}$ is defined with respect to the coordinate $\boldsymbol{r}$, so

$$\langle \boldsymbol{r}, t|\boldsymbol{p}|\boldsymbol{\Psi}\rangle = \frac{\hbar}{i}\boldsymbol{\nabla}\psi(\boldsymbol{r}, t). \qquad (V.1.27)$$

Hence the action of the momentum operator $\boldsymbol{p}$ on a vector $|\Psi\rangle$ is the same as the gradient of the representative $\psi(\boldsymbol{r}, t)$ of $|\Psi\rangle$. This is called the "Schrödinger representation" and its operator form is

$$\boldsymbol{p} = \frac{\hbar}{i}\frac{\partial}{\partial \boldsymbol{q}}, \qquad (V.1.28)$$

where the components q_1, q_2, q_3 of $\boldsymbol{q}$ in three-dimensional Cartesian space are position operators. The operator $\boldsymbol{p}$ operates according to

$$\boldsymbol{p}|\boldsymbol{r}, t\rangle = \frac{\hbar}{i}\frac{\partial}{\partial \boldsymbol{q}}|\boldsymbol{r}, t\rangle = \frac{\hbar}{i}\frac{\partial}{\partial \boldsymbol{r}}|\boldsymbol{r}, t\rangle. \qquad (V.1.29)$$

V.1.B. Momentum Representation

In place of $\boldsymbol{q}$ representation we may use $\boldsymbol{p}$ representation and define another important representation in quantum mechanics. The representation of an arbitrary state vector $|\Psi\rangle$, as in the previous case, is completely defined by taking its scalar product with the eigenvectors of $\boldsymbol{p}$ representation. Thus

$$\langle \boldsymbol{p}, t|\Psi\rangle = \phi(\boldsymbol{p}, t), \qquad (V.1.30)$$

as an ordinary function of momenta and time, is defined as the components (or representation for various values of $\boldsymbol{p}$) of the vector $|\Psi\rangle$ in $\boldsymbol{p}$ representation. The scalar product of two state vectors $|\Psi\rangle$ and $|\Phi\rangle$ in $\boldsymbol{p}$ representation is defined by

$$\langle \Phi|\Psi\rangle = \int \langle \Phi|\boldsymbol{p}, t\rangle\, d^3\boldsymbol{p}\, \langle \boldsymbol{p}, t|\Psi\rangle = \int f^*(\boldsymbol{p}, t)\phi(\boldsymbol{p}, t)\, d^3\boldsymbol{p}, \qquad (V.1.31)$$

where $f^*(\boldsymbol{p}, t) = \langle \Phi|\boldsymbol{p}, t\rangle$.

The vectors $|\Psi\rangle$ and $|\Phi\rangle$ are the same state vectors we used in both $\boldsymbol{q}$ and $\boldsymbol{p}$ representations, so the scalar products ($V.1.24$) and ($V.1.31$) are equal. We note that the functions $\psi(\boldsymbol{r}, t)$ and $\phi(\boldsymbol{p}, t)$ are related by

$$\langle \boldsymbol{r}, t|\Psi\rangle = \int \langle \boldsymbol{r}, t|\boldsymbol{p}, t\rangle\, d^3\boldsymbol{p}\, \langle \boldsymbol{p}, t|\Psi\rangle$$

or

$$\psi(\boldsymbol{r}, t) = (2\pi\hbar)^{-3/2} \int e^{(i/\hbar)\boldsymbol{r}\cdot\boldsymbol{p}}\phi(\boldsymbol{p}, t)\, d^3\boldsymbol{p}. \qquad (V.1.32)$$

The last result shows that the components (or representatives) of a state vector $|\Psi\rangle$ with respect to $\boldsymbol{q}$ and $\boldsymbol{p}$ representations are related by a Fourier integral transformation. This means that the transformation function $\exp[(i/\hbar)\boldsymbol{r}\cdot\boldsymbol{p}]$ for various values of $\boldsymbol{p}$ provides a complete set for the expansion of $\psi(\boldsymbol{r}, t)$.

The position operator $\boldsymbol{q}$ in momentum representation is represented by

$$\begin{aligned}\langle \boldsymbol{p}, t|\boldsymbol{q}|\boldsymbol{p}', t\rangle &= \int \langle \boldsymbol{p}, t|\boldsymbol{q}|\boldsymbol{r}, t\rangle\, d^3x\, \langle \boldsymbol{r}, t|\boldsymbol{p}', t\rangle \\ &= \frac{1}{h^3}\int \boldsymbol{r} e^{-(i/\hbar)(\boldsymbol{p}-\boldsymbol{p}')\cdot\boldsymbol{r}}\, d^3x \\ &= -\frac{\hbar}{i}\frac{1}{h^3}\frac{\partial}{\partial \boldsymbol{p}}\int e^{(i/\hbar)(\boldsymbol{p}-\boldsymbol{p}')\cdot\boldsymbol{r}}\, d^3x \\ &= -\frac{\hbar}{i}\frac{\partial}{\partial \boldsymbol{p}}[\delta(\boldsymbol{p}-\boldsymbol{p}')].\end{aligned} \tag{V.1.33}$$

The position operator $\boldsymbol{q}$ can operate on a vector $|\boldsymbol{\Psi}\rangle$ to produce another vector $\boldsymbol{q}|\boldsymbol{\Psi}\rangle$. The vector $\boldsymbol{q}|\boldsymbol{\Psi}\rangle$ can be represented by

$$\begin{aligned}\langle \boldsymbol{p}, t|\boldsymbol{q}|\boldsymbol{\Psi}\rangle &= \int \langle \boldsymbol{p}, t|\boldsymbol{q}|\boldsymbol{p}', t\rangle\, d^3\boldsymbol{p}'\, \langle \boldsymbol{p}', t|\boldsymbol{\Psi}\rangle \\ &= -\frac{\hbar}{i}\int \frac{\partial}{\partial \boldsymbol{p}}[\delta(\boldsymbol{p}-\boldsymbol{p}')]\, d^3\boldsymbol{p}'\, \phi(\boldsymbol{p}', t) \\ &= i\hbar\frac{\partial}{\partial \boldsymbol{p}}\phi(\boldsymbol{p}, t).\end{aligned} \tag{V.1.34}$$

Hence the action of the position operator $\boldsymbol{q}$ on a vector $|\boldsymbol{\Psi}\rangle$ is the same as the momentum gradient of the representative $\phi(\boldsymbol{p}, t)$ of $|\boldsymbol{\Psi}\rangle$. This is called "momentum representation" and its operator form is

$$\boldsymbol{q} = i\hbar\frac{\partial}{\partial \boldsymbol{p}}, \tag{V.1.35}$$

which operates according to

$$\boldsymbol{q}|\boldsymbol{p}, t\rangle = i\hbar\frac{\partial}{\partial \boldsymbol{p}}|\boldsymbol{p}, t\rangle. \tag{V.1.36}$$

Since the position and momentum operators $\boldsymbol{q}$ and $\boldsymbol{p}$ are Hermitian, it follows that the operators $\partial/\partial\boldsymbol{p}$ and $\partial/\partial\boldsymbol{q}$ are anti-Hermitian operators.

It must be noted that in both the Schrödinger and momentum representations the operators $\boldsymbol{q}$ and $\boldsymbol{p}$ are time-independent.

V.2. The Time Development of the State of a Dynamical System

Let us suppose that the state of a dynamical system—that is, any particular motion among all possible ones—at the instant t_0 is represented by a most general type of vector $|\boldsymbol{\Psi}, t_0\rangle$. By analogy with (*I.6.7*) we may operate by the unitary operator (*V.1.4*) on the state $|\boldsymbol{\Psi}, t_0\rangle$ and obtain the state at another time t by

$$|\boldsymbol{\Psi}, t\rangle = U(tt_0)|\boldsymbol{\Psi}, t_0\rangle = \int |\boldsymbol{r}, t\rangle\, d^3\boldsymbol{r}\, \langle \boldsymbol{r}, t_0|\boldsymbol{\Psi}, t_0\rangle. \tag{V.2.1}$$

From the unitarity of U, as in (*I.6.2*), it follows that the position eigenstate $|\boldsymbol{r}, t\rangle$ and the unitary operator U satisfy equations of the form

$$i\frac{dU}{dt} = SU, \tag{V.2.2}$$

$$i\frac{d}{dt}|\boldsymbol{r}, t\rangle = S|\boldsymbol{r}, t\rangle, \tag{V.2.3}$$

where S is a more general Hermitian operator than the one used in (*I.6.2*). In this case S is the generator of "rotations" *in infinite-dimensional unitary space*. By differentiating (*V.2.1*) with respect to time and using (*V.2.2*) we get

$$i\frac{d}{dt}|\boldsymbol{\Psi}, t\rangle = S|\boldsymbol{\Psi}, t\rangle, \tag{V.2.4}$$

where the Hermitian operator S has the dimensions of an angular frequency. A very general and also a formal derivation of the fundamental equation of quantum mechanics, the Schrödinger equation, can be based on the following statements.

(a) We use Planck's formula $E = h\nu$ relating the energy and frequency of a wave or "particle oscillator" and heuristically identify (by analogy with the procedure of Chapter II) the frequency operator S by

$$S = \frac{1}{\hbar}H, \tag{V.2.5}$$

where H is an energy operator (see Section V.3).

(b) The Hermitian operator H is a function of the operators $\boldsymbol{q}$ and $\boldsymbol{p}$, so in Schrödinger's representation it is of the form $H(\boldsymbol{p}, \boldsymbol{q}, t) \equiv H[(\hbar/i)\boldsymbol{\nabla}, \boldsymbol{r}, t]$. The operator H, by analogy with classical mechanics, is called the Hamiltonian operator of the dynamical system. In most cases of practical interest it is to be obtained from the classical Hamiltonian by replacing coordinates and momenta by their operator forms in the Schrödinger representation—that is, the commutation relations between the $\boldsymbol{q}$ and the $\boldsymbol{p}$).

Under the above assumptions the time development of a state vector $|\boldsymbol{\Psi}, t\rangle$ in the Schrödinger representation is given by a linear equation,

$$i\hbar\frac{d}{dt}|\boldsymbol{\Psi}, t\rangle = H|\boldsymbol{\Psi}, t\rangle. \tag{V.2.6}$$

The more usual form of this equation is given in terms of the components or representatives of the state vector $|\boldsymbol{\Psi}, t\rangle$. This is obtained by multiplying on the left by the bra vector $\langle\boldsymbol{r}, t_0|$, as

$$i\hbar\frac{\partial}{\partial t}\psi(\boldsymbol{r}, t) = H\psi(\boldsymbol{r}, t), \tag{V.2.7}$$

where the operator H is now a function of $(\hbar/i)(\partial/\partial\mathbf{r})$ and of $\mathbf{r}$, and it is obtained from $H(\boldsymbol{q}, \boldsymbol{p})$ by

$$\begin{aligned}
\langle \mathbf{r}, t_0|H(\boldsymbol{q}, \boldsymbol{p}) &= \int \langle \mathbf{r}, t_0|H|\mathbf{r}', t_0\rangle\, d^3x'\, \langle \mathbf{r}', t_0| \\
&= \int \langle \mathbf{r}, t_0|H\left(\mathbf{r}', \frac{\hbar}{i}\frac{\partial}{\partial \mathbf{r}'}\right)|\mathbf{r}', t_0\rangle\, d^3x'\, \langle \mathbf{r}', t_0| \\
&= \int H\left(\mathbf{r}', \frac{\hbar}{i}\frac{\partial}{\partial \mathbf{r}'}\right)\langle \mathbf{r}, t_0|\mathbf{r}', t_0\rangle\, d^3x'\, \langle \mathbf{r}', t_0| \\
&= \int H\left(\mathbf{r}', \frac{\hbar}{i}\frac{\partial}{\partial \mathbf{r}'}\right)\delta(\mathbf{r} - \mathbf{r}')\, d^3x'\, \langle \mathbf{r}', t_0|.
\end{aligned}$$

Hence

$$\langle \mathbf{r}, t_0|H(\boldsymbol{q}, \boldsymbol{p}) = H\left(\mathbf{r}, \frac{\hbar}{i}\frac{\partial}{\partial \mathbf{r}}\right)\langle \mathbf{r}, t_0|.$$

Equation (*V.2.7*) is Schrödinger's wave equation. The above "derivation" is of formal significance only, since no specific assumptions about the state $|\boldsymbol{\Psi}, t\rangle$ were made; only the analogy with the concept of rotation has been used. The introduction of Planck's hypothesis was also quite ad hoc, since its use was not initiated by deeper physical motivations.

A physical formulation of quantum mechanics must be based on Planck's original motivation for introducing the constant $\hbar$ and also on de Broglie's postulate of wave and particle duality of matter. One such formulation of quantum mechanics actually comes from a reinterpretation of the electromagnetic field (as in Chapter II).

The unitary operator $U(t, t_0)$, which transforms a state $|\boldsymbol{\Psi}, t_0\rangle$ at time t_0 to another state $|\boldsymbol{\Psi}, t\rangle$ at time t satisfies the equation

$$i\hbar\frac{dU}{dt} = HU. \qquad (V.2.8)$$

Both equations (*V.2.6*) and (*V.2.8*), as in (*I.7.3*), can be cast as integral equations,

$$|\boldsymbol{\Psi}, t\rangle = |\boldsymbol{\Psi}, t_0\rangle - \frac{i}{\hbar}\int_{t_0}^{t} \epsilon_+(t, t_1)H(t_1)|\boldsymbol{\Psi}, t_1\rangle\, dt_1 \qquad (V.2.9)$$

and

$$U(tt_0) = I - \frac{i}{\hbar}\int_{t_0}^{t} \epsilon_+(t, t_1)H(t)U(t_1t_0)\, dt_1, \qquad (V.2.10)$$

where the function $\epsilon_+(t, t_1)$ is defined by (*I.7.2*), and where we used the boundary condition

$$U(t_0t_0) = I. \qquad (V.2.11)$$

V.2.A. Interpretation of States and Dynamical Variables in Schrödinger's Equation

Schrödinger's equation gives the time evolution of the state vector $|\boldsymbol{\Psi}, t\rangle$ of a dynamical system. The state vector itself is not an observable. The two basic observables of Schrödinger's equation are Planck's constant h and the Hamiltonian H of the system. The role of $|\boldsymbol{\Psi}, t\rangle$ or its representative $\langle \boldsymbol{r}, t|\boldsymbol{\Psi}, t\rangle = \psi(\boldsymbol{r}, t)$ in the interpretation of quantum mechanics is of the greatest importance. Quantum mechanics postulates a statistical background for the laws of physics.

Statistical concepts were already used in classical physics. The kinetic theory of gases, thermodynamics, and Brownian motion are among the best examples in classical physics of theories that have used statistical concepts in their descriptions. Brownian motion, as treated by Einstein, demonstrates that the molecular motion and its statistical character can be made visible. For example, the movement of the suspended particles in Brownian motion can be regarded as a process of diffusion under the action of osmotic pressure and viscosity of the liquid. According to Einstein's theory of Brownian motion, the actual velocity of the suspended particle, produced by the impacts of the molecules of the liquid on it, is unobservable. What one observes in a finite time interval Δt are random displacements of the particles. The probability of these random displacements is calculated from a diffusion equation.*

Another example of classical probability physics is the statistical mechanics of Maxwell, Boltzmann, Gibbs, and of others. Statistical mechanics deals, in general, with the statistical behavior of a virtual assembly of equal mechanical systems. A state of the single system among the large number of systems is described by a set of generalized coordinates and momenta which can be depicted as a point in $2n$-dimensional "phase space." The energy is assumed to be a function of these variables. In this theory also one introduces a distribution function satisfying Liouville's equation,

$$\frac{df}{dt} = 0. \qquad (V.2.12)$$

In deriving this equation it is assumed that the distribution function f is a function of coordinates and momenta and that each system of the assembly obeys Hamilton's equations of motion (*I.1.4*). For example, a one-particle distribution function f as a function of 3-momenta and 3-coordinates is used to interpret the quantity $f\, d^3x\, d^3\boldsymbol{p}$ as the probability of finding a particle in

---

* This example shows clearly that in classical probability description of physical laws the probability itself obeys a differential equation.

the volume element d^3x, with momenta around $\boldsymbol{p}$ in the momentum volume element $d^3\boldsymbol{p}$. In this way one is enabled to define regions of "equal weight" and apply the laws of probability.*

From the above discussion it is clear that Schrödinger's equation is not of the type of a diffusion equation or Liouville's equation, where one can calculate probabilities directly. A probability is a nonnegative number. Such a number, resembling f in (*V.2.12*) but by no means the same as f, can be obtained from (*V.2.6*). The complex conjugate state $\langle \boldsymbol{\Psi}, t|$ satisfies, as follows from (*V.2.6*), the equation

$$-i\hbar \frac{d}{dt} \langle \boldsymbol{\Psi}, t| = \langle \boldsymbol{\Psi}, t|H. \tag{V.2.13}$$

By using (*V.2.6*) together with (*V.2.13*) we easily derive the equation

$$\frac{dP}{dt} = 0 \tag{V.2.14}$$

for the conservation of the probability

$$\begin{aligned} P = \langle \boldsymbol{\Psi}, t|\boldsymbol{\Psi}, t\rangle &= \int \langle \boldsymbol{\Psi}, t|\boldsymbol{r}, t\rangle \, d^3\boldsymbol{r} \, \langle \boldsymbol{r}, t|\boldsymbol{\Psi}, t\rangle \\ &= \int \psi^*(\boldsymbol{r}, t)\psi(\boldsymbol{r}, t) \, d^3\boldsymbol{r}. \end{aligned} \tag{V.2.15}$$

For the maximum probability of 1 we shall assume that the wave function $\psi(\boldsymbol{r}, t)$ is normalized, and we shall write (*V.2.15*) in the form

$$P = \int |\psi|^2 \, d^3x = 1. \tag{V.2.16}$$

The wave function ψ is a "probability amplitude" and

$$|\psi|^2 \, d^3x$$

is the probability that a particle (with mass) can be found in a volume element d^3x.

Statements (*V.2.15*) and (*V.2.16*) can also be made in terms of the Fourier transform $\psi(\boldsymbol{p}, t)$ of the wave function $\psi(\boldsymbol{r}, t)$, for

$$\begin{aligned} P = \langle \boldsymbol{\Psi}, t|\boldsymbol{\Psi}, t\rangle &= \int \langle \boldsymbol{\Psi}, t|\boldsymbol{p}, t\rangle \, d^3p \, \langle \boldsymbol{p}, t|\boldsymbol{\Psi}, t\rangle \\ &= \int |\phi(\boldsymbol{p}, t)|^2 \, d^3\boldsymbol{p} = 1. \end{aligned} \tag{V.2.17}$$

The probability that a particle (with or without mass) can be found with momenta around $\boldsymbol{p}$ in the momentum volume element $d^3\boldsymbol{p}$ is

$$|\phi(\boldsymbol{p}, t)|^2 \, d^3\boldsymbol{p}.$$

---

* In quantum mechanics one abandons continuous distribution of "equal statistical weight" in phase space. In the derivation of Planck's distribution law, for instance, it is assumed that only those states whose energies are multiples of $h\nu$ have finite statistical weight.

In general, if α is any observable of a dynamical system, then its average value with respect to a state $|\boldsymbol{\Psi}, t\rangle$ is defined by

$$\begin{aligned}\langle\alpha\rangle &= \langle\boldsymbol{\Psi}, t|\alpha|\boldsymbol{\Psi}, t\rangle \\ &= \int \psi^*(\boldsymbol{r}, t)(\langle\boldsymbol{r}, t|\alpha|\boldsymbol{r}', t\rangle)\psi(\boldsymbol{r}', t)\, d^3x\, d^3x'. \end{aligned} \tag{V.2.18}$$

For example, if α is chosen as the position vector operator $\boldsymbol{q}$, then its average value in the state $|\boldsymbol{\Psi}, t\rangle$ is

$$\begin{aligned}\langle\boldsymbol{q}\rangle &= \int \psi^*(\boldsymbol{r}, t)\boldsymbol{r}'\delta(\boldsymbol{r} - \boldsymbol{r}')\psi(\boldsymbol{r}', t)\, d^3x\, d^3x' \\ &= \int \boldsymbol{r}|\psi(\boldsymbol{r}, t)|^2\, d^3x. \end{aligned} \tag{V.2.19}$$

The average value of an observable is the same in both of the states $|\boldsymbol{\Psi}, t\rangle$ and $e^{i\delta}|\boldsymbol{\Psi}, t\rangle$, where δ is a real number.

The average value of an observable can equivalently be defined also with respect to the momentum-space-wave function $\phi(\boldsymbol{p}, t)$ by

$$\begin{aligned}\langle\alpha\rangle &= \langle\boldsymbol{\Psi}, t|\alpha|\boldsymbol{\Psi}, t\rangle \\ &= \int \phi^*(\boldsymbol{p}, t)(\langle\boldsymbol{p}, t|\alpha|\boldsymbol{p}', t\rangle)\phi(\boldsymbol{p}', t)\, d^3\boldsymbol{p}\, d^3\boldsymbol{p}'. \end{aligned} \tag{V.2.20}$$

In particular, for $\alpha = \boldsymbol{p}$ we obtain the average value of the momentum in a state $|\boldsymbol{\Psi}, t\rangle$ in the form

$$\langle\boldsymbol{p}\rangle = \int \boldsymbol{p}|\phi(\boldsymbol{p}, t)|^2\, d^3\boldsymbol{p}. \tag{V.2.21}$$

The function $\psi(\boldsymbol{r}, t)$, used in the definition of probability and the average value of an observable, must further be qualified with respect to its transformation properties in the sense discussed in Chapter I. Therefore the wave function ψ must be represented in the form ψ_A, where the subscript A refers to scalar, vector, spinor, or some other transformation property of the wave function. For the description of some dynamical systems the function ψ_A can have scalar, vector, and spinor properties simultaneously, where each transformation property refers to a different degree of freedom, such as spin, parity, isotopic spin, and so on. Under these circumstances the probability density $|\psi|^2$ and the average value $\langle\alpha\rangle$ must be defined according to

$$|\psi|^2 = \sum_A \psi_A^* \psi_A \tag{V.2.22}$$

and

$$\langle\alpha\rangle = \sum_{AB} \int \psi_A^*(\boldsymbol{r}, t)(\langle\boldsymbol{r}, t|\alpha_{AB}|\boldsymbol{r}', t\rangle)\psi_B(\boldsymbol{r}', t)\, d^3\boldsymbol{r}\, d^3\boldsymbol{r}', \tag{V.2.23}$$

where we assume that the observable α_{AB} also has the implied transformation properties.

V.2.B. Other Forms of Schrödinger's Equation

Instead of $\boldsymbol{q}$ or $\boldsymbol{p}$ representation we could choose a representation where the Hamiltonian has a diagonal form. We also assume that it is time-independent. Let us suppose that the time-independent Hamiltonian operator, together with a set of operators Γ, forms a complete set of commuting observables with simultaneous eigenstates $|E, \gamma\rangle$, where E is the eigenvalue of H, the energy of the system. For a state $|\boldsymbol{\Psi}, t\rangle$, the wave function of the system is

$$\psi(E, \gamma, t) = \langle E, \gamma|\boldsymbol{\Psi}, t\rangle. \tag{V.2.24}$$

By taking the representative of equation (*V.2.6*) with respect to an eigenstate $|E, \gamma\rangle$, we obtain the Schrödinger equation in the form

$$i\hbar\frac{\partial}{\partial t}\langle E, \gamma|\boldsymbol{\Psi}, t\rangle = \langle E, \gamma|H|\boldsymbol{\Psi}, t\rangle$$

or

$$i\hbar\frac{\partial}{\partial t}\psi(E, \gamma, t) = E\psi(E, \gamma, t). \tag{V.2.25}$$

Equation (*V.2.25*) is solved by

$$\psi(E, \gamma, t) = e^{-(i/\hbar)E(t-t_0)}\psi(E, \gamma, t_0), \tag{V.2.26}$$

where the variables Γ, in practice, are usually chosen as the coordinates of the dynamical system. In the latter case, (*V.2.25*) yields the eigenvalue equation

$$H(\boldsymbol{r}, -i\hbar\boldsymbol{\nabla})\psi(\boldsymbol{r}) = E\psi(\boldsymbol{r}). \tag{V.2.27}$$

Another useful form of the Schrödinger equation can be given in momentum representation. This can be done by projecting (or taking a representative of) equation (*V.2.6*), by multiplying scalarly from the left with the eigenvector $\langle p, t|$ of the momentum operator p. Thus we obtain

$$i\hbar\frac{\partial}{\partial t}\phi(\boldsymbol{p}, t) = \langle \boldsymbol{p}, t|H|\boldsymbol{\Psi}, t\rangle,$$

where

$$\begin{aligned}
&\langle \boldsymbol{p}, t|H|\boldsymbol{\Psi}, t\rangle \\
&\quad = \int \langle \boldsymbol{p}, t|\boldsymbol{r}, t\rangle\, d^3x\, \langle \boldsymbol{r}, t|H|\boldsymbol{r}', t\rangle\, d^3x\, \langle \boldsymbol{r}', t|\boldsymbol{\Psi}, t\rangle \\
&\quad = \frac{1}{h^3}\int e^{(i/\hbar)\boldsymbol{r}\cdot\boldsymbol{p}}\, d^3x\, \delta(\boldsymbol{r} - \boldsymbol{r}')H\left(\boldsymbol{r}', -i\hbar\frac{\partial}{\partial \boldsymbol{r}'}\right) e^{-(i/\hbar)\boldsymbol{r}'\cdot\boldsymbol{p}'}\phi(\boldsymbol{p}', t)\, d^3x'\, d^3\boldsymbol{p}' \\
&\quad = \frac{1}{h^3}\int e^{(i/\hbar)\boldsymbol{r}\cdot\boldsymbol{p}}\, d^3x\, H\left(\boldsymbol{r}, -i\hbar\frac{\partial}{\partial \boldsymbol{r}}\right) e^{-(i/\hbar)\boldsymbol{r}\cdot\boldsymbol{p}'}\phi(\boldsymbol{p}', t)\, d^3\boldsymbol{p}'.
\end{aligned}$$

Hence the Schrödinger equation in momentum representation takes the form

$$i\hbar\frac{\partial}{\partial t}\phi(\boldsymbol{p}, t) = \frac{1}{h^3}\int e^{(i/\hbar)\boldsymbol{r}\cdot\boldsymbol{p}}\, d^3x\, H\left(\boldsymbol{r}, -i\hbar\frac{\partial}{\partial \boldsymbol{r}}\right) e^{-(i/\hbar)\boldsymbol{r}\cdot\boldsymbol{p}'}\phi(\boldsymbol{p}', t)\, d^3\boldsymbol{p}. \tag{V.2.28}$$

For a particle with mass m and potential energy $V(\boldsymbol{r})$ the Hamiltonian is given by

$$H = -\frac{\hbar^2}{2m}\nabla^2 + V(\boldsymbol{r}). \qquad (V.2.29)$$

In this case equation ($V.2.28$) becomes an integral differential equation in momentum space,

$$i\hbar\frac{\partial}{\partial t}\phi(\boldsymbol{p}, t) = \frac{\boldsymbol{p}^2}{2m}\phi(\boldsymbol{p}, t) + \int V(\boldsymbol{p} - \boldsymbol{p}')\phi(\boldsymbol{p}', t)\, d^3\boldsymbol{p}, \qquad (V.2.30)$$

where $V(\boldsymbol{p} - \boldsymbol{p}')$ is the Fourier transform of the potential

$$V(\boldsymbol{p} - \boldsymbol{p}') = \frac{1}{h^3}\int e^{(i/\hbar)\boldsymbol{r}\cdot(\boldsymbol{p}-\boldsymbol{p}')}V(\boldsymbol{r})\, d^3x. \qquad (V.2.31)$$

For a free particle ($V = 0$) the momentum-space-wave function is a solution of the wave equation

$$i\hbar\frac{\partial}{\partial t}\phi(\boldsymbol{p}, t) = \frac{\boldsymbol{p}^2}{2m}\phi(\boldsymbol{p}, t)$$

in the form

$$\phi(\boldsymbol{p}, t) = \phi_0(\boldsymbol{p})e^{-(i/\hbar)(\boldsymbol{p}^2/2m)(t-t_0)}, \qquad (V.2.32)$$

where $\phi_0(\boldsymbol{p})$ is the wave function at time $t = t_0$. The probability that the particle has its momentum in the range $\boldsymbol{p}$, $\boldsymbol{p} + d\boldsymbol{p}$ at time t, or

$$|\phi|^2\, d^3\boldsymbol{p} = |\phi_0|^2\, d^3\boldsymbol{p},$$

is equal to the probability that the particle has the same momentum in the same range at any other time.

By using ($V.1.32$) we can obtain the wave function in the coordinate space

$$\psi(\boldsymbol{r} - \boldsymbol{r}_0, t - t_0) = (h)^{-3/2}\int e^{(i/\hbar)\boldsymbol{p}\cdot(\boldsymbol{r}-\boldsymbol{r}_0)}e^{-(i/\hbar)(\boldsymbol{p}^2/2m)(t-t_0)}\phi_0(\boldsymbol{p})\, d^3\boldsymbol{p}, \qquad (V.2.33)$$

where we chose $\boldsymbol{r}_0$ as the origin of coordinates. A free particle can be described as a superposition of plane waves. From ($V.2.33$) we observe that the contributions to the integral arising from different values of $\boldsymbol{p}$, at the point $\boldsymbol{r} = \boldsymbol{r}_0$, will add up to phase and the resulting wave function (and therefore the probability density $|\psi|^2$) at $\boldsymbol{r} = \boldsymbol{r}_0$ will assume large values. But for $\boldsymbol{r} \neq \boldsymbol{r}_0$, because of the rapid oscillations of $\exp[(i/\hbar)\boldsymbol{r}\cdot\boldsymbol{p}]$, the contributions for large deviations of $\boldsymbol{r}$ from $\boldsymbol{r}_0$ will tend to cancel one another. Therefore the wave function ($V.2.33$) represents a "wave packet," where we assume that ϕ_0 is not a rapidly oscillating function.

The probability density

$$|\psi|^2 = \frac{1}{h^3}\int \exp\left[\frac{i}{\hbar}(\boldsymbol{r} - \boldsymbol{r}_0)\cdot(\boldsymbol{p} - \boldsymbol{p}')\right] \times \exp\left[-\frac{i(t - t_0)}{2m\hbar}(\boldsymbol{p}^2 - \boldsymbol{p}'^2)\right]\phi_0^*(\boldsymbol{p}')\phi_0(\boldsymbol{p})\, d^3\boldsymbol{p}\, d^3\boldsymbol{p}' \qquad (V.2.34)$$

will, for accurate knowledge of the momentum, decrease with time. For example, for a constant initial momentum wave function—that is, $\phi_0(\boldsymbol{p}) = A$, where A is a constant—the integral (*V.2.34*) can easily be performed. We use the formulas

$$\int_{-\infty}^{\infty} e^{-\lambda^2 a - i\lambda u}\, d\lambda = \sqrt{\left(\frac{\pi}{a}\right)}\, e^{-(u^2/4a)} \tag{V.2.35}$$

and

$$\int_{-\infty}^{\infty} e^{-i\lambda^2 a - \lambda u}\, d\lambda = \sqrt{\left(\frac{\pi}{ia}\right)}\, e^{iu^2/4a} \tag{V.2.36}$$

and write the probability density $|\psi|^2$, for $\phi_0 = A$, in the form

$$|\psi|^2 = |A|^2 m^3 \frac{1}{|t - t_0|^3}. \tag{V.2.37}$$

Hence, it is clearly seen that the probability of finding the particle in the volume element d^3x, or

$$|\psi|^2\, d^3x = |A|^2 m^3 \frac{d^3x}{|t - t_0|^3}, \tag{V.2.38}$$

decreases as the inverse cube of time.

V.3. Heisenberg's Equations of Motion and Further Developments of Transformation Theory

A form of quantum mechanics different from that of Schrödinger's but entirely equivalent to it is Heisenberg's formulation of the theory. A comparison of classical and quantum mechanical theories can be made more directly in terms of Heisenberg's formulation. In Heisenberg's representation all linear operators are time-dependent, while state vectors are time-independent.

Consider the position and momentum operators $\boldsymbol{q}_0$ and $\boldsymbol{p}_0$ at a fixed time t_0. In accordance with the rule of unitary transformation we can construct from q_0 and p_0 the position and momentum operators q and p at a later time t by

$$\boldsymbol{q}(t) = U^\dagger \boldsymbol{q}_0 U, \tag{V.3.1}$$

$$\boldsymbol{p}(t) = U^\dagger \boldsymbol{p}_0 U, \tag{V.3.2}$$

where the unitary operator U satisfies Schrödinger's equation (*V.2.8*). From (*V.3.1*) and (*V.3.2*), by differentiation we obtain

$$\begin{aligned} i\hbar \frac{d\boldsymbol{q}}{dt} &= i\hbar \frac{dU^\dagger}{dt} \boldsymbol{q}_0 U + i\hbar U^\dagger \boldsymbol{q}_0 \frac{dU}{dt} \\ &= -U^\dagger H \boldsymbol{q}_0 U + U^\dagger \boldsymbol{q}_0 H U \\ &= -U^\dagger H U U^\dagger \boldsymbol{q}_0 U + U^\dagger \boldsymbol{q} U U^\dagger H U \\ &= -H(t)\boldsymbol{q}(t) + \boldsymbol{q}(t) H(t). \end{aligned}$$

Hence

$$i\hbar \frac{d\boldsymbol{q}}{dt} = [\boldsymbol{q}, H(t)] \qquad (V.3.3)$$

and also

$$i\hbar \frac{d\boldsymbol{p}}{dt} = [\boldsymbol{p}, H(t)], \qquad (V.3.4)$$

where

$$H(t) = U^{\dagger}HU.$$

From (*V.3.3*) and (*V.3.4*) it follows that Heisenberg's equations of motion can also be written as

$$\frac{d\boldsymbol{q}}{dt} = \frac{\partial H(t)}{\partial \boldsymbol{p}} \qquad (V.3.5)$$

and

$$\frac{d\boldsymbol{p}}{dt} = -\frac{\partial H(t)}{\partial \boldsymbol{q}}, \qquad (V.3.6)$$

which are operator equations of motion in quantum mechanics corresponding to Hamilton's equations of motion in classical mechanics. The above formulation of quantum mechanics is also an explicit statement on Bohr's "correspondence principle," which states that quantum description of a dynamical system must, for large quantum numbers or for $\hbar \longrightarrow 0$ or for some other asymptotic limit such as large mass or small wavelength, reduce to the classical description.

Furthermore, equations (*V.3.5*) and (*V.3.6*) constitute a good justification for the relation (*V.2.5*) between the frequency operator S and the Hamiltonian of the system.

From equations (*V.3.3*) and (*V.3.4*) we infer that in general all dynamical variables that remain unchanged during the motion must commute with the Hamiltonian. Conversely, dynamical variables commuting with the Hamiltonian are constants of the motion.

If $\alpha(t)$ is any Heisenberg operator (observable or not), then it will satisfy Heisenberg's equations of motion,

$$i\hbar \frac{d\alpha}{dt} = i\hbar \frac{\partial \alpha}{\partial t} + [\alpha, H], \qquad (V.3.7)$$

where $\partial/\partial t$ refers to explicit time-dependence of α. Also, if $|\boldsymbol{\Psi}, t_0\rangle$ is a fixed Heisenberg state vector, then it is related to a Schrödinger state vector $|\boldsymbol{\Psi}, t\rangle$ by

$$|\boldsymbol{\Psi}, t_0\rangle = U^{\dagger}|\boldsymbol{\Psi}, t\rangle. \qquad (V.3.8)$$

If a dynamical variable is found in a state $|\boldsymbol{\Psi}, t_0\rangle$ at a fixed instant t_0, then the probability of finding it in any other state $|\boldsymbol{\eta}, t\rangle$ following a measurement on the system at a later time t is defined by

$$|\langle \boldsymbol{\eta}, t|\boldsymbol{\Psi}, t_0\rangle|^2 = |\langle \boldsymbol{\eta}, t|U^\dagger|\boldsymbol{\Psi}, t\rangle|^2. \tag{V.3.9}$$

Classical equations (*III.1.10*) become operator equations in quantum mechanics,

$$q(t) = q(t_0) + \frac{t}{i\hbar}[q, H] + \frac{1}{2!}\left(\frac{t}{i\hbar}\right)^2 [[q, H], H] + \cdots,$$

$$(V.3.10)$$

$$p(t) = p(t_0) + \frac{t}{i\hbar}[p, H] + \frac{1}{2!}\left(\frac{t}{i\hbar}\right)^2 [[p, H], H] + \cdots,$$

where the commutators are evaluated at time t_0. Equations (*V.3.10*) for time-independent H can be written as

$$q(t) = e^{(i/\hbar)tH} q_0 e^{-(i/\hbar)tH}, \tag{V.3.11}$$

$$p(t) = e^{(i/\hbar)tH} p_0 e^{-(i/\hbar)tH}, \tag{V.3.12}$$

where $e^{-(i/\hbar)tH}$ is a unitary operator. Thus if $|\boldsymbol{\Psi}, t_0\rangle$ is the state at time t_0, then the state at time t is given by

$$|\boldsymbol{\Psi}, t\rangle = e^{-(i/\hbar)(t-t_0)H}|\boldsymbol{\Psi}, t_0\rangle, \tag{V.3.13}$$

and it describes a "stationary state." In particular, if $|\boldsymbol{\Psi}, t_0\rangle$ happens to be an eigenstate of energy H, then the stationary state wave function is

$$\psi(\mathbf{r}, t) = \langle \mathbf{r}, t_0|\boldsymbol{\Psi}, t\rangle = e^{-(i/\hbar)E(t-t_0)}\psi_0(\mathbf{r}). \tag{V.3.14}$$

V.3.A. The Free Particle in Heisenberg Representation

The average value of a Heisenberg dynamical variable $\alpha(t)$ is defined by

$$\langle\alpha(t)\rangle = \langle \boldsymbol{\Psi}, t_0|\alpha(t)|\boldsymbol{\Psi}, t_0\rangle, \tag{V.3.15}$$

where $|\boldsymbol{\Psi}, t_0\rangle$ is a Heisenberg state vector. From (*V.3.15*) it follows that

$$\frac{d}{dt}\langle\alpha\rangle = \left\langle\frac{1}{i\hbar}[\alpha, H]\right\rangle. \tag{V.3.16}$$

For $\alpha = \mathbf{q}$ and $\mathbf{p}$ we obtain

$$\frac{d}{dt}\langle\mathbf{q}\rangle = \left\langle\frac{d\mathbf{q}}{dt}\right\rangle = \left\langle\frac{\partial H}{\partial \mathbf{p}}\right\rangle,$$

$$(V.3.17)$$

$$\frac{d}{dt}\langle\mathbf{p}\rangle = \left\langle\frac{d\mathbf{p}}{dt}\right\rangle = \left\langle-\frac{\partial H}{\partial \mathbf{q}}\right\rangle.$$

Hence we see that the average position and average momentum of the particle, as position and momentum of the center of a wave packet, will move with the average values of $\partial H/\partial\mathbf{p}$ and $-\partial H/\partial\mathbf{q}$. For a free particle, with $H = \mathbf{p}^2/2m$, we have

$$\frac{d}{dt}\langle \boldsymbol{q} \rangle = \left\langle \frac{\boldsymbol{p}}{m} \right\rangle,$$
$$\frac{d}{dt}\langle \boldsymbol{p} \rangle = 0, \tag{V.3.18}$$

which means that the average motion of a free particle obeys Newton's first law of motion.

The operator equations (*V.3.5*) and (*V.3.6*) for a free particle can be solved as

$$\boldsymbol{q} = \frac{t}{m}\boldsymbol{p} + \boldsymbol{q}_0, \qquad \boldsymbol{p} = \boldsymbol{p}_0. \tag{V.3.19}$$

These equations could also be obtained from (*V.3.11*) and (*V.3.12*) with $H = \boldsymbol{p}^2/2m$.

Despite the great similarity to classical free particle equations, the physical interpretations of (*V.3.19*) are quite different from the classical case. In order to see this difference we begin by defining "the measure of spread" in the value of a dynamical variable α by

$$(\Delta\alpha)^2 = \langle(\alpha - \langle\alpha\rangle)^2\rangle = \langle\alpha^2\rangle - (\langle\alpha\rangle)^2, \tag{V.3.20}$$

where $(\Delta\alpha)^2$ is the *average square deviation* of α from its average value $\langle\alpha\rangle$.

The average square deviation of the position operator $\boldsymbol{q}$, as follows from (*V.3.19*), is

$$(\Delta q)^2 = \frac{t^2}{m^2}(\Delta p_0)^2 + (\Delta q_0)^2 + \frac{t}{m}\langle q_0 p_0 + p_0 q_0\rangle - \frac{2t}{m}\langle p_0\rangle\langle q_0\rangle. \tag{V.3.21}$$

We see from this result that the average square deviation of position of a free particle, will, after a certain time, increase indefinitely. The spread is a minimum only at the initial time.

V.3.B. The Velocity of the Photon

The momentum operator $\boldsymbol{p}$ commutes with the Hamiltonian H [see (*II.1.28*)] and it is, therefore, a constant of the motion. The velocity of the photon as a time-dependent operator can be obtained from Heisenberg's equations of motion,

$$\boldsymbol{V} = \frac{d\boldsymbol{r}}{dt} = \frac{1}{i\hbar}[\boldsymbol{r}, H] = c\boldsymbol{K}. \tag{V.3.22}$$

For a plane wave moving in the p_3 direction we had $\mathfrak{m} = K_3$, so in this case $V_3 = cK_3$. Hence the eigenvalues of the velocity operator are $+c$, $-c$, and 0. The value $V_3 = 0$ is excluded by the transverse condition $\boldsymbol{p}\cdot\boldsymbol{\eta} = 0$. Thus a measurement of the velocity in the p_3 direction is certain to lead to the result $\pm c$. The velocity of a photon is either parallel or antiparallel to its spin, depending on its state of polarization. This result is valid for all massless particles with any spin.

The noncommutation of the velocity operators V_1, V_2, and V_3 means that they cannot in general possess simultaneously well-defined values. Although the velocity operator V does not commute with the Hamiltonian H, its projection in the direction of the momentum p commutes with H. From

$$[V_i, H] = ic\epsilon_{ijk}p_jV_k$$

we obtain

$$(\boldsymbol{p}\cdot\boldsymbol{V})H - H(\boldsymbol{p}\cdot\boldsymbol{V}) = 0, \tag{V.3.23}$$

where we use the commutation relations $[p_i, V_j] = 0$ and $[p_i, H] = 0$.

We may, therefore, regard the component of the velocity along the direction of the momentum as a constant of the motion. The expectation value of $V_p = (1/p)\boldsymbol{p}\cdot\boldsymbol{V}$ is

$$\begin{aligned}\langle V_p\rangle &= \int \langle\eta|\frac{1}{p}\boldsymbol{p}\cdot\boldsymbol{V}|\eta\rangle\, d^3\boldsymbol{r}\\ &= \int \langle\eta|\frac{\lambda}{\hbar}H|\eta\rangle\, d^3\boldsymbol{r}.\end{aligned}$$

Hence

$$\langle V_p\rangle = \frac{\lambda}{\hbar}\int E\langle\eta|\eta\rangle\, d^3\boldsymbol{r} = \frac{\lambda}{\hbar}E = \frac{\lambda}{h}h\nu = \lambda\nu = c. \tag{V.3.24}$$

The time variation of the velocity is given by

$$\frac{d\boldsymbol{V}}{dt} = \frac{1}{i\hbar}[\boldsymbol{V}, H] = \frac{c}{\hbar}\boldsymbol{p}\times\boldsymbol{V}.$$

It can also be written as

$$i\hbar\frac{d\boldsymbol{V}}{dt} = H\boldsymbol{V}, \tag{V.3.25}$$

and its solution is

$$\boldsymbol{V} = e^{-(i/\hbar)tH}\boldsymbol{V}_0, \tag{V.3.26}$$

where $\boldsymbol{V}_0$ is a constant velocity operator and is equal to the value of $\boldsymbol{V}$ at $t = 0$. The oscillatory nature of (*V.3.26*) shows that $\boldsymbol{V}$ has the eigenvalues $\pm c$.

V.4. The Derivation of Uncertainty Relations

To every pair of canonically conjugate observables α and β corresponds an uncertainty relation. This means that the observables α and β cannot be diagonalized simultaneously. Let ξ be the commutator of α and β,

$$[\alpha, \beta] = \xi, \tag{V.4.1}$$

where ξ is a linear anti-Hermitian operator. In a state $|\Psi\rangle$ the measures of spread in α and β are given by

$$\Delta\alpha = \sqrt{\langle\alpha_c^2\rangle}, \qquad \Delta\beta = \sqrt{\langle\beta_c^2\rangle},$$

where the Hermitian operators

$$\alpha_c = \alpha - \langle\alpha\rangle \quad \text{and} \quad \beta_c = \beta - \langle\beta\rangle$$

satisfy the same commutation relation, $[\![\alpha_c, \beta_c]\!] = \xi$.

If we assume that $|\Psi\rangle$ is a unit ($\langle\Psi|\Psi\rangle = 1$) state vector, then

$$\begin{aligned}(\Delta\alpha)^2(\Delta\beta)^2 &= \langle\Psi|\alpha_c^2|\Psi\rangle\langle\Psi|\beta_c^2|\Psi\rangle \\ &= [\langle\Psi|\alpha_c)(\alpha_c|\Psi\rangle][\langle\Psi|\beta_c)(\beta_c|\Psi\rangle].\end{aligned}$$

The right side is the product of the squares of the two vectors $\alpha_c|\Psi\rangle$ and $\beta_c|\Psi\rangle$. Applying Schwarz's inequality we obtain

$$(\Delta\alpha)^2(\Delta\beta)^2 \geqq |\langle\Psi|\alpha_c\beta_c|\Psi\rangle|^2. \tag{V.4.2}$$

If we write the operator $\alpha_c\beta_c$ in the form

$$\alpha_c\beta_c = \tfrac{1}{2}(\alpha_c\beta_c + \beta_c\alpha_c) + \tfrac{1}{2}[\![\alpha_c, \beta_c]\!],$$

we obtain

$$(\Delta\alpha)^2(\Delta\beta)^2 \geqq |\tfrac{1}{2}\langle\alpha_c\beta_c + \beta_c\alpha_c\rangle + \tfrac{1}{2}\langle\xi\rangle|^2,$$

where the term $(\frac{1}{2})\langle\xi\rangle$ on the right is pure imaginary, so the right side is of the form $|a + ib|^2$ with $|a| \geqq |b|$. Using Schwarz's inequality once more, we get

$$(\Delta\alpha)^2(\Delta\beta)^2 \geqq \tfrac{1}{4}|\langle\xi\rangle|^2$$

or

$$\Delta\alpha\Delta\beta \geqq \tfrac{1}{2}|\langle[\![\alpha, \beta]\!]\rangle|. \tag{V.4.3}$$

This is the most general form of Heisenberg's uncertainty principle.

From (*V.4.3*) we may derive the uncertainty relation between uncertainties of time and energy. Let α be the Hamiltonian of a dynamical system assumed to be independent of time and let β be any other observable of the same dynamical system. The uncertainty relation (*V.4.3*) yields

$$\Delta H\Delta\beta \geqq \tfrac{1}{2}|\langle[\![H, \beta]\!]\rangle|$$

or

$$\Delta H\Delta\beta \geqq \frac{1}{2}\hbar\left|\left\langle\frac{d\beta}{dt}\right\rangle\right|,$$

where ΔH can be regarded as the measure of spread in the energy of the system and therefore $\Delta H = \Delta E$. State vectors in Schrödinger's formulation and linear operators in Heisenberg's formulation of quantum mechanics depend on time. Time itself forms a continuum and it is a measurable physical entity. But there is no particular Hermitian operator whose eigenspectrum is time itself. However, for any observable not commuting with the Hamiltonian we can calculate a measure of spread in time. For example, for a wave packet moving in the x direction, the uncertainty in time at which the center of packet passes the point $x = x_1$ would be approximately equal to the uncertainty in x divided by the group velocity of the wave packet:

$$\Delta t = \frac{\Delta x}{\frac{d}{dt}\langle x \rangle} = \frac{\Delta x}{\frac{\partial E}{\partial p}} = \frac{m\Delta x}{p}.$$

Thus by taking β in the above to be the coordinate q for a wave packet, we can deduce the uncertainty relation

$$\Delta E \Delta t \geqq \tfrac{1}{2}\hbar. \tag{V.4.4}$$

As another example of uncertainty relations, consider the measurement of the orbital angular momentum L_3. In polar coordinates it has the form $i\hbar(\partial/\partial\phi)$. The angle ϕ is, from 0 to 2π, a continuous variable, as against the discrete eigenvalues of L_3. From (*V.4.3*) we have

$$\Delta L_3 \Delta\beta \geqq \tfrac{1}{2}|\langle [\![L_3, \beta]\!] \rangle|.$$

If we assume that β commutes with the coordinates we can write

$$[\![L_3, \beta]\!] = -i\hbar \frac{\partial\beta}{\partial\phi}$$

and obtain

$$\Delta L_3 \Delta\beta \geqq \frac{1}{2}\hbar \left| \left\langle \frac{\partial\beta}{\partial\phi} \right\rangle \right|.$$

Hence the uncertainty $\Delta\phi = \Delta\beta / \left| \left\langle \frac{\partial\beta}{\partial\phi} \right\rangle \right|$ in the azimuthal angle ϕ and the uncertainty ΔL_3 in L_3 obey the relation

$$\Delta L_3 \Delta\phi \geqq \tfrac{1}{2}\hbar. \tag{V.4.5}$$

An accurate measurement of L_3 will cause a spread in ϕ and vice versa. In this sense, ϕ and L_3 are to be regarded as canonically conjugate observables.

The components of the total angular momentum $\boldsymbol{J}$ also satisfy the uncertainty relations:

$$\Delta J_1 \Delta J_2 \geqq \tfrac{1}{2}|\langle [\![J_1, J_2]\!] \rangle| = \tfrac{1}{2}\hbar|\langle J_3 \rangle|.$$

Hence, if the measurement is carried out in an eigenstate of J_3, we have

$$\Delta J_1 \Delta J_2 \geqq \tfrac{1}{2}\hbar(m\hbar). \tag{V.4.6}$$

Here also, eventually, an uncertainty in J_1 or J_2 can be related to uncertainty in an angle $J_1/m\hbar$ or $J_2/m\hbar$, respectively. The uncertainties in the measurements of J_1 and J_2 mean that the angular momentum vector $\boldsymbol{J}$ will sweep out a narrow cone around the z direction and it will never coincide with it. This follows also from the fact that the maximum value j of m is smaller than the length $\hbar\sqrt{j(j+1)}$ of the angular momentum vector.

V.4.A. Some Direct Applications of Uncertainty Relations

1. *Energy Spread in the Formation of a Compound Nucleus.*

According to Bohr's theory of the compound nucleus, low-energy neutron-nucleus reactions can take place in two stages: (a) the formation of a compound nucleus consisting of the neutron and original target nucleus, and (b) decay of the compound nucleus. It is assumed that once a neutron has entered the target nucleus it will very rapidly share its kinetic energy among the nuclear constituents and form a compound nucleus in an excited state. A compound nucleus formed in an excited state may have a certain statistical trend toward some modes of decay, which may include γ radiation, neutron re-emission, or emission of one or more particles. These processes will, of course, compete and each mode of decay can be characterized by a mean life τ (a certain measure of spread in time which the excited state would have if all the other possible modes of decay were not operating). The mean life τ of the excited state may be calculated by

$$\frac{1}{\tau} = \frac{1}{\tau_1} + \frac{1}{\tau_2} + \cdots + \frac{1}{\tau_n},$$

where n is the number of possible modes of decay. In accordance with the uncertainty in energy and time spreads of an excited state of the compound nucleus, we write

$$\Gamma\tau = \hbar, \qquad (V.4.7)$$

where Γ is called the width of the excited state. We can define a partial width Γ_i for each lifetime τ_i by $\Gamma_i = \hbar/\tau_i$, so the total energy spread is

$$\Gamma = \sum_i \Gamma_i.$$

2. *The Magnetic Moment of a Free Electron.*

It has been stated by Bohr* that "it is not possible by means of a Stern-Gerlach experiment to determine the magnetic moment of a free electron, or to prepare a beam of electrons with the magnetic moments all pointing in the same direction."

The magnetic moment of a bound electron is measured by means of a Stern-Gerlach experiment. A beam of atoms enters a region in which there is an inhomogeneous magnetic field in a direction perpendicular to the direction of motion of the atoms. If the electrons in the atom are rotating with angular

---

* N. F. Mott, *Proc. Roy. Soc. London, A*, **124** (1929), 440.
N. F. Mott and H. S. W. Massey, *The Theory of Atomic Collisions*, Oxford Univ. Press, Oxford, 1949, p. 63.

momentum $\boldsymbol{L}$, then according to (*I.6.22*) their energy would be given by $(e/mc)\mathfrak{H}\cdot\boldsymbol{L}$. Quantum mechanically the energy is half of the classical value and $\boldsymbol{L}$ is, of course, the angular momentum operator. The contribution from the spin is $-\boldsymbol{\mu}\cdot\mathfrak{H}$, where $\boldsymbol{\mu} = (e\hbar/2mc)\boldsymbol{\sigma}$ is the magnetic moment operator. Because of the quantization of angular momentum the beam of atoms collected at some distance from the field will leave $2(2l + 1)$ spots on a detecting screen; in other words, one can measure l and spin of the electron by counting the number of spots.

Now let us suppose that the position of an electron is known with an accuracy Δr and that we wish to determine its magnetic moment at a point at a distance r from Δr. A meaningful measurement would require a measure of spread in the electron position, satisfying the relation

$$\Delta r \ll r. \tag{V.4.8}$$

The magnetic field corresponding to a magnetic moment μ is

$$\mathfrak{H} \cong \frac{\mu}{r^3}, \tag{V.4.9}$$

and the magnetic field due to the motion of electrons is

$$\mathfrak{H}_e = \frac{ep}{mcr^2}. \tag{V.4.10}$$

From the uncertainty relation $\Delta r\Delta p \geqq (\frac{1}{2})\hbar$, we deduce that for a small Δr the spread in p is large; therefore we cannot measure $\mathfrak{H}_e$ with sufficient accuracy. However, if the uncertainty Δp in p is such that $\mathfrak{H}$ is much larger than $\mathfrak{H}_e$, then we have

$$\frac{\mu}{r^3} \gg \frac{e\Delta p}{mcr^2}. \tag{V.4.11}$$

Hence, using $\Delta p\Delta r \geqq (\frac{1}{2})\hbar$, we obtain

$$\Delta r \gg r, \tag{V.4.12}$$

which contradicts (*V.4.8*). The conclusion is, therefore, that it is not possible to measure the magnetic moment of a free electron in this way.

3. *The Fundamental Unit of Length of a Gravitational Field.*

Let us assume that the interaction of a gravitational and electromagnetic field can give rise to some discrete regions where the electromagnetic field is large but not infinite. Let R_c be such a region of the field, with linear dimensions of the order of a length r_c. (In order to be consistent with the relativistic transformation properties of a field, we shall regard the length r_c as an uncertainty in the location of the region R_c.) If we neglect any possible "dielectric" property of R_c, the minimum time T required for a light signal to propagate across the region R_c can be taken to be

$$T = \frac{r_c}{c}. \qquad (V.4.13)$$

We assume that R_c is a seat of a large number of electric charges of one sign and its momentum spread is such that the relation

$$\Delta p r_c = \hbar \qquad (V.4.14)$$

can be used to predict the length r_c. If q_c is the maximum value of the field in R_c, then the total energy and charge content in it are respectively given by

$$E = q_c^2 r_c^3 \qquad (V.4.15)$$

and

$$Q = q_c r_c^2. \qquad (V.4.16)$$

The latter is a consequence of Gauss' theorem in electrostatics. The total energy E and the minimum time T are related by

$$ET = (q_c^2 r_c^3)\frac{r_c}{c} = \hbar. \qquad (V.4.17)$$

In order that the energy E be contained within a region of dimensions r_c^3 and not blow up, the gravitational field in R_c must provide enough attraction between various parts of R_c to balance the Coulomb repulsion. Hence the gravitational attraction,

$$(\Delta p/c)^2(G/r_c^2),$$

must be balanced, exactly, by the Coulomb repulsion,

$$(r_c^2 q_c)^2/r_c^2,$$

produced by the total charge Q. Thus

$$\left(\frac{\Delta p}{c}\right)^2 \frac{G}{r_c^2} = \frac{(r_c^2 q_c)^2}{r_c^2}, \qquad (V.4.18)$$

where G is the gravitational constant. From $(V.1.14)$, $(V.4.17)$, and $(V.1.18)$ we obtain the results

$$r_c = \sqrt{\left(\frac{\hbar G}{c^3}\right)} \qquad (V.4.19)$$

and

$$q_c = \frac{c^3}{G}\sqrt{\left(\frac{c}{\hbar}\right)}. \qquad (V.4.20)$$

The spread in momentum for the maximum possible "smallness" r_c of R_c containing an energy E is

$$\Delta p = \sqrt{\left(\frac{\hbar c^3}{G}\right)}. \qquad (V.4.21)$$

The mass and charge of R_c are respectively given by

$$M_c = \frac{\Delta p}{c}\sqrt{\left(\frac{\hbar c}{G}\right)}, \tag{V.4.22}$$

$$Q = \sqrt{(\hbar c)} \tag{V.4.23}$$

and the ratio of charge-to-mass ratio of R_c to charge-to-mass ratio of an elementary particle is just the well-known dimensionless number

$$\frac{\left(\dfrac{Q}{M_c}\right)^2}{\left(\dfrac{e}{m}\right)^2} = \frac{m^2 G}{e^2}. \tag{V.4.24}$$

V.4.B. Problems

1. According to a Stern-Gerlach experiment, a hydrogen atom with $l = 0$ of its electron (S state) has a magnetic moment equal to $e\hbar/2mc$ (one *Bohr magneton*). By using uncertainty relations, prove that for a hydrogen atom whose magnetic moment direction is unknown it is impossible to discover this direction by an experiment. Consider the possibility of measuring the magnetic field $\mathcal{H}$ outside the atom by observing the deflection of an electron passing the atom at a distance r. (Hint: calculate the magnetic field $\mathcal{H}$ at the point where the electron is passing, the force on the electron due to $\mathcal{H}$, the time during which the field acts on the electron, the momentum of the electron. For the deflection to be observable, it must be greater than the natural spreading of the beam.)

2. The wave function (*V.2.33*) represents a wave packet if: (a) $\phi(p)$ vanishes everywhere except in a small region around a wave number $k_0 = (1/\hbar)p_0$, (b) $\phi(p)$ reaches its maximum at $k = k_0$.

Show that the center of the wave packet defined by

$$\left(\frac{\partial f}{\partial k}\right)_{k=k_0} = 0$$

moves with the velocity (that is, the *group velocity* of monochromatic progressive waves)

$$\boldsymbol{v}_g = \left(\frac{\partial \omega}{\partial \boldsymbol{k}}\right)_{\boldsymbol{k}=\boldsymbol{k}_0} = \frac{\hbar \boldsymbol{k}_0}{m},$$

where $f = \boldsymbol{k}\cdot\boldsymbol{r} - \omega t$, $\boldsymbol{p} = \hbar\boldsymbol{k}$, and $\omega = \boldsymbol{p}^2/2m\hbar$.

3. The measurement of the position of a particle is possible only if it is practically a free particle. Why?

4. Let the state of a particle be represented by a normalized function $\psi(x)$. Assuming that the average value of the position in this state is zero, derive the relations

$$\int_{-\infty}^{\infty} \left|\frac{d\psi}{dx}\right|^2 dx = \frac{1}{\hbar^2}\,\Delta p^2,$$

$$\int_{-\infty}^{\infty} \left(x\,\frac{d\psi^*}{dx}\,\psi + x\,\frac{d\psi}{dx}\,\psi^*\right) dx = -1.$$

Hence, by using the inequality

$$\int_{-\infty}^{\infty} \left|ax\psi + \frac{d\psi}{dx}\right|^2 dx \geqq 0$$

(due to H. Weyl), derive the uncertainty relation

$$\Delta q \Delta p \geqq \tfrac{1}{2}\hbar.$$

Show also that the uncertainties in p and q assume their minimum values in a state

$$\phi = \left(\frac{1}{\alpha\pi}\right)^{1/4} e^{-x^2/2\alpha}, \qquad (V.4.25)$$

where

$$\alpha = 2(\Delta q)^2.$$

5. By taking the Fourier transform of the wave function (*V.4.25*) in the previous problem, according to the rule

$$\phi(p) = \frac{1}{\sqrt{h}} \int A e^{-(i/\hbar)xp} e^{-x^2/2\alpha}\, dx,$$

derive the uncertainty relation for the minimum uncertainties in q and p, where $A = (\alpha\pi)^{-1/4}$.

6. A beam of particles is incident normally at a a plane of a slit of width d. The accuracy with which the co-ordinates of the particles in the direction of the slit are known, of course, since $\Delta q = d$. By using the wave properties of the particles and the diffraction law $\sin\theta \cong \lambda/d$, where λ is the de Broglie wavelength of the particles, prove that the uncertainty in the momentum (parallel to the screen containing the slit) obeys the law $\Delta p \Delta q \cong \hbar$.

V.5. Transformation Functions and Infinitesimal Unitary Transformations

Formally, the knowledge of a unitary transformation provides a complete solution of a quantum mechanical problem. For this reason a closer study of the unitary transformations is essential. In particular, the propagation of a wave in space and time can be described in terms of the representatives of a unitary operator. From definition (*V.1.19*) of the unitary operator its representatives in q representation can be obtained in the form

$$\langle \mathbf{r}, t | \mathbf{r}', t' \rangle, \qquad (V.5.1)$$

where

$$\langle \boldsymbol{r}, t|\boldsymbol{r}', t'\rangle = \langle \boldsymbol{r}, t|U(t't)|\boldsymbol{r}', t\rangle.$$

For $t = t'$ we have $U(t't) = I$, so

$$\lim_{t=t'} \langle \boldsymbol{r}, t|\boldsymbol{r}', t'\rangle = \delta(\boldsymbol{r} - \boldsymbol{r}'). \qquad (V.5.2)$$

For the special case of a free particle the unitary operator $U(t't)$ is given by

$$U(t't) = e^{-(i/\hbar)(\boldsymbol{p}^2/2m)(t'-t)}. \qquad (V.5.3)$$

The corresponding transformation function follows from (*V.5.3*):

$$\begin{aligned}\langle \boldsymbol{r}, t|\boldsymbol{r}', t'\rangle &= \langle \boldsymbol{r}, t|U(t't)|\boldsymbol{r}', t\rangle \\ &= \langle \boldsymbol{r}, t|e^{-(i/\hbar)(\boldsymbol{p}^2/2m)(t'-t)}|\boldsymbol{r}', t\rangle \\ &= \int \langle \boldsymbol{r}, t|\boldsymbol{p}, t\rangle\, d^3\boldsymbol{p}\, \langle \boldsymbol{p}, t|e^{-(i/\hbar)(\boldsymbol{p}^2/2m)(t'-t)}|\boldsymbol{r}', t\rangle.\end{aligned}$$

Using expression (*V.1.21*) for the transformation functions $\langle \boldsymbol{r}, t|\boldsymbol{p}, t\rangle$, we obtain

$$\langle \boldsymbol{r}, t|\boldsymbol{r}', t'\rangle = \frac{1}{h^3}\int e^{(i/\hbar)\boldsymbol{p}\cdot(\boldsymbol{r}-\boldsymbol{r}')}e^{-(i/\hbar)(\boldsymbol{p}^2/2m)(t'-t)}\, d^3\boldsymbol{p}.$$

If this integral is factorized into three integrals of the type (*V.2.36*), we obtain

$$\langle \boldsymbol{r}, t|\boldsymbol{r}', t'\rangle = \left[\frac{m}{2\pi i\hbar(t'-t)}\right]^{3/2} e^{im(\boldsymbol{r}-\boldsymbol{r}')^2/2\hbar(t'-t)}. \qquad (V.5.4)$$

This satisfies condition (*V.5.2*), since the volume integral of $\langle \boldsymbol{r}, t|\boldsymbol{r}', t'\rangle$ is equal to 1.

The momentum space representation of the transformation function, as follows from (*V.5.3*), is

$$\begin{aligned}\langle \boldsymbol{p}, t|U(t't)|\boldsymbol{p}', t\rangle &= \langle \boldsymbol{p}, t|\boldsymbol{p}', t'\rangle \\ &= e^{-(i/\hbar)(\boldsymbol{p}^2/2m)(t'-t)}\delta(\boldsymbol{p} - \boldsymbol{p}'), \qquad (V.5.5)\end{aligned}$$

which is also the Fourier transform of (*V.5.4*).

The physical interpretation of the transformation function $\langle \boldsymbol{r}, t|\boldsymbol{r}', t'\rangle$, in accordance with the probability interpretation of quantum mechanics, is to be based on the meaning of $|\langle \boldsymbol{r}, t|\boldsymbol{r}', t'\rangle|^2$. It is the probability that $\boldsymbol{q}$ has the value $\boldsymbol{r}'$ at time t' if it had the value $\boldsymbol{r}$ at time t (where $\boldsymbol{q}$ is diagonal). It contains the entire history of the dynamical system in the time interval (t, t'). The transformation function $\langle \boldsymbol{r}t|\boldsymbol{r}'t\rangle$, as defined by (*V.5.4*), is the propagator of a free particle.

A rather suggestive relation that is found in the more general formulation of quantum mechanics is obtained by writing

$$\langle \boldsymbol{r}, t|\boldsymbol{r}', t'\rangle = e^{(i/\hbar)S}, \qquad (V.5.6)$$

where the complex function S is given as

$$S = S_c + \frac{3}{2i}\hbar \log\left[\frac{m}{2\pi i\hbar(t' - t)}\right], \qquad (V.5.7)$$

and

$$S_c = \frac{m(\boldsymbol{r} - \boldsymbol{r}')^2}{2(t - t')}$$

is the extremum action function of a free classical particle.

From the integral equation (*V.2.10*) for the unitary operator $U(tt_0)$, by taking the representatives of $U(tt_0)$ in $\boldsymbol{q}$ representation, we can derive an integral equation for the transformation function itself,

$$\langle \boldsymbol{r}, t|U(t't)|\boldsymbol{r}', t\rangle = \delta(\boldsymbol{r} - \boldsymbol{r}') - \frac{i}{\hbar}\int_t^{t'} \epsilon_+(t', t_1)\langle \boldsymbol{r}, t|H(t_1)U(t_1t)|\boldsymbol{r}', t\rangle\, dt_1.$$

Hence

$$\langle \boldsymbol{r}, t|\boldsymbol{r}', t'\rangle = \delta(\boldsymbol{r} - \boldsymbol{r}') - \frac{i}{\hbar}\int_t^{t'} \epsilon_+(t', t_1)H\left(\boldsymbol{r}, -i\hbar\frac{\partial}{\partial \boldsymbol{r}}, t_1\right)\langle \boldsymbol{r}, t|\boldsymbol{r}', t_1\rangle\, dt_1 \qquad (V.5.8)$$

is the required integral equation incorporating the boundary condition (*V.5.2*) and the direction of flow of time. The corresponding differential equation is

$$\left(i\hbar\frac{\partial}{\partial t} - H\right)G(\boldsymbol{r}, \boldsymbol{r}', t, t') = \delta(\boldsymbol{r} - \boldsymbol{r}')\delta(t - t'), \qquad (V.5.9)$$

where "Green's function," $G(\boldsymbol{r}, \boldsymbol{r}', t, t')$, is defined by

$$G = \begin{cases} \langle \boldsymbol{r}, t|\boldsymbol{r}', t'\rangle & \text{for } t > t', \\ 0 & \text{for } t < t'. \end{cases} \qquad (V.5.10)$$

Equation (*V.5.9*) is usually called "Green's function equation." For $H = \boldsymbol{p}^2/2m$ it is satisfied by the free particle "propagator function" (*V.5.4*). It is related to the motion of a free particle in time.

There will be other occasions where we shall need to solve an equation of the type (*V.5.9*). In this connection we solve this equation for the special case of a free particle, using the method of Fourier transformation. We put

$$G(\boldsymbol{r} - \boldsymbol{r}', t - t') = \left(\frac{1}{2\pi}\right)^4 \int \hbar e^{i\boldsymbol{k}\cdot\boldsymbol{R}}e^{-i\omega\tau}\overline{G}(\boldsymbol{k}, \omega)\, d^3\boldsymbol{k}\, d\omega, \qquad (V.5.11)$$

$$\delta(\boldsymbol{r} - \boldsymbol{r}')\delta(t - t') = \left(\frac{1}{2\pi}\right)^4 \int e^{i\boldsymbol{k}\cdot\boldsymbol{R}}e^{-i\omega\tau}\, d^3\boldsymbol{k}\, d\omega, \qquad (V.5.12)$$

where $\boldsymbol{R} = \boldsymbol{r} - \boldsymbol{r}'$ and $\tau = t - t'$. Substituting in (*V.5.9*) we get

$$\overline{G}(\boldsymbol{k}, \omega) = \frac{1}{\hbar\omega - \dfrac{p^2}{2m}} + A\delta\left(\hbar\omega - \frac{p^2}{2m}\right), \qquad (V.5.13)$$

where we use the relation (*III.3.24*) for δ functions and where A is a constant. The boundary condition that $t' > t$ in the integral (*V.5.8*) can be taken over in the present case by choosing the constant A as $A = i\pi$, in which case (*V.5.13*) becomes

$$\bar{G}(\boldsymbol{k}, \omega) = \frac{1}{\hbar\omega - \dfrac{p^2}{2m}}, \qquad (V.5.14)$$

where ω contains a small negative imaginary part—that is, $-i\epsilon$, with $\epsilon > 0$ [see (*III.3.16*)].

The integrand (*V.5.11*) will have no poles on the energy axis of the complex plane. We may use (*III.3.18*) together with (*V.5.14*) and cast the integral for the propagator function in the form

$$G = i\left(\frac{1}{2\pi}\right)^4 \int_0^\infty du\, exp\left[-iu\left(\omega - \frac{\hbar k^2}{2m}\right)\right] \int_{-\infty}^{\infty} e^{i\boldsymbol{k}\cdot\boldsymbol{R}} e^{-i\omega\tau}\, d^3\boldsymbol{k}\, d\omega.$$

To integrate this we choose the vector $\boldsymbol{R}$ as the polar axis in $\boldsymbol{k}$ space and perform the angle integrations in

$$\int e^{i\boldsymbol{k}\cdot\boldsymbol{R}} e^{-i\omega\tau}\, d^3\boldsymbol{k} = \int_0^\infty dk \int_\Omega k^2 e^{ikR\cos\theta} \sin\theta\, e^{-i\omega\tau}\, d\theta\, d\phi$$

$$= 2\pi \frac{1}{iR} \int_0^\infty k e^{-i\omega\tau}(e^{ikR} - e^{-ikR})\, dk.$$

Hence Green's function becomes

$$G = \left(\frac{1}{2\pi}\right)^3 \frac{1}{R} \int\int_0^\infty e^{-i\omega(\tau+u)}\, d\omega\, du \int_0^\infty k e^{i(u\hbar/2m)k^2}(e^{ikR} - e^{-ikR})\, dk$$

$$= \left(\frac{1}{2\pi}\right)^3 \frac{1}{R} \int\int_0^\infty du\, e^{-i\omega(\tau+u)}\, d\omega \int_{-\infty}^{\infty} k e^{ikR} e^{(iu\hbar/2m)k^2}\, dk$$

$$= \left(\frac{1}{2\pi}\right)^2 \frac{1}{R} \int_{-\infty}^{\infty} k e^{ikR} e^{-(i\tau/2m)\hbar k^2}\, dk$$

$$= \frac{1}{2}\left(\frac{1}{2\pi}\right)^2 \frac{1}{iR}\frac{\partial}{\partial R} \int_{-\infty}^{\infty} e^{ikR} e^{-(i\tau/2m)\hbar k^2}\, dk.$$

Using the integral relation (*V.2.36*) we obtain

$$G = \left[\frac{m}{2\pi i\hbar\tau}\right]^{3/2} e^{(im/2\hbar\tau)R^2}, \qquad (V.5.15)$$

which agrees with (*V.5.4*).

V.5.A. Infinitesimal Unitary Transformations

Unitary transformations in the infinitesimal neighborhood of the unit operator can induce infinitesimal changes of observables and state vectors. For example, the unitary operator

$$U = e^{-(i/\hbar)\Delta t H},$$

for small enough time interval Δt, can effectively be replaced by

$$U = I - \frac{i}{\hbar}\Delta t H. \tag{V.5.16}$$

This is an infinitesimal unitary transformation operator. In general, an infinitesimal unitary transformation operator has the form

$$U = I - \frac{i}{\hbar}F, \tag{V.5.17}$$

where F is an infinitesimal [in the sense defined in $(I.5.D)$] Hermitian operator. Its inverse is given by

$$U^{-1} = U^{\dagger} = 1 + \frac{i}{\hbar}F.$$

The changes induced by infinitesimal unitary transformation in a vector $|\boldsymbol{\Psi}\rangle$ and in an operator α are respectively given by

$$i\hbar\delta|\boldsymbol{\Psi}\rangle = F|\boldsymbol{\Psi}\rangle \tag{V.5.18}$$

and

$$i\hbar\delta\alpha = [\alpha, F], \tag{V.5.19}$$

where

$$\delta|\boldsymbol{\Psi}\rangle = U|\boldsymbol{\Psi}\rangle - |\boldsymbol{\Psi}\rangle$$

and

$$\delta\alpha = U^{\dagger}\alpha U - \alpha.$$

The infinitesimal Hermitian operator F is the generator of the unitary transformation. The change in the ket $\langle\boldsymbol{\Psi}|$ is obtained as

$$i\hbar\delta\langle\boldsymbol{\Psi}| = -\langle\boldsymbol{\Psi}|F. \tag{V.5.20}$$

Consider a complete commuting set of operators α (for example, $\alpha = q$ or $\alpha = p$) and the eigenstates $|\alpha'\rangle$ corresponding to eigenvalues α'. An arbitrary state $|\boldsymbol{\Psi}\rangle$ is completely described by the functions

$$\psi(\alpha') = \langle\alpha'|\boldsymbol{\Psi}\rangle.$$

If β is a complete commuting set similar to α then its eigenstates $|\beta'\rangle$ corresponding to eigenvalues β' can be used to describe the arbitrary state $|\boldsymbol{\Psi}\rangle$ by

$$\psi(\beta') = \langle\beta'|\boldsymbol{\Psi}\rangle.$$

The two descriptions $\psi(\alpha')$ and $\psi(\beta')$ are related by

$$\psi(\alpha') = \int \langle\alpha'|\beta'\rangle\, d\beta'\, \langle\beta'|\boldsymbol{\Psi}\rangle$$

or

$$\psi(\alpha') = \int \langle\alpha'|\beta'\rangle\psi(\beta')\, d\beta', \tag{V.5.21}$$

where $\langle\alpha'|\beta'\rangle$ is a transformation function.

A change in $\psi(\alpha')$ under an infinitesimal unitary transformation generated by a Hermitian operator F_α is

$$\delta\psi(\alpha') = \delta\langle\alpha'|\Psi\rangle = \frac{1}{\hbar}\langle\alpha'|F_\alpha|\Psi\rangle, \tag{V.5.22}$$

which can also be written as

$$\delta\psi(\alpha') = \frac{i}{\hbar}\int\langle\alpha'|F_\alpha|\alpha''\rangle\, d\alpha''\, \psi(\alpha''). \tag{V.5.23}$$

We can find the change in the transformation function $\langle\alpha'|\beta'\rangle$ induced by the two generators F_α and F_β, in the form

$$\delta\langle\alpha'|\beta'\rangle = \delta(\langle\alpha'|)|\beta'\rangle + \langle\alpha'|(\delta|\beta'\rangle) = \frac{i}{\hbar}\langle\alpha'|(F_\alpha - F_\beta)|\beta'\rangle. \tag{V.5.24}$$

V.5.B. The Dirac-Schwinger Action Principle

An alternative formulation of quantum theory can be based on the Lagrangian formulation of classical mechanics. Consider two sets of complete commuting observables, α and β. We can set up two representations—a representation in which α is diagonal and a second representation in which β is diagonal. Let us suppose that α and β are Heisenberg dynamical variables related by a unitary transformation:

$$\beta = U^\dagger \alpha U. \tag{V.5.25}$$

Thus if $|\alpha' t_0\rangle$ are eigenstates of α with eigenvalue α', then the eigenstates of β are

$$|\beta' t\rangle = U(tt_0)|\alpha', t_0\rangle, \tag{V.5.26}$$

where $\alpha' = \beta'$, since a unitary transformation does not change the eigenvalue spectrum. The two representations are connected by a transformation function, $\langle\beta'' t|\alpha' t_0\rangle$, where $\beta'' = \alpha''$.

Now using ($V.5.24$), we may write

$$\langle\beta'' t|\alpha' t_0\rangle = \langle\beta'' t|U^\dagger|\beta' t\rangle. \tag{V.5.27}$$

From the group property

$$U(tt')U(t't_0) = U(tt_0), \tag{V.5.28}$$

it follows that

$$U^\dagger(tt_0) = U(t_0 t),$$

where the property ($V.5.26$) can be derived from

$$U(tt_0) = \int|\beta' t\rangle\, d\alpha'\, \langle\alpha' t_0| = \int|\alpha' t\rangle\, d\alpha'\, \langle\alpha' t_0|. \tag{V.5.29}$$

Thus $U^\dagger(tt_0)$ describes the development of the system from time t to time t_0. The change of $U^\dagger$ under infinitesimal unitary transformations induced by F_α and F_β can be obtained from

$$\delta U^{\dagger} = \delta \int |\alpha' t_0\rangle \, d\alpha' \, \langle \beta' t|$$

as

$$\begin{aligned}\delta U^{\dagger} &= \int \delta(|\alpha' t_0\rangle) \, d\alpha' \, \langle \beta' t| + \int |\alpha' t_0\rangle \, d\alpha' \, \delta(\langle \beta' t| \\ &= \frac{1}{i\hbar}\left(\int F_{\alpha}|\alpha' t_0\rangle \, d\alpha' \, \langle \beta' t| - \int |\alpha' t_0\rangle \, d\alpha' \, \langle \beta' t| F_{\beta}\right)\end{aligned}$$

or

$$\delta U^{\dagger} = \frac{1}{i\hbar}(F_{\alpha}U^{\dagger} - U^{\dagger}F_{\beta}). \tag{V.5.30}$$

The representatives of $\delta U^{\dagger}$ with respect to the eigenvectors of β at time t are

$$\langle \beta'' t|\delta U^{\dagger}|\beta' t\rangle = \frac{1}{i\hbar}[\langle \beta'' t|F_{\alpha}U^{\dagger}|\beta' t\rangle - \langle \beta'' t|U^{\dagger}F_{\beta}|\beta' t\rangle].$$

Hence

$$\langle \beta'' t|\delta U^{\dagger}|\beta' t\rangle = \frac{1}{i\hbar}[\langle \beta'' t|F_{\alpha}|\alpha' t_0\rangle - \langle \beta'' t|F_{\beta}|\alpha' t_0\rangle]$$

or

$$i\hbar\langle \beta'' t|\delta U^{\dagger}|\beta' t\rangle = \langle \beta'' t|(F_{\alpha} - F_{\beta})|\alpha' t_0\rangle.$$

Comparing this with (*V.5.22*), we obtain

$$\delta\langle \beta'' t|\alpha' t_0\rangle = \langle \beta'' t|\delta U^{\dagger}|\beta' t\rangle, \tag{V.5.31}$$

so we have a differential characterization of the change of the transformation function in terms of the representatives of the change in the unitary operator U, which relates the two complete set of observables α and β.

From the unitary property $U^{\dagger}U = I$ we infer (see Section 1.6) that $iU\delta U^{\dagger}$ is a Hermitian operator. Accordingly we write

$$\delta U^{\dagger} = \frac{i}{\hbar} U^{\dagger}\delta W_{tot}, \tag{V.5.32}$$

where δW_{tot} is a Hermitian operator. By means of this observation, the change in the transformation function can be cast in the form

$$\delta\langle \beta'' t|\alpha' t_0\rangle = \frac{i}{\hbar}\langle \beta'' t|\delta W_{tot}|\alpha' t_0\rangle. \tag{V.5.33}$$

This is the basic starting point of Schwinger's action principle.*

From the composition law

$$\langle \beta'' t|\gamma' \tau\rangle = \int \langle \beta'' t|\alpha' t_0\rangle \, d\alpha' \, \langle \alpha' t_0|\gamma' \tau\rangle,$$

we obtain

$$\langle \beta'' t|\delta W_{\tau t}|\gamma' \tau\rangle = \langle \beta'' t|\delta W_{tot}|\alpha' t_0\rangle + \langle \alpha' t_0|\delta W_{\tau t_0}|\gamma' \tau\rangle.$$

---

*J. Schwinger, *Phys. Rev.* **82** (1951), 914.

Hence, because of the completeness of α, β, and γ, we have

$$\delta W_{\tau t} = \delta W_{t_0 t} + \delta W_{\tau t_0}. \qquad (V.5.34)$$

This is the additive law of composition of the infinitesimal transformation. Schwinger's action principle consists in assuming that the Hermitian operator $W_{t_0 t}$ is of the form

$$W_{t_0 t} = \int_{t_0}^{t} L(t)\, dt \qquad (V.5.35)$$

and obeys the additive requirement (*V.5.34*). Finally, inserting (*V.5.35*) in (*V.5.33*), we get for the change of transformation function the expression

$$\delta\langle\beta''t|\alpha't_0\rangle = \frac{i}{\hbar}\langle\beta''t|\delta\int_{t_0}^{t} L(t)\, dt\,|\alpha't_0\rangle, \qquad (V.5.36)$$

where the operator L is a function of the sets α and β.

Now let us assume the existence of a commutation relation between α and β of the form

$$[\alpha, \beta] = i\hbar f, \qquad (V.5.37)$$

say, where f is the commutator of α and β. We use (*V.5.37*) and subject the differential expression $\delta\int_{t_0}^{t} L(t)\, dt$ to a process of ordering in such a way that β in L stands everywhere to the left of α. For an L ordered in this way the operators α and β will act directly on their respective eigenvectors in (*V.5.36*). If $\mathcal{O}$ is the operation of ordering, then we write

$$\mathcal{O}\left(\delta\int_{t_0}^{t} L\, dt\right) = \mathcal{O}(\delta W_{t_0 t}) = \delta\mathcal{W}_{tt_0},$$

where the ordered differential operator $\delta\mathcal{W}_{tt_0}$ is equal to δW. But the ordered operator $\mathcal{O}W_{t_0 t} = \mathcal{W}_{tt_0}$, obtained by integration, is not equal to the original Hermitian operator $W_{t_0 t}$ and also $\mathcal{W}_{tt_0}$ itself is not Hermitian.

Equation (*V.5.33*) can now be replaced by

$$\delta\langle\beta''t|\alpha't_0\rangle = \frac{i}{\hbar}\langle\beta''t|\delta\mathcal{W}_{tt_0}(\beta, \alpha, t, t_0)|\alpha't_0\rangle$$

$$= \frac{i}{\hbar}\,\delta\mathcal{W}_{tt_0}(\beta'', \alpha', t, t_0)\langle\beta''t|\alpha't_0\rangle. \qquad (V.5.38)$$

This can be written as

$$\delta\left[\log\langle\beta''t|\alpha't_0\rangle - \frac{1}{\hbar}\mathcal{W}_{tt_0}(\beta'', \alpha', t, t_0)\right] = 0.$$

Hence we get*

$$\langle\beta''t|\alpha't_0\rangle = e^{(i/\hbar)\mathcal{W}_{tt_0}(\beta'',\alpha',t,t_0)}, \qquad (V.5.39)$$

where the constant of integration is additively incorporated in $\mathcal{W}_{tt_0}$. The

---

* P. A. M. Dirac, *Physikalische Zeitschrift der Sowjet-Union,* Vol. 3, 1938.

constant of integration is to be determined from the normalization requirement

$$\int \langle \beta'' t | \alpha' t' \rangle \, d\alpha' \, \langle \alpha' t' | \beta' t \rangle = \delta(\beta'' - \beta') \qquad (V.5.40)$$

The meaning of the function $\mathcal{W}_{tt_0}$ can be understood by taking a special problem where $\alpha = q_0 = q(t_0)$ and $\beta = q(t)$. We have the equations

$$\langle \boldsymbol{r}, t | \boldsymbol{q} | \boldsymbol{r}_0, t_0 \rangle = \boldsymbol{r} \langle \boldsymbol{r}, t | \boldsymbol{r}_0, t_0 \rangle,$$

$$\langle \boldsymbol{r}, t | \boldsymbol{p} | \boldsymbol{r}_0, t_0 \rangle = -i\hbar \frac{\partial}{\partial \boldsymbol{r}} \langle \boldsymbol{r}, t | \boldsymbol{r}_0, t_0 \rangle, \qquad (V.5.41)$$

and

$$\langle \boldsymbol{r}, t | \boldsymbol{q}_0 | \boldsymbol{r}_0, t_0 \rangle = \boldsymbol{r}_0 \langle \boldsymbol{r}, t | \boldsymbol{r}_0, t_0 \rangle,$$

$$\langle \boldsymbol{r}, t | \boldsymbol{p}_0 | \boldsymbol{r}_0, t_0 \rangle = i\hbar \frac{\partial}{\partial \boldsymbol{r}_0} \langle \boldsymbol{r}, t | \boldsymbol{r}_0, t_0 \rangle. \qquad (V.5.42)$$

Therefore

$$\langle \boldsymbol{r}, t | \mathcal{W}_{tt_0}(\boldsymbol{q}, \boldsymbol{q}_0, t, t_0) | \boldsymbol{r}_0, t_0 \rangle = \mathcal{W}_{tt_0}(\boldsymbol{r}, t_0, \boldsymbol{r}_0, t_0) \langle \boldsymbol{r}, t | \boldsymbol{r}_0, t_0 \rangle \qquad (V.5.43)$$

and

$$\langle \boldsymbol{r}, t | \boldsymbol{r}_0, t_0 \rangle = e^{(i/\hbar)\mathcal{W}_{tt_0}(\boldsymbol{r}, \boldsymbol{r}_0, t, t_0)}. \qquad (V.5.44)$$

Substituting in the second relation of $(V.5.41)$ we get

$$\langle \boldsymbol{r}, t | \boldsymbol{p} | \boldsymbol{r}_0, t_0 \rangle = \frac{\partial \mathcal{W}_{tt_0}(\boldsymbol{r}, \boldsymbol{r}_0, t, t_0)}{\partial \boldsymbol{r}} \langle \boldsymbol{r}, t | \boldsymbol{r}_0, t_0 \rangle,$$

which can be written as

$$\langle \boldsymbol{r}, t | \frac{\partial \mathcal{W}_{tt_0}(\boldsymbol{q}, \boldsymbol{q}_0, t, t_0)}{\partial \boldsymbol{q}} | \boldsymbol{r}_0, t_0 \rangle = \frac{\partial \mathcal{W}_{tt_0}(\boldsymbol{r}, \boldsymbol{r}_0, t, t_0)}{\partial \boldsymbol{r}} \langle \boldsymbol{r}, t | \boldsymbol{r}_0, t_0 \rangle.$$

Hence the quantum definition of the momentum similar to the classical definition, $(I.1.5)$, is given by

$$\boldsymbol{p} = \frac{\partial \mathcal{W}_{tt_0}(\boldsymbol{q}, \boldsymbol{q}_0, t, t_0)}{\partial \boldsymbol{q}}, \qquad (V.5.45)$$

where, because of the ordered form of the operator $\mathcal{W}_{tt_0}$, the differentiation with respect to the operator $\boldsymbol{q}$ is well defined. In the same way we can show that

$$\boldsymbol{p}_0 = -\frac{\partial \mathcal{W}_{tt_0}}{\partial \boldsymbol{q}_0}. \qquad (V.5.46)$$

The commutation relations of $(III.4.2)$ can now be written as

$$\left[q_i, \frac{\partial \mathcal{W}_{tt_0}}{\partial \boldsymbol{q}_j} \right] = i\hbar \delta_{ij}. \qquad (V.5.47)$$

The function $\mathcal{W}_{tt_0}(\boldsymbol{r}, \boldsymbol{r}_0, t, t_0)$ is the classical analogue of the action function S.

Because of $(V.2.3)$, the transformation function $\langle \boldsymbol{r}, t | \boldsymbol{r}_0, t_0 \rangle$ is a solution of Schrödinger's equation

$$\left(i\hbar \frac{\partial}{\partial t} - H \right) \langle \boldsymbol{r}, t | \boldsymbol{r}_0, t_0 \rangle = 0 \qquad (V.5.48)$$

This can be used to derive the quantum Hamilton-Jacobi equation. First we note from (*V.5.44*) that

$$i\hbar \frac{\partial}{\partial t}\langle \mathbf{r}, t|\mathbf{r}_0, t_0\rangle = -\frac{\partial \mathcal{W}_{tt_0}(\mathbf{r}, \mathbf{r}_0, t, t_0)}{\partial t}\langle \mathbf{r}, t|\mathbf{r}_0, t_0\rangle, \qquad (V.5.49)$$

which can be written as

$$\langle \mathbf{r}, t|\left(-\frac{\partial \mathcal{W}_{tt_0}(\mathbf{q}, \mathbf{q}_0, t, t_0)}{\partial t}\right)|\mathbf{r}_0, t_0\rangle = -\frac{\partial \mathcal{W}_{tt_0}}{\partial t}\langle \mathbf{r}, t|\mathbf{r}_0, t_0\rangle. \qquad (V.5.50)$$

Moreover, from (*V.5.48*) and (*V.5.49*), we write

$$\langle \mathbf{r}, t|H|\mathbf{r}_0, t_0\rangle = H\left(\mathbf{r}, -i\hbar\frac{\partial}{\partial \mathbf{r}}, t\right)\langle \mathbf{r}, t|\mathbf{r}_0, t_0\rangle$$

$$= i\hbar\frac{\partial}{\partial t}\langle \mathbf{r}, t|\mathbf{r}_0, t_0\rangle = \langle \mathbf{r}, t|\left(-\frac{\partial \mathcal{W}_{tt_0}}{\partial t}\right)|\mathbf{r}_0, t_0\rangle.$$

Hence we infer the quantum Hamilton-Jacobi equation,

$$-\frac{\partial \mathcal{W}_{tt_0}(\mathbf{q}, \mathbf{q}_0, t, t_0)}{\partial t} = H\left(\mathbf{q}, \frac{\partial \mathcal{W}_{tt_0}}{\partial \mathbf{q}}, t\right), \qquad (V.5.51)$$

where the Hamiltonian is an ordered operator. Like Heisenberg's equations of motion, (*V.3.5*) and (*V.3.6*), the quantum Hamilton-Jacobi equation is of the same form as the classical Hamilton-Jacobi equation.

V.5.C. Examples of Transformation Functions

(a) *The free particle.* From the Hamiltonian and from the free particle solutions of (*V.3.19*) we have

$$H = \frac{\mathbf{p}^2}{2m} = \frac{m}{2t^2}(\mathbf{q} - \mathbf{q}_0)^2.$$

By using the quantum form of the Poisson-bracket expression (*III.1.47*), or

$$[q_i(t), q_j(t_0)] = i\hbar\frac{t - t_0}{m}\delta_{ij},$$

we obtain the ordered Hamiltonian

$$H = \frac{m}{2t^2}\left(\mathbf{q}^2 + \mathbf{q}_0^2 - 2\mathbf{q}\cdot\mathbf{q}_0 - \frac{3i\hbar}{m}t\right).$$

With the ordered Hamiltonian we have the Hamilton-Jacobi equation,

$$-\frac{\partial \mathcal{W}}{\partial t} = \frac{m}{2t^2}\left(\mathbf{q}^2 + \mathbf{q}_0^2 - 2\mathbf{q}\cdot\mathbf{q}_0 - \frac{3i\hbar}{m}t\right).$$

Hence the action operator $\mathcal{W}$ is given by

$$\mathcal{W} = \frac{m}{2t}(\mathbf{q}^2 + \mathbf{q}_0^2 - 2\mathbf{q}\cdot\mathbf{q}_0) + \frac{3i\hbar}{2}\log At, \qquad (V.5.52)$$

where A is a constant of integration to be determined. The transformation function, from (*V.5.44*), follows as

$$\langle \mathbf{r}, t|\mathbf{r}_0, 0\rangle = \exp\left\{\frac{i}{\hbar}\left[\frac{m}{2t}(\mathbf{r}-\mathbf{r}_0)^2 + \frac{3i\hbar}{2}\log At\right]\right\}.$$

To determine the constant A we use (*V.5.40*) in the form

$$\int \langle \mathbf{r}', t|\mathbf{r}_0, 0\rangle\, d^3\mathbf{r}_0\, \langle \mathbf{r}_0, 0|\mathbf{r}, t\rangle = \delta(\mathbf{r}'-\mathbf{r}).$$

Hence the integral relation

$$\int \exp\left\{\frac{i}{\hbar}\left[\frac{m}{2t}(\mathbf{r}'-\mathbf{r}_0)^2 + \frac{3i\hbar}{2}\log At\right]\right\} \exp\left\{-\frac{i}{\hbar}\left[\frac{m}{2t}(\mathbf{r}_0-\mathbf{r})^2 - \frac{3i\hbar}{2}\log At\right]\right\} d^3\mathbf{r}_0 = \delta(\mathbf{r}'-\mathbf{r})$$

yields

$$\exp\left[-3\log At\left(\frac{2\pi i\hbar t}{m}\right)^3\right]\delta(\mathbf{r}-\mathbf{r}')\exp\left[\frac{im}{2\hbar t}(\mathbf{r}'^2-\mathbf{r}^2)\right] = \delta(\mathbf{r}-\mathbf{r}').$$

Noting the relation

$$\delta(\mathbf{r}-\mathbf{r}')\exp\left[\frac{im}{2\hbar t}(\mathbf{r}'^2-\mathbf{r}^2)\right] = \delta(\mathbf{r}-\mathbf{r}'),$$

we obtain

$$A = \frac{2\pi i\hbar}{m}$$

so

$$\langle \mathbf{r}t|\mathbf{r}_0t_0\rangle = \left(\frac{m}{2\pi i\hbar t}\right)^{3/2}\exp\left[\frac{im}{2\hbar t}(\mathbf{r}-\mathbf{r}_0)^2\right]. \qquad (V.5.53)$$

(b) *One-dimensional free harmonic oscillator*. The Hamiltonian for a free harmonic oscillator is

$$H = \frac{p^2}{2m} + \frac{1}{2}m\omega^2q^2. \qquad (V.5.54)$$

Heisenberg's equations of motion will yield a quantum analogue of the classical solutions, (*III.1.32*), in the form

$$q = q_0\cos\omega t + \frac{1}{m\omega}p_0\sin\omega t \qquad (V.5.55)$$

$$p = -m\omega q_0\sin\omega t + p_0\cos\omega t.$$

The corresponding commutator of $q(t)$ and $q(t_0)$, as follows from the quantum version of the classical relation, (*III.1.46*), is

$$[q(t), q(t_0)] = i\hbar\frac{\sin\omega(t-t_0)}{m\omega}. \qquad (V.5.56)$$

Eliminating p_0 in (*V.5.55*), substituting in the expression of the Hamiltonian, and using the commutation relation (*V.5.56*), we obtain the ordered Hamiltonian,

$$H = \frac{1}{2}\frac{m\omega^2}{\sin^2 \omega t}(q^2 + q_0^2) - \frac{m\omega^2 \cos \omega t}{\sin^2 \omega t} qq_0 + \frac{1}{2} i\hbar\omega \cot \omega t. \qquad (V.5.57)$$

By integrating the Hamilton-Jacobi equation we obtain the action operator

$$\mathcal{W} = \frac{1}{2} m\omega \cot \omega t \left(q^2 + q_0^2 - \frac{2}{\cos \omega t} qq_0\right) + \frac{1}{2} i\hbar \log (A \sin \omega t). \qquad (V.5.58)$$

Hence the transformation function for a free harmonic oscillator is

$$\langle x, t | x_0, t_0\rangle = e^{(i/\hbar)\mathcal{W}(x,x_0,t)}, \qquad (V.5.59)$$

where

$$\mathcal{W}(x, x_0, t) = \frac{1}{2} m\omega \cot \omega t \left(x^2 + x_0^2 - \frac{2xx_0}{\cos \omega t}\right) + \frac{1}{2} i\hbar \log \left(\frac{2\pi i\hbar}{m\omega} \sin \omega t\right). \qquad (V.5.60)$$

V.5.D. Problems

1. By using the relativistic free particle Hamiltonian in the form

$$H = c\sqrt{(\boldsymbol{p}^2 + m^2c^2)} \cong mc^2 \left(1 + \frac{1}{2}\frac{\boldsymbol{p}^2}{m^2c^2} - \frac{1}{8}\frac{\boldsymbol{p}^4}{m^4c^4}\right), \qquad (V.5.61)$$

calculate the first-order relativistic correction to the transformation function of a free particle.

2. Calculate the transformation function for a relativistic spinless particle. Assume the Hamiltonian

$$H = c\sqrt{(\boldsymbol{p}^2 + m^2c^2)}$$

and define the transformation function by

$$\langle \boldsymbol{r}, t | U | \boldsymbol{r}', t\rangle = \langle \boldsymbol{r}, t | \boldsymbol{r}', t'\rangle,$$

where

$$U = \exp\left[-\frac{i}{\hbar} c\sqrt{(\boldsymbol{p}^2 + m^2c^2)}(t' - t)\right], \qquad (V.5.62)$$

$$\boldsymbol{p} = -i\hbar\boldsymbol{\nabla}$$

(Note that $\langle \boldsymbol{r}, t | \boldsymbol{r}', t'\rangle$ is not Green's function.) Use the method employed in Section 5. Show that the required transformation function is

$$\langle \boldsymbol{r}, t | \boldsymbol{r}', t'\rangle = \frac{c\kappa^2\tau}{4\pi(c^2\tau^2 - R^2)}$$

$$\left[H_0^{(1)}(\kappa\sqrt{(c^2\tau^2 - R^2)}) - \frac{2}{\kappa\sqrt{(c^2\tau^2 - R^2)}} H_1^{(1)}(\kappa\sqrt{(c^2\tau^2 - R^2)})\right]. \qquad (V.5.63)$$

The Hankel function relations

$$\frac{d}{dx}\left[\frac{1}{x} H_1^{(1)}(x)\right] = \frac{1}{x} H_0^{(1)}(x) - \frac{2}{x^2} H_1^{(1)}(x)$$

and

$$\int_{-\infty}^{\infty} \exp(ixy) \exp[ib\sqrt{(a^2 + x^2)}]\, dx = -\frac{\pi ab}{b^2 - y^2} H_1^{(1)}[a\sqrt{(b^2 - y^2)}] \quad (V.5.64)$$

are used, where $\tau = t' - t$ and $\kappa = mc/\hbar$.

Show that the transformation function defined in this way satisfies the equation

$$\left(\nabla^2 - \frac{1}{c^2}\frac{\partial^2}{\partial t^2} - \kappa^2\right)\langle \mathbf{r}, t|\mathbf{r}', t'\rangle = 0, \quad (V.5.65)$$

which is the *Klein-Gordon equation.*

3. Find the transformation function for a particle moving under the influence of a constant force, the Hamiltonian being

$$H = \frac{p^2}{2m} - aq, \quad (V.5.66)$$

where a is a numerical constant and q is the position operator in one dimension.

CHAPTER VI

SYMMETRY PRINCIPLES AND QUANTUM STATISTICS

VI.1. Parity of a Dynamical System

Studies of the symmetry properties of dynamical systems constitute the most important application of the transformation theory. Statements pertaining to the conservation of a particular symmetry of physical phenomena are usually laws of nature. For example, the indistinguishability of two or more electrons from one another can be regarded as a symmetry of nature. The invariance or noninvariance of a physical law under a certain group of coordinate transformations is a symmetry property describing the particular law. The fact that a neutrino can distinguish a left-handed coordinate system from a right-handed one is a symmetry property of the neutrino. The corresponding symmetry property for the photon is its indifference to left- and right-handed systems, since both correspond to possible states for the photon. The intrinsic parity of a π-meson—that is, the parity of π in its rest frame—is -1 and for this reason it is described by a pseudoscalar wave function. As another example we mention the time symmetry between particles and antiparticles where particles and antiparticles correspond to *"motion" along the time axis* in opposite directions.

The above are only a few examples among many symmetry properties of natural phenomena. For a partial understanding of the role of symmetry operations and their relations to dynamical variables we shall investigate the symmetry properties of Schrödinger's equation. We define a parity operator with the properties

$$\mathcal{P}\boldsymbol{q}\mathcal{P}^{-1} = -\boldsymbol{q}, \qquad (VI.1.1)$$

$$\mathcal{P}\boldsymbol{p}\mathcal{P}^{-1} = -\boldsymbol{p}, \qquad (VI.1.2)$$

where $\boldsymbol{q}$ and $\boldsymbol{p}$ are position and momentum operators, respectively. The parity operator $\mathcal{P}$ can operate on the eigenstates $|\boldsymbol{r}, t\rangle$ and $|\boldsymbol{p}, t\rangle$ of position and momentum, respectively. Thus from

$$\boldsymbol{q}\mathcal{P}|\boldsymbol{r}, t\rangle = -\mathcal{P}\boldsymbol{q}|\boldsymbol{r}, t\rangle = -\boldsymbol{r}\mathcal{P}|\boldsymbol{r}, t\rangle, \qquad (VI.1.3)$$

it follows that if $|\boldsymbol{r}, t\rangle$ is an eigenstate of $\boldsymbol{q}$ with eigenvalue $\boldsymbol{r}$, then $\mathcal{P}|\boldsymbol{r}, t\rangle$ is another eigenstate of $\boldsymbol{q}$ with eigenvalue $-\boldsymbol{r}$.

Thus, in essence, parity operation is a coordinate transformation of the type $x_i' = -x_i$, for $i = 1, 2, 3$, which is a transformation from the right-handed to the left-handed coordinate system. It anticommutes with $\boldsymbol{q}$ or $\boldsymbol{p}$,

$$[\boldsymbol{q}, \mathcal{P}]_+ = 0, \qquad (VI.1.4)$$

$$[\boldsymbol{p}, \mathcal{P}]_+ = 0, \qquad (VI.1.5)$$

but commutes with even powers of $\boldsymbol{q}$ and of $\boldsymbol{p}$; that is,

$$\begin{aligned} [\boldsymbol{q}^{2n}, \mathcal{P}] &= 0, \\ [\boldsymbol{p}^{2n}, \mathcal{P}] &= 0. \end{aligned} \qquad (VI.1.6)$$

If $|\boldsymbol{\Psi}, t\rangle$ is a state of a dynamical system we can define a "mirror state" by

$$|\boldsymbol{\Psi}', t\rangle = \mathcal{P}|\boldsymbol{\Psi}, t\rangle. \qquad (VI.1.7)$$

The representative of this state in $\boldsymbol{q}$ representation is

$$\begin{aligned} \langle \boldsymbol{r}, t|\mathcal{P}|\boldsymbol{\Psi}, t\rangle &= \int \langle \boldsymbol{r}, t|\mathcal{P}|\boldsymbol{r}', t\rangle d^3x' \langle \boldsymbol{r}', t|\boldsymbol{\Psi}, t\rangle \\ &= \int \langle \boldsymbol{r}, t|-\boldsymbol{r}', t\rangle \psi(\boldsymbol{r}', t) d^3x' \\ &= \int \delta(\boldsymbol{r} + \boldsymbol{r}')\psi(\boldsymbol{r}', t) d^3x'. \end{aligned}$$

Hence

$$\langle \boldsymbol{r}, t|\mathcal{P}|\boldsymbol{\Psi}, t\rangle = \psi(-\boldsymbol{r}, t)$$

and the effect of $\mathcal{P}$ on a function of position is to replace it by its mirror function. Thus

$$\mathcal{P}\psi(\boldsymbol{r}, t) = \psi(-\boldsymbol{r}, t)$$

and

$$\mathcal{P}^2\psi(\boldsymbol{r}, t) = \psi(\boldsymbol{r}, t)$$

so

$$\mathcal{P}^2 = 1 \qquad (VI.1.8)$$

and its eigenvalues are ± 1. In the above equations the number of position coordinates (that is, the number of particles) are not restricted; the parity operator will operate on equal footing on all of them.

The probability of finding a particle at $\boldsymbol{r}$ in the state $\mathcal{P}\psi$ is equal to the probability of finding it at $-\boldsymbol{r}$ in the state $\psi(\boldsymbol{r}, t)$. We shall assume that (for a large number of dynamical systems) $\mathcal{P}$ is a linear Hermitian operator and that it commutes with the Hamiltonian (in most cases):

$$[\mathcal{P}, H] = 0. \tag{VI.1.9}$$

Equation (*VI.1.9*) means that:

(a) *$\mathcal{P}$ is a constant of the motion,*
(b) *The Hamiltonian is a scalar,*
(c) *$\mathcal{P}$ can be used to form together with H a complete commuting set of observables.*

Because of the anticommutation relations (*VI.1.4*) and (*VI.1.5*), the parity of a system cannot simultaneously be measured with its position or momentum. But parity can be measured simultaneously with the Hamiltonian and also for the case $\boldsymbol{p} = 0$, corresponding to the "intrinsic parity" of the system measured in its rest frame. Parity commutes also with the total angular momentum operator $\boldsymbol{J}$.

The eigenfunctions of orbital angular momentum of a particle—that is, the spherical harmonics $Y_{lm}(\theta, \phi)$—are also eigenfunctions of parity operator $\mathcal{P}$ (since $\mathcal{P}$ and $\boldsymbol{L}$ commute) with eigenvalues $(-1)^l$. Hence we say that parity of a one-particle state of orbital angular momentum l is given by $P = (-1)^l$, which is usually called "orbital parity." For odd or even values of l, parity is odd or even, respectively. If P_i, for $i = 1, 2, \cdots, n$, are parities of the constituents of an n-particle system, then the parity of the whole system is defined as the product of the parities of $n - 1$ relative orbital angular momentum states; that is, $P = (-1)^{l_1 + l_2 + \cdots + l_{m-1}}$, where $l_1, l_2, l_3, \cdots, l_{n-1}$ are orbital momenta of the particles.

VI.1.A. The Time-Reversed State of a Dynamical System

The classical equations of motion are symmetrical with respect to past and future. The same applies in the form of "microscopic reversibility" for classical statistical ensembles. Here the property of microscopic reversibility is expressed in terms of "correlation functions," as

$$\langle f_i(t) f_j(t + \tau) \rangle = \langle f_i(t) f_j(t - \tau) \rangle,$$

where the average value is calculated over a microcanonical ensemble of systems. The functions f_i, for $i = 1, 2, \cdots$ are state variables of the statistical system. Thus correlation between a value $f_i(t)$ at a time t and a value $f_j(t + \tau)$ at a time τ later is the same as the correlation between $f_i(t)$ and a value of f_j at a time τ earlier.

Quantum mechanical laws also possess similar time-reversal invariance properties. The displacement in time of the state of the dynamical system, from a fixed time $t = 0$ to time t, is given by [see (*V.2.9*)]

$$|\boldsymbol{\Psi}, t\rangle = |\boldsymbol{\Psi}, 0\rangle - \frac{i}{\hbar}\int_0^t \epsilon_+(t, t_1)H(t_1)|\boldsymbol{\Psi}, t_1\rangle\, dt_1. \qquad (VI.1.10)$$

By replacing t by $-t$ we obtain the time-reversed description of the dynamical system in terms of the state vector $|\boldsymbol{\Psi}, -t\rangle$, which satisfies the integral equation

$$|\boldsymbol{\Psi}, -t\rangle = |\boldsymbol{\Psi}, 0\rangle - \frac{i}{\hbar}\int_0^{-t} \epsilon_+(-t, t_1)H(t_1)|\boldsymbol{\Psi}, t_1\rangle\, dt_1.$$

By making the transformation $t_1 \longrightarrow -t_1$ in the integral, we get

$$|\boldsymbol{\Psi}, -t\rangle = |\boldsymbol{\Psi}, 0\rangle + \frac{i}{\hbar}\int_0^t \epsilon_+(-t, -t_1)H(-t_1)|\boldsymbol{\Psi}, -t_1\rangle\, dt_1,$$

where the function $\epsilon_+(-t, -t_1)$ is defined by

$$\epsilon_+(-t, -t_1) = -\epsilon_-(t, t_1) = \begin{cases} 1 & \text{if } t \leqq t_1, \\ 0 & \text{if } t > t_1. \end{cases}$$

Hence the time-reversed state satisfies the equation

$$|\boldsymbol{\Psi}, -t\rangle = |\boldsymbol{\Psi}, 0\rangle - \frac{i}{\hbar}\int_0^t \epsilon_-(t, t_1)H(-t_1)|\boldsymbol{\Psi}, -t_1\rangle\, dt_1. \qquad (VI.1.11)$$

If we require that the time development of the system from the present ($t = 0$) to a future time t in a state $|\boldsymbol{\Psi}, t\rangle$ be the same as its time development from the future time t to the "present past" in a state $|\boldsymbol{\Psi}, -t\rangle$, then the two states will, naturally, be related by a quantum mechanical operation $\mathfrak{J}$:

$$|\boldsymbol{\Psi}, -t\rangle = \mathfrak{J}|\boldsymbol{\Psi}, t\rangle. \qquad (VI.1.12)$$

The Schrödinger and Heisenberg dynamical variables are related by unitary transformations and therefore every dynamical variable (via Heisenberg's equations of motion) has a well-defined time development. This means that a time-reversal operation will affect all the dynamical variables of a system. For example, in a state $|\boldsymbol{\Psi}, -t\rangle$ all velocities and spins of a dynamical system have opposite directions to those in the state $|\boldsymbol{\Psi}, t\rangle$.

In order to see the fundamental significance of statement (*VI.1.12*) let us work with the solutions of equations (*VI.1.10*) and (*VI.1.11*). Symbolic forms of the solutions are obtainable from the generalization of the solution (*I.7.9*) for a time-dependent rotation operator. Thus we can write

$$|\boldsymbol{\Psi}, t\rangle = P\exp\left[-\frac{i}{\hbar}\int_0^t H(t')\, dt'\right]|\boldsymbol{\Psi}, 0\rangle \qquad (VI.1.13)$$

and

$$|\boldsymbol{\Psi}, -t\rangle = \overline{P}_c\exp\left[\left(-\frac{i}{\hbar}\int_0^t H(-t')\, dt'\right)\right]|\boldsymbol{\Psi}, 0\rangle, \qquad (VI.1.14)$$

where the effect of the operator $\overline{P}_c$ is to order the operators in reverse order to the ordering of operators by P, followed by Hermitian conjugation. More explicitly, let us use the notation P_{LE} for the operation of ordering of operators from earlier time to later time and P_{EL} for ordering in the reverse order. Thus we have

$$\overline{P}_c = P_{EL}\overline{C}$$

and

$$P_{EL}^{\dagger} = P_{EL}^{-1}, \qquad P_{LE}^{\dagger} = P_{LE}^{-1}.$$

The effect of $P_{EL}\overline{C}$ on the operators following it is equivalent to ordering the operators from later time to the earlier time, plus Hermitian conjugation.

From (*VI.1.12*), (*VI.1.13*), and (*VI.1.14*) it follows that

$$\begin{aligned} \mathfrak{J}P_{LE} &= P_{EL}\overline{C}, \\ H(t) &= H(-t), \end{aligned}$$

so the time-reversal operation $\mathfrak{J}$ is

$$\mathfrak{J} = P_{EL}P_{LE}^{-1}\overline{C},$$

where $P_{EL}P_{LE}^{-1}$ is a unitary operator U. Thus for the most general form of the time reversal-operation $\mathfrak{J}$, we have

$$\mathfrak{J} = U\overline{C}. \qquad (VI.1.15)$$

The operator $\mathfrak{J}$, as defined by (*VI.1.15*), is an antiunitary operator. In deriving (*VI.1.15*) we have used the assumption $H(t) = H(-t)$, or rather

$$\mathfrak{J}H(t)\mathfrak{J}^{-1} = H(-t). \qquad (VI.1.16)$$

If (*VI.1.16*) was not true, the time-reversal operation $\mathfrak{J}$ would not be a symmetry element in quantum mechanics. The unitary operator U in (*VI.1.15*) is, further, restricted by the transformation property (the spin) of the dynamical system. Statement (*VI.1.16*) implies that (because of the antiunitary nature of $\mathfrak{J}$) the Hamiltonian of a dynamical system cannot contain any complex function in its structure. For example, a coupling constant representing the strength of a particular interaction must be a real number. A complex coupling constant would violate the time-reversal invariance of a dynamical system.

Another important property of the time-reversal operator $\mathfrak{J}$, not shared by parity operation, comes from its repeated operation. Thus, for example,

$$\mathfrak{J}^2 = U\overline{C}U\overline{C} = UU^* = aI.$$

From the unitarity of U it follows that

$$U^* = aU^{-1} = aU^{\dagger} = a(aU^{-1}) = a^2U^{-1}.$$

Hence, taking the transpose of both sides, we get

$$U^{\dagger} = a^2U^{\dagger}$$

or

$$a^2 = 1;$$

therefore

$$a = \pm 1$$

yields the result

$$\mathfrak{J}^2 = \pm 1. \qquad (VI.1.17)$$

For a single particle with spin $\frac{1}{2}$ we have $\mathfrak{J}^2 = -1$; with spin 1 we have $\mathfrak{J}^2 = 1$ (see Chapter VIII). For an n-particle system the time-reversal operator is of the form $\mathfrak{J} = \mathfrak{J}_1 \mathfrak{J}_2 \cdots \mathfrak{J}_n$, where $\mathfrak{J}_1, \mathfrak{J}_2, \cdots, \mathfrak{J}_n$ are time-reversal operators for individual particles.

In accordance with the correspondence with classical theory we can assume that the position operator $\boldsymbol{q}$ commutes with $\mathfrak{J}$. But from Schrödinger's representation of the momentum operator and from the antilinearity of $\mathfrak{J}$ it follows that $\mathfrak{J}$ and $\boldsymbol{p}$ anticommute:

$$\mathfrak{J}\boldsymbol{p}\mathfrak{J}^{-1} = -\boldsymbol{p}. \qquad (VI.1.18)$$

The operator $\mathfrak{J}$ anticommutes also with the orbital angular momentum and therefore with the spin operator itself:

$$\mathfrak{J}\boldsymbol{s}\mathfrak{J}^{-1} = -\boldsymbol{s}. \qquad (VI.1.19)$$

The transformation properties of $\boldsymbol{p}$ and $\boldsymbol{s}$ under $\mathfrak{J}$ operation imply certain restrictions on the possible forms of a time-reversal invariant Hamiltonian. The observables $\boldsymbol{p}$ and $\boldsymbol{s}$ can occur in the Hamiltonian H only in a time-reversal invariant combination, with themselves or with other observables of a dynamical system. For example, the operators $\boldsymbol{s}\cdot\boldsymbol{\mathcal{H}}$, $\boldsymbol{L}\cdot\boldsymbol{s}$, $\boldsymbol{p}^2$, $\boldsymbol{p}\cdot\boldsymbol{s}$, are typical linear Hermitian operators that are invariant under time-reversal operation.

VI.1.B. Problems

1. Prove that at a fixed time, say $t = 0$, the wave function corresponding to a time-reversed state is just the complex conjugate of the wave function of the original state. Prove also that the wave function in a momentum space corresponding to a time-reversed state is $\phi^*(-\boldsymbol{p})$.

2. The absolute value of the scalar product of any two states $|\boldsymbol{\Psi}\rangle$ and $|\boldsymbol{\Phi}\rangle$, or $|\langle\boldsymbol{\Phi}|\boldsymbol{\Psi}\rangle|$, does not change under time-reversal operation, where $\langle\boldsymbol{\Phi}|\boldsymbol{\Psi}\rangle$ is called the "transition probability amplitude." If α is an observable, producing transition from the state $|\boldsymbol{\Psi}\rangle$ to the state $|\boldsymbol{\Phi}\rangle$, then the transition probability amplitude $\langle\boldsymbol{\Phi}|\alpha|\boldsymbol{\Psi}\rangle$ satisfies the equation

$$[\langle\boldsymbol{\Phi}'|\alpha(t)|\boldsymbol{\Psi}'\rangle]^* = \langle\boldsymbol{\Phi}|\alpha(-t)|\boldsymbol{\Psi}\rangle, \qquad (VI.1.20)$$

where

$$\alpha(-t) = \mathfrak{J}^{-1}\alpha\mathfrak{J}, \qquad |\boldsymbol{\Psi}'\rangle = \mathfrak{J}|\boldsymbol{\Psi}\rangle, \qquad |\boldsymbol{\Phi}'\rangle = \mathfrak{J}|\boldsymbol{\Phi}\rangle.$$

3. The unitary operator

$$S(\infty, -\infty) = P_{LE}\left[\exp\left(-\frac{i}{\hbar}\int_{-\infty}^{\infty} H(t)\,dt\right)\right], \qquad (VI.1.21)$$

which connects the states at infinite past to states at infinite future, is called the *collision matrix* (or *S matrix*) in quantum mechanics. Prove that its time-reversed form is given by*

$$\mathfrak{J}S\mathfrak{J}^{-1} = S^{-1} = S^{\dagger}. \qquad (VI.1.22)$$

VI.2. The Pauli Principle

The existence of indistinguishable particles is a symmetry of nature that lies in a deeper level than the symmetries contained in the space and time parities discussed above. A system is said to consist of N indistinguishable particles if no observable change is made when any two of its members are interchanged. The basic quantities describing each member of the N-particle system can be divided into two classes.

(a) Dynamical variables: all particles have the same magnitude of spin but not necessarily the same directions of spin; each member has a position, or momentum, and a Hamiltonian operator associated with it; the dynamical variables' spin, orbital angular momentum, energy, momentum, and position obey the corresponding uncertainty relations.

(b) Intrinsic properties: all particles of the system have the same electric charge and mass.

A system of N particles satisfying the above conditions may be called "dynamically equivalent" particles. If we ignore the interaction between the particles, then the total Hamiltonian is the sum of the Hamiltonians of individual particles,

$$\boldsymbol{H} = H(1) + H(2) + \cdots + H(N),$$

where we used the symbols 1, 2, $\cdots$, N to represent the dynamical variables on which each Hamiltonian depends. The total Hamiltonian is symmetrical with respect to the interchange of the particles. Since the interactions of the particles are neglected, each particle obeys the corresponding Schrödinger equation:

$$i\hbar\frac{d}{dt}|\boldsymbol{\Psi}_i, t\rangle = H(i)|\boldsymbol{\Psi}_i, t\rangle, \qquad \text{for } i = 1, 2, \cdots, N. \qquad (VI.2.1)$$

---

* L. Wolfenstein and J. Ashkin, *Phys. Rev.*, **85** (1952), 947–949.
R. H. Dalitz, *Proc. Phys. Soc., London, A*, **65** (1952), 175–178.
E. P. Wigner and L. Eisenbud, *Phys. Rev.*, **72** (1947), 29–41.
F. Coester, *Phys. Rev.*, **84** (1951), 1259; **89** (1953), 619–620.

The assembly of an N-particle system as a whole obeys the Schrödinger equation

$$i\hbar \frac{d}{dt} |\boldsymbol{\Psi}, t\rangle = \boldsymbol{H}|\boldsymbol{\Psi}, t\rangle, \qquad (VI.2.2)$$

where the state $|\boldsymbol{\Psi}, t\rangle$ is some symmetrical function of the states $|\boldsymbol{\Psi}_i, t\rangle$. If $|\boldsymbol{\Psi}_i\rangle$ is a stationary state for the ith particle, with energy eigenvalue E_{in} for $n = 1, 2, \cdots$, then the corresponding stationary state $|\boldsymbol{\Psi}\rangle$ of the assembly satisfies the equation

$$\boldsymbol{H}|\boldsymbol{\Psi}\rangle = E|\boldsymbol{\Psi}\rangle, \qquad (VI.2.3)$$

where the total energy eigenvalue E is given by

$$E = E_i^a + E_j^b + E_k^c + \cdots + E_s^q.$$

where

$$i, j, k, \cdots, s = 1, 2, \cdots, N$$

and

$$i \neq j \neq k \neq \cdots \neq s,$$

so the energy of, for example, the ith particle can be E_1^a or E_2^a, and so on. The eigenstate corresponding to energy E can be written as

$$|\boldsymbol{\Psi}\rangle = |\boldsymbol{\Psi}_i^a\rangle|\boldsymbol{\Psi}_j^b\rangle \cdots |\boldsymbol{\Psi}_s^q\rangle, \qquad (VI.2.4)$$

so any one of these with $i = 1, 2, \cdots, N$, $j = 1, 2, \cdots, N, \cdots$, $s = 1, 2, \cdots, N$ are possible eigenfunctions corresponding to the same energy E. We can interchange the particles and corresponding states without changing the energy E. Every possible interchange of the particles leads to another state for the assembly. In this way we see that to a given eigenvalue E of the assembly correspond many states, so there is a *degeneracy* arising from the *exchange process*. At a given time we can form certain linear combinations of the eigenstates $(VI.2.4)$ to remove the degeneracy. There are only two possibilities. (a) *Symmetrical states* can be formed by adding all possible products of individual eigenstates of the type $(VI.2.4)$, obtained by permutations among the particles of the assembly:

$$|\boldsymbol{\Psi}_s\rangle = \sum_P P|\boldsymbol{\Psi}_i^a\rangle|\boldsymbol{\Psi}_j^b\rangle \cdots |\boldsymbol{\Psi}_s^q\rangle, \qquad (VI.2.5)$$

where $\sum_P$ means the sum over all permutations P. There is only one symmetrical state for a given total energy E. The degeneracy is thus removed. (b) *Antisymmetrical* states can be formed in a determinantal form:

$$|\boldsymbol{\Psi}_A\rangle = \begin{vmatrix} |\boldsymbol{\Psi}_1^a\rangle & |\boldsymbol{\Psi}_2^a\rangle & \cdots & |\boldsymbol{\Psi}_N^a\rangle \\ |\boldsymbol{\Psi}_1^b\rangle & |\boldsymbol{\Psi}_2^b\rangle & \cdots & |\boldsymbol{\Psi}_N^b\rangle \\ \cdots & \cdots & \cdots & \cdots \\ |\boldsymbol{\Psi}_1^q\rangle & |\boldsymbol{\Psi}_2^q\rangle & \cdots & |\boldsymbol{\Psi}_N^q\rangle \end{vmatrix}. \qquad (VI.2.6)$$

The antisymmetrical state $|\Psi_A\rangle$ of the assembly represents a state where the particle states $a, b, \cdots, q$ are occupied and where occupation of any state by each particle is equally likely. The occupation of any of the two states $|\Psi_a\rangle$ and $|\Psi_b\rangle$ by any two particles, where $|\Psi_a\rangle$ and $|\Psi_b\rangle$ are the same, does not correspond to a state for the assembly since in this case $|\Psi_A\rangle = 0$. Hence we see that two particles cannot occupy the same state; that is, spin direction, momentum and energy eigenvalue, position, and so on, cannot be the same. This is *Pauli's exclusion principle.* For example, the wave function of a two-electron system, if symmetrical with respect to the coordinates of the electrons, must be antisymmetrical with respect to the spin wave function of the two-electron system.

Because of the symmetrical structure of the Hamiltonian of the N-particle assembly, the corresponding state as a solution of the Schrödinger's equation will vary with time according to the particular symmetry (symmetrical or antisymmetrical) with which it started initially. This is believed to be a basic law of nature; it is not required for the formulation of quantum mechanics but it can be brought into quantum mechanics by formulating the particular statistics required by the symmetries of the states.

For symmetrical states it is possible for two or more particles to be in the same state. The statistics implied by this description seems to have some similarity to classical statistics where one uses the concept of *Gibbs ensemble.* It is important to point out that the statistics implied by the symmetrical states of quantum ensembles (*Bose statistics*) is considerably different from classical statistics.

VI.2.A. Density Matrix

According to the discussion in (*V.2.17*), the classical distribution function f, as follows from (*V.2.12*), satisfies the equation of conservation,

$$\frac{\partial f}{\partial t} = -[f, H]_c, \tag{VI.2.7}$$

where the number of similar particles is given by $\int f \, d\Gamma = N$, with

$$d\Gamma = \prod_{i=1}^{N} dq_i \, dp_i$$

as the phase space element. In this description all N similar dynamical systems move independently without mutual interaction. The distribution function f can be used to calculate the average value of any dynamical variable $A(q, p)$ according to

$$\langle A \rangle = \int Af \, d\Gamma. \tag{VI.2.8}$$

In quantum mechanics the phase space at a given time t cannot be defined unambiguously. For example for one-particle distribution we can, at best, imagine a "cell" in phase space whose dimensions are of the order of $(\Delta q \Delta p)^3 \cong \hbar^3$. In quantum mechanics we may sometimes have to consider a motion of a dynamical system which is not completely specified. Such possibilities occur quite frequently—for example in atomic and nuclear phenomena involving polarization, spin orientations, and angular correlations. In these cases the possible information is less that maximum information attained in a "pure state," where we can talk of states of definite spin orientation, represented by state vectors. In situations where the information is less than maximum possible information, we introduce, by analogy with classical statistical description, the concept of a "density matrix" to represent such states. The use of the density matrix is of special importance for the description of many-body phenomena. The idea of the density matrix description was first introduced by von Neumann.

The states of dynamical systems introduced so far are *"pure states" characterized by the possibility of performing an experiment in the particular state leading to a prediction with certainty*. The particular state is assumed to be an eigenvector of a Hermitian operator which forms a complete commuting set, with itself or with some other set of Hermitian operators. If a beam of photons, for example, is transmitted 100% through a suitably oriented *Nicol prism*, then we say that each photon of the beam is linearly polarized. This is an example of a pure state. No other state of polarization has this property with respect to the same prism. In this case the information on the system is maximum. However, a beam of photons with partial polarization is not, with certainty, transmitted or reflected by a prism. In this case the information is less than the maximum. It is possible to analyze a nonpure state into pure states. We first assume a certain probability law and consider a dynamical system that can be found in one of the many possible states according to this law.

For the sake of simplicity let us consider a complete set of discrete orthonormal states $|\beta_n\rangle$ and expand a pure state $|\boldsymbol{\Psi}\rangle$ according to

$$|\boldsymbol{\Psi}\rangle = \sum_{n=1}^{\infty} |\beta_n\rangle\langle\beta_n|\boldsymbol{\Psi}\rangle = \sum_{n=1}^{\infty} a_n|\beta_n\rangle, \qquad (VI.2.9)$$

where the expansion coefficients, the representatives of $|\boldsymbol{\Psi}\rangle$, define the pure state completely. Let us consider various other pure states represented by $|\boldsymbol{\Psi}^{(s)}\rangle$. Each pure state can be expanded according to

$$|\boldsymbol{\Psi}^{(s)}\rangle = \sum_{n=1}^{\infty} a_n^{(s)}|\beta_n\rangle, \qquad (VI.2.10)$$

and the average value of an observable α with respect to any one of these pure states is given by

$$\langle\alpha\rangle_s = \langle\boldsymbol{\Psi}^{(s)}|\alpha|\boldsymbol{\Psi}^{(s)}\rangle = \sum_{nn'} a_{n'}^{*(s)} a_n^{(s)} \langle\beta_n{}'|\alpha|\beta_n\rangle.$$

Calculation of the probability of a certain experimental result where the dynamical system is in a nonpure state proceeds as follows.

(a) We assume a probability P_s for each pure state $|\boldsymbol{\Psi}^{(s)}\rangle$.

(b) The average value of a dynamical variable α is then defined by taking the average of $\langle\alpha\rangle_s$ with the corresponding probabilities P_s. Because of the possibility that each P_s is different, this procedure corresponds to an incoherent superposition of the pure state's average values of α. Hence the resultant average value of α is

$$\langle\alpha\rangle = \sum_s \langle\alpha\rangle_s P_s. \qquad (VI.2.11)$$

It can be rewritten as

$$\langle\alpha\rangle = \sum_{nn'} \sum_s a_{n'}^{*(s)} a_n^{(s)} \langle\beta_n{}'|\alpha|\beta_n\rangle P_s$$

$$= \sum_{nn'} \langle\beta_n{}'|\alpha|\beta_n\rangle\langle\beta_n|\rho|\beta_n{}'\rangle,$$

where

$$\langle\beta_n|\rho|\beta_n{}'\rangle = \sum_s a_{n'}^{*(s)} a_n^{(s)} P_s$$

$$= \sum_s \langle\boldsymbol{\Psi}^{(s)}|\beta_n{}'\rangle\langle\beta_n|\boldsymbol{\Psi}^{(s)}\rangle P_s.$$

Hence

$$\rho = \sum_s |\boldsymbol{\Psi}^{(s)}\rangle P_s \langle\boldsymbol{\Psi}^{(s)}| \qquad (VI.2.12)$$

is the quantum density operator. With this definition the resultant average value of α becomes

$$\langle\alpha\rangle = \sum_n \langle\beta_n|\alpha\rho|\beta_n\rangle = \mathrm{tr}\,(\alpha\rho). \qquad (VI.2.13)$$

From the definition of the density operator ρ we see that it is a Hermitian operator and therefore its eigenvalues are real. A comparison of (*VI.2.13*) with the classical average value (*VI.2.8*) shows that the phase space integration of the classical observable A times the classical distribution function f is replaced in quantum mechanics by the diagonal sum of the quantum observable α times the quantum density function ρ with respect to a complete set of eigenvectors. If the representation is taken as a continuous one, then the discrete sum in (*VI.2.13*) is replaced by

$$\langle \alpha \rangle = \int \langle \beta' | \alpha \rho | \beta' \rangle \, d\beta'. \tag{VI.2.14}$$

If α corresponds to an identity operation, then its mean value must be unity. This leads to the restriction

$$\text{tr } \rho = 1. \tag{VI.2.15}$$

From the application of the concept of the norm of an operator [see (*I.5.21*)] to ρ, it follows that the density matrix is further restricted by

$$\text{tr } (\rho^2) \leqq 1. \tag{VI.2.16}$$

If the pure states $|\boldsymbol{\Psi}^{(s)}\rangle$ are solutions of Schrödinger's equation, then the density matrix, as can easily be seen, satisfies the equation

$$i\hbar \frac{d\rho}{dt} = -[\rho, H], \tag{VI.2.17}$$

which differs from the Heisenberg equations of motion for a dynamical variable in the minus sign on the right. It has a formal resemblance (except in the total time derivative) to classical conservation equation (*VI.2.7*) for the classical distribution function f.

Furthermore, from the definition of ρ we deduce the statement

$$\langle \beta_n | \rho | \beta_n \rangle = \sum_s |a_n^{(s)}|^2 P_s \tag{VI.2.18}$$

on the probability of the observable β, which are diagonal in $|\beta_n\rangle$ representation (having the values β_n).

A density matrix of finite order N is formed from N pure states $|\boldsymbol{\Psi}^{(s)}\rangle$ for $s = 1, 2, \cdots, N$. The conditions of Hermiticity and (*VI.2.15*) imply that the density matrix ρ is completely defined by $N^2 - 1$ parameters. Hence a state possessing N pure states can be identified by $N^2 - 1$ data. For example, the spin of Co^{60} is 5 and it has $(2s + 1) = 11$ pure states of spin orientation. Therefore the description of a specific state of spin orientation generally requires $(11)^2 - 1 = 120$ independent data.

To illustrate the above formalism let us consider orientation of particles of spin $\frac{1}{2}\hbar$.* In this case one has two pure states of opposite (up and down) spin orientations and hence the density matrix is a 2×2 matrix. In a nonpure state the degree and direction of spin orientation is described by a vector,

$$\boldsymbol{q} = \langle \boldsymbol{\sigma} \rangle = \text{tr } (\boldsymbol{\sigma}\rho), \tag{VI.2.19}$$

where the $\boldsymbol{\sigma}$ are Pauli spin matrices. For definite spin orientation in a pure state, one has $|\boldsymbol{q}| = 1$, in a state of random orientation, $|\boldsymbol{q}| = 0$. The fact that

---

* U. Fano, *Rev. Mod. Phys.*, **29** (1957), 75.

the Pauli matrices σ_i together with I_2 form a complete algebra can serve to express ρ in the form*

$$\rho = a_1\sigma_1 + a_2\sigma_2 + a_3\sigma_3 + a_4,$$

where from tr $\rho = 1$ and tr $\sigma_i = 0$ we have

$$2a_4 = 1, \qquad a_4 = \tfrac{1}{2}.$$

Using the expression (*VI.2.19*) for the vector $\boldsymbol{q}$, we obtain $q_i = 2a_i$, where we use the easily established formula $\text{tr}\,(\sigma_i\sigma_j) = 2\delta_{ij}$.
Hence the density matrix is

$$\rho = \tfrac{1}{2}(I_2 + \boldsymbol{\sigma}\cdot\boldsymbol{q}). \qquad (VI.2.20)$$

This result can be applied to the treatment of Larmor precession of spin orientation in a magnetic field. The energy of an electron in a magnetic field $\boldsymbol{\mathcal{H}}$ with magnetic moment $\boldsymbol{\mu}$ is

$$H = -\boldsymbol{\mu}\cdot\boldsymbol{\mathcal{H}}, \qquad (VI.2.21)$$

where $\boldsymbol{\mu} = (e/2mc)\hbar\boldsymbol{\sigma}$.

If we use the equation of motion (*VI.2.17*) for ρ, with the Hamiltonian operator given by (*VI.2.21*) and the definition of ρ as in (*VI.2.20*), we find the classical result

$$\frac{d\boldsymbol{q}}{dt} = \frac{e}{mc}\,\boldsymbol{q}\times\boldsymbol{\mathcal{H}} \qquad (VI.2.22)$$

[see (*I.4.23*) and (*I.6.20*)].

A second example can be constructed from the classical anology of a system in thermodynamic equilibrium at a temperature T. The classical Gibbs distribution of such a system can be taken over in quantum mechanics in the form

$$\rho = Ae^{-H/\kappa T}, \qquad (VI.2.23)$$

where A is a normalization constant defined by

$$A = (\text{tr}\, e^{-H/\kappa T})^{-1}$$

and H is the quantum Hamiltonian of the system. From (*VI.2.23*) we see that ρ commutes with H, so the energy of an assembly in a steady state $d\rho/dt = 0$ can be measured, as well as the probability that it remains in this state.

VI.2.B. Bose-Einstein Statistics

A deeper understanding of classical and quantum probability and statistics concepts may be obtained from a comparison of the basic ideas of Boltzmann and Bose-Einstein (and also of Fermi-Dirac) distributions. The classical phase space can be imagined to consist of a large number of small "cells,"

---

* H. A. Tolhoek and S. R. deGroot, *Phys. Rev.*, **83** (1951), 189.

each of size a_i, where $i = 1, 2, \cdots$, the total volume of phase space being Γ. Consider the distribution of N particles (or systems) over the cells. Let n_i be the number of particles in η_i states (or cells) so that the *mean occupation numbers* are n_i/η_i, where $i = 1, 2, \cdots$. In Boltzmann statistics it is assumed that the mean occupation numbers of all states are small compared to unity, so the distribution of the particles over different states is independent of one another. If each one of n_i particles is put into one of η_i states the result is $(\eta_i)^{n_i}$ distributions. The probability that n_i particles will be found in cell number 1, that n_2 particles will be found in cell number 2, and so on, with "equal a priori probability" (that is, all points in phase space are equally probable) is given by

$$P_B = \prod_i \frac{(\eta_i)^{n_i}}{n_i!} \qquad (VI.2.24)$$

This is the basis of the Boltzmann distribution for a system of particles not in equilibrium. Derivation of equilibrium state distribution, as the most probable distribution, follows from the *entropy** of the system of particles:

$$S = \kappa \log P_B. \qquad (VI.2.25)$$

Hence

$$S = \kappa \sum_i [n_i \log \eta_i - \log (n_i!)].$$

For very large n_i we can use the formula

$$\log n! = \log 1 + \log 2 + \cdots + \log n$$
$$\cong \int_0^n \log x \, dx = n \log \frac{n}{e} \qquad (VI.2.26)$$

and obtain the entropy in the form

$$S_B = \kappa \sum_i n_i \log \left(\frac{e\eta_i}{n_i}\right).$$

In terms of the average occupation number, $\bar{n}_i = n_i/\eta_i$, we have

$$S = \kappa \sum_i \eta_i \bar{n}_i \log \left(\frac{e}{\bar{n}_i}\right), \qquad (VI.2.27)$$

where

$$\sum_i n_i = \sum_i \eta_i \bar{n}_i = N,$$
$$\sum_i E_i n_i = \sum_i E_i \eta_i \bar{n}_i = E,$$

where E is the total energy. With these conditions, and from the method of

* E. Schrödinger, *Statistical Thermodynamics*, Cambridge University Press, Cambridge, 1948.

Lagrange's undetermined multipliers, we find the condition for maximum entropy (the equilibrium state) as

$$\frac{\partial}{\partial \bar{n}_i}\left(\frac{S}{\kappa} + AN + BE\right) = 0$$

or

$$\eta_i(A + BE_i - \log \bar{n}_i) = 0,$$

where A and B are constants. Hence the most probable distribution is

$$n_i = Fe^{-E_i/\kappa T},$$

where F is a constant; the constant B is identified in thermodynamics as $-1/\kappa T$, where κ is the *Boltzmann constant.*

For the Bose-Einstein distribution the restriction of *equal a priori probability* is relaxed; there can be any number of particles in each state. The probability (*VI.2.24*) is modified to become the total number of ways of distributing n_i particles amongst η_i states. In this case, instead of a large number of small cells, as in the Boltzmann picture, we have a large number of cells with no restrictions on their sizes. We may envisage the phase space as consisting of a one-dimensional array of cells of various sizes, including the possibility of equal cells as well as cells of zero dimensions. If there are η_i states, then the cells are partitioned from one another by $\eta_i - 1$ phase space walls. We may further separate each of the n_i particles distributed over η_i states arranged along the one-dimensional array by additional phase space walls. Thus the total number of walls in the array is $\eta_i + n_i - 1$. The number of ways in which one can choose $\eta_i - 1$ walls out of $\eta_i + n_i - 1$ objects is the required probability for the Bose-Einstein distribution, or

$$P_{BE} = \prod_i \frac{(n_i + \eta_i - 1)!}{n_i!(n_i - 1)!}. \qquad (VI.2.28)$$

The corresponding entropy, following the procedure for the Boltzmann distribution, is

$$S_{BE} = \kappa \sum_i \eta_i[(1 + \bar{n}_i) \log (1 + n_i) - \bar{n}_i \log \bar{n}_i], \qquad (VI.2.29)$$

which for $n_i \ll \eta_i$ reduces to the corresponding entropy for Boltzmann distribution. For very large n_i, equation (*VI.2.29*) becomes

$$S_{BE} = \kappa \sum_i \eta_i \log \left(\frac{en_i}{\eta_i}\right), \qquad (VI.2.30)$$

which would follow from S_B by replacing n_i by η_i and η_i by n_i. The most probable distribution for a Bose-Einstein system is therefore

$$n_i = \frac{G\eta_i}{e^{E_i/\kappa T} - G}, \qquad (VI.2.31)$$

where G is a constant.

Consider now a two-particle system and the only two possible states that it can occupy. According to Boltzmann statistics, if the two-particle system is in thermodynamic equilibrium at very high temperatures, the probability of finding any one of the particles in either state is equal (*equal a priori probability*). The distribution consists of a probability of $\frac{1}{4}$ that both particles are in state I, a probability $\frac{1}{4}$ that both particles are in state II, and a probability $\frac{1}{2}$ that one particle is in states I and II.

If we apply the Bose-Einstein distribution, we use the symmetrical states of the two particles. From (*VI.2.4*) we can form, for a two-particle system, three symmetrical states,

$$\begin{aligned} |\boldsymbol{\Psi}_1\rangle &= |\boldsymbol{\Psi}_I^a\rangle|\boldsymbol{\Psi}_I^b\rangle, \\ |\boldsymbol{\Psi}_2\rangle &= |\boldsymbol{\Psi}_{II}^a\rangle|\boldsymbol{\Psi}_{II}^b\rangle, \\ |\boldsymbol{\Psi}_3\rangle &= |\boldsymbol{\Psi}_I^a\rangle|\boldsymbol{\Psi}_{II}^b\rangle + |\boldsymbol{\Psi}_I^b\rangle|\boldsymbol{\Psi}_{II}^a\rangle, \end{aligned} \tag{VI.2.32}$$

where a and b are used to designate the two particles. From the quantum mechanical density function (*VI.2.23*) for two particles at high temperatures it follows that $\rho = A$ and that the three states (*VI.2.32*) are equally probable. The probability of each state $|\boldsymbol{\Psi}_i\rangle$, for $i = 1, 2, 3$, to occur is just $\frac{1}{3}$. Hence the *Bose-Einstein probability that two particles are in the same state is greater than the classical probability*.

Furthermore, in the Bose-Einstein description of a gas consisting of particles with mass in a volume V there is a limit to the maximum possible density of the gas. The compression of a gas beyond a certain density gives rise to the so-called *Bose-Einstein condensation* phenomenon. The *superfluidity* exhibited by liquid helium is attributed to Einstein condensation where, beyond a certain density of the liquid, the decrease of the volume does not affect pressure and density. The condensation phenomenon does not occur with H_e^3. The spins of H_e^4 and H_e^3 nuclei are 0 and $\frac{1}{2}$; the spin 0 obeys *Bose-Einstein* statistics but the spin $\frac{1}{2}$ obeys *Fermi-Dirac* statistics. In general, *all nuclei with odd mass number obey Fermi statistics and all nuclei with even mass number obey Bose statistics*. Therefore a natural expectation is that there exists a close connection between spin and statistics of a particle.

VI.2.C. Fermi-Dirac Statistics

Fermi-Dirac statistics is the statistical description of systems of particles obeying Pauli's exclusion principle. In this case each quantum state can be occupied by one particle at most. Therefore, the numbers n_i are of the same order of magnitude as the number of states η_i. The probability P_B or P_{BE} of Boltzmann or Bose-Einstein statistics is replaced by the number of ways of distributing n_i individual particles over η_i states, with at most one particle in each. Hence

$$P_{FD} = \prod_i \frac{\eta_i!}{n_i!(\eta_i - n_i)!}, \tag{VI.2.33}$$

and the corresponding Fermi-Dirac equilibrium distribution is

$$\bar{n}_i = \frac{D\eta_i}{e^{E_i/\varkappa T} + D}, \tag{VI.2.34}$$

where D is a constant. It is shown in statistical mechanics that (for a gas of identical particles) the decrease of temperature at a fixed density leads, in the case of Fermi statistics, to an increase in the pressure as compared to the value for ordinary gas (Fermi degeneracy of the gas).

Since a Fermi gas of identical particles has an antisymmetric wave function, we say that the quantum mechanical exchange effect sets up an additional effective "repulsion" between particles. As was pointed out previously, the exchange effect for a Bose gas (symmetric wave function) gives rise to the condensation phenomenon and hence to an effective "attraction" between the particles.

VI.3. Isotopic Spin

It has been pointed out in the discussion of Pauli's principle that the intrinsic properties of the particles described by charge and mass are not directly involved in the application of this principle, even though mass and charge play the primary role in the indistinguishability of the particles. A possible answer to the solution of the problem may be found in a further increase (in addition to energy and angular momentum quantum numbers) of the number of permissible quantum states of a dynamical system. Historically, the experimental observation of the charge independence of nuclear forces between protons and neutrons was the main motivation for a further generalization of the concept of indistinguishability; that is, as far as nuclear forces were concerned the positive charge of the proton and the zero charge of the neutron did not play any role. Therefore, like two electrons, one with spin $\frac{1}{2}$ and the other with spin $-\frac{1}{2}$, the nucleons (protons and neutrons) could be regarded as two different charge states of the "same" particle. By analogy with the spin degree of freedom for particles, it follows that we may look for an observable whose two eigenstates correspond to protons and neutrons with eigenvalues describing charge and chargeless properties of the particles. The observable in question has been called "isotopic spin." If we assume that the total isotopic spin of the "nucleon" is $\frac{1}{2}$, then we assign the eigenvalue $\frac{1}{2}$ to the proton and the value $-\frac{1}{2}$ to the neutron. Thus proton and neutron correspond to *isotopic spin-up* and *isotopic spin-down,* respectively. We can thus introduce an *isotopic spin space.*

For convenience we shall use the abbreviation "I spin" for "isotopic spin." The I spin formalism can be developed in a way completely analogous to ordinary spin—or rather, to angular momentum formalism. If the idea of I spin degree of freedom were confined to neutron-proton systems only, it would be somewhat difficult to believe in its validity as an isolated law of nature. We must look for a possible degree of freedom for I spin for all dynamical systems. Therefore we can begin by postulating the existence of a linear vector Hermitian operator T_i, for $i = 1, 2, 3$, like angular momentum J_i, satisfying the angular momentum commutation relations

$$[T_i, T_j] = i\epsilon_{ijk}T_k. \tag{VI.3.1}$$

With respect to the I spin concept all dynamical systems (for example, elementary particles) can be put into two classes. (a) Dynamical systems with integral "intrinsic I spin," $T = 0$ and $T = 1$. (b) Dynamical systems with half-integral "intrinsic I spin," $T = \frac{1}{2}$. We shall use the notation $\frac{1}{2}\tau_i$ for operators of I spin $\frac{1}{2}$, which are of the same formal structure as Pauli spin matrices σ_i, and they satisfy the commutation relation (*VI.3.1*). The operators of I spin 1, or κ_i, for $i = 1, 2, 3$, have the same formal structure as ordinary matrices of spin 1 (that is, the K matrices).

The charge of the nucleon can be represented by

$$Q_N = e^+(\tfrac{1}{2}\tau_3 + \tfrac{1}{2}), \tag{VI.3.2}$$

where τ_3 is the third component of the I spin matrices τ_i. Thus proton and neutron correspond to eigenvalues $\frac{1}{2}$ and $-\frac{1}{2}$ of τ_3 respectively. Hence we say that the nucleon is a particle with total I spin value $\frac{1}{2}$. In a similar way a typical particle of I spin 1 is called a π meson and its charge is defined by

$$Q_\pi = e^+\kappa_3, \tag{VI.3.3}$$

where κ_3 is the third component of the I spin matrices κ_i. Its eigenvalues are $+1$, -1, and 0 (see Section I.8), so altogether there are three π mesons corresponding to charges e^+, $-e^+$, and 0. We can use two representations, where in each one τ_3 and κ_3 are diagonal and define I spin $\frac{1}{2}$ and I spin 1 spaces spanned by the eigenvectors of τ_3 and κ_3, respectively. In this case the wavefunction of a particle is either a spinor in space of I spin $\frac{1}{2}$ (as for the nucleon) or a vector (or a scalar) in space of I spin 1 (or space of I spin 0). The π mesons constitute a vector in space of I spin 1. Thus the most general form of the wave function of I spin 1 is of the form

$$\begin{aligned} |\pi\rangle &= |1\rangle\langle 1|\pi\rangle + |-1\rangle\langle -1|\pi\rangle + |0\rangle\langle 0|\pi\rangle \\ &= \pi_+|1\rangle + \pi_-|-1\rangle + \pi_0|0\rangle. \end{aligned} \tag{VI.3.4}$$

(See Section I.8.)

The eigenvectors $|1\rangle$, $|-1\rangle$, and $|0\rangle$ are called positive, negative, and neutral axes, respectively. A rotation around the neutral axis of I spin space is generated by the operator κ_3:

$$|\pi'\rangle = e^{i\phi\kappa_3}|\pi\rangle.$$

Hence, as in Section I.8, we obtain the gauge transformations of the first kind,

$$\begin{aligned} |\pi'_+\rangle &= e^{i\phi}|\pi_+\rangle, \\ |\pi'_-\rangle &= e^{-i\phi}|\pi_-\rangle, \\ |\pi'_0\rangle &= |\pi_0\rangle, \end{aligned} \qquad (VI.3.5)$$

which leaves the length of the vector unchanged: $\langle\pi|\pi\rangle = \langle\pi'|\pi'\rangle = \langle\pi_c|\pi_c\rangle$. The quantity $\langle\pi|\pi\rangle$ is related to the probability of finding three π mesons. In this way we see that the three π mesons can be described in terms of a single wave function which transforms like a vector in space of I spin 1. In a similar way the nucleon representing the proton or neutron transforms like a spinor in space of I spin $\frac{1}{2}$.

In general, strongly coupled particles—interactions where electromagnetic forces can be neglected—can be related to a charge multiplet with an I spin quantum number T and multiplicity $(2T + 1)$. We may use the concept of "orbital I spin," as implied by the commutation relations (*VI.3.1*), and we can assign (for light nuclei where the Coulomb interaction is negligible compared to nuclear interaction) a T value to each nuclear level. In particular, one can use the conservation of I spin, as for the case of ordinary spin, in nuclear reactions leading to some selection rules.

The conservation of I spin is, of course, valid only for reactions that are independent of charge. In this sense all strong interactions leave charge multiplets, corresponding to eigenvalues $T_3 = -T, -T+1, \cdots, T$, rigorously degenerate. Hence, electromagnetic interactions, being essentially charge-dependent, will not conserve total I spin. The electromagnetic interactions, if taken into account, can differentiate between proton-proton and neutron-neutron interactions and hence between proton and neutron, and thus remove I spin multiplet degeneracy of the nucleon. The T_3 component of the I spin, being a function of charge, will commute with the Hamiltonian of a photon and a charged particle system, since the coupling between the last two depends on charge. Hence the electromagnetic interaction will not affect the conservation of T_3.

VI.3.A. Isotopic Spin of a Meson-Nucleon System

The I spin wave functions of a two-nucleon system are eigenfunctions of the third component of the total intrinsic I spin:

$$\boldsymbol{\tau} = \tfrac{1}{2}(\boldsymbol{\tau}_a + \boldsymbol{\tau}_b). \qquad (VI.3.6)$$

The wave functions consist of three symmetric and one antisymmetric (with respect to the interchange of nucleons) functions (see Section *IV.1.A*, problem 1),

$$
\begin{aligned}
|nn\rangle &= |an\rangle|bn\rangle, \\
|pn\rangle &= \frac{1}{\sqrt{2}}\,[|ap\rangle|bn\rangle + |an\rangle|bp\rangle], \\
|pp\rangle &= |ap\rangle|bp\rangle, \\
|pn\rangle &= \frac{1}{\sqrt{2}}\,[|ap\rangle|bn\rangle - |an\rangle|bp\rangle],
\end{aligned}
\tag{VI.3.7}
$$

where the symbols p and n signify proton and neutron, respectively. Now we can generalize the Pauli principle by including I spin as an additional quantum number into the possible number of quantum states. If the I spin wave function is one of the first three in (*VI.3.7*), then in accordance with the generalized Pauli principle the space and spin wave functions must be antisymmetric; if the two-nucleon system is in the fourth I spin state of (*VI.3.7*), then space and spin wave function must be symmetric.

For the symmetric triplet state in (*VI.3.7*) we can say that the I spins of the nucleons are parallel and add up to total I spin 1. For the singlet state the I spins are antiparallel and add up to total I spin 0.

For a meson-nucleon system the appropriate I spin operator is the sum of meson and nucleon I spins:

$$
\boldsymbol{T} = \tfrac{1}{2}\boldsymbol{\tau} + \boldsymbol{\kappa}. \tag{VI.3.8}
$$

From the rule of addition of angular momenta it follows that the resultant total I spin values are $\boldsymbol{T} = \frac{3}{2}$ and $T = \frac{1}{2}$. The corresponding wave functions (see Section *IV.3.B*) are

$$
\begin{aligned}
|\pi_- n\rangle &= |a\pi_-\rangle|bn\rangle, \\
|\pi_- p,\, \pi_0 n\rangle &= \frac{1}{\sqrt{3}}\,|a\pi_-\rangle|bp\rangle + \sqrt{\frac{2}{3}}\,|a\pi_0\rangle|bn\rangle, \\
|\pi_0 p,\, \pi_+ n\rangle &= \sqrt{\frac{2}{3}}\,|a\pi_0\rangle|bp\rangle + \frac{1}{\sqrt{3}}\,|a\pi_+\rangle|bn\rangle, \\
|\pi_+ p\rangle &= |a\pi_+\rangle|bp\rangle,
\end{aligned}
\tag{VI.3.9}
$$

for I spin value $T = \frac{3}{2}$ and $T_3(\frac{3}{2}) = -\frac{3}{2}, -\frac{1}{2}, \frac{1}{2}, \frac{3}{2}$ states, and

$$
\begin{aligned}
|\pi_0 n,\, \pi_- p\rangle &= \frac{1}{\sqrt{3}}\,|a\pi_0\rangle|bn\rangle - \sqrt{\frac{2}{3}}\,|a\pi_-\rangle|bp\rangle, \\
|\pi_0 p,\, \pi_+ n\rangle &= -\frac{1}{\sqrt{3}}\,|a\pi_0\rangle|bp\rangle + \sqrt{\frac{2}{3}}\,|a\pi_+\rangle|bn\rangle,
\end{aligned}
\tag{VI.3.10}
$$

for I spin value $T = \frac{1}{2}$ and $T_3(\frac{1}{2}) = \frac{1}{2}, -\frac{1}{2}$ states. For two-π-meson systems (as follows from problem 4 of Section *IV.1.A*) there are altogether 9 I spin states corresponding to the total I spins, $T = 0$, $T = 1$, and $T = 2$.

Finally, formula (*VI.3.2*) for the charge can be generalized to an A-nucleon system by writing for the total charge

$$Q_A = e^+(T_3 + \tfrac{1}{2}A), \qquad (VI.3.11)$$

where T_3 is the third component of the total I spin vector operator

$$T = \sum_{n=1}^{A} \tfrac{1}{2}\tau(n). \qquad (VI.3.12)$$

Thus the total I spin T is the sum (in accordance with the addition rule for angular momenta) of the individual I spins of the nucleons. Hence total I spin T assumes integral values for even A and half-integral values for odd A.

VI.3.B. The Conservation of Heavy Particles

Experimental evidence on nuclear and elementary particle reactions leads to the empirical statement that *"heavy" particles cannot be transformed into particles whose masses are less than that of the proton. This means that if in any reaction a heavy particle is annihilated or is lost, then another heavy particle will take its place.* The best evidence in favor of the conservation of heavy particles is, of course, the stability of nuclear matter.

Since the neutron is a heavy particle, then a semi-theoretical formulation of conservation of "heaviness" must be based on the conservation of charge via I spin degree of freedom. The definition of charge by (*VI.3.2*) is not symmetrical with respect to the assignment of I spin. There is, of course, no theoretical reason for excluding the possibilities of assigning the I spin value $-\frac{1}{2}$ for a charged heavy particle and the value $\frac{1}{2}$ for a neutral heavy particle. In this case formula (*VI.3.2*) can be replaced by

$$\overline{Q}_N = e^+(\tfrac{1}{2}\tau_3 - \tfrac{1}{2}). \qquad (VI.3.13)$$

The corresponding heavy particles are the one with I spin $-\frac{1}{2}$ and charge $-e^+$ (antiproton) and the other with I spin $\frac{1}{2}$ and charge zero (antineutron). The actual theoretical basis for these particles will be discussed in the relativistic form of quantum mechanics. In this section the experimental facts on the existence of antiproton and antineutron are sufficient for an understanding of laws formulated in (*VI.3.2*) and (*VI.3.13*).

Evidently the definitions of Q_N and $\bar{Q}_N$ imply the existence of a new quantum number, called "the baryon number." In terms of the baryon number N we can combine (*VI.3.2*) and (*VI.3.13*) into a single statement

$$Q = e^+(\tfrac{1}{2}\tau_3 + \tfrac{1}{2}N), \qquad (VI.3.14)$$

where the baryon number $N = 1$ corresponds to proton and neutron and the baryon number $N = -1$ to antiproton and antineutron. To complete the picture we can define the charge of the mesons and nucleons (and antinucleons) by

$$Q = e^+(T_3 + \tfrac{1}{2}N), \qquad (VI.3.15)$$

where $T_3 = \frac{1}{2}\tau_3$ for odd baryon numbers with $N = \pm 1$, and $T_3 = \kappa_3$ for even baryon numbers with $N = 0$. Hence *the baryon content of the meson is zero.* The absolute conservation of Q means that the conservation of T_3 is the same as the conservation of N.

However, this last statement does not exclude the possibility that there may still exist a quantum number that is absolutely conserved. Because *conservation of heavy particles implies that in any elementary particle reaction the number of nucleons minus the number of antinucleons remains unchanged.* But there is nothing to prevent us from generalizing the heavy particle conservation into a conservation law: in any elementary particle reaction the number of heavy particles minus the number of heavy antiparticles is unchanged (proton and antiproton being the heavy particles with lowest mass). Thus, in addition to the absolute conservation of electric charge, one can introduce* another quantum number that is also absolutely conserved. This quantum number is called the *baryon charge* n. It can assume the values 1, for baryons = nucleons + hyperons; -1, for antibaryons = antinucleons + antihyperons; and 0 for mesons (π *mesons* + K *mesons*).

Therefore the most general form of electric charge (after separating out from N the absolutely conserved baryon charge n) is a combination of three quantum numbers of I spin T_3, baryon charge n, and "*strangeness*" quantum number $\mathcal{S}$,

$$\frac{1}{e^+} Q = T_3 + \tfrac{1}{2}\, n + \tfrac{1}{2}\, \mathcal{S}, \qquad (VI.3.16)$$

where the conservation of T_3 is now the same as the conservation of the integral "quantum number" $\mathcal{S}$, *the strangeness.* The general conservation law (*VI.3.16*) applies only for nucleons, hyperons, and mesons. The strangeness quantum number $\mathcal{S}$ assumes the value 0 for nucleons (antinucleons) and for π mesons. All strongly coupled particles with $\mathcal{S} \neq 0$ are called "strange" particles. The quantum number $\mathcal{S}$ is conserved for all T_3 conserving interactions. Therefore, for all electromagnetic and strong interactions, strangeness is conserved.

For I spin (T_3) nonconserving interactions (weak interactions) a change $\frac{1}{2}\Delta S$ must be the same as the change ΔT_3, since $T_3 + \frac{1}{2}\mathcal{S}$ is conserved. The observable $T_3 + \frac{1}{2}\mathcal{S}$ can be regarded as a further generalization of the I spin

---

* M. Gell-Mann and A. H. Rosenfeld, *Annual Review of Nuclear Science,* Volume 7, Annual Reviews, Inc., Palo Alto, Calif., 1957, p. 413.

concept, where T_3 and $\frac{1}{2}\mathcal{S}$ may be compared to having an "orbital I spin" and "spin I spin," respectively. Thus the sum of T_3 and $\frac{1}{2}\mathcal{S}$ is always conserved. However, the above theory of strangeness, as proposed by Gell-Mann, is not necessarily complete, since there may still be a possibility to extract from $T_3 + \frac{1}{2}\mathcal{S}$ another absolutely conserved quantum number like Q and the baryon charge n. Furthermore, it has not yet been possible to derive the observationally *"correct" law* (*VI.3.16*) from a basic theory such as quantum electrodynamics.

Now, if we assume that the only possible total intrinsic I spin values for strongly interacting particles are 0, $\frac{1}{2}$, and 1 and that the baryon charge, like the electric charge, can assume the values 1, -1, and 0, then the strangeness quantum number $\mathcal{S}$ is limited to values -2, -1, 0, 1, and 2. Hence strangeness, like $l = 2$ and the corresponding $2l + 1$ values of the magnetic quantum number m, has the total strangeness number $\mathcal{S}^2 = \mathfrak{s}(\mathfrak{s} + 1)$, where $\mathfrak{s} = 2$. From these arguments we reach the important conclusion that the concept of isotopic spin has some important and deep-seated bearing on the problem of the elementary particle and that it is as yet in its infancy stage.

A law similar to that for the conservation of the baryon charge exists for light fermions or leptons (electron, muon, neutrino, plus the corresponding antiparticles—positron, positive muon, and antineutrino); the law is called conservation of the lepton charge. *Lepton charge is defined as the number of leptons minus the number of antileptons.* The fact that total I spin is not conserved by electromagnetic and weak interactions implies that the I spin concept as introduced for strongly interacting particles is not involved in the conservation of the lepton charge. With respect to the two distinct laws of conservation of the lepton and baryon charges, all elementary fermions can be put into two classes—leptons (antileptons) and baryons (antibaryons). Baryons can further be classified as nucleons (antinucleons) and hyperons (antihyperons). All elementary fermions, such as particles of spin $-\frac{1}{2}$, are assumed to be described by spinor wave functions. All mesons are bosons with spin 0 and they can be put into two classes with respect to the strangeness quantum number $\mathcal{S}$. The value $\mathcal{S} = 0$ corresponds to π mesons and $\mathcal{S} = +1$ and -1 to four K mesons. All mesons are assumed to be described by pseudoscalar wave functions. The photon is the only known particle of spin 1 and is described by a vector wave function.

The lepton conservation law is best illustrated by the nuclear β decay and muon (μ) decay processes. A proton can capture an electron and produce a neutrino,

$$p + e^- \longrightarrow n + \nu, \qquad (VI.3.17)$$

where we use the symbols p, n, e^-, ν for proton, neutron, electron, and neutrino, respectively. We use the convention that the neutral massless particle in reaction (*VI.3.17*) is to be called neutrino. From (*VI.3.17*) we can infer the energetically possible—that is, forced reaction—from conservation of the electric charge,

$$p \longrightarrow n + e^+ + \nu, \qquad (VI.3.18)$$

where we shall assume that proton and neutron have lepton charges of zero. If we assign a lepton charge of $+1$ to the neutrino, then the conservation of the lepton charge implies a lepton charge of -1 for the positron e^+. In this sense, if the neutrino is a lepton, the positron is an antilepton.

Next let us consider the free decay of a neutron,

$$n \longrightarrow p + e^- + \bar{\nu}, \qquad (VI.3.19)$$

where the symbol $\bar{\nu}$ is meant for another possible massless particle of spin $\frac{1}{2}$. Since the electron has a lepton charge of $+1$, then the $\bar{\nu}$ particle must have the lepton charge of -1 and therefore $\bar{\nu}$ is an antilepton (antineutrino).

An interesting elementary particle reaction involving leptons alone is the free decay of a positive muon:

$$\mu^+ \longrightarrow e^+ + \nu + \bar{\nu}. \qquad (VI.3.20)$$

From the conservation of the lepton charge it follows that μ^+ and e^+ have equal lepton charges. Hence μ^+ is an antilepton. According to the lepton conservation law all mesons have zero lepton charge. Therefore, the reaction

$$\pi^+ \longrightarrow \mu^+ + \nu \qquad (VI.3.21)$$

cannot take place with an antineutrino; but $\bar{\nu}$ is produced in the reaction

$$\pi^- \longrightarrow \mu^- + \bar{\nu}. \qquad (VI.3.22)$$

We must point out that a capture reaction, with the same strength of interaction as the electron capture, occurs also for μ^-:

$$\mu^- + p \longrightarrow n + \nu. \qquad (VI.3.23)$$

Hence we see that the electromagnetic properties of muons (μ^+, μ^-) and electrons (e^+, e^-) are essentially the same. It is, therefore, logical to expect the existence of other decays that conserve the lepton charge:

$$\pi^- \longrightarrow e^- + \bar{\nu} \qquad (VI.3.24)$$

and also

$$\pi^+ \longrightarrow e^+ + \nu. \qquad (VI.3.25)$$

These reactions have, actually, been observed.*

Another interesting evidence in favor of lepton conservation comes from the observed radioactive β decays of π mesons,

$$\pi^+ \longrightarrow e^+ + \nu + \gamma, \qquad (VI.3.26)$$
$$\pi^- \longrightarrow e^- + \bar{\nu} + \gamma, \qquad (VI.3.27)$$

* Fazzini, Fidecaro, Merrison, Paul, and Tollestrup, *Phys. Rev. Letters,* **1** (1958), 247.

where the symbol γ is used for a photon. Finally, the lepton-conserving reactions

$$\mu^+ \longrightarrow e^+ + \gamma, \qquad (VI.3.28)$$

$$\mu^- \longrightarrow e^- + \gamma \qquad (VI.3.29)$$

have also been observed.*

VI.3.C. Isotopic Spin and Nuclear Levels

We have seen that the degree of freedom for isotopic spin is confined only to heavy particles; leptons do not possess this symmetry. The only degree of freedom for lepton charge, with the exception of neutrinos, is invariance under "charge conjugation." This invariance is a symmetry principle which is valid for electromagnetic and nuclear interactions but which fails for weak interactions (nuclear β decay, μ decay, and so on). The charge conjugation symmetry means that the laws of nature remain unchanged if all positive charges are replaced by negative charges and vice versa, or, in more general form: *the laws of nature remain invariant with respect to interchange of a particle with its antiparticle, and vice versa.* This symmetry breaks down for all processes involving the neutrino or antineutrino. The conclusion is that electromagnetic interactions (because of their charge dependence) do not conserve total I spin and weak interactions violate charge conjugation (also parity). We may add that the absence of an I spin for leptons is also inferred from the absence of strong interactions for leptons. Thus, from the point of view of I spin, there seems to be an impenetrable wall between leptons and baryons. This situation does not arise with ordinary spin, where baryons and leptons have the same spin. But baryons and leptons do not have the same interaction properties; for example, the proton can interact strongly with the neutron and it can also interact electromagnetically with the electron, but the electron cannot interact strongly with any particle. Therefore the I spin degree of freedom of a system is closely related to its strong coupling property. Hence the interaction of baryons and mesons must be invariant with respect to rotations in I spin space, which is equivalent to the conservation of total I spin or the charge independence of nuclear forces.

We shall now give a mathematical formulation of the application of I spin to nuclear interactions. Consider the I spin operators

$$\tau_+ = \tfrac{1}{2}(\tau_1 + i\tau_2) \qquad \text{and} \qquad \tau_- = \tfrac{1}{2}(\tau_1 - i\tau_2),$$

---

* Many physicists believe that there are two kinds of neutrino pairs, so the two neutrinos occurring in (VI.3.20) need not necessarily be antiparticles but just different neutrinos obeying the lepton conservation law. Thus $\mu^+ \longrightarrow e^+ + \nu_e + \bar{\nu}_\mu$, $\pi^+ \longrightarrow \mu^+ + \nu_\mu \longrightarrow e^+ + \nu_e$, and so on, are possible decays, with ν_e and ν_μ being different from ν and $\bar{\nu}$.

which satisfy the commutation relations

$$\begin{aligned} [\tau_+ \; \tau_-] &= \tau_3, \\ [\tau_3 \; \tau_+] &= 2\tau_+, \\ [\tau_3 \; \tau_-] &= -2\tau_-, \end{aligned} \qquad (VI.3.30)$$

where

$$\tau_+\tau_- = \tfrac{1}{2}\tau_3 + \tfrac{1}{2}, \qquad (VI.3.31)$$

$$\tau_-\tau_+ = -\tfrac{1}{2}\tau_3 + \tfrac{1}{2}. \qquad (VI.3.32)$$

The charge of the nucleon can be expressed by

$$Q_N = e^+\tau_+\tau_-. \qquad (VI.3.33)$$

If we replace e^+ by $-e^+$ and take the Hermitian conjugate of Q_N, we obtain the charge of the antinucleon:

$$\bar{Q}_N = -Q_N^+ = -e^+\tau_-\tau_+ \qquad (VI.3.34)$$

The last result (the charge conjugation) can also be obtained by a unitary transformation induced by τ_2 and replacing e^+ by $-e^+$:

$$\tau_2^+\tau_+\tau_-\tau_2 = \tau_2\tau_+\tau_-\tau_2 = \tau_-\tau_+.$$

The operators $\tau_+\tau_-$ and $\tau_-\tau_+$ are projection operators and therefore their eigenvalues are $+1$ and 0. The I spin eigenstates in a representation where τ_3 is diagonal are

$$|1\rangle = \begin{bmatrix}1\\0\end{bmatrix}, \qquad |-1\rangle = \begin{bmatrix}0\\1\end{bmatrix}.$$

The operators τ_+ and τ_- act on the proton and neutron states $|1\rangle$ and $|-1\rangle$, respectively, according to

$$\begin{aligned} \tau_+|1\rangle &= 0, & \tau_+|-1\rangle &= |1\rangle, \\ \tau_-|1\rangle &= |-1\rangle, & \tau_-|-1\rangle &= 0. \end{aligned}$$

Thus τ_+ is an operator which annihilates a proton state and converts a neutron state into a proton state. Similarly, τ_- converts a proton state into a neutron state and annihilates a neutron state. For the operators $\tau_+\tau_-$ and $\tau_-\tau_+$ we have

$$\begin{aligned} \tau_-\tau_+|1\rangle &= 0, & \tau_-\tau_+|-1\rangle &= |-1\rangle, \\ \tau_+\tau_-|1\rangle &= |1\rangle, & \tau_+\tau_-|-1\rangle &= 0. \end{aligned}$$

Such processes of conversion occur in β decay of the nucleus, which involves the conversion of one neutron to a proton, while positive β decay involves the conversion of a proton into a neutron. Besides β decay, nuclear forces are dependent on exchange effects (exchange forces) where the proton and neutron are interconverted one into the other; the operators τ_+ and τ_- provide a convenient tool for the description of such processes.

For a two-nucleon system [see (*VI.3.7*)] we define the charge exchange operator by

$$P_{ab}^{\boldsymbol{\tau}} = \tau^2 - 1 = \tfrac{1}{2}(1 + \boldsymbol{\tau}_a \cdot \boldsymbol{\tau}_b), \qquad (VI.3.35)$$

where $\boldsymbol{\tau} = \frac{1}{2}(\boldsymbol{\tau}_a + \boldsymbol{\tau}_b)$ and the eigenvalues of the total I spin are 0 and 1. Therefore the eigenvalues of the charge exchange operator are obtained from

$$P_{ab}^{\tau} = T(T+1) - 1,$$

where $T = 0$ for the singlet state [the fourth state in (*VI.3.7*)] and $T = 1$ for the triplet states [the first three states in (*VI.3.7*)] of two-nucleon systems.

The charge states (*VI.3.7*) are simultaneous eigenstates of τ_3 and T^2, so we obtain $P_{ab}^{\tau}|nn\rangle = |nn\rangle$, $P_{ab}^{\tau}|pn\rangle = |pn\rangle$, and $P_{ab}^{\tau}|pp\rangle = |pp\rangle$ for the symmetric triplet states and $P_{ab}^{\tau}|pn\rangle = -|pn\rangle$ for the antisymmetric singlet state of (*VI.3.7*).

The energy levels, phase shifts are the same for all triplet charge state wave functions. Hence we deduce that the behavior of states depends on the total I spin and not on τ_3 (neglecting Coulomb effects). This result is very similar to ordinary spin theory where the levels depend on the total spin s and not on s_3, so long as one neglects spin-orbit forces. Furthermore, the symmetry character of the wave function depends on the total I spin and not on τ_3. The ground state of a deuteron, for example, where $l = 0$ and $s = 1$ (triplet spin state), is symmetric in a space-spin wave function. It must, therefore, be antisymmetric in the charge state; that is, $T = 0$ and the corresponding wave function is given by the fourth equation in (*VI.3.7*).

By analogy with P_{ab}^{τ} we can define a spin exchange operator by

$$P_{ab}^{\sigma} = \mathbf{S}^2 - 1 = \tfrac{1}{2}(1 + \boldsymbol{\sigma}_a \cdot \boldsymbol{\sigma}_b), \qquad (VI.3.36)$$

where $\mathbf{S} = \frac{1}{2}(\boldsymbol{\sigma}_a + \boldsymbol{\sigma}_b)$.

Now let $P_{ab}^{\boldsymbol{r}}$ be the space exchange operator of two nucleons. In accordance with the generalized Pauli principle under the operation of interchange of position, spin, and I spin of two nucleons, the wave function must change sign:

$$P_{ab}^{\boldsymbol{r}} P_{ab}^{\boldsymbol{\tau}} P_{ab}^{\boldsymbol{\sigma}} \psi = -\psi. \qquad (VI.3.37)$$

Multiplying both sides by $P_{ab}^{\boldsymbol{\tau}}$ and $P_{ab}^{\boldsymbol{\sigma}}$ and noting that $(P_{ab}^{\boldsymbol{\sigma}})^2 = (P_{ab}^{\boldsymbol{\tau}})^2 = 1$, we obtain

$$P_{ab}^{\boldsymbol{r}} \psi = -P_{ab}^{\boldsymbol{\sigma}} P_{ab}^{\boldsymbol{\tau}} \psi$$

for all the wave functions ψ satisfying the generalized Pauli principle. Hence we can write

$$\begin{aligned} P_{ab}^{\boldsymbol{r}} &= -P_{ab}^{\boldsymbol{\sigma}} P_{ab}^{\boldsymbol{\tau}} \\ &= -\tfrac{1}{4}(1 + \boldsymbol{\sigma}_a \cdot \boldsymbol{\sigma}_b)(1 + \boldsymbol{\tau}_a \cdot \boldsymbol{\tau}_b) \end{aligned} \qquad (VI.3.38)$$

The interchange of the position vectors $\boldsymbol{r}_1$ and $\boldsymbol{r}_2$ (the Majorana exchange) is equivalent to reversing the sign of the relative coordinate $\boldsymbol{r} = \boldsymbol{r}_1 - \boldsymbol{r}_2$. In a two-particle system this is the same as the parity operation. Thus the nuclear force depends on the relative angular momentum of the nucleons. The operation by $P_{ab}^{\boldsymbol{r}}$ does not change the state for even l and it changes its sign for odd l.

The charge independence or I spin degeneracy of nuclear forces can be removed by treating the Coulomb energy and mass difference of nucleons as a small perturbation. This implies the existence of I spin multiplets.

From (*VI.3.11*), for the charge of an A-nucleon system, and setting $Q_A/e^+ = Z$, we obtain

$$T_3 = \tfrac{1}{2}(Z - N), \qquad (VI.3.39)$$

where Z and N refer to the number of protons and neutrons in the nucleus, respectively, and where $A = Z + N$. For odd A the total I spin, defined by (*VI.3.12*), assumes half-integral values. Thus for $T = \frac{1}{2}$ we have $T_3 = \frac{1}{2}$, $T_3 = -\frac{1}{2}$. For $A = 15$, the mass number, (*VI.3.39*) yields the two nuclei with $Z = 7, N = 8$ and $Z = 8, N = 7$. These are called *mirror nuclei*; the number of neutrons in one of them equals the number of protons in the other.

The $2T + 1$ nuclei $(A, T), (A, T - 1), \cdots, (A, -T)$, corresponding to the total I spin T and the $2T + 1$ values of T_3, are called isobaric nuclei; they are all described by the wave function ψ for the nucleus (A, T_3), and they all have the same energy, provided we neglect the Coulomb energy. If $T_3 > 0$ then the original nucleus contains more protons than neutrons. If we replace one of the protons by a neutron, the corresponding I spin is $T_3 - 1$ and the maximum number of identical particles (protons) is decreased by one. The process of replacing a proton by a neutron should not lead to a possible value of I spin less than $-T_3$, since otherwise there is the possibility of violating the Pauli principle. Thus T_3 is the maximum value of I spin for which the exchange of a proton by a neutron is allowed.

The isobaric nuclei (A, T_3) with $T_3 = -T, \cdots, T$ are said to form an isotopic multiplet with total I spin T. According to I spin multiplet theory* when Coulomb and mass difference effects are negligible, the level structure of isobaric nuclei can be (approximately) predicted simultaneously.

VI.3.D. Problems

1. It is conceivable that very high-energy electron-electron or electron-nucleon scattering may lead to meson production, in which case the electromagnetic coupling is negligible compared to the strong coupling of meson production. (The production cross-section is very small, but in principle it is possible.) Can one, then, assign an isotopic spin to leptons?

2. Is it possible to develop an I spin theory for particles whose strong interactions are negligible compared to their electromagnetic and weak

---

* L. Eisenbud and E. P. Wigner, *Nuclear Structure*, Princeton Univ. Press, Princeton, 1958.

interactions? In such a scheme, leptons and antileptons will appear as doubly degenerate I spin triplets whose degeneracy can be removed by their lepton charge.

3. Show that for a meson-nucleon system the projection operator

$$P_c = \tfrac{5}{4} - \tfrac{1}{3}\boldsymbol{T}^2 = \tfrac{1}{3}(I - \boldsymbol{\tau}\cdot\boldsymbol{\kappa}),$$

where $\boldsymbol{T} = \frac{1}{2}\boldsymbol{\tau} + \boldsymbol{\kappa}$, annihilates $T = \frac{3}{2}$ states and leaves $T = \frac{1}{2}$ states unchanged.

4. Show that for an A-nucleon system the antisymmetric I spin wave function is

$$\Psi = \left[\frac{A!}{N!(A-N)!}\right]^{-1/2} \sum_P \epsilon_P P \psi_I, \qquad (VI.3.40)$$

where

$$\psi_I = \psi_I(\boldsymbol{r}_1, \boldsymbol{s}_1; \boldsymbol{r}_2, \boldsymbol{s}_2; \cdots; \boldsymbol{r}_N, \boldsymbol{s}_N; \boldsymbol{r}_{N+1}\boldsymbol{s}_{N+1}; \cdots; \boldsymbol{r}_A, \boldsymbol{s}_A)$$
$$\times |T_{1p}, T_{2p}, \cdots, T_{Np}\rangle |T_{(N+1)n}, \cdots, T_{An}\rangle,$$

and $S_i = \pm 1$, where $i = 1, 2, \cdots$ for the A spin directions of the nucleons; $T_{1p} = T_{2p} = \cdots = T_{Np} = 1$ and $T_{(N+1)n} = \cdots = T_{An} = -1$ for the proton and neutron I spins. Furthermore, the I spin states are of the form $|T_{1p}\rangle|T_{2p}\rangle \cdots |T_{Np}\rangle$ and $|T_{(N+1)n}\rangle \cdots |T_{An}\rangle$. The sum is to be taken over all permutations P of the A subscripts (including the identity permutation, which does not affect the subscripts), and ϵ_p is $+1$ for even permutation, -1 for odd permutation.*

5. Prove that for a two-meson system with I spins $\boldsymbol{\kappa}_a$ and $\boldsymbol{\kappa}_b$, respectively, the operator $\boldsymbol{\kappa}_a \cdot \boldsymbol{\kappa}_b$ is an exchange operator. The total I spins $T = 1$ and $T = 2$ correspond to antisymmetric and symmetric states and the effect of $\boldsymbol{\kappa}_a \cdot \boldsymbol{\kappa}_b$ on the state $T = 0$ consists of multiplying it by -2. Write down the 9 I spin states of a two meson system and explain the reasons for the antisymmetric and symmetric properties of the I spin states corresponding to total I spins $T = 1$ and $T = 2$, respectively. How would you reconcile these results with the fact that mesons obey Bose-Einstein statistics?

---

* L. W. Nordheim and F. L. Yost, *Phys. Rev.* **51** (1937), 942.

CHAPTER VII

HARMONIC OSCILLATOR REPRESENTATIONS

VII.1. The Fock Representation

For a direct illustration and also as an extension of the various concepts introduced in the previous chapters, we shall work out in detail the quantum theory of a harmonic oscillator. The present treatment contains also the foundations of field quantization, which in this book is applied only to massless particles.

A free harmonic oscillator is the simplest dynamical system in quantum mechanics. The Hamiltonian of the oscillator can be obtained from the Hamiltonian of the classical oscillator (*III.1.36*) by treating the quantity

$$b = \frac{1}{\sqrt{2m}}(p + imq) \tag{VII.1.1}$$

as a linear operator. Thus the Hamiltonian is given by

$$H = \tfrac{1}{2}(b^*b + bb^*),$$

where b satisfies the commutation relation

$$[b^*, b] = \hbar\omega. \tag{VII.1.2}$$

Hence H becomes

$$H = \tfrac{1}{2}\hbar\omega + bb^*.$$

It is more convenient to work with the linear operators

$$\begin{aligned} a_+ &= \frac{1}{\sqrt{\hbar\omega}}\, b \;= \frac{1}{\sqrt{2m\hbar\omega}}(p + im\omega q), \\ a_- &= \frac{1}{\sqrt{\hbar\omega}}\, b^* = \frac{1}{\sqrt{2m\hbar\omega}}(p - im\omega q), \end{aligned} \tag{VII.1.3}$$

and the commutation relation

$$[a_-, a_+] = 1. \tag{VII.1.4}$$

The Hamiltonian assumes a simple form:

$$H = \hbar\omega(a_+a_- + \tfrac{1}{2}) = \hbar\omega(a_-a_+ - \tfrac{1}{2}). \qquad (VII.1.5)$$

The harmonic oscillator representation to be discussed in this section is due to Fock* and it has further been extended and applied by Dirac† to the theory of second quantization.

From the commutation relation (*VII.1.4*) we can easily deduce a more general commutation relation,

$$[a_-, a_+^n] = na_+^{n-1}, \qquad (VII.1.6)$$

where n is a positive integer. The commutation relations (*VII.1.4*) and (*VII.1.6*) imply that the operator a_- acts like an operator of differentiation of the form d/da_+.

The Fock representation of harmonic oscillator assumes that H has a minimum energy eigenvalue E_0, corresponding to an eigenstate $|E_0\rangle$,

$$H|E_0\rangle = E_0|E_0\rangle. \qquad (VII.1.7)$$

Hence we obtain

$$\hbar\omega a_+a_-|E_0\rangle = (E_0 - \tfrac{1}{2}\hbar\omega)|E_0\rangle$$

and

$$\hbar\omega a_-a_+a_-|E_0\rangle = (E_0 - \tfrac{1}{2}\hbar\omega)a_-|E_0\rangle.$$

Using the Hamiltonian, the last relation leads to

$$Ha_-|E_0\rangle = (E_0 - \hbar\omega)a_-|E_0\rangle,$$

which contradicts our original assumption that E_0 was the minimum energy eigenvalue. Therefore the state $a_-|E_0\rangle$ must satisfy the equation

$$a_-|E_0\rangle = 0. \qquad (VII.1.8)$$

By using this equation we can calculate the minimum value E_0 of the energy. From (*VII.1.8*) we can write

$$\hbar\omega a_+a_-|E_0\rangle = 0$$

or

$$(H - \tfrac{1}{2}\hbar\omega)|E_0\rangle = 0,$$
$$(E_0 - \tfrac{1}{2}\hbar\omega)|E_0\rangle = 0.$$

Hence

$$E_0 = \tfrac{1}{2}\hbar\omega \qquad (VII.1.9)$$

is the minimum energy eigenvalue of a harmonic oscillator. From the commutation relation (*VII.1.6*) we have

$$a_-a_+^n = a_+^na_- + na_+^{n-1}.$$

---

* V. Fock, *Z. Phys.*, **49** (1928), 339. *Phys. Z. Soviet: USSR*, **6** (1934), 425.
† P. A. M. Dirac, *Ann. Inst.*, H. Poincaré, **XI–1** (1949).

Operating on both sides with a_+ and using the expression of the Hamiltonian we obtain

$$(H - \tfrac{1}{2}\hbar\omega)a_+^n = n\hbar\omega a_+^n + \hbar\omega a_+^{n+1}a_-.$$

Operating on the state $|E_0\rangle$ and using the condition (*VII.1.8*) we get the eigenvalue equation

$$(H - \tfrac{1}{2}\hbar\omega)a_+^n|E_0\rangle = n\hbar\omega a_+^n|E_0\rangle$$

or

$$H|E_n\rangle = \hbar\omega(n + \tfrac{1}{2})|E_n\rangle, \qquad (VII.1.10)$$

where the eigenstates $|E_n\rangle$, corresponding to eigenvalues

$$E_n = \hbar\omega(n + \tfrac{1}{2}), \qquad (VII.1.11)$$

are defined by

$$|E_n\rangle = a_+^n|E_0\rangle. \qquad (VII.1.12)$$

The vectors $a_+^n|E_0\rangle$ for $n = 0, 1, 2, \cdots$ can form a complete set and therefore a representation. To see this, let us introduce a dynamical variable defined by

$$N = a_+a_-, \qquad (VII.1.13)$$

where N has eigenvalues $0, 1, 2, \cdots$ and the Hamiltonian assumes the form

$$H = \hbar\omega(N + \tfrac{1}{2}). \qquad (VII.1.14)$$

If $|E_0\rangle$ is a unit vector, then the length of the vector $a_+^n|E_0\rangle$ is given by

$$\begin{aligned}\langle E_0|a_-^n a_+^n|E_0\rangle &= \langle E_0|a_-^{n-1}(a_+^n a_- + na_+^{n-1})|E_0\rangle \\ &= n\langle E_0|a_-^{n-1}a_+^{n-1}|E_0\rangle = n(n-1)\langle E_0|a_-^{n-2}a_+^{n-2}|E_0\rangle \\ &= \cdots = n!\langle E_0|E_0\rangle = n!.\end{aligned}$$

Thus the length of the vector is

$$\langle E_0|a_-^n a_+^n|E_0\rangle = n!. \qquad (VII.1.15)$$

From (*VII.1.8*) and (*VII.1.15*) it easily follows that

$$\langle E_n|E_m\rangle = 0 \qquad \text{if } n \neq m.$$

In general we have

$$\langle E_m|E_n\rangle = n!\delta_{mn}, \qquad (VII.1.16)$$

which proves that $|E_n\rangle$ with $n = 0, 1, 2, \cdots$ form a complete set of vectors. Hence we can define a unit operator by

$$I = \sum_{n=0}^{\infty} \lambda_n|E_n\rangle\langle E_n|,$$

where $\sqrt{\lambda_n}$ is the normalization factor. Any oscillator state $|\eta\rangle$ can be expressed as

$$\begin{aligned}|\eta\rangle &= \sum_{n=0}^{\infty} \lambda_n|E_n\rangle\langle E_n|\eta\rangle = \sum_{n=0}^{\infty} \eta_n a_+^n|E_0\rangle \\ &= F(a_+)|E_0\rangle, \qquad (VII.1.17)\end{aligned}$$

where $\eta_n = \lambda_n \langle E_n | \eta \rangle$ and the operator $F(a_+)$ is

$$F(a_+) = \sum_{n=0}^{\infty} \eta_n a_+^n. \tag{VII.1.18}$$

The vector $|\eta\rangle$, representing any oscillator state, can be normalized according to

$$\begin{aligned} \langle \eta | \eta \rangle &= \sum_{n,m} \eta_n^* \eta_m \langle E_0 | a_-^n a_+^m | E_0 \rangle \\ &= \sum_n n! |\eta_n|^2 = 1, \end{aligned} \tag{VII.1.19}$$

where $n!|\eta_n|^2$ is the probability of finding the oscillator in its nth excited state—that is, the state where its energy is $[n + \frac{1}{2}]\hbar\omega$.

The theory can be extended to the case of many oscillators represented by $a_i^{(+)}$, $a_j^{(-)}$, satisfying the commutation relations

$$\begin{aligned} a_i^{(+)} a_j^{(+)} - a_j^{(+)} a_i^{(+)} &= 0, \\ a_i^{(-)} a_j^{(-)} - a_j^{(-)} a_i^{(-)} &= 0, \\ a_i^{(-)} a_j^{(+)} - a_j^{(+)} a_i^{(-)} &= \delta_{ij}. \end{aligned} \tag{VII.1.20}$$

The operator corresponding to N is

$$N_i = a_i^{(+)} a_i^{(-)}. \tag{VII.1.21}$$

The stationary states of the oscillators are

$$|E_{n_1 n_2} \cdots \rangle = (a_1^{(+)})^{n_1} (a_2^{(+)})^{n_2} \cdots |E_0\rangle \tag{VII.1.22}$$

where $n_1, n_2, \cdots$ are eigenvalues of $N_1, N_2, \cdots$. The length of the vector $|E_{n_1 n_2} \cdots \rangle$ is

$$\langle E_{n_1 n_2} \cdots | E_{n_1 n_2} \cdots \rangle = n_1! n_2! \cdots. \tag{VII.1.23}$$

The state of minimum energy $|E_0\rangle$ satisfies the equation

$$a_i^{(-)} |E_0\rangle = 0 \tag{VII.1.24}$$

for all oscillators, so $|E_0\rangle$ is of the form

$$|E_0\rangle = |E_{01}\rangle |E_{02}\rangle |E_{03}\rangle \cdots. \tag{VII.1.25}$$

Any state of the oscillators represented by $|\eta_{12} \cdots \rangle$ can be expanded according to

$$\begin{aligned} |\eta_{12} \cdots \rangle &= \sum_{n_1 n_2 \cdots} \cdots \eta_{n_1 n_2} \cdots (a_1^{(+)})^{n_1} (a_2^{(+)})^{n_2} \cdots |E_0\rangle \\ &= F(a_{12} \cdots) |E_0\rangle. \end{aligned} \tag{VII.1.26}$$

The state $|\eta_{12} \cdots \rangle$ can be normalized by

$$\sum_{n_1 n_2 \cdots} |\eta_{n_1 n_2} \cdots |^2 n_1! n_2! \cdots = 1, \tag{VII.1.27}$$

where the coefficient $|\eta_{n_1 n_2} \cdots |^2 n_1! n_2! \cdots$ is the probability of finding the oscillators in the states corresponding to $n_1, n_2, \cdots$.

VII.1.A. An Ensemble of Bosons and the Stationary States of a System of Oscillators

Consider a system of n bosons. We shall construct a state vector which will be symmetrical with respect to all the particles. Let us write the oscillator states of the form

$$\begin{aligned} |\alpha_1'\rangle &= (a_1^{(+)})^{n_1}|E_{01}\rangle, \\ |\alpha_2'\rangle &= (a_2^{(+)})^{n_2}|E_{02}\rangle, \\ |\alpha_3'\rangle &= (a_3^{(+)})^{n_3}|E_{03}\rangle, \\ &\cdots\cdots\cdots\cdots\cdots\cdots. \end{aligned} \tag{VII.1.28}$$

Each of these can be regarded as a symmetrical state since we may, for example, write

$$|\alpha_1'\rangle = a_1^{(+)}a_1^{(+)} \cdots a_1^{(+)}|E_{01}\rangle,$$

where the operators $a_1^{(+)}$ are repeated n_1 times; therefore the interchange of the same n_1 operators among themselves will not change the state $|\alpha_1'\rangle$. If we were to label each one of $a_1^{(+)}$, then there would be $n_1!$ possible ways of permuting n_1 objects (in this case bosons) without changing the state $|\alpha_1'\rangle$. We may, therefore, look upon the state $|\alpha_1'\rangle$ as a symmetrical state of n_1 bosons. In the same way we can say that there are n_2 bosons in the state $|\alpha_2'\rangle$, and so on. Hence the symmetrical state corresponding to n bosons with "occupation numbers" $n_1, n_2, \cdots$ is given by

$$|\alpha_1'\alpha_2' \cdots \alpha_j'\rangle = (a_1^{(+)})^{n_1}(a_2^{(+)})^{n_2} \cdots (a_j^{(+)})^{n_j}|E_0\rangle, \tag{VII.1.29}$$

where $n_1 + n_2 + \cdots + n_j = n$.

We may regard the state $|\alpha_1'\alpha_2' \cdots \alpha_j'\rangle$ as arising from the symmetrization of an arbitrary state $|\alpha_r\alpha_s \cdots \alpha_q\rangle$, where

$$\alpha_r + \alpha_s + \cdots + \alpha_q = n_1\alpha_1 + n_2\alpha_2 + \cdots. \tag{VII.1.30}$$

Thus we can write

$$|\alpha_1'\alpha_2' \cdots \alpha_j'\rangle = S|\alpha_r\alpha_s \cdots \alpha_q\rangle, \tag{VII.1.31}$$

where the symmetrization operator is defined by

$$S = \frac{1}{\sqrt{n!}}\Sigma P, \tag{VII.1.32}$$

with P implying $n!$ permutations of n bosons. From (*VII.1.23*) we see that the length of the state vector $|\alpha_1'\alpha_2' \cdots \alpha_j'\rangle$ is just $n_1!n_2! \cdots n_j!$, so (*VII.1.31*) yields

$$\langle\alpha_r\alpha_s \cdots \alpha_q|S^2|\alpha_r\alpha_s \cdots \alpha_q\rangle = n_1!n_2! \cdots n_j! \tag{VII.1.33}$$

as the length of the state vector of n bosons occupying the states $|\alpha_1\rangle$, $|\alpha_2\rangle, \cdots, |\alpha_j\rangle$, with occupation numbers $n_1, n_2, \cdots, n_j$, respectively.

We may use state vectors of the form (*VII.1.31*) and set up a complete set of vectors as

$$|E_0\rangle,\ |\alpha_r\rangle,\ S|\alpha_r\alpha_s\rangle,\ \cdots,\ S|\alpha_r\alpha_s\ \cdots\ \alpha_q\rangle, \tag{VII.1.34}$$

where $|E_0\rangle$ is the state with no bosons present, the $|\alpha_r\rangle$ are the states with one boson present, the $S|\alpha_r\alpha_s\rangle$ are the states with two bosons present, and so forth. It is evident from definition (*VII.1.31*) and from (*VII.1.29*) that all these states of various number of bosons are orthogonal. For an ensemble of one boson we have

$$|\alpha_r\rangle = a_r^{(+)}|E_0\rangle. \tag{VII.1.35}$$

It means that the operator $a_r^{(+)}$ "creates" one boson from the "vacuum state" $|E_0\rangle$. The vector representing any boson state is given by

$$|\alpha\rangle = \sum_r \lambda_r a_r^{(+)}|E_0\rangle. \tag{VII.1.36}$$

Hence, multiplying with $a_s^{(-)}$, we get

$$\begin{aligned} a_s^{(-)}|\alpha\rangle &= \sum_r \lambda_r a_s^{(-)} a_r^{(+)}|E_0\rangle \\ &= \sum_r \lambda_r[a_r^{(+)}a_s^{(-)} + \delta_{rs}]|E_0\rangle = \lambda_s|E_0\rangle, \end{aligned}$$

which corresponds to a state of no boson present. Therefore, the operator $a_s^{(-)}$ corresponds to an "absorption (or annihilation) operator" from the state $|\alpha_s\rangle$.

The operation with $a_s^{(-)}$ on the general state (*VII.1.29*) yields

$$\begin{aligned} &a_s^{(-)}(a_1^{(+)})^{n_1}(a_2^{(+)})^{n_2}\ \cdots\ (a_s^{(+)})^{n_s}\ \cdots\ |E_0\rangle \\ &\quad = (a_1^{(+)})^{n_1}(a_2^{(+)})^{n_2}\ \cdots\ [(a^{(+)})^{n_s}a_s^{(-)} + n_s(a_s^{(+)})^{n_s-1}]|E_0\rangle \qquad (VII.1.37) \\ &\quad = n_s(a_1^{(+)})^{n_1}(a_2^{(+)})^{n_2}\ \cdots\ (a_s^{(+)})^{n_s-1}\ \cdots\ |E_0\rangle, \end{aligned}$$

so operation by $a_s^{(-)}$ decreases the number of bosons in the state $|\alpha_s\rangle$ by 1. A general state of an ensemble of bosons can be represented by (*VII.1.26*) in the form

$$\Psi(a^+)|E_0\rangle = \sum_{n_1 n_2 \cdots} \lambda_{n_1 n_2} \ldots (a_1^{(+)})^{n_1}(a_2^{(+)})^{n_2}\ \cdots\ |E_0\rangle, \tag{VII.1.38}$$

where the various terms of $\Psi(a^+)$ are related to the number of bosons according to the degree of each term.

Let us now assume that the states $|\alpha_r\rangle$ for a boson corresponds to the stationary states with energy levels E_1, E_2, $\cdots$. Thus we have

$$|\alpha_r\rangle = |E_r\rangle e^{-(i/\hbar)tE_r}. \tag{VII.1.39}$$

Hence the time dependence of $a_r^{(+)}$ is given by

$$a_r^{(+)} = (a_r^+)_0 e^{-(i/\hbar)tE_r}. \tag{VII.1.40}$$

which shows [see (*III.1.35*)] that the time dependence of $a_r^{(+)}$ is like that of a harmonic oscillator with frequency $\omega_r = E_r/\hbar$. This means that an ensemble of bosons have the same description as a system of harmonic oscillators having frequencies $E_r/\hbar$. In terms of occupation numbers the total energy of the ensemble of bosons is

$$H = \sum_r N_r E_r = \sum_r E_r a_r^{(+)} a_r^{(-)}, \qquad (VII.1.41)$$

where the occupation number operator $N_r = a_r^{(+)} a_r^{(-)}$ has the eigenvalues n_r. Hence a set of harmonic oscillators can represent a noninteracting assembly of bosons in stationary states. According to this picture the nth quantum state of one of the oscillators of the set represents a state where there are n bosons.

VII.1.B. An Ensemble of Fermions and Stationary States of a System of Oscillators

We may envisage a system of oscillators obeying Fermi-Dirac statistics; that is, we assume that it is not possible to have more than one particle in a given state. The commutation relations (*VII.1.20*) for Bose-Einstein oscillators have now to be replaced by the anticommutation relations of Fermi-Dirac oscillators:

$$\begin{aligned} a_i^{(+)} a_j^{(+)} + a_j^{(+)} a_i^{(+)} &= 0, \\ a_i^{(-)} a_j^{(-)} + a_j^{(-)} a_i^{(-)} &= 0, \\ a_i^{(-)} a_j^{(+)} + a_j^{(+)} a_i^{(-)} &= \delta_{ij}. \end{aligned} \qquad (VII.1.42)$$

We shall see that the anticommutation relations are the only possibility consistent with Fermi-Dirac statistics.

From the first two anticommutation relations we find that

$$(a_r^{(+)})^2 = 0, \qquad (a_r^{(-)})^2 = 0. \qquad (VII.1.43)$$

The occupation number operator is defined by

$$N_r = a_r^{(+)} a_r^{(-)}. \qquad (VII.1.44)$$

Hence

$$\begin{aligned} N_r^2 &= a_r^{(+)} a_r^{(-)} a_r^{(+)} a_r^{(-)} = a_r^{(+)} (1 - a_r^{(+)} a_r^{(-)}) a_r^{(-)} \\ &= a_r^{(+)} a_r^{(-)}. \end{aligned}$$

Thus

$$N_r^2 = N_r \qquad (VII.1.45)$$

implies that N_r is a projection operator and its eigenvalues are 0 or 1. (This property of N_r, required by Fermi-Dirac statistics, could not be obtained from the commutation relations obeyed by $a_i^{(+)}$ and $a_i^{(-)}$.)

In a way similar to that used for bosons we can define a vacuum state by

$$N_r|E_0\rangle = 0, \qquad \langle E_0|E_0\rangle = 1.$$

Hence we get

$$\langle E_0|a_r^{(+)}a_r^{(-)}|E_0\rangle = 0,$$

meaning that the length of the vector $a_r^{(-)}|E_0\rangle$ is zero. Therefore we must have

$$a_r^{(-)}|E_0\rangle = 0. \qquad (VII.1.46)$$

The vector $a_r^{(+)}|E_0\rangle$ is of unit length;

$$\begin{aligned}\langle E_0|a_r^{(-)}a_r^{(+)}|E_0\rangle &= \langle E_0|(1 - a_r^{(+)}a_r^{(-)})|E_0\rangle \\ &= \langle E_0|E_0\rangle = 1.\end{aligned}$$

Furthermore, the occupation number N_r operates on a state according to

$$\begin{aligned}N_r a_r^{(+)}|E_0\rangle &= a_r^{(+)}a_r^{(-)}a_r^{(+)}|E_0\rangle \\ &= a_r^{(+)}(1 - a_r^{(+)}a_r^{(-)})|E_0\rangle = a_r^{(+)}|E_0\rangle. \qquad (VII.1.47)\end{aligned}$$

Hence $a_r^{(+)}|E_0\rangle$ is an eigenstate of N_r belonging to eigenvalue 1.

A simultaneous eigenstate of all occupation number operators N_1, N_2, $\cdots$ can be constructed as

$$|\alpha_1'\alpha_2' \cdots \alpha_j'\rangle = a_r^{(+)}a_s^{(+)} \cdots a_q^{(+)}|E_0\rangle, \qquad (VII.1.48)$$

where now the states α_r, α_s, $\cdots$ are all different since two identical particles cannot be in the same state. Mathematical expression of this fact is contained in the anticommutation relations (*VII.1.42*) and what follows from them (*VII.1.43*). Because of the anticommutation relations the state represented by (*VII.1.48*) is antisymmetric and of unit length. It can be regarded as arising from the antisymmetrization of a general state $|\alpha_r\alpha_s \cdots \alpha_q\rangle$, or

$$A|\alpha_r\alpha_s \cdots \alpha_q\rangle = a_r^{(+)}a_s^{(+)} \cdots a_q^{(+)}|E_0\rangle, \qquad (VII.1.49)$$

where $r \neq s \neq \cdots \neq q$, and

$$A = \frac{1}{\sqrt{n!}}\sum_P \pm P \qquad (VII.1.50)$$

is the antisymmetrization operator with $+$ sign for even permutations and $-$ sign for odd permutations of the fermions. Ensembles of fermions can be described in terms of complete set of vectors,

$$|E_0\rangle,\ |\alpha_r\rangle,\ A|\alpha_r\alpha_s\rangle,\ \cdots,\ A|\alpha_r\alpha_s \cdots \alpha_q\rangle,\ \cdots, \qquad (VII.1.51)$$

which are orthogonal and normalized, with $|E_0\rangle$ corresponding to a state with no fermion present, $|\alpha\rangle$ to states with one fermion present, and so on.

A general state of an ensemble of fermions is of the form

$$\Psi(a^{(+)})|E_0\rangle = \sum_{rs \cdots q} \lambda_{rs \cdots q} a_r^{(+)}a_s^{(+)} \cdots a_q^{(+)}|E_0\rangle. \qquad (VII.1.52)$$

The operator function of the $a^{(+)}$,

$$\Psi(a^+) = \sum_{rs \cdots q} \lambda_{rs \cdots q} a_r^{(+)}a_s^{(+)} \cdots a_q^{(+)},$$

consists of noninteracting occupied fermion states alone. The operators $a_r^{(+)}$

and $a_r^{(-)}$ are the respective operators of "creation" and "annihilation" of fermions.

VII.1.C. The Matrix Representation of Oscillator Operators

We introduce normalized eigenstates of the occupation number operator N by

$$|n\rangle = \frac{1}{\sqrt{n!}}|E_n\rangle = \frac{1}{\sqrt{n!}}a_n^+|E_0\rangle, \qquad (VII.1.53)$$

where

$$\langle n|n'\rangle = \frac{1}{\sqrt{(n!n'!)}}\langle E_n|E_n'\rangle = \delta_{nn'},$$
$$N|n\rangle = n|n\rangle, \qquad N = a_+a_-. \qquad (VII.1.54)$$

Thus the vectors $|n\rangle$ form a complete set and they can be used to set up a representation. The following operator relations can easily be established:

$$a_+|n\rangle = \frac{1}{\sqrt{n!}}a_+^{n+1}|E_0\rangle = \frac{\sqrt{(n+1)}}{\sqrt{(n+1)!}}|E_{n+1}\rangle = \sqrt{(n+1)}|n+1\rangle$$

or

$$a_+|n\rangle = \sqrt{(n+1)}|n+1\rangle. \qquad (VII.1.55)$$

Similarly,

$$a_-|n\rangle = \sqrt{n}|n-1\rangle. \qquad (VII.1.56)$$

We may now obtain the representatives of the position and momentum operators of a harmonic oscillator from

$$q = i\sqrt{\left(\frac{\hbar}{2m\omega}\right)}(a_- - a_+),$$

$$p = \sqrt{\left(\frac{\hbar\omega m}{2}\right)}(a_- + a_+),$$

as

$$q_{n+1,n} = \langle n+1|q|n\rangle = i\sqrt{\left[\frac{\hbar(n+1)}{2m\omega}\right]}, \qquad (VII.1.57)$$

$$q_{n-1,n} = \langle n-1|q|n\rangle = i\sqrt{\left(\frac{\hbar n}{2m\omega}\right)}, \qquad (VII.1.58)$$

$$p_{n+1,n} = \sqrt{\left[\frac{\hbar\omega m(n+1)}{2}\right]}, \qquad (VII.1.59)$$

$$p_{n-1,n} = \sqrt{\left(\frac{\hbar\omega mn}{2}\right)}. \qquad (VII.1.60)$$

Hence q and p have representatives for those transitions in which the quantum number n of the oscillator increases or decreases by one.

VII.2. The Schrödinger Representation of a Harmonic Oscillator

VII.2.A. One-Dimensional Oscillator

The Schrödinger wave equation for a harmonic oscillator is

$$\left(-\frac{\hbar^2}{2m}\frac{d^2}{dq^2} + \frac{1}{2}m\omega^2 q^2\right)\psi = E\psi. \qquad (VII.2.1)$$

Putting

$$x = \sqrt{\left(\frac{m\omega}{\hbar}\right)}\, q$$

we obtain

$$\frac{d^2\psi}{dx^2} + \left(\frac{2E}{\hbar\omega} - x^2\right)\psi = 0 \qquad (VII.2.2)$$

The wave function must remain finite for $x = \pm\infty$. For large x the term $2E/\hbar\omega$ can be neglected; then the solution satisfying the boundary conditions is of the form $\exp\left(-\frac{1}{2}x^2\right)$. Thus in the presence of the term $2E/\hbar\omega$ the wave function is of the form

$$\psi = e^{-1/2x^2}\eta(x).$$

Using the wave equation (*VII.2.2*) we obtain

$$\frac{d^2\eta}{dx^2} - 2x\frac{d\eta}{dx} + \left(\frac{2E}{\hbar\omega} - 1\right)\eta = 0, \qquad (VII.2.3)$$

where the function $\eta(x)$ must be finite for all finite x, and for large x it must be such that the wave function $\psi(x)$ shall tend to zero. The solutions satisfying these boundary conditions are Hermite polynomials defined by

$$H_n(x) = (-1)^n e^{x^2}\frac{d^n}{dx^n}\left(e^{-x^2}\right). \qquad (VII.2.4)$$

The normalized eigenfunctions of the oscillator are

$$\psi_n(x) = \left[\frac{m\omega}{\pi\hbar(2^n n!)^2}\right]^{1/4} \exp\left[-\tfrac{1}{2}(m\omega/\hbar)x^2\right] H_n\left[x\sqrt{\left(\frac{m\omega}{\hbar}\right)}\right], \qquad (VII.2.5)$$

where

$$\int_{-\infty}^{\infty}[\psi_n(x)]^2\, dx = 1.$$

The corresponding eigenvalues are obtained from setting $(2E/\hbar\omega) - 1 = 2n$.

It is interesting to observe that an equivalent discussion of the oscillator can be given in a momentum representation. In this case we treat the momentum operator p as an ordinary number and we replace the position operator by its momentum representation:

$$q = i\hbar \frac{d}{dp}.$$

The Hamiltonian is

$$H = \frac{1}{2m} p^2 - \frac{1}{2} m\omega^2\hbar^2 \frac{d^2}{dp^2}. \qquad (VII.2.6)$$

The corresponding wave equation,

$$H\phi(p) = E\phi(p),$$

can be written as

$$\frac{d^2\phi}{dy^2} + \left(\frac{2E}{\omega\hbar} - y^2\right)\phi = 0, \qquad (VII.2.7)$$

where the dimensionless variable y is given by $y = p/\sqrt{(m\omega\hbar)}$. The boundary conditions are imposed for small and large momenta of the oscillator. For large p the wave function $\phi(p)$ must tend to zero and it must be finite for zero momentum. The momentum space eigenfunctions are given by

$$\phi_n(p) = \left[\frac{1}{2\hbar m\omega\pi(2^n n!)^2}\right]^{1/4} e^{-(1/2)(p^2/m\omega\hbar)} H_n\left(\frac{p}{\sqrt{m\omega\hbar}}\right). \qquad (VII.2.8)$$

The above results can be obtained directly from the operator formulation of the harmonic oscillator. We shall discuss it in detail. Let $|p\rangle$ be the normalized eigenstates of the momentum operator p corresponding to the eigenvalue p. Consider the representatives of equations ($VII.1.55$) and ($VII.1.8$) in momentum representation,

$$\langle p|a_+|n\rangle = \sqrt{(n+1)}\langle p|n+1\rangle = \phi_{n+1}(p)\sqrt{(n+1)}, \qquad (VII.2.9)$$

$$\langle p|a_-|E_0\rangle = 0, \qquad (VII.2.10)$$

where $\phi_{n+1}(p) = \langle p|n+1\rangle$. The representative $\langle p|a_+|n\rangle$ can be written as

$$\langle p|a_+|n\rangle = \int \langle p|a_+|p'\rangle\phi_n(p')\, dp',$$

where

$$\langle p|a_+|p'\rangle = \frac{1}{\sqrt{(2m\omega\hbar)}}\left[p\delta(p-p') - \hbar m\omega \frac{\partial}{\partial p}\delta(p-p')\right]. \qquad (VII.2.11)$$

Hence

$$\langle p|a_+|n\rangle = \frac{p}{\sqrt{(2m\hbar\omega)}}\phi_n(p) - \sqrt{\left(\frac{\hbar m\omega}{2}\right)}\frac{d}{dp}\phi_n(p). \qquad (VII.2.12)$$

Equation ($VII.2.9$) now leads to

$$\phi_{n+1} = \frac{p}{\sqrt{[2(n+1)m\hbar\omega]}}\phi_n - \sqrt{\left[\frac{\hbar m\omega}{2(n+1)}\right]}\frac{d\phi_n}{dp}. \qquad (VII.2.13)$$

A similar procedure applied to equation (*VII.2.10*) leads to

$$\frac{d\phi_0}{dp} + \frac{p}{\hbar m\omega}\,\phi_0 = 0, \qquad (VII.2.14)$$

where $\phi_0 = \langle p|E_0\rangle = \langle p|0\rangle$ is the *normal state* momentum wave function. Equation (*VII.2.14*) is solved by

$$\phi_0 = Ae^{-(1/2)(p^2/\hbar m\omega)}.$$

The constant A is determined from the normalization

$$\int_{-\infty}^{\infty} \phi_0^2\, dp = 1$$

as

$$A = \left[\frac{1}{2\pi\hbar m\omega}\right]^{1/4},$$

so

$$\phi_0 = \left[\frac{1}{2\pi\hbar m\omega}\right]^{1/4} e^{-(1/2)(p^2/\hbar m\omega)}. \qquad (VII.2.15)$$

In terms of y, equation (*VII.2.13*) reads as

$$\phi_{n+1} = \frac{1}{\sqrt{[2(n+1)]}}\left(-\frac{d}{dy} + y\right)\phi_n$$

$$= -\frac{1}{\sqrt{[2(n+1)]}}\, e^{(1/2)y^2}\frac{d}{dy}\,(e^{-(1/2)y^2}\phi_n).$$

By successive iteration we obtain

$$\phi_n = \frac{(-1)^n}{\sqrt{(2^n n!)}}\, e^{(1/2)y^2}\frac{d^n}{dy^n}\,(e^{-(1/2)y^2}\phi_0). \qquad (VII.2.16)$$

Using the definitions of ϕ_0, as given by (*VII.2.15*), and of the Hermite polynomials, we obtain (*VII.2.8*).

VII.2.B. The Three-Dimensional Oscillator

The quantum Hamiltonian corresponding to the classical Hamiltonian (*III.1.41*) is

$$H = \tfrac{1}{2}\hbar\omega \sum_{i=1}^{3} (a_i^+ a_i^- + a_i^- a_i^+), \qquad (VII.2.17)$$

where

$$a_i^+ = \frac{1}{\sqrt{(2m\omega\hbar)}}\,(p_i + im\omega q_i),$$

$$a_i^- = \frac{1}{\sqrt{(2m\omega\hbar)}}\,(p_i - im\omega q_i),$$

and

$$[a_i^-, a_j^+] = \delta_{ij}. \qquad (VII.2.18)$$

The Hamiltonian can also be written as

$$H = \hbar\omega(N + \tfrac{3}{2}), \tag{VII.2.19}$$

where

$$N = N_1 + N_2 + N_3,$$

$$N_1 = a_1^+ a_1^-, \qquad N_2 = a_2^+ a_2^-, \qquad N_3 = a_3^+ a_3^-.$$

Hence the corresponding eigenvalues are

$$E_n = \hbar\omega(n + \tfrac{3}{2}), \tag{VII.2.20}$$

where $n = n_1 + n_2 + n_3$. The corresponding eigenstates of N are

$$|n\rangle = |n_1\rangle|n_2\rangle|n_3\rangle = \frac{1}{\sqrt{(n_1!n_2!n_3!)}}(a_1^+)^{n_1}(a_2^+)^{n_2}(a_3^+)^{n_3}|E_0\rangle, \tag{VII.2.21}$$

$$N|n\rangle = n|n\rangle,$$

where

$$a_1^-|E_0\rangle = a_2^-|E_0\rangle = a_3^-|E_0\rangle = 0.$$

The number of ways that n can be written as a sum of three nonnegative integers is $(\frac{1}{2})(n+1)(n+2)$, so the eigenvalues are $(\frac{1}{2})(n+1)(n+2)$-fold degenerate. If the x_1, x_2, and x_3 components of the oscillations ω_1, ω_2, ω_3 are not equal, then the potential energy is given by (*III.1.38*) and the degeneracy is lifted. In the latter case the energy levels are

$$E_{n_1} = \hbar\omega_1(n_1 + \tfrac{1}{2}), \qquad E_{n_2} = \hbar\omega_2(n_2 + \tfrac{1}{2}), \qquad E_{n_3} = \hbar\omega_3(n_3 + \tfrac{1}{2}).$$

The total energy is $E_{n_1} + E_{n_2} + E_{n_3}$.

The wave functions for the degenerate case are

$$\psi_{n_1n_2n_3}(r) = \left[\frac{m^3\omega^3}{\pi^3\hbar^3(2^n n_1!n_2!n_3!)^2}\right]^{1/4} e^{-(m\omega/2\hbar)r^2}$$

$$H_{n_1}\left[x_1\sqrt{\left(\frac{m\omega}{\hbar}\right)}\right] H_{n_2}\left[x_2\sqrt{\left(\frac{m\omega}{\hbar}\right)}\right] H_{n_3}\left[x_3\sqrt{\left(\frac{m\omega}{\hbar}\right)}\right]. \tag{VII.2.22}$$

For a one-dimensional oscillator in the normal state, represented by ψ_0 (a Gaussian type wave function), the maximum occurs at the origin. Furthermore, the probability of finding the oscillator outside its classical region (the region between the two ends of its oscillations) does not vanish, even though in such states its total energy is less than its potential energy. The latter arises from the uncertainties in the position and momentum of the oscillator. A particle's capability, in quantum mechanics, to penetrate a potential barrier higher than its total energy is usually called the "tunnel effect."

VII.2.C. Problems

1. Show that the average values of p^2 and q^2 with respect to harmonic oscillator states are given by

$$\langle p^2 \rangle = (n + \tfrac{1}{2})\hbar\omega m,$$

$$\langle q^2 \rangle = (n + \tfrac{1}{2}) \frac{\hbar}{m\omega}.$$

Hence prove that the measure of spreads in q and p satisfy

$$\Delta q \Delta p = (n + \tfrac{1}{2})\hbar.$$

Thus the harmonic oscillator level $n = 0$ (zero-point energy) corresponds, with its Gaussian type wave function, to a state of minimum uncertainty.

2. Consider the differential equation

$$\frac{d^2u}{dx^2} - x\frac{du}{dx} + nu = 0 \qquad (VII.2.23)$$

and the equation obtained from it by replacing n by $-n$ and x by ix:

$$\frac{d^2f}{dx^2} + x\frac{df}{dx} + nf = 0. \qquad (VII.2.24)$$

Show that for $n = 1$ the equation (*VII.2.24*) is satisfied by

$$u = \frac{1}{\sqrt{(2\pi)}} \int_{-\infty}^{\infty} \frac{\exp(-\frac{1}{2}y^2)}{x + y + i\epsilon}\, dy, \qquad (VII.2.25)$$

where ϵ is a small positive number. By integrating differential equation (*VII.2.24*), prove that integral (*VII.2.25*) can be reduced to

$$u = xe^{-(1/2)x^2} \int_0^x e^{(1/2)y^2}\, dy - \sqrt{\left(\frac{\pi}{2}\right)}\, e^{-(1/2)x^2}x.$$

3. Using expression (*IV.3.17*) for the square of angular momentum, show that the simultaneous eigenfunctions of $\boldsymbol{L}^2$, H [see (*VII.2.19*)], and L_3 can be expressed as

$$\psi_{nlm} = \frac{1}{r} h_{nl}(r) Y_{lm}(\theta, \phi),$$

where h_{nl} are solutions of

$$\left[-\frac{\hbar^2}{2m}\frac{d^2}{dr^2} + \frac{l(l+1)\hbar^2}{2mr^2} + \tfrac{1}{2}m\omega^2 r^2\right] h_{nl} = (n + \tfrac{1}{2})\,\hbar\omega h_{nl},$$

and n, l, m are eigenvalues of H, $\boldsymbol{L}^2$, and L_3, respectively.

4. By using a power series expansion of the one-dimensional oscillator wave function,

$$\psi(x) = a_0 + a_1 x + a_2 x^2 + \cdots,$$

show that the expansion coefficients obey the recursion formula

$$a_{s+2} = -\frac{2(n-s)}{(s+1)(s+2)}\, a_s,$$

where

$$2n = \frac{2E}{\hbar\omega} - 1.$$

Show that the higher terms of ψ differ from those for e^{x^2} only by a multiplicative constant, so for large values of $|x|$, $\psi(x)$ will behave like e^{x^2}. Hence the only acceptable wave function can be obtained by breaking off the series after a finite number of terms, leaving a polynomial. The value of E which causes the series to break off after the sth term is $E = \hbar\omega[s + \frac{1}{2}]$.

5. Solve Heisenberg's equations of motion for the oscillator and hence show that the average values of q and p lead to the classical form of the oscillator.

6. Use definition (*VI.2.23*) of the density operator for a system in thermodynamic equilibrium and calculate the average energy of an oscillator in thermodynamic equilibrium. [Hint: put $H = \hbar\omega(N + \frac{1}{2})$.] Then

$$\operatorname{tr} e^{-(1/\kappa T)H} = \sum_{n=0}^{\infty} \langle n|e^{-(1/\kappa T)H}|n\rangle = \sum_{n=0}^{\infty} \exp\left[-\frac{\hbar\omega}{\kappa T}\left(n + \frac{1}{2}\right)\right].$$

Now use $\langle E\rangle = \operatorname{tr}(\rho H)$ to obtain Planck's formula,

$$\langle E\rangle = \tfrac{1}{2}\,\hbar\omega + \frac{\hbar\omega}{e^{\hbar\omega/\kappa T} - 1}.$$

7. By using the expansions

$$|q\rangle = \sum_{n=0}^{\infty} |n\rangle\langle n|q\rangle,$$

$$|p\rangle = \sum_{n=0}^{\infty} |n\rangle\langle n|p\rangle,$$

give expressions for the expansion of a delta function in terms of oscillator wave functions. Hence derive the expansion of $e^{(i/\hbar)qp}$. Comment on your results.

8. By using the theory of harmonic oscillators as developed in this chapter, set up a similar approach for the representation of angular momentum discussed in Chapter IV. In particular, compare the set of irreducible eigenvectors (*IV.1.38*) for the total angular momentum and the complete set of eigenvectors (*VII.1.34*) for a system of harmonic oscillators. Use the resemblance between the operators J_+, J_- and a_+, a_-.

CHAPTER VIII

THE LORENTZ GROUP

VIII.1. The Three-Dimensional Complex Orthogonal Representation

The notion of spin comes from the Lorentz covariance properties of the equations of quantum mechanics. The integral and half-integral spin concepts are closely associated with the transformation property of the field representing a particle (scalar, vector, tensor, or spinor fields). Spin is an intrinsic property of a field. For these and other reasons we have to discover all possible representations of the Lorentz group.

It has been shown in Section I.9 that real orthogonal transformations in three-dimensional space are *homomorphic* (one-to-two correspondence) onto unitary transformations in the spinor plane. The proper Lorentz transformation (for instance, three velocity components and three angles of rotation) as a six-parameter representation of a *homogeneous Lorentz group*—and also *improper Lorentz transformations*—can have a complex space representation.* Every complex linear manifold is suitable for the representation of the Lorentz group. For example, the three-dimensional unitary space cannot be used for the representation of the Lorentz group. This is because of the Euclidean nature of this space and also because of the requirement of 8 parameters ($n^2 - 1 = 3^2 - 1$) for the representation of the three-dimensional unitary unimodular group.

We may envisage a three-dimensional linear manifold spanned by the special type of complex vectors formed from space and time components of an antisymmetric tensor field.

The representation of the Lorentz group by a three-dimensional complex orthogonal group is also suggested by the fact that the Lorentz-invariant path length $ds^2 = 0$ of a plane electromagnetic wave can be replaced by the two Lorentz-invariant statements that the electric and magnetic vectors of the wave are (a) of equal magnitude and (b) perpendicular to one another.

At each point of the wave we can set up an "invariant coordinate system"

* B. Kurşunoğlu, *J. Math. Phys.*, **2**, No. 1 (1961), 22–32.

with the electric vector $\mathcal{E}$ and magnetic vector $\mathcal{H}$, choosing the third axis of the coordinate system in the direction of its propagation (or its spin direction).

Let $f_{\alpha\beta}$ be any antisymmetric 4×4 matrix, which under a Lorentz transformation of coordinates transforms like the antisymmetric combination

$$|a\supset\subset b| - |b\supset\subset a|$$

of two 4-vectors $|a\supset$ and $|b\supset$.

Thus, if $f'(x')$ is the matrix resulting from a Lorentz transformation $|x'\supset = L|x\supset$, we have

$$f' = Lf\tilde{L}, \tag{VIII.1.1}$$

where

$$f = [f_{\alpha\beta}] = \begin{bmatrix} 0 & f_{12} & -f_{31} & f_{14} \\ -f_{12} & 0 & f_{23} & f_{24} \\ f_{31} & -f_{23} & 0 & f_{34} \\ -f_{14} & -f_{24} & -f_{34} & 0 \end{bmatrix}. \tag{VIII.1.2}$$

In accordance with the notation of Chapter II, we define the bra $\subset\chi|$ by

$$\subset\chi| = [\chi_1, \chi_2, \chi_3]. \tag{VIII.1.3}$$

The bra $\langle\chi|$ is defined by

$$\langle\chi| = [\chi_1^*, \chi_2^*, \chi_3^*] = (|\chi\rangle)^\dagger.$$

We must now distinguish between two types of scalar products of two vectors $|\chi\rangle$ and $|\zeta\rangle$ belonging to the three-dimensional complex space.

(a) The Lorentz-invariant scalar product of $|\chi\rangle$ and $|\zeta\rangle$ is

$$\subset\zeta|\chi\supset = \zeta_1\chi_1 + \zeta_2\chi_2 + \zeta_3\chi_3. \tag{VIII.1.4}$$

(b) The Hermitian (or gauge-invariant) scalar product of $|\chi\rangle$ and $|\zeta\rangle$ is

$$\langle\zeta|\chi\rangle = \zeta_1^*\chi_1 + \zeta_2^*\chi_2 + \zeta_3^*\chi_3. \tag{VIII.1.5}$$

In particular, for $|\zeta\rangle = |\chi\rangle$ we have

$$\subset\chi|\chi\supset = \chi_1^2 + \chi_2^2 + \chi_3^2 = \Omega + 2i\Lambda \tag{VIII.1.6}$$

and

$$\langle\chi|\chi\rangle = |\chi_1|^2 + |\chi_2|^2 + |\chi_3|^2 = \mathcal{E}^2 + \mathcal{H}^2, \tag{VIII.1.7}$$

where

$$\Omega = \mathcal{H}^2 - \mathcal{E}^2 = \tfrac{1}{2}f^{\mu\nu}f_{\mu\nu},$$

which is a scalar,

$$\Lambda = \mathcal{E}\cdot\mathcal{H} = \tfrac{1}{4}f^{\mu\nu}\phi_{\mu\nu}, \tag{VIII.1.8}$$

which is a pseudoscalar, and

$$\phi^{\mu\nu} = \tfrac{1}{2}\epsilon^{\mu\nu\rho\sigma}f_{\rho\sigma}, \tag{VIII.1.9}$$

which is called the dual tensor of $f_{\mu\nu}$. The quantities $\epsilon^{\mu\nu\rho\sigma}$ constitute a contravariant tensor of fourth rank, antisymmetric with respect to the interchange of any two indices. The $\epsilon^{\mu\nu\rho\sigma}$ is $+1$ when $\mu\nu\rho\sigma$ assumes the values of even permutations of (1234), -1 for values of odd permutations of (1234), and zero for any two equal indices. They transform like an axial quantity as

$$\epsilon'^{\mu\nu\rho\sigma} = L^{\mu}_{\alpha}L^{\nu}_{\beta}L^{\rho}_{\gamma}L^{\sigma}_{\delta}\epsilon^{\alpha\beta\gamma\delta} = \det(L)\epsilon^{\mu\nu\rho\sigma},$$

so the transformation of $\epsilon^{\mu\nu\rho\sigma}$ depends on the sign of det (L). It is seen from (*VIII.1.6*) and (*VIII.1.7*) that the former is Lorentz-invariant and the latter is gauge-invariant; that is, the transformation

$$|\chi_{\delta}\rangle = e^{i\delta}|\chi\rangle \qquad (VIII.1.10)$$

does not change (*VIII.1.7*) for an arbitrary, invariant, real phase variable $\delta(x)$. All vectors of the complex three-dimensional manifold are of the form (*VIII.1.10*) or its complex conjugate.

The ket $|\chi_{\delta}\rangle$ can further be qualified as a complex vector by its transformation properties. For this purpose we introduce complex orthogonal transformations which leave (*VIII.1.6*) unchanged. If R is the transformation matrix of a complex ket, we obtain another ket belonging to the same complex space by

$$|\chi'\rangle = R|\chi_{\delta}\rangle = Re^{i\delta}|\chi\rangle. \qquad (VIII.1.11)$$

Hence

$$\subset\chi'|\chi'\supset = \subset\chi|e^{i\delta}\tilde{R}Re^{i\delta}|\chi\supset = \subset\chi|\chi\supset.$$

so the invariance of (*VIII.1.6*) under R transformations requires that all R transformations must satisfy

$$\tilde{R}R = R\tilde{R} = e^{-2i\delta}. \qquad (VIII.1.12)$$

These conditions on R correspond to six complex or twelve real equations; therefore, of the eighteen parameters fixing R (plus the phase δ), six are independent. The six parameters together with a given δ will fix a member of the complex group (extended complex group for $\delta \neq 0$).

We shall be interested in the two subgroups of the extended group corresponding to the two special values of δ.

(a) $\delta = 0$, and

$$\tilde{R}R = R\tilde{R} = I. \qquad (VIII.1.13)$$

This is the complex orthogonal group. The determinant of R is $+1$ or -1. Thus we have to distinguish between a pure complex rotation group with determinant $+1$ and a rotation reflection group—which includes transformation matrices—with determinant -1. The identity element of the group is the unit matrix I_3. Because of the nonunitary nature of R its eigenvalues are not all of unit magnitude.

(b) $\delta = \pi/2$, and

$$\tilde{R}R = R\tilde{R} = -I. \qquad (VIII.1.14)$$

This is the antiorthogonal group. The determinant of R, in this case, is $+i$ or $-i$. We shall see presently that antiorthogonal and improper R transformations are equivalent to antilinear operations on the vectors of the complex space.

The complex conjugate of any ket $|\chi\rangle$ is transformed by the complex conjugates of R transformations satisfying the orthogonality and antiorthogonality conditions,

$$\tilde{R}^*R^* = R^*\tilde{R}^* = I \tag{VIII.1.15}$$

and

$$\tilde{R}^*R^* = R^*\tilde{R}^* = -I, \tag{VIII.1.16}$$

respectively.

If $\overline{C}$ is the operator of complex conjugation (antiunitary operator), then it can operate on $|\chi\rangle$ to produce

$$|\chi^*\rangle = \overline{C}|\chi\rangle$$

and

$$|\chi'^*\rangle = \overline{C}|\chi'\rangle = \overline{C}R|\chi\rangle = \overline{C}R\overline{C}|\chi^*\rangle = R^*|\chi^*\rangle, \tag{VIII.1.17}$$

where we use the antiunitary operator property*

$$\overline{C}^2 = I. \tag{VIII.1.18}$$

For the proper complex orthogonal group a member R can be assumed to be a function of an invariant parameter τ. It satisfies the equation [as follows from differentiating (*VIII.1.13*)]

$$i\frac{dR}{d\tau} = ZR, \tag{VIII.1.19}$$

where Z is a complex antisymmetric 3×3 matrix, namely,

$$\tilde{Z} = -Z,$$

and

$$Z = i\begin{bmatrix} 0 & -a_3 - ib_3 & a_2 + ib_2 \\ a_3 + ib_3 & 0 & -a_1 - ib_1 \\ -a_2 - ib_2 & a_1 + ib_1 & 0 \end{bmatrix} = a^jK_j + ib^jK_j, \tag{VIII.1.20}$$

where a^j and b^j, for $j = 1, 2, 3$, are real numbers. Hence the six generators of the proper complex orthogonal group are

$$K_i, \qquad iK_i. \tag{VIII.1.21}$$

The former generates pure rotations and the latter corresponds to velocity transformations. Typical proper R transformations are

---

* The subgroup of the extended group considered here is a four-sheet group corresponding to four different values of the determinants of R transformations.

$$R_1 = \exp[i(\psi + i\lambda)K_1], \qquad (VIII.1.22)$$
$$R_2 = \exp[i(\phi + i\epsilon)K_2], \qquad (VIII.1.23)$$
$$R_3 = \exp[i(\theta + i\rho)K_3]. \qquad (VIII.1.24)$$

A Lorentz transformation of the electromagnetic field can now be effected by a complex orthogonal matrix. Let us consider the R_1-transformation which has the matrix form

$$R_1 = \begin{bmatrix} 1 & 0 & 0 \\ 0 & \cos(\psi + i\lambda) & \sin(\psi + i\lambda) \\ 0 & -\sin(\psi + i\lambda) & \cos(\psi + i\lambda) \end{bmatrix}, \qquad (VIII.1.25)$$

where

$$\cos(\psi + i\lambda) = \cos\psi \cosh\lambda - i\sin\psi \sinh\lambda,$$
$$\sin(\psi + i\lambda) = \sin\psi \cosh\lambda + i\cos\psi \sinh\lambda,$$

and

$$\tanh\lambda = \frac{v}{c}.$$

The Lorentz transformation by R_1 corresponds to a rotation around the x_1 direction by an angle ψ and a uniform motion along the same direction with velocity v.

From

$$|\chi'\rangle = R_1|\chi\rangle \qquad (VIII.1.26)$$

we obtain

$$\chi_1' = \chi_1,$$

$$\chi_2' = \gamma\left[\chi_2\left(\cos\psi - i\frac{v}{c}\sin\psi\right) + \chi_3\left(\sin\psi + i\frac{v}{c}\cos\psi\right)\right], \qquad (VIII.1.27)$$

$$\chi_3' = \gamma\left[-\chi_2\left(\sin\psi + i\frac{v}{c}\cos\psi\right) + \chi_3\left(\cos\psi - i\frac{v}{c}\sin\psi\right)\right],$$

where

$$\gamma = \left(1 - \frac{v^2}{c^2}\right)^{-1/2}.$$

Equating the real and imaginary parts of $(VIII.1.27)$, we obtain the transformation laws of the electromagnetic field as

$$\mathcal{E}_1' = \mathcal{E}_1,$$

$$\mathcal{E}_2' = \gamma\left[\left(\mathcal{E}_2 - \frac{v}{c}\mathcal{H}_3\right)\cos\psi + \left(\mathcal{E}_3 + \frac{v}{c}\mathcal{H}_2\right)\sin\psi\right],$$

$$\mathcal{E}_3' = \gamma\left[\left(\mathcal{E}_3 + \frac{v}{c}\mathcal{H}_2\right)\cos\psi + \left(-\mathcal{E}_2 + \frac{v}{c}\mathcal{H}_3\right)\sin\psi\right],$$

$$\mathcal{H}_1' = \mathcal{H}_1, \qquad (VIII.1.28)$$

$$\mathcal{H}_2' = \gamma\left[\left(\mathcal{H}_2 + \frac{v}{c}\mathcal{E}_3\right)\cos\psi + \left(\mathcal{H}_3 - \frac{v}{c}\mathcal{E}_2\right)\sin\psi\right],$$

$$\mathcal{H}_3' = \gamma\left[\left(\mathcal{H}_3 - \frac{v}{c}\mathcal{E}_2\right)\cos\psi - \left(\mathcal{H}_2 + \frac{v}{c}\mathcal{E}_3\right)\sin\psi\right],$$

which for $\psi = 0$ reduce to

$$\begin{aligned} &\mathcal{E}_1' = \mathcal{E}_1, \quad &\mathcal{E}_2' = \gamma\left(\mathcal{E}_2 - \frac{v}{c}\mathcal{H}_3\right), \quad &\mathcal{E}_3' = \gamma\left(\mathcal{E}_3 + \frac{v}{c}\mathcal{H}_2\right), \\ &\mathcal{H}_1' = \mathcal{H}_1, \quad &\mathcal{H}_2' = \gamma\left(\mathcal{H}_2 + \frac{v}{c}\mathcal{E}_3\right), \quad &\mathcal{H}_3' = \gamma\left(\mathcal{H}_3 - \frac{v}{c}\mathcal{E}_2\right). \end{aligned} \tag{VIII.1.29}$$

VIII.1.A. The Transformation of Electromagnetic Energy and Momentum Density

Energy, momentum, and stress properties of the classical electromagnetic field are described by a symmetric second-rank tensor $T_{\alpha\beta}$, defined by

$$T_{\alpha\beta} = \tfrac{1}{2}a_{\alpha\beta}\Omega - f_{\alpha\mu}f^{\mu}_{\beta}, \tag{VIII.1.30}$$

where

$$T_{44} = \tfrac{1}{2}(\mathcal{E}^2 + \mathcal{H}^2),$$
$$T_{i4} = (\mathcal{E} \times \mathcal{H})_i,$$

and the space components T_{ij} are associated with the stress properties (components of momentum current) of the field. Further properties of $T_{\alpha\beta}$ are

$$T^{\alpha}_{\mu}T^{\mu}_{\beta} = \delta^{\alpha}_{\beta}(\tfrac{1}{4}\Omega^2 + \Lambda^2) = \tfrac{1}{4}\delta^{\alpha}_{\beta}|\chi^2|^2 \tag{VIII.1.31}$$

and

$$(\tfrac{1}{4}\Omega^2 + \Lambda^2) = \left(\frac{\mathcal{E}^2 + \mathcal{H}^2}{2}\right)^2 - (\mathcal{E} \times \mathcal{H})^2. \tag{VIII.1.32}$$

A comparison of (*VIII.1.32*) with the square of the momentum vector p_μ of a material particle ($p_\mu p^\mu = p_4^2 - \boldsymbol{p}^2$) suggests that there exists a Lorentz-covariant representation of the energy and momentum properties of the electromagnetic field. Thus, if we take

$$S_\mu = \frac{1}{c}\,T_{\mu\nu}V^\nu, \tag{VIII.1.33}$$

where V^ν is a unit vector, or

$$V_\nu V^\nu = 1, \tag{VIII.1.34}$$

then we obtain

$$\begin{aligned} c^2 S_\mu S^\mu &= T_{\mu\sigma}V^\sigma T^{\mu\rho}V_\rho \\ &= \delta^{\rho}_{\sigma}V^\sigma V_\rho(\tfrac{1}{4}\Omega^2 + \Lambda^2) \\ &= \tfrac{1}{4}\Omega^2 + \Lambda^2. \end{aligned}$$

Hence the energy and momentum density vector S_μ defined by (*VIII.1.33*) transforms Lorentz-covariantly for all types of electromagnetic waves and it reduces to

$$cS_4 = \tfrac{1}{4}(\mathcal{E}^2 + \mathcal{H}^2),$$
$$cS_i = (\mathcal{E} \times \mathcal{H})_i$$

for $V_i = 0$, $V_4 = 1$.

The complex space representation of S_μ and $T_{\mu\nu}$ can be obtained, by inspection, as

$$S_\mu = \frac{1}{2c}\langle\chi|B_{\mu\nu}V^\nu|\chi\rangle, \tag{VIII.1.35}$$

$$T_{\mu\nu} = \tfrac{1}{2}\langle\chi|B_{\mu\nu}|\chi\rangle, \tag{VIII.1.36}$$

where the ten 3×3 matrices $B_{\mu\nu}$ are given by

$$\begin{aligned} B_{44} &= I_3, \qquad B_{4i} = B_{i4} = K_i, \\ B_{ij} &= B_{ji} = K_iK_j + K_jK_i - I_3\delta_{ij}, \end{aligned} \tag{VIII.1.37}$$

and, like $T_{\mu\nu}$, they satisfy the trace property

$$a^{\mu\nu}B_{\mu\nu} = 0. \tag{VIII.1.38}$$

If $v^i = 0$, then S_μ can be written as

$$S_\mu = \frac{1}{2c}\langle\chi|K_\mu|\chi\rangle. \tag{VIII.1.39}$$

The B matrices, as follows from the definitions ($VIII.1.37$), have the matrix forms

$$B_{11} = \begin{bmatrix} -1 & 0 & 0 \\ 0 & 1 & 0 \\ 0 & 0 & 1 \end{bmatrix}, \quad B_{22} = \begin{bmatrix} 1 & 0 & 0 \\ 0 & -1 & 0 \\ 0 & 0 & 1 \end{bmatrix}, \quad B_{33} = \begin{bmatrix} 1 & 0 & 0 \\ 0 & 1 & 0 \\ 0 & 0 & -1 \end{bmatrix}$$

$$B_{23} = B_1 = \begin{bmatrix} 0 & 0 & 0 \\ 0 & 0 & -1 \\ 0 & -1 & 0 \end{bmatrix},$$

$$B_{31} = B_2 = \begin{bmatrix} 0 & 0 & -1 \\ 0 & 0 & 0 \\ -1 & 0 & 0 \end{bmatrix}, \tag{VIII.1.40}$$

$$B_{12} = B_3 = \begin{bmatrix} 0 & -1 & 0 \\ -1 & 0 & 0 \\ 0 & 0 & 0 \end{bmatrix}.$$

the remaining B have already been defined as K matrices.

All B matrices are Hermitian. The matrices B_{ij} satisfy the relations

$$B_{11}^2 + B_{22}^2 + B_{33}^2 = 3l_3 \tag{VIII.1.41}$$

and

$$B_1^2 + B_2^2 + B_3^2 = 2l_3. \tag{VIII.1.42}$$

The eigenvalues of any B_i, for $i = 1, 2, 3$, are $+1$, -1, and 0. The normalized eigenvectors of B_3, for example, are real vectors

$$|1\rangle = \frac{1}{\sqrt{2}}\begin{bmatrix} 1 \\ -1 \\ 0 \end{bmatrix}, \qquad |-1\rangle = \frac{1}{\sqrt{2}}\begin{bmatrix} 1 \\ 1 \\ 0 \end{bmatrix}, \qquad |0\rangle = \begin{bmatrix} 0 \\ 0 \\ 1 \end{bmatrix}. \tag{VIII.1.43}$$

Furthermore,

$$B_1^3 = B_1, \qquad B_2^3 = B_2, \qquad B_3^3 = B_3 \qquad (VIII.1.44)$$

and

$$B_1^2 = K_1^2, \qquad B_2^2 = K_2^2, \qquad B_3^2 = K_3^2, \qquad (VIII.1.45)$$

$$\tilde{B}_i = B_i, \qquad \tilde{K}_i = -K_i. \qquad (VIII.1.46)$$

From the above properties of B and K matrices we see that the transformation operators, such as

$$A(\theta) = e^{i\theta K_3}, \qquad G(\theta) = e^{i\theta B_3}, \qquad (VIII.1.47)$$

induce the transformations

$$|\chi'\rangle = e^{i\theta K_3}|\chi\rangle, \qquad (VIII.1.48)$$

$$|\chi_b\rangle = e^{i\theta B_3}|\chi\rangle. \qquad (VIII.1.49)$$

The operator (*VIII.1.48*) is both energy-conserving and also a Lorentz transformation operator, since

$$\langle\chi'|\chi'\rangle = \langle\chi|e^{-i\theta K_3}e^{i\theta K_3}|\chi\rangle = \langle\chi|\chi\rangle$$

and

$$\subset\chi'|\chi'\supset = \subset\chi|e^{i\theta\tilde{K}_3}e^{i\theta K_3}|\chi\supset$$

$$= \subset\chi|e^{-i\theta K_3}e^{i\theta K_3}|\chi\supset = \subset\chi|\chi\supset.$$

The operator (*VIII.1.49*), because of the property (*VIII.1.46*), effects only an energy-conserving transformation:

$$\langle\chi_b|\chi_b\rangle = \langle\chi|e^{-i\theta B_3}e^{i\theta B_3}|\chi\rangle = \langle\chi|\chi\rangle.$$

The nonsingular matrices B_{11}, B_{22}, B_{33} are the generators of diagonal unitary transformation operators; these transformations also are energy-conserving.

The transformation properties of B matrices, under simultaneous complex orthogonal and Lorentz transformations, can be obtained from the vector and tensor transformation properties of S_μ and $T_{\mu\nu}$ as defined by (*VIII.1.35*) and (*VIII.1.36*), respectively.

The tensor $T_{\mu\nu}$ in another Lorentz frame has the form

$$T'_{\mu\nu} = \tfrac{1}{2}\langle\chi'|B_{\mu\nu}|\chi'\rangle, \qquad (VIII.1.50)$$

where $|\chi'\rangle$ is a function of the new coordinates x'^μ, related to the old coordinates x^μ by a Lorentz transformation,

$$x'^\mu = L^\mu_\nu x^\nu,$$

and $|\chi'\rangle$ itself is transformed by an R transformation according to

$$|\chi'\rangle = R|\chi\rangle.$$

If we apply these transformations, together with

$$T'_{\mu\nu} = L^\alpha_\mu L^\beta_\nu T_{\alpha\beta}$$

in the definition (*VIII.1.50*) of $T'_{\mu\nu}$, we obtain

$$L^\alpha_\mu L^\beta_\nu T_{\alpha\beta} = \tfrac{1}{2}\langle\chi|R^\dagger B_{\mu\nu}R|\chi\rangle. \qquad (VIII.1.51)$$

If we substitute for $T_{\alpha\beta}$ on the left from (*VIII.1.36*) and require that the transformation hold for all complex vectors of the complex space, we get the transformation rules of B matrices:

$$R^\dagger B_{\mu\nu} R = L_\mu^\alpha L_\nu^\beta B_{\alpha\beta}. \tag{VIII.1.52}$$

The R matrix is a function of the coefficients L_ν^μ alone.

The symmetry properties of a space formed from $|\chi\rangle$ vectors are of great physical interest. We shall study some of these properties by the application of the improper Lorentz transformations corresponding to Lorentz matrices F, $-F$, and $-I_4$. But F and $-F$ correspond to space- and time-reflection transformations of coordinates, respectively [see (*I.10.4*)]. In R space, the corresponding transformation can be obtained by replacing L_μ^α by a_μ^α, which leads to

$$R^\dagger B_{\mu\nu} R = a_\mu^\alpha a_\nu^\beta B_{\alpha\beta}. \tag{VIII.1.53}$$

Hence various B matrices transform according to

$$R^\dagger R = I, \tag{VIII.1.54}$$

$$R^\dagger K_i R = -K_i, \tag{VIII.1.55}$$

$$R^\dagger B_{ij} R = B_{ij}. \tag{VIII.1.56}$$

We shall study five different R transformations satisfying (*VIII.1.54*) and (*VIII.1.55*).

(a) The R transformation corresponding to the F matrix in Lorentz space can be taken to be the "parity" operator $\mathcal{P}$, which is a linear unitary space-reflection operator and transforms the B matrices according to

$$\mathcal{P}^2 = I, \tag{VIII.1.57}$$

$$\mathcal{P}^{-1} K_i \mathcal{P} = -K_i, \tag{VIII.1.58}$$

$$\mathcal{P}^{-1} B_{ij} \mathcal{P} = B_{ij}. \tag{VIII.1.59}$$

When electric and magnetic vectors are regarded as classical functions of space and time, the parity operator $\mathcal{P}$ acts on a ket $|\chi(\boldsymbol{r}, t)\rangle$ to produce another ket $|\chi'\rangle$:

$$|\chi'\rangle = \mathcal{P}|\chi(\boldsymbol{r}, t)\rangle = -|\chi^*(-\boldsymbol{r}, t)\rangle = -\overline{C}|\chi(-\boldsymbol{r}, t)\rangle. \tag{VIII.1.60}$$

In the above we used the transformation properties of $\mathcal{E}$ and $\mathcal{H}$ under space reflections (see Section I.4). On operating twice with $\mathcal{P}$ we obtain the original state,

$$\mathcal{P}|\chi'\rangle = \mathcal{P}^2|\chi\rangle = |\chi\rangle.$$

The matrices B_{ij}, where $i, j = 1, 2, 3$, remain unchanged under parity operation.

(b) The fact that the elements of K matrices and of B_{ij} matrices are pure imaginary and real numbers, respectively, suggest the choice of R as the antilinear operator of the complex conjugation

$$R = \pm\overline{C}, \qquad (VIII.1.61)$$

which satisfy (*VIII.1.54*) and (*VIII.1.56*). At this point we note that $\mathcal{P}$ and $-\overline{C}$ operations on a ket $|\chi\rangle$ are not equivalent operations.

The antilinear operator $\overline{C}$ can be regarded as the "metric"! of the complex space and in this sense it corresponds to the Lorentz metric F of Lorentz space. We may now use the ordinary ket notation and define the scalar product of two complex vectors, without the necessity of introducing two types of scalar products, by

$$\langle\chi|\overline{C}|\chi\rangle = \chi_i^*\chi_i^*, \qquad (VIII.1.62)$$

where the effect of the antilinear operator $\overline{C}$ is to replace the expression following it by its complex conjugate. We can also define an antilinear operator $\overline{C}_L$, whose effect is to replace the expression "preceding" it by its complex conjugate. Thus if b is a complex number, then

$$\overline{C}b = b\overline{C}_L = b^* \qquad (VIII.1.63)$$

and

$$\overline{C}b\overline{C}_L = b\overline{C}_L^2 = b^*C_L = b.$$

Hence

$$\overline{C}_L^2 = 1. \qquad (VIII.1.64)$$

With the use of $\overline{C}_L$ the scalar product of two vectors $|\chi\rangle$ and $|\eta\rangle$ is defined as

$$\langle\chi|\overline{C}_L|\eta\rangle = \chi_i\eta_i$$

and

$$\langle\chi|\overline{C}_L|\chi\rangle = \chi_i\chi_i. \qquad (VIII.1.65)$$

The vector $\langle\chi|C_L = \langle\chi^*| = \subset\chi|$ is called the "adjoint" of $|\chi\rangle$.

(c) The R transformation corresponding to the coordinate time-reflecting ($-F$) Lorentz matrix can be taken as the time-reflection operator of the complex space. We shall now prove that time-reversal operation in R space is an antiunitary operation.*

To find the R transformation corresponding to $-F$ in Lorentz space we shall posit

$$R = V\overline{C}, \qquad (VIII.1.66)$$

where V is a unitary operator,

$$V^\dagger V = I$$

The definition of R by (*VIII.1.66*) automatically satisfies (*VIII.1.54*), and its substitution in (*VIII.1.55*) yields

---

* Space and time reflections of coordinates in Lorentz space are affected by the transformations $|x'\supset = F|x\supset$ or $x'^i = -x^i$ and $t' = t$, and $|x'\supset = -F|x\supset$ or $x'^i = x^i$ and $t' = -t$, respectively.

$$\tilde{V}K_iV^* = K_i. \qquad (VIII.1.67)$$

If R operates on vectors of the type $|\chi\rangle$, then the simplest choice for V is to take

$$V = I_3, \qquad (VIII.1.68)$$

so the corresponding time-reversal operator $\mathfrak{J}$ of three-dimensional complex space has the form

$$\mathfrak{J} = I_3\overline{C}. \qquad (VIII.1.69)$$

A more general form of the time-reversal operator which can operate on vectors of the form $e^{i\delta}|\chi\rangle$ is

$$\mathfrak{J} = e^{i\delta}I_3\overline{C}, \qquad (VIII.1.70)$$

which satisfies

$$\mathfrak{J}^2 = I. \qquad (VIII.1.71)$$

The operator $\mathfrak{J}$, as defined by $(VIII.1.70)$ for $\delta = 0$, $\delta = \pi$, and $\delta = 2\pi$, is the complex orthogonal, and for $\delta = \pi/2$ it is an antiorthogonal operator:

$$\tilde{\mathfrak{J}}\mathfrak{J} = I, \qquad \text{for } \delta = 0,\ \pi,\ 2\pi,$$

$$\tilde{\mathfrak{J}}\mathfrak{J} = -I, \qquad \text{for } \delta = \frac{\pi}{2}.$$

The K matrices under $\mathfrak{J}$ transform according to

$$\tilde{\mathfrak{J}}K_i\mathfrak{J} = -K_ie^{+2i\delta} \qquad (VIII.1.72)$$

and

$$\mathfrak{J}^{-1}K_i\mathfrak{J} = -K_i. \qquad (VIII.1.73)$$

For the case $\delta = \pi/2$, the parity transformation $(VIII.1.58)$ and time-reversal transformation $(VIII.1.72)$ prove that K_i transforms like a polar vector. The vector iK_i behaves differently under $\mathfrak{J}$ transformations, since

$$\tilde{\mathfrak{J}}iK_i\mathfrak{J} = iK_ie^{-2i\delta} \qquad (VIII.1.74)$$

and

$$\mathfrak{J}^{-1}iK_i\mathfrak{J} = iK_i, \qquad (VIII.1.75)$$

so iK_i for $\delta = \pi/2$ behaves like an axial vector.

(d) A Lorentz transformation reflecting both space and time coordinates is represented by

$$|x'\supset = -I_4|x\supset \qquad (VIII.1.76)$$

or

$$x'^i = -x^i, \qquad t' = -t.$$

In this case the transformation rules $(VIII.1.52)$ of $B_{\mu\nu}$ become

$$R^\dagger B_{\mu\nu}R = B_{\mu\nu}$$

or

$$R^\dagger R = I, \qquad R^\dagger K_iR = K_i, \qquad R^\dagger B_{ij}R = B_{ij}. \qquad (VIII.1.77)$$

These equations are satisfied by the successive application of time-reversal and space-reflection operators. Thus the R transformation in complex space, corresponding to simultaneous reflection of space and time coordinates in Lorentz space, can be represented as

$$S_R = \mathfrak{I}\mathcal{P} = e^{i\delta}\overline{C}\mathcal{P}. \qquad (VIII.1.78)$$

The notation S_R is that of Pauli, meaning *strong reflection.** Actually strong reflection also includes, in addition to reflection of space and time coordinates, reflection of the field.

(e) A strong reflection transformation can be represented by

$$S_{(R)} = -e^{i\delta}\overline{C}\mathcal{P}, \qquad (VIII.1.79)$$

which can operate on $e^{i\delta}|\chi\rangle$ to produce

$$|\chi'\rangle = S_{(R)}e^{i\delta}|\chi\rangle = |\chi(-\boldsymbol{r})\rangle.$$

The change of sign of the field can be regarded as the change of sign of its source, the electric charge.

VIII.2. The Two-Valued Representation of the Complex Orthogonal Group

The complex orthogonal transformations (*VIII.1.11*) and (*VIII.1.13*) can be represented by a similarity transformation

$$Q' = U^{-1}QU, \qquad (VIII.2.1)$$

where

$$Q = i\begin{bmatrix} \chi_3 & \chi_- \\ \chi_+ & -\chi_3 \end{bmatrix}, \qquad Q' = i\begin{bmatrix} \chi_3' & \chi_-' \\ \chi_+' & -\chi_3' \end{bmatrix}, \qquad (VIII.2.2)$$

$$\chi_\pm = \chi_1 \pm i\chi_2.$$

The factor i in the definition of Q, as will be seen presently, is required for invariance reasons. The 2×2 complex matrix U is subject to the condition

$$\det U = 1 \qquad (VIII.2.3)$$

providing two equations among the four complex elements of U. Thus U matrices can constitute a six-parameter representation of the complex orthogonal group. The determinant of (*VIII.2.1*) is

$$\chi_1'^2 + \chi_2'^2 + \chi_3'^2 = \chi_1^2 + \chi_2^2 + \chi_3^2. \qquad (VIII.2.4)$$

Furthermore, in terms of Pauli matrices, (*VIII.2.1*) can be written as

$$i\boldsymbol{\sigma}\cdot\boldsymbol{\chi}' = U^{-1}i\boldsymbol{\sigma}\cdot\boldsymbol{\chi}U, \qquad (VIII.2.5)$$

where the factor i on both sides of the equation, because of possible antilinear

---

* W. Pauli, *Niels Bohr and the Development of Physics*, Pergamon Press, London, 1955.

U operations, cannot be canceled out. It is also important to observe that the square of (*VIII.2.5*) reproduces (*VIII.2.4*), showing that

$$i\boldsymbol{\sigma}\cdot\boldsymbol{\chi} = i\boldsymbol{\sigma}\cdot\boldsymbol{\mathcal{E}} - \boldsymbol{\sigma}\cdot\boldsymbol{\mathcal{H}} \qquad (VIII.2.6)$$

transforms in a Lorentz-invariant way. We may look upon (*VIII.2.6*) as a scalar product of two six-vectors ($i\boldsymbol{\sigma}$, $\boldsymbol{\sigma}$) and ($\boldsymbol{\mathcal{E}}$, $\boldsymbol{\mathcal{H}}$), where the transformation properties of $i\boldsymbol{\sigma}$ and $\boldsymbol{\sigma}$ are not the same, since the invariance of (*VIII.2.6*) requires that $i\boldsymbol{\sigma}$ and $\boldsymbol{\sigma}$ transform like polar and axial vectors, respectively.

The generators of U transformations, corresponding to the generators K_i and iK_i of R transformations, are, of course, σ_i and $i\sigma_i$, respectively. The U transformations

$$U(\theta_i) = \pm \exp\left[\frac{-i\theta_i}{2}\sigma_i\right], \qquad (VIII.2.7)$$

for $i = 1, 2, 3$ (not summed over i), as rotation operators, and

$$U(\lambda_i) = \pm \exp\left[\frac{\lambda_i}{2}\sigma_i\right], \qquad (VIII.2.8)$$

for $i = 1, 2, 3$ (not summed over i), as velocity transformation operators can provide a double-valued six-parameter representation of the proper complex orthogonal group.

Under a Lorentz transformation of coordinates the ket $|\chi(x)\rangle$ will be transformed by the corresponding R matrix according to $|\chi'\rangle = R|\chi\rangle$; correspondingly, a two-component ket $|u(x)\rangle$ of the "spinor" space will be transformed by the corresponding U matrix according to

$$|u'\rangle = U|u\rangle, \qquad (VIII.2.9)$$

where

$$|u\rangle = \begin{bmatrix} u_1 \\ u_2 \end{bmatrix}.$$

If we replace χ_i' in (*VIII.2.5*) by

$$\chi_i' = R_{ij}\chi_j, \qquad (VIII.2.10)$$

and note that (*VIII.2.5*) must hold for all proper R transformations of the complex space, we obtain

$$i\sigma_i R_{ij} = U^{-1} i\sigma_j U \qquad (VIII.2.11)$$

as the transformation rules of the $\boldsymbol{\sigma}$. The U matrix is a function of the coefficients R_{ij} alone. It can easily be verified that the six-parameter group of U matrices (*VIII.2.7*) and (*VIII.2.8*) satisfy (*VIII.2.11*).

Quantities transforming according to (*VIII.2.9*), with the transformation matrix U satisfying (*VIII.2.11*), are called two-component spinors, corresponding to the complex vectors of R space. Further properties of spinors will be discussed in the next section.

To find the U transformations corresponding to improper R transformations it is necessary, because of the antilinear operations involved, to use (*VIII.2.5*) instead of (*VIII.2.11*). An interesting U transformation is one corresponding to parity operation in complex three-dimensional space:

$$|\chi'\rangle = \mathcal{P}|\chi\rangle.$$

Substituting in (*VIII.2.5*) we get

$$-i\sigma_i\chi_i^* = U^{-1}i\sigma_i\chi_i U. \qquad (VIII.2.12)$$

The left side can be written as

$$\mathcal{P}^{-1}i\sigma_i^L\chi_i\mathcal{P} = U^{-1}i\sigma_i\chi_i U, \qquad (VIII.2.13)$$

where σ_i^L are left-handed Pauli matrices (see Section I.8), so space-reflection operation is not an invariant transformation in the two-component spinor space; that is to say, there exists no U transformation corresponding to $\mathcal{P}$ transformation in R space that can leave (*VIII.2.5*) invariant.

Next we consider the transformation $R = \overline{C}$ in (*VIII.2.5*), and obtain

$$i\sigma_i\chi_i^* = U^{-1}i\sigma_i\chi_i U, \qquad (VIII.2.14)$$

which, like (*VIII.2.12*), obviously implies an antilinear U operation, and which differs from (*VIII.2.12*) only by a plus sign on the left.

Let us posit

$$U = \Gamma\overline{C},$$

where Γ is a 2×2 matrix to be calculated. From (*VIII.2.14*) we obtain

$$\begin{aligned} i\sigma_i\chi_i^* &= \overline{C}^{-1}\Gamma^{-1}i\sigma_i\chi_i\Gamma\overline{C} = \overline{C}\Gamma^{-1}i\sigma_i\chi_i\Gamma\overline{C} \\ &= -(\Gamma^*)^{-1}i\sigma_i^L\chi_i^*\Gamma^*, \end{aligned}$$

where we use the operator property of the $\boldsymbol{\sigma}$,

$$\overline{C}\sigma_i\overline{C} = \sigma_i^* = \sigma_i^L.$$

The special matrix

$$f = i\sigma_2 = \begin{bmatrix} 0 & 1 \\ -1 & 0 \end{bmatrix} \qquad (VIII.2.15)$$

transforms the $\boldsymbol{\sigma}$ according to

$$f^{-1}\sigma_i f = -\sigma_i^L, \qquad (VIII.2.16)$$

where

$$f^{-1} = -f, \qquad f^2 = -I. \qquad (VIII.2.17)$$

Thus we can conveniently choose $\Gamma = f$ and obtain

$$i\sigma_i\chi_i^* = -f^{-1}i\sigma_i^L\chi_i^*f = i\sigma_i\chi_i^*.$$

Hence, the required antilinear U transformation (up to an arbitrary phase factor) is

$$U = \mathfrak{J} = f\overline{C}. \qquad (VIII.2.18)$$

The antilinear operator $\mathfrak{J}$ obtained above has the following properties.

(a) It satisfies

$$\mathfrak{J}^2 = -I. \tag{VIII.2.19}$$

[Compare with (*VIII.1.71*).]

(b) It transforms a spinor $|u\rangle$ according to

$$|u'\rangle = \mathfrak{J}|u\rangle = \begin{bmatrix} 0 & 1 \\ -1 & 0 \end{bmatrix}\begin{bmatrix} u_1^* \\ u_2^* \end{bmatrix} = \begin{bmatrix} u_2^* \\ -u_1^* \end{bmatrix}. \tag{VIII.2.20}$$

(c) It is the time-reversal operator of the spinor space (see Chapter IX).

The transformations of $i\sigma_i$ and σ_i under $\mathfrak{J}$ are given by

$$\mathfrak{J}^{-1}i\sigma_i\mathfrak{J} = i\sigma_i \tag{VIII.2.21}$$

and

$$\mathfrak{J}^{-1}\sigma_i\mathfrak{J} = -\sigma_i. \tag{VIII.2.22}$$

Hence, under time reversal operation, $i\sigma_i$ and σ_i transform like a polar and an axial vector, respectively. Thus the choice of (*VIII.2.2*) for the Q matrix is now justified, since

$$i\boldsymbol{\sigma}\cdot\boldsymbol{\chi} = i\boldsymbol{\sigma}\cdot\boldsymbol{\mathcal{E}} - \boldsymbol{\sigma}\cdot\boldsymbol{\mathcal{H}}$$

shows clearly that the invariance comes from multiplying, scalarly, the polar vector $\boldsymbol{\mathcal{E}}$ by $i\boldsymbol{\sigma}$ and the axial vector $\boldsymbol{\mathcal{H}}$ by $\boldsymbol{\sigma}$.

We must point out that (*VIII.2.14*) can also be satisfied by taking

$$U = \mathfrak{J}_L = \overline{C}_L f,$$

which operates on the bra vectors of u space according to

$$\langle u|\overline{C}_L f = [u_1^*, u_2^*]\overline{C}_L f = [u_1, u_2]f = [u_2, -u_1]. \tag{VIII.2.23}$$

VIII.3. Two-Component Spinors

The preceding discussion of spinors and their transformation properties was based on the one-to-two correspondence of the transformations of three-dimensional complex vectors and two-dimensional spinors. We must also study the transformation properties of three Pauli matrices σ_i together with a 2×2 unit matrix $\sigma_4 = I_2$ directly in terms of Lorentz transformations carried out in Lorentz space.

We can begin by observing that the relativistic invariant (*I.10.2*) can be expressed as a determinant of a 2×2 matrix M defined by

$$M = \begin{bmatrix} ct + x_3 & x_- \\ x_+ & ct - x_3 \end{bmatrix} = x^\mu\sigma_\mu, \tag{VIII.3.1}$$

where

$$\sigma_4 = I_2.$$

Hence

$$\det M = c^2t^2 - x_1^2 - x_2^2 - x_3^2. \qquad (VIII.3.2)$$

Unlike the case of $(\boldsymbol{\sigma}\cdot\boldsymbol{\chi})^2$, in the present representation $(x^\mu\sigma_\mu)^2$ is not a Lorentz-invariant expression. This leads to some limitations on the transformation properties of σ_μ and also on the invariants formed with the use of σ_μ. A certain class of Lorentz transformation of coordinates x_μ into x'^μ can, formally, be expressed as a similarity transformation:

$$M' = S^{-1}MS.$$

Because of the Hermitian character of M, however, we must use a transformation of the form

$$M' = S^\dagger MS, \qquad (VIII.3.3)$$

so the Hermitian conjugations of both sides yield the same equation. We can also write $(VIII.3.3)$ as

$$x'^\mu\sigma_\mu = S^\dagger x^\mu\sigma_\mu S, \qquad (VIII.3.4)$$

where

$$\det S = 1 \qquad (VIII.3.5)$$

and S is not assumed to be a unitary 2×2 matrix. The determinental condition $(VIII.3.5)$ is required for two reasons:

(a) to reduce the number of parameters specifying an S from 8 to 6;
(b) to maintain $(VIII.3.2)$ for the transformed coordinates x'^μ, since

$$\det(x'^\mu\sigma_\mu) = \det S^\dagger\cdot\det(x^\mu\sigma_\mu)\cdot\det S = \det(x^\mu\sigma_\mu)$$

or

$$ct'^2 - x_1'^2 - x_2'^2 - x_3'^2 = c^2t^2 - x_1^2 - x_2^2 - x_3^2.$$

We shall see in the following that the Lorentz invariance obtained by a determinantal operation alone does not [because $(\sigma_\mu x^\mu)^2$ is not an invariant] entail the entire Lorentz group as an invariance group.

Let us stipulate the existence of a class of Lorentz transformations satisfying $(VIII.3.4)$ such that if L transforms x^μ according to

$$|x'\supset = L|x\supset, \qquad (VIII.3.6)$$

then S will transform a two-component spinor $|u\rangle$ by

$$|u'\rangle = S|u\rangle, \qquad (VIII.3.7)$$

where the components u_α and u'_α, for $\alpha = 1, 2$, of $|u\rangle$ and $|u'\rangle$ are functions of x^μ and x'^μ, respectively. To obtain further properties of S we consider the transformation of a spinor relation,

$$|v\rangle = \sigma^\mu p_\mu|u\rangle. \qquad (VIII.3.8)$$

The requirement of Lorentz invariance implies that in the transformed coordinate system we must have

$$|v'\rangle = \sigma^\mu p'_\mu |u'\rangle. \tag{VIII.3.9}$$

By applying the transformations (*VIII.3.6*) and (*VIII.3.7*), we replace (*VIII.3.9*) by

$$S|v\rangle = \sigma^\mu L^\nu_\mu p_\nu S|u\rangle.$$

Hence, comparing with (*VIII.3.8*) and requiring that the invariance hold for every $|u\rangle$ and $|v\rangle$, we obtain

$$S^{-1}\sigma^\mu S L^\nu_\mu = \sigma^\nu.$$

Using

$$L^\nu_\mu L^\rho_\nu = a^\rho_\mu$$

we get

$$S^{-1}\sigma_\mu S = L^\nu_\mu \sigma_\nu \tag{VIII.3.10}$$

as transformation rules of σ_μ and also as relations to define an S transformation as a function of the coefficients L^μ_ν. The relations (*VIII.3.10*) are valid for all proper Lorentz transformations.*

Because of the very important role played by $\boldsymbol{\sigma}$ matrices in quantum mechanics we shall consider their transformation properties in some detail.

For improper Lorentz transformations it is convenient to replace (*VIII.3.10*) by

$$S^{-1}\sigma_\mu S = L^\nu_\mu \Sigma_\nu, \tag{VIII.3.11}$$

where the Σ_ν are either ordinary or left-handed Pauli matrices.

(a) Space-reflection transformation satisfies

$$S^{-1}\sigma_\mu S = a^\nu_\mu \Sigma_\nu. \tag{VIII.3.12}$$

A comparison with (*VIII.2.16*) and (*VIII.2.22*) shows that we have two alternatives for S transformations.

(i) We can take $S = f$ and set $\Sigma_i = \sigma_i^L$, so the f matrix can be interpreted as the "metric" of the spinor space whose vectors transform by S transformations.

(ii) We can also take $S = \mathfrak{J} = f\bar{C}$ and set $\Sigma_i = \sigma_i$ which yields (*VIII.2.22*).

(b) Time-reflection transformation satisfies $S^{-1}\sigma_\mu S = -a^\nu_\mu \Sigma_\nu$ or $\Sigma_4 = \sigma_4$ and $\Sigma_i = S^{-1}\sigma_i S$.

---

* There are quite a few differences between the two spinor spaces defined in Section VIII.2 and in the present section. Some of these differences must be noted: (a) condition (*VIII.2.3*) on the determinent of U is not necessary; (b) condition (*VIII.3.5*) for S transformation is necessary to maintain Lorentz invariance; (c) U transformations are functions of R_{ij}, while S transformations are directly related to L^μ_ν; (d) the matrices σ_i and $i\sigma_i$ transform in U and R space like a six-vector, while σ_i or $i\sigma_i$ is only the space part of a four-vector σ_μ in S space and Lorentz space.

If $\Sigma_i = \sigma_i^L$, then S is the operator of the complex conjugation $\bar{C}$. For $\Sigma_i = \sigma_i$, the σ_μ transform like the coordinates where $t' = -t$ and $x'^i = x^i$.

VIII.3.A. Examples of Improper and Antilinear Transformations

In a way similar to that of (*VIII.1.39*) we can study the transformation of the four-vector

$$s'_\mu = \frac{1}{2c}\langle u'|\sigma_\mu|u'\rangle, \tag{VIII.3.13}$$

which transforms as

$$s'_\mu = \frac{1}{2c}\langle u'|\sigma_\mu|u'\rangle = \frac{1}{2c}\langle u|S^\dagger\sigma_\mu S|u\rangle. \tag{VIII.3.14}$$

For $S = f$ and $S^\dagger = f^\dagger = -f$, we obtain

$$s'_4 = s_4, \qquad s'_i = -\frac{1}{2c}\langle u|\sigma_i^L|u\rangle \neq s_i.$$

Hence s_μ does not transform as a proper vector under $S = f$; actually it does not transform as a vector at all.

Next, for $S = f\bar{C}$ we get

$$s'_4 = s_4, \qquad s'_i = -s_i.$$

In this case s_μ transforms like the coordinates themselves—that is, as a vector.

With $S = \overline{C}$ the situation is similar to $S = f$.

We see that a four-vector of the form (*VIII.3.13*) does not transform like an ordinary vector under all types of Lorentz transformations. These aspects of distinguishing one set of Lorentz transformations from another set are a distinct feature of expressions involving σ_μ linearly.

VIII.3.B. Further Development of Spinor Transformations

The "metric" f of spinor space can be used to raise or lower spinor indices. We can develop spinor algebra in a form quite similar to that of tensors. The metric f can be considered as a second-rank spinor $f_{\alpha\beta}$, where α, $\beta = 1, 2$. We can also define a contravariant metric tensor $f^{\alpha\beta}$ by the rule

$$f^{\alpha\gamma}f_{\beta\gamma} = f^{\gamma\alpha}f_{\gamma\beta} = \delta^\alpha_\beta, \tag{VIII.3.15}$$

where, it should be noted, the uncontracted indices α and β are taken both as first or second indices in $f^{\alpha\gamma}$ and $f_{\beta\gamma}$. The contravariant metric $f^{\alpha\beta}$ is not to be understood as the inverse of the matrix

$$f = \begin{bmatrix} 0 & 1 \\ -1 & 0 \end{bmatrix}.$$

Actually the matrix representation of $f^{\alpha\beta}$ is equal to f.

The invariant scalar product of two spinors $|u\rangle$ and $|v\rangle$ is defined by

$$f^{\alpha\beta}u_\alpha v_\beta = u_1v_2 - u_2v_1.$$

In ket notation we must use the operators $\overline{C}_Lf$ and $f\overline{C}$ to define scalar products. Thus

$$\langle u|\overline{C}_Lf|v\rangle = [u^{1*}, u^{2*}]\overline{C}_Lf\begin{bmatrix} v^1 \\ v^2 \end{bmatrix}$$

$$= [u^1, u^2]\begin{bmatrix} v^2 \\ -v^1 \end{bmatrix} = u^1v^2 - u^2v^1. \qquad (VIII.3.16)$$

Also,

$$\langle u|f\overline{C}|v\rangle = [-u^2, u^1]\begin{bmatrix} v^{1*} \\ v^{2*} \end{bmatrix} = u^1v^{2*} - u^2v^{1*}. \qquad (VIII.3.17)$$

From (*VIII.3.16*) we see that the scalar product of a spinor with itself vanishes. By analogy with the proper representations of the Lorentz group we can use the metric f to infer that all two-valued two-dimensional representations of the Lorentz group by S transformation matrices must satisfy the condition

$$\tilde{S}fS = f. \qquad (VIII.3.18)$$

The reader can, as a good exercise, show that all S transformations discussed in the previous sections, including the U transformations (*VIII.2.7*) and (*VIII.2.8*), satisfy condition (*VIII.3.18*).

By taking the complex conjugate of

$$|u'\rangle = S|u\rangle,$$

we find that the complex conjugate of a spinor is transformed by the complex conjugate of S, as

$$|u'^*\rangle = S^*|u^*\rangle. \qquad (VIII.3.19)$$

The metric of the complex conjugate space is the reciprocal of f; that is, $-f$ ($= f_c$, say). The covariant and contravariant components of $|u^*\rangle$ are related by

$$u^{*\alpha} = f_c^{\alpha\beta}u_\beta^* = -f^{\alpha\beta}u_\beta^*.$$

Hence

$$u^{1*} = u_2^*, \qquad u^{*2} = -u_1^*.$$

The same connections for $|u\rangle$ are

$$u_\alpha = f_{\alpha\beta}u^\beta$$

or

$$u_1 = u^2, \qquad u_2 = -u^1.$$

We see that the components of $|u^*\rangle$ are transformed as the covariant components u_α of $|u\rangle$. This result has been obtained from using $-f$ as the metric of the complex conjugate space. But $-f$ in spinor space corresponds to $-F$ in Lorentz space. The matrix $-F$, as a Lorentz matrix of class $L_{44} = -1$, transforms coordinates by reflecting time and leaving the space coordinates unchanged. Hence we infer that time-reflection transformation in Lorentz space corresponds to the operation of complex conjugation in spinor space.

Spinors transforming like the product of two spinors of rank one are called spinors of rank two. The metric f is an example of a covariant second-rank spinor. Pauli matrices are spinors of rank two.

VIII.4. The Stereographic Projections of the Complex Representation

The fundamental invariant of the complex space

$$Q^2 = \chi_1^2 + \chi_2^2 + \chi_3^2 = \langle\chi|\overline{C}_L|\chi\rangle \tag{VIII.4.1}$$

and its complex conjugate

$$Q^{*2} = \chi_1^{*2} + \chi_2^{*2} + \chi_3^{*2} = \langle\chi|\overline{C}|\chi\rangle \tag{VIII.4.2}$$

will vanish for a plane electromagnetic wave. With respect to the point $Q^2 = 0$, the invariant Q^{*2} is to be regarded as the image of Q^2 in a space consisting of the three points 0, Q^2, Q^{*2}.

The functional relationship between the points Q^2 and Q^{*2} is such that they are situated from the point $Q^2 = 0$ and from one another at "invariant distances." The points Q^2 and Q^{*2}, being related by an antilinear transformation, cannot be transformed into one another by means of a linear unitary transformation. Under R transformations the "lattice" $(0, Q^2, Q^{*2})$ remains an invariant structure of the complex space. A more general complex space can be defined by including the gauge group in the complex group.

Two important Hermitian operators related to complex space can be obtained by adding and subtracting (*VIII.4.1*) and (*VIII.4.2*), to give

$$\tfrac{1}{2}(Q^2 + Q^{*2}) = \langle\chi|Y|\chi\rangle = \Omega \tag{VIII.4.3}$$

and

$$\tfrac{1}{2}(Q^2 - Q^{*2}) = \langle\chi|D|\chi\rangle = -2i\Lambda, \tag{VIII.4.4}$$

where

$$Y^\dagger = Y = \tfrac{1}{2}(\overline{C} + \overline{C}_L), \tag{VIII.4.5}$$

$$D^\dagger = -D = \tfrac{1}{2}(\overline{C}_L - \overline{C}) \tag{VIII.4.6}$$

are linear (!) Hermitian and anti-Hermitian operators, respectively. The operators Y and D both satisfy the algebraic equations

$$Y^3 = Y \tag{VIII.4.7}$$

and

$$D^3 = D. \tag{VIII.4.8}$$

Thus, both Y and D have eigenvalues $+1$, -1, and 0. Both Y and D belong to the complex representation of the Lorentz group.

The effect of the linear unitary operator $\overline{C}C_L$ can be seen by observing that the Hermitian scalar product of two complex vectors $|\chi\rangle$ and $|\eta\rangle$ is

$$\langle\eta|\chi\rangle = \langle\chi|\overline{C}_L\overline{C}|\eta\rangle. \qquad (VIII.4.9)$$

The double-valued representation of the rotation group can be based on the stereographic projection* of a unit sphere about the origin onto the equatorial plane $x_3 = 0$, with the south pole as the center of projection. To the point x_1, x_2, x_3 on the sphere corresponds the point x_1', x_2', 0 on the plane, and the formulas for the projections are

$$x_1 + ix_2 = \frac{2a}{1 + aa^*} = x_+,$$

$$x_1 - ix_2 = \frac{2a^*}{1 + aa^*} = x_-,$$

$$x_3 = \frac{1 - aa^*}{1 + aa^*},$$

where

$$a = x_1' + ix_2' = \frac{u_2}{u_1}$$

and u_1, u_2 are homogeneous complex coordinates which enable us to include the south pole of the sphere in the projection. In terms of the coordinates u_1 and u_2 we have

$$x_+ = \frac{2u_1^*u_2}{|u_1|^2 + |u_2|^2}, \qquad x_- = \frac{2u_1u_2^*}{|u_1|^2 + |u_2|^2}, \qquad x_3 = \frac{|u_1|^2 - |u_2|^2}{|u_1|^2 + |u_2|^2}.$$

Let us now put

$$\zeta_2 = \begin{bmatrix} -x_+ & x_3 \\ x_3 & x_- \end{bmatrix},$$

where

$$\det \zeta_2 = -(x_1^2 + x_2^2 + x_3^2) = -1.$$

By using the projection formulas we can write

$$\xi_2 = \lambda^2\langle u|[(\boldsymbol{\tau} \times \boldsymbol{\sigma})_2 - i\tau_2]|u\rangle, \qquad (VIII.4.10)$$

where

$$\lambda = (|u_1|^2 + |u_2|^2)^{-1/2}.$$

The $\boldsymbol{\tau}$ matrices are of the same type as the $\boldsymbol{\sigma}$ matrices but they refer to a different degree of freedom of the sphere and therefore commute with the $\boldsymbol{\sigma}$.

The form of (*VIII.4.10*) suggests that we can complete it by a vector-matrix operator as

---

* See H. Weyl, *Theory of Groups and Quantum Mechanics*, Dover, New York, 1931.

$$\zeta_i = \lambda^2 \langle u | [(\boldsymbol{\tau} \times \boldsymbol{\sigma})_i - i\tau_i] | u \rangle \tag{VIII.4.11}$$

and obtain three possible projections of the point (x_1, x_2, x_3) on the unit sphere. The matrices ζ_1 and ζ_3 are given by

$$\zeta_1 = -i \begin{bmatrix} x_+ & -x_3 \\ x_3 & x_- \end{bmatrix}, \qquad \zeta_3 = -i \begin{bmatrix} x_3 & x_- \\ -x_+ & x_3 \end{bmatrix}$$

and their determinants are

$$\det \zeta_1 = \det \zeta_2 = \det \zeta_3 = -(x_1^2 + x_2^2 + x_3^2).$$

Thus the three possible stereographic projections represented by ζ_i, where $i = 1, 2, 3$, form a vector, and they satisfy

$$\zeta_1^2 + \zeta_2^2 + \zeta_3^2 = x_1^2 + x_2^2 + x_3^2 = +1,$$

so the operator ζ_i lies on the unit sphere. In terms of the $\boldsymbol{\sigma}$ and $\boldsymbol{K}$ matrices, (*VIII.4.11*) can be written as

$$\zeta_i = -i(\sigma^\mu K_\mu)^{ij} \langle u_I | \tau_j | u_I \rangle \tag{VIII.4.12}$$

or as

$$\zeta_i = -i(\sigma^\mu K_\mu)^{ij} x_j, \tag{VIII.4.13}$$

where

$$|u_I\rangle = \lambda |u\rangle = \lambda \begin{bmatrix} u_1 \\ u_2 \end{bmatrix}.$$

Hence, each unitary transformation

$$|u'\rangle = U|u\rangle, \qquad U^\dagger U = I$$

on the equatorial plane (the spinor plane) corresponds to a rotation of the sphere. In this way we obtain all possible rotations of the sphere.

It is interesting to note that the operator $-i\sigma^\mu K_\mu$ is related to the projection operator

$$P_c = \tfrac{1}{3}\sigma^\mu K_\mu. \tag{VIII.4.14}$$

The projection operator property of P_c can be seen by taking its square, as defined in (*VIII.4.14*):

$$P_c^2 = \tfrac{1}{9}(I - \boldsymbol{\sigma}\cdot\boldsymbol{K})^2 = \tfrac{1}{9}[I - 2\boldsymbol{\sigma}\cdot\boldsymbol{K} + (\boldsymbol{\sigma}\cdot\boldsymbol{K})^2].$$

we can express $(\boldsymbol{\sigma}\cdot\boldsymbol{K})^2$ as

$$\begin{aligned}(\boldsymbol{\sigma}\cdot\boldsymbol{K})^2 &= \sigma_i K_i \sigma_j K_j = \sigma_i \sigma_j K_i K_j = (\delta_{ij} + i\epsilon_{ijk}\sigma_k) K_i K_j \\ &= \boldsymbol{K}^2 + i\epsilon_{ijk} K_i K_j = (2 - \boldsymbol{\sigma}\cdot\boldsymbol{K}).\end{aligned}$$

Hence

$$\begin{aligned}P_c^2 &= \tfrac{1}{9}[I - 2\boldsymbol{\sigma}\cdot\boldsymbol{K} + 2 - \boldsymbol{\sigma}\cdot\boldsymbol{K}] \\ &= \tfrac{1}{3}(I - \boldsymbol{\sigma}\cdot\boldsymbol{K}) = P_c.\end{aligned}$$

The spin operators

$$s_i = K_i + \tfrac{1}{2}\sigma_i \tag{VIII.4.15}$$

commute with P_c and satisfy the usual commutation relations

$$[s_i, s_j] = i\epsilon_{ijk} s_k. \tag{VIII.4.16}$$

The operators s_i can operate on the product of the kets of σ-spin and K-spin spaces, respectively.

We may now generalize the above results to the complex space. The projection of the "complex sphere" onto a spinor plane consists of three second-rank spinors which together transform like a complex vector; each one by itself transforms as a second-rank spinor. For the projection of $|\chi\rangle$ we can write

$$|\zeta\rangle = -i(\sigma^\mu K_\mu)|\chi\rangle$$

or

$$\begin{bmatrix} \zeta^1 \\ \zeta^2 \\ \zeta^3 \end{bmatrix} = \begin{bmatrix} -iI_2 & \sigma_3 & -\sigma_2 \\ -\sigma_3 & -iI_2 & \sigma_1 \\ \sigma_2 & -\sigma_1 & -iI_2 \end{bmatrix} \begin{bmatrix} \chi_1 \\ \chi_2 \\ \chi_3 \end{bmatrix}, \qquad (VIII.4.17)$$

where the spinor indices of the ζ and σ are suppressed.

The formulas of stereographic projection are

$$\chi_+ = \frac{2Qa}{1+ab}, \qquad \chi_- = \frac{2Qb}{1+ab}, \qquad \chi_3 = Q\frac{1-ab}{1+ab}, \qquad (VIII.4.18)$$

where

$$a = \chi_1' + i\chi_2', \qquad b = \chi_1' - i\chi_2'.$$

We note that b is not equal to the complex conjugate of a. If we put $a = u_2/u_1$, $b = v_2/v_1$ in (*VIII.4.18*), we get

$$\chi_+ = \frac{2Qu_2v_1}{u_1v_1 + u_2v_2}, \qquad \chi_- = \frac{2Qu_1v_2}{u_1v_1 + u_2v_2}, \qquad \chi_3 = Q\frac{u_1v_1 - u_2v_2}{u_1v_1 + u_2v_2}, \qquad (VIII.4.19)$$

which satisfy

$$\chi_+\chi_- + \chi_3^2 = Q^2$$

and

$$\det\begin{bmatrix} -\chi_+ & \chi_3 \\ \chi_3 & \chi_- \end{bmatrix} = -Q^2.$$

In comparing these with the projection of the real sphere we see that the stereographic projections of the complex sphere are given by

$$\zeta^i = -i(\sigma^\mu K_\mu)^{ij} \subset v_I|\tau_j|u_I \supset, \qquad (VIII.4.20)$$

where

$$\subset v_I| = A[v_1, v_2], \qquad |u_I\supset = A\begin{bmatrix} u_1 \\ u_2 \end{bmatrix},$$

in which

$$A = \frac{1}{\sqrt{(u_1v_1 + u_2v_2)}}.$$

From (*VIII.4.17*) we have

$$\zeta^1 = -i\begin{bmatrix} \chi_+ & -\chi_3 \\ \chi_3 & \chi_- \end{bmatrix}, \qquad \zeta^2 = \begin{bmatrix} -\chi_+ & \chi_3 \\ \chi_3 & \chi_- \end{bmatrix},$$
$$\zeta^3 = -i\begin{bmatrix} \chi_3 & \chi_- \\ -\chi_+ & \chi_3 \end{bmatrix}, \qquad (VIII.4.21)$$

where the ζ matrices satisfy

$$(\zeta^1)^2 + (\zeta^2)^2 + (\zeta^3)^2 = Q^2 \qquad (VIII.4.22)$$

and

$$\det \zeta^1 = \det \zeta^2 = \det \zeta^3 = -Q^2,$$
$$\det(\zeta^1 + \zeta^2) = \det(\zeta^2 + \zeta^3) = \det(\zeta^3 + \zeta^1) = -2Q^2,$$
$$\det(\zeta^1 + \zeta^2 + \zeta^3) = -3Q^2.$$

All possible rotations of the "complex sphere" can be obtained by U transformations of the type discussed in Section *VIII.1*:

$$|u'\rangle = U|u\rangle, \qquad |v'\rangle = U|v\rangle.$$

An important special case corresponds to $Q^2 = 0$. Here the three spinors ζ^i, for $i = 1, 2, 3$, are equivalent. From (*VIII.4.18*) we can write

$$\frac{1}{a}\chi_+ + a\chi_- = 2Q, \qquad \frac{1}{b}\chi_- + b\chi_+ = 2Q,$$

so for $Q = 0$ we obtain

$$a^2b^2 = 1$$

or

$$(ab - 1)(ab + 1) = 0.$$

The case $ab - 1 = 0$ corresponds to $\chi_1 = \chi_2 = \chi_3 = 0$. For $ab + 1 = 0$, we infer on physical grounds that $Q/(ab + 1)$ must, for $Q = 0$ and $ab + 1 = 0$, be a finite quantity; otherwise the χ would be infinite for an electromagnetic plane wave. For simplicity we shall take

$$\lim_{Q=0}\left(\frac{2Q}{ab + 1}\right) = 1,$$

which can be regarded as a normalization condition on the spinors $|u\rangle$ and $|v\rangle$.

Thus formulas (*VIII.4.19*) become

$$\chi_+ = u_2v_1, \qquad \chi_- = u_1v_2, \qquad \chi_3 = \tfrac{1}{2}(u_1v_1 - u_2v_2), \qquad (VIII.4.23)$$

subject to the condition $u_1v_1 + u_2v_2 = 0$ or $v_1/u_2 = -v_2/u_1 = -\alpha$, say, where α is a complex number. By using $v_1 = -\alpha u_2$ and $v_2 = \alpha u_1$, the expressions (*VIII.4.23*) take the forms $\chi_+ = -\alpha u_2^2$, $\chi_- = \alpha u_1^2$, $\chi_3 = -\alpha u_1 u_2$. Hence

$$\begin{aligned} \chi_1 &= \tfrac{1}{2}\alpha(u_1^2 - u_2^2), \\ \chi_2 &= \tfrac{1}{2}i\alpha(u_1^2 + u_2^2), \qquad (VIII.4.24) \\ \chi_3 &= -\alpha u_1 u_2. \end{aligned}$$

The vanishing of Q^2 is independent of a particular complex number α; it can, therefore, be absorbed into the spinor $|u\rangle$ and expressions (*VIII.4.24*) then become

$$\begin{aligned} \chi_1 &= \tfrac{1}{2}(u_1^2 - u_2^2), \\ \chi_2 &= \tfrac{1}{2}i(u_1^2 + u_2^2), \qquad (VIII.4.25) \\ \chi_3 &= -u_1 u_2. \end{aligned}$$

The entire complex sphere in this case reduces to a plane containing the electric vector $\mathcal{E}$ and magnetic vector $\mathcal{H}$ of the plane wave. We shall call this particular plane the "neutral plane."

We can use the transformations (*VIII.4.25*) to transform the momentum vector P_μ, defined by

$$P_\mu = \frac{1}{2c} \langle \chi | K_\mu | \chi \rangle.$$

Because $Q^2 = 0$, the vector P_μ is a null-vector and the transformations (*VIII.4.25*) do not, of course, change this property of P_μ. In terms of the new variables u_1 and u_2, the components of P_μ are given by

$$\begin{aligned} cP_1 &= \tfrac{1}{2} \sqrt{(cP_4)}(u_1^* u_2 + u_1 u_2^*), \\ cP_2 &= -\tfrac{1}{2} \sqrt{(cP_4)} i (u_1^* u_2 - u_2^* u_1), \\ cP_3 &= \tfrac{1}{2} \sqrt{(cP_4)}(u_1^* u - u_2^* u_2), \\ cP_4 &= \tfrac{1}{4} (u_1^* u_1 + u_2^* u_2)^2. \end{aligned}$$

These can be expressed as

$$P_\mu = \frac{1}{2c} \langle u_I | \sigma_\mu | u_I \rangle, \qquad (VIII.4.26)$$

where the spinor $|u_I\rangle$ is related to $|u\rangle$ by

$$|u_I\rangle = (cP_4)^{1/4} |u\rangle, \qquad (VIII.4.27)$$

The vector P_μ defined in terms of the kets $|\chi\rangle$ satisfies, because of Maxwell's equations, the conservation equation,

$$\frac{\partial P_\mu}{\partial x_\mu} = 0. \qquad (VIII.4.28)$$

The same vector P_μ, expressed in terms of the spinor $|u\rangle$, will satisfy the conservation equation (*VIII.4.28*) provided the spinor $|u\rangle$ satisfies the equation

$$\sigma^\mu \frac{\partial}{\partial x^\mu} |u\rangle = 0. \qquad (VIII.4.29)$$

This is the wave equation for a field of spin $\frac{1}{2}\hbar$ without mass and charge. It will be discussed in detail in Chapter IX.

VIII.5. The Four-Dimensional Spin Representation of the Lorentz Group

A four-dimensional spin representation of the proper Lorentz group in a C_4 that contains no subspace other than itself and the null space (irreducibility) requires a complete algebra of four-dimensional matrices. The Kronecker product of two square matrices A and B of order $m \times m$ and $n \times n$, respectively, is defined as a matrix of order $mn \times mn$. Its matrix representation is

$$A \oplus B = \begin{bmatrix} a_{11}B & a_{12}B & \cdots & a_{1n}B \\ a_{21}B & a_{22}B & \cdots & a_{2n}B \\ \cdots & \cdots & \cdots & \cdots \\ \cdots & \cdots & \cdots & \cdots \\ a_{n1}B & a_{n2}B & \cdots & a_{nn}B \end{bmatrix},$$

where the symbol $\oplus$ between any two matrices signifies the Kronecker product of the respective matrices.

By using the matrices σ_μ, where $\mu = 1, 2, 3, 4$, we can form 16 (4×4) matrices by means of Kronecker products

$$A_{\mu,\nu} = \sigma_\mu \oplus \sigma_\nu, \tag{VIII.5.1}$$

which can constitute 16 basic matrices of a particular C_4 (four-dimensional spinor space). All sixteen matrices $A_{\mu,\nu}$ are contained in Table VIII.5 of Kronecker products.

TABLE VIII.5. The matrices $A_{\mu,\nu}$.

	I_2	σ_1	σ_2	σ_3
I_2	$I_2 \oplus I_2$	$I_2 \oplus \sigma_1$	$I_2 \oplus \sigma_2$	$I_2 \oplus \sigma_3$
σ_1	$\sigma_1 \oplus I_2$	$\sigma_1 \oplus \sigma_1$	$\sigma_1 \oplus \sigma_2$	$\sigma_1 \oplus \sigma_3$
σ_2	$\sigma_2 \oplus I_2$	$\sigma_2 \oplus \sigma_1$	$\sigma_2 \oplus \sigma_2$	$\sigma_2 \oplus \sigma_3$
σ_3	$\sigma_3 \oplus I_2$	$\sigma_3 \oplus \sigma_1$	$\sigma_3 \oplus \sigma_2$	$\sigma_3 \oplus \sigma_3$

All matrices of C_4 can be expressed as a linear combination of the above 16 (4×4) matrices. Because of the irreducibility of the σ matrices and the definition of the Kronecker product,* the 4×4 matrices of Table VIII.5 cannot be transformed into one another by means of the matrix transformation rule defined in (*I.4.8*).

The matrix multiplication of two Kronecker products $A \oplus B$ and $C \oplus D$ of square matrices A, B, C, D of order $n \times n$ is defined by

$$(A \oplus B)(C \oplus D) = AC \oplus BD, \tag{VIII.5.2}$$

where AC and BD are ordinary matrix multiplications of the square matrices of the same order.

---

* For a detailed discussion of the Kronecker product in the theory of groups and its relevance to the irreducibility concept, the reader should consult F. D. Murnaghan, *The Theory of Group Representations*, Johns Hopkins Press, Baltimore, 1938, p. 38.

If A and B are nonsingular square matrices of dimension n, it follows from (*VIII.5.2*) that

$$(A \oplus B)(A^{-1} \oplus B^{-1}) = I_n \oplus I_n = I_{2n}$$

and

$$A \oplus B = (A \oplus I_n)(I_n \oplus B). \qquad (VIII.5.3)$$

Hence

$$\begin{aligned} \det (A \oplus B) &= \det (A \oplus I_n) \det (I_n \oplus B) \\ &= (\det A)^n (\det B)^n = \det (AB)^n. \end{aligned} \qquad (VIII.5.4)$$

We can now show that all elements of Table VIII.5 can be constructed from the 4×4 matrices

$$\alpha_i = \sigma_i \oplus \sigma_i, \qquad \beta = \sigma_3 \oplus I_2. \qquad (VIII.5.5)$$

(a) The matrix multiplication of the α and β is

$$\begin{aligned} \alpha_5 = \alpha_1\alpha_2\alpha_3\beta &= (\sigma_1 \oplus \sigma_1)(\sigma_1 \oplus \sigma_2)(\sigma_1 \oplus \sigma_3)(\sigma_3 \oplus I_2) \\ &= (\sigma_1\sigma_1 \oplus \sigma_1\sigma_2)(\sigma_1\sigma_3 \oplus \sigma_3 I_2) = (I_2 \oplus i\sigma_3)(-i\sigma_2 \oplus \sigma_3) \\ &= \sigma_2 \oplus I_2. \end{aligned}$$

Thus

$$\alpha_5 = \sigma_2 \oplus I_2. \qquad (VIII.5.6)$$

(b) The matrix multiplication of the $\boldsymbol{\alpha}$ and β with α_5 yield

$$\begin{aligned} i\alpha_5\alpha_1 &= (i\sigma_2 \oplus I_2)(\sigma_1 \oplus \sigma_1) = \sigma_3 \oplus \sigma_1, \\ i\alpha_5\alpha_2 &= (i\sigma_2 \oplus I_2)(\sigma_1 \oplus \sigma_2) = \sigma_3 \oplus \sigma_2, \\ i\alpha_5\alpha_3 &= (i\sigma_2 \oplus I_2)(\sigma_1 \oplus \sigma_3) = \sigma_3 \oplus \sigma_3, \\ -i\alpha_5\beta &= (-i\sigma_2 \oplus I_2)(\sigma_3 \oplus I_2) = \sigma_1 \oplus I_2. \end{aligned} \qquad (VIII.5.7)$$

(c) Antisymmetric combinations of the $\boldsymbol{\alpha}$ give

$$\begin{aligned} \frac{1}{2i}(\alpha_i\alpha_j - \alpha_j\alpha_i) &= \frac{1}{2i}(\sigma_1 \oplus \sigma_i)(\sigma_1 \oplus \sigma_j) - (\sigma_1 \oplus \sigma_j)(\sigma_1 \oplus \sigma_i) \\ &= \frac{1}{2i} I_2 \oplus (\sigma_i\sigma_j - \sigma_j\sigma_i) = \epsilon_{ijk} I_2 \oplus \sigma_k. \end{aligned}$$

Hence

$$I_2 \oplus \sigma_i = -\tfrac{1}{2}i\epsilon_{ijk}\alpha_j\alpha_k$$

or

$$I_2 \oplus \boldsymbol{\sigma} = -\tfrac{1}{2}i\boldsymbol{\alpha} \times \boldsymbol{\alpha}. \qquad (VIII.5.8)$$

(d) From antisymmetric combinations of $\boldsymbol{\alpha}$ and β we obtain

$$\frac{1}{2i}(\beta\boldsymbol{\alpha} - \boldsymbol{\alpha}\beta) = \sigma_2 \oplus \boldsymbol{\sigma} = -i\beta\boldsymbol{\alpha}, \qquad (VIII.5.9)$$

By using the definitions of the $\boldsymbol{\alpha}$ and β it is easy to show by means of the Kronecker products that they satisfy the anticommutation relations

$$\alpha_\mu\alpha_\nu + \alpha_\nu\alpha_\mu = 2\delta_{\mu\nu}I_4, \qquad (VIII.5.10)$$

where

$$I_4 = I_2 \oplus I_2$$

and

$$\alpha_4 = \beta.$$

We shall construct a different set of Dirac matrices by defining

$$\boldsymbol{\gamma} = i\beta\boldsymbol{\alpha}, \qquad \gamma_4 = i\beta, \tag{VIII.5.11}$$

where the γ_i, for $i = 1, 2, 3$, are Hermitian and γ_4 is anti-Hermitian; that is,

$$\gamma_i^\dagger = \gamma_i, \qquad \gamma_4^\dagger = -\gamma_4, \tag{VIII.5.12}$$

and

$$\gamma_1^2 = \gamma_2^2 = \gamma_3^2 = I_4, \qquad \gamma_4^2 = -I_4.$$

The anticommutation rules for γ matrices can be worked out from the Kronecker products:

$$\gamma_\mu\gamma_\nu + \gamma_\nu\gamma_\mu = -2a_{\mu\nu}I_4. \tag{VIII.5.13}$$

On comparing (*VIII.5.13*) with (*VIII.5.10*) we see that γ matrices are more suitable for relativistic considerations. In particular, the square of the operator $\gamma^\mu p_\mu$, as follows from using (*VIII.5.13*), is

$$\begin{aligned}(\gamma^\mu p_\mu)^2 &= \gamma^\mu p_\mu \gamma^\nu p_\nu = \tfrac{1}{2}(\gamma^\mu\gamma^\nu + \gamma^\nu\gamma^\mu)p_\mu p_\nu \\ &= -a^{\mu\nu}p_\mu p_\nu = \boldsymbol{p}^2 - p_0^2,\end{aligned}$$

a Lorentz-invariant expression. The last result implies that the rationalization of the Lorentz-invariant square root,

$$mc = \sqrt{(p_0^2 - \boldsymbol{p}^2)}$$

in terms of γ matrices requires the use of the Hermitian γ_i, for $i = 1, 2, 3$, and the anti-Hermitian γ_4 (or vice-versa). We cannot, because of (*VIII.5.13*), at the same time have all γ matrices Hermitian and also maintain Lorentz-invariance.

In γ representation all 16 matrices of the complete four-dimensional matrix algebra assume a more symmetrical form than in $\boldsymbol{\alpha}$ representation. Thus

$$\gamma_5 = \gamma_1\gamma_2\gamma_3\gamma_4 = -\beta\alpha_5 = i\sigma_1 \oplus I_2 \tag{VIII.5.14}$$

has the matrix form

$$\gamma_5 = \begin{bmatrix} 0 & iI_2 \\ iI_2 & 0 \end{bmatrix}, \tag{VIII.5.15}$$

where

$$\gamma_5^\dagger = -\gamma_5. \tag{VIII.5.16}$$

The γ_5 matrix can also be written as

$$\gamma_5 = \frac{1}{4!}\,\epsilon^{\mu\nu\rho\sigma}\gamma_\mu\gamma_\nu\gamma_\rho\gamma_\sigma, \tag{VIII.5.17}$$

$$\gamma_5^2 = -I_4. \tag{VIII.5.18}$$

Because of the vector transformation properties of the γ, the operator γ_5, as the product of four γ, changes its sign under (a) reflection of coordinates, and (b) reflection of time. It transforms like a pseudoscalar under reflection of both space and time.

A very important property of γ_5 is its anticommutation with all the other four γ:

$$\gamma_5\gamma_\mu + \gamma_\mu\gamma_5 = 0. \tag{VIII.5.19}$$

The anticommutation relations (*VIII.5.13*) and (*VIII.5.19*) can be combined into a single set,

$$\Gamma_A\Gamma_B + \Gamma_B\Gamma_A = -2M_{AB}I_4, \tag{VIII.5.20}$$

where, for $A = 1, 2, 3, 4, 5$,

$$\Gamma_A \equiv (\gamma_\mu, \gamma_5), \qquad M_{\mu 5} = M_{5\mu} = 0, \qquad M_{55} = 1, \qquad M_{\mu\nu} = a_{\mu\nu}.$$

The square of the four-dimensional operator

$$\Gamma_A p^A = \gamma^\mu p_\mu + imc\gamma_5$$

is given by

$$(\Gamma^A p_A)^2 = \mathbf{p}^2 - p_0^2 + m^2c^2. \tag{VIII.5.21}$$

The remaining members of the γ matrices include the matrices $\gamma_5\gamma_\mu$, which transform (to be seen later) like the components of a *pseudovector*.

The spin tensor operator $\gamma_\mu\gamma_\nu$ is directly related to (*VIII.5.8*) and (*VIII.5.9*), since

$$\gamma_i\gamma_j - \gamma_j\gamma_i = \alpha_i\alpha_j - \alpha_j\alpha_i$$

and

$$\gamma_i = \frac{i}{2}(\beta\alpha_i - \alpha_i\beta).$$

We define the spin matrices by

$$\sigma_{\mu\nu} = -\tfrac{1}{2}i(\gamma_\mu\gamma_\nu - \gamma_\nu\gamma_\mu), \tag{VIII.5.22}$$

where the space parts of $\sigma_{\mu\nu}$,

$$\sigma_{23} = -i\gamma_2\gamma_3, \qquad \sigma_{31} = -i\gamma_3\gamma_1, \qquad \sigma_{12} = -i\gamma_1\gamma_2,$$

or

$$\sigma_{ij} = \epsilon_{ijk}\begin{bmatrix}\sigma_k & 0\\ 0 & \sigma_k\end{bmatrix}, \tag{VIII.5.23}$$

are Hermitian, and the time parts,

$$\sigma_{14} = \gamma_1\beta, \qquad \sigma_{24} = \gamma_2\beta, \qquad \sigma_{34} = \gamma_3\beta,$$

or

$$\sigma_{i4} = \begin{bmatrix}0 & -i\sigma_i\\ -i\sigma_i & 0\end{bmatrix} = -i\alpha_i, \tag{VIII.5.24}$$

are anti-Hermitian. The squares of $\boldsymbol{\sigma}$ matrices satisfy

$$\begin{aligned}\sigma_{23}^2 = \sigma_{31}^2 = \sigma_{12}^2 &= I_4,\\ \sigma_{14}^2 = \sigma_{24}^2 = \sigma_{34}^2 &= -I_4.\end{aligned} \tag{VIII.5.25}$$

Some of the most frequently used commutation and anticommutation relations are

$$\tfrac{1}{2}[\sigma_{\mu\nu}, \gamma_\rho] = \tfrac{1}{2}(\sigma_{\mu\nu}\gamma_\rho - \gamma_\rho\sigma_{\mu\nu}) = i(\gamma_\mu a_{\rho\nu} - \gamma_\nu a_{\mu\rho}), \qquad (VIII.5.26)$$

$$\tfrac{1}{2}[\sigma_{\mu\nu}, \gamma_\rho]_+ = \tfrac{1}{2}(\sigma_{\mu\nu}\gamma_\rho + \gamma_\rho\sigma_{\mu\nu}) = -i\epsilon_{\mu\nu\rho\sigma}\gamma^\sigma\gamma_5, \qquad (VIII.5.27)$$

$$\gamma_\mu\gamma_\nu\gamma_\rho = -\epsilon_{\mu\nu\rho\sigma}\gamma_5\gamma^\sigma + a_{\mu\rho}\gamma_\nu - a_{\mu\nu}\gamma_\rho - a_{\rho\nu}\gamma_\mu,$$

$$\tfrac{1}{2}[\sigma_{\mu\nu}, \sigma_{\alpha\beta}]_+ = -\gamma_5\epsilon_{\mu\nu\alpha\beta} + a_{\mu\alpha}a_{\nu\beta} - a_{\mu\beta}a_{\nu\alpha}, \qquad (VIII.5.28)$$

$$[\sigma_{\mu\nu}, \gamma_5] = 0, \qquad (VIII.5.29)$$

$$\tfrac{1}{2}[\sigma_{\mu\nu}, \sigma_{\alpha\beta}] = ia_{\alpha\nu}\sigma_{\mu\beta} + ia_{\beta\nu}\sigma_{\alpha\mu} - ia_{\alpha\mu}\sigma_{\nu\beta} - ia_{\mu\beta}\sigma_{\alpha\nu}. \qquad (VIII.5.30)$$

By introducing

$$S_{\mu\nu} = \tfrac{1}{2}\sigma_{\mu\nu}, \qquad (VIII.5.31)$$

from (*VIII.4.30*), we obtain

$$[S_{\mu\nu}, S_{\alpha\beta}] = ia_{\alpha\nu}S_{\mu\beta} + ia_{\beta\nu}S_{\alpha\mu} - ia_{\alpha\mu}S_{\nu\beta} - ia_{\mu\beta}S_{\alpha\nu}. \qquad (VIII.5.32)$$

It is interesting to compare this with the classical relations (*III.1.25*). The commutation rules (*VIII.5.26*) become

$$\begin{aligned} [S_{\mu\nu}, \gamma_\rho] &= ia_{\mu\rho}\gamma_\nu - ia_{\rho\nu}\gamma_\mu \\ [S_{\mu\nu}, \gamma_5\gamma_\rho] &= ia_{\mu\rho}\gamma_5\gamma_\nu - ia_{\rho\nu}\gamma_5\gamma_\mu. \end{aligned} \qquad (VIII.5.33)$$

Also note that the generators $M_{(\mu\nu)}$ of the proper Lorentz transformations as defined by (*I.10.23*) satisfy the same commutation relations as $S_{\mu\nu}$ defined by (*VIII.5.31*):

$$[M_{(\mu\nu)}, M_{(\alpha\beta)}] = ia_{\alpha\nu}M_{(\mu\beta)} + ia_{\beta\nu}M_{(\alpha\mu)} - ia_{\alpha\mu}M_{(\nu\beta)} - ia_{\mu\beta}M_{(\alpha\nu)}. \qquad (VIII.5.34)$$

Finally we observe from Table VIII.5 that all 4×4 matrices with imaginary elements are those containing the Pauli matrix σ_2 only once in the Kronecker products of the $\boldsymbol{\sigma}$. All matrices in the third row and the third column contain σ_2 and, with the exception of the element $\sigma_2 \oplus \sigma_2$, all change sign under the operation of complex conjugation. We may look for a unitary transformation which will transform the element $\sigma_2 \oplus \sigma_2 = -\gamma_2$ into itself. Thus, if U is the unitary transformation operator, then we require

$$U^\dagger\gamma_2 U = \gamma_2.$$

The unitary operator U must obviously be a linear operator of the form

$$U = a + b\gamma_2,$$

where a and b are constants to be defined from the unitarity condition $U^\dagger U = I$ or from the transformation requirement on γ_2. This results in the definition

$$U = \frac{1}{\sqrt{2}}[I + i\gamma_2]. \qquad (VIII.5.35)$$

Application of the unitary transformation operator (*VIII.5.35*) onto the elements of Table VIII.5 transforms all of them into pure imaginary and antisymmetric matrices, except for $\boldsymbol{\alpha}$ matrices, which are transformed into symmetric matrices with real elements. This particular representation of Dirac matrices is called the "Majorana representation" and is quite useful in the study of the various symmetry elements of the elementary particle physics.

In the Majorana representation the matrices β, α_i, and γ_5 of the usual representation are given as

$$\beta_M = U^\dagger \beta U = -\alpha_2, \qquad \alpha_M^1 = \alpha_1, \qquad \alpha_M^2 = -\beta,$$
$$\alpha_M^3 = \alpha_3, \qquad \gamma_5^M = i\gamma_5\gamma_2. \qquad (VIII.5.36)$$

VIII.5.A. The Lorentz Transformations Induced by γ Generators

The spinors of four-dimensional space, whose complete matrix algebra is determined by the 16 matrices I_4, γ_5, γ_μ, $\gamma_5\gamma_\mu$, $\gamma_\mu\gamma_\nu$ are defined by their transformation rules. If $|\psi\rangle$ is a four-dimensional spinor, as a function of space and time, it transforms according to

$$|\psi'\rangle = S|\psi\rangle, \qquad (VIII.5.37)$$

where

$$|\psi\rangle = \begin{bmatrix} \psi_1 \\ \psi_2 \\ \psi_3 \\ \psi_4 \end{bmatrix}.$$

and $|\psi'\rangle$ are functions of x^μ and x'^μ, respectively. The coordinates x'^μ and x^μ are related by a Lorentz transformation. The transformation matrix S of the spinor space is a 4×4 matrix and is a function of the coefficients L_ν^μ alone.

In order to find a two-valued four-dimensional representation of the Lorentz group we consider the transformation of a spinor $|\phi\rangle$ defined by

$$|\phi\rangle = \gamma^\mu p_\mu |\psi\rangle, \qquad (VIII.5.38)$$

where

$$p_\mu p^\mu \neq 0.$$

In another Lorentz frame the spinor $|\phi\rangle$ must have the form

$$|\phi'\rangle = \gamma^\mu p'_\mu |\psi'\rangle. \qquad (VIII.5.39)$$

By applying the transformation (*VIII.5.37*) and the corresponding Lorentz transformation, we obtain the conditions

$$S^{-1}\gamma_\mu S = L_\mu^\nu \gamma_\nu \qquad (VIII.5.40)$$

for the matrix S and the transformation laws of the γ.

The "metrical" properties of the four-dimensional spinor space are described by a special S operator corresponding to the Lorentz matrix F. The "metric" of the spinor space follows, therefore, by replacing L^{ν}_{μ} on the right side of (*VIII.5.40*) by a^{ν}_{μ}:

$$S^{-1}\gamma_\mu S = a^{\nu}_{\mu}\gamma_\nu \tag{VIII.5.41}$$

or

$$\gamma_i S + S\gamma_i = 0, \qquad \gamma_4 S - S\gamma_4 = 0.$$

Thus the metric (up to an unimportant phase factor) is uniquely defined by taking

$$S_p = \beta. \tag{VIII.5.42}$$

It transforms γ matrices according to

$$\beta^{-1}\gamma_i\beta = -\gamma_i, \qquad \beta^{-1}\gamma_4\beta = \gamma_4, \qquad \beta^{-1}\gamma_5\beta = -\gamma_5, \tag{VIII.5.43}$$

which is like F transforming the coordinates according to

$$|x'\supset = F|x\supset$$

or

$$x'^i = -x^i \quad \text{and} \quad x'^4 = x^4.$$

The S transformation in spinor space corresponding to $-F$ transformation in Lorentz space is

$$S^{-1}\gamma_\mu S = -a^{\nu}_{\mu}\gamma_\nu \tag{VIII.5.44}$$

or

$$\gamma_i S - S\gamma_i = 0, \qquad \gamma_4 S + S\gamma_4 = 0.$$

Hence

$$S_T = \beta\gamma_5 \tag{VIII.5.45}$$

and it transforms the γ according to

$$\begin{aligned}(\beta\gamma_5)^{-1}\gamma_i(\beta\gamma_5) &= \gamma_i,\\ (\beta\gamma_5)^{-1}\gamma_4(\beta\gamma_5) &= -\gamma_4,\\ (\beta\gamma_5)^{-1}\gamma_5(\beta\gamma_5) &= -\gamma_5,\end{aligned} \tag{VIII.5.46}$$

which are like the transformation of coordinates by $-F$, as

$$|x'\supset = -F|x\supset$$

or

$$x'^i = x^i, \qquad x'^4 = -x^4.$$

The antilinear operation of complex conjugation can be used to construct a symmetry operation in four-dimensional spinor space. From (*VIII.5.39*) and (*VIII.5.37*) we have

$$|\phi\rangle = S^{-1}\gamma^\mu L^{\nu}_{\mu}p_\nu S|\psi\rangle.$$

For $L^{\nu}_{\mu} = -a^{\nu}_{\mu}$ and $S = \mathfrak{I} = \beta\gamma_5\overline{C}$ it becomes

$$|\phi\rangle = \overline{C}\gamma_5\beta\gamma^\mu a^{\nu}_{\mu}p_\nu\beta\gamma_5\overline{C}|\psi\rangle.$$

If we operate on both sides by $\overline{C}$ we obtain

$$|\phi^*\rangle = \gamma^\mu p_\mu|\psi^*\rangle. \tag{VIII.5.47}$$

From this result we infer that the time-reversal operator of the four-dimensional spinor space is given by

$$\mathfrak{J} = \beta\gamma_5\overline{C}, \tag{VIII.5.48}$$

where

$$\mathfrak{J}^2 = -1. \tag{VIII.5.49}$$

For the identity transformation $L^\mu_\nu = \delta^\mu_\nu$ the corresponding S is just the unit matrix of C_4.

For the Lorentz transformation of class $L_{44} \leqq -1$, corresponding to the reflection of both space and time coordinates, we set $L^\mu_\nu = -\delta^\mu_\nu$ in (*VIII.5.40*) and obtain

$$S^{-1}\gamma_\mu S = -\gamma_\mu$$

or

$$\gamma_\mu S + S\gamma_\mu = 0.$$

Hence the S transformation in this case is just

$$S_R = \gamma_5, \tag{VIII.5.50}$$

which is a further result indicating the intimate relationship between the γ_5 operator and improper transformations in spinor space.

The scalar product of two spinors $|\psi\rangle$ and $|\phi\rangle$ in terms of the metric β of spinor space, follows as

$$\langle\psi|\beta|\phi\rangle = \psi_1^*\phi_1 + \psi_2^*\phi_2 - \psi_3^*\phi_3 - \psi_4^*\phi_4, \tag{VIII.5.51}$$

which is a Lorentz-invariant expression (a scalar).

In particular, the invariant square of the spinor $|\psi\rangle$ is

$$\langle\psi|\beta|\psi\rangle = \langle\bar{\psi}|\psi\rangle, \tag{VIII.5.52}$$

where

$$\langle\bar{\psi}| = \langle\psi|\beta \tag{VIII.5.53}$$

is called the adjoint spinor corresponding to the spinor $|\psi\rangle$. It is instructive to compare this with $\subset p|F$ or the contravariant components p^μ of the momentum p_μ.

The S transformations for the two-valued representations of the Lorentz group satisfy a condition similar to (*I.10.9*) for Lorentz space. Let $|\psi'\rangle$ be the spinor in the transformed coordinate system, so

$$|\psi'\rangle = S|\psi\rangle.$$

If (*VIII.5.52*) is to remain invariant under Lorentz transformations, we must have

$$\langle\psi'|\beta|\psi'\rangle = \langle\psi|\beta|\psi\rangle \tag{VIII.5.54}$$

satisfied for any spinor $|\psi\rangle$; that is,

$$S^\dagger\beta S = \pm\beta, \tag{VIII.5.55}$$

where $+$ and $-$ signs on the right apply for proper (and for the class $L_{44} \geqq 1$)

and for improper (and for the class $L_{44} \leqq -1$) Lorentz transformations, respectively. For example, the S transformations $S = \beta\gamma_5$ and $S = \gamma_5$, corresponding to Lorentz transformation matrices $-F$ and $-I$, respectively, will satisfy (*VIII.5.55*) with the minus sign on the right.

From a comparison of the commutation relations (*VIII.5.32*) and (*VIII.5.34*) we easily infer that we can use the spin tensor $\sigma_{\mu\nu}$ to set up a six-parameter two-valued representation of the homogeneous proper Lorentz group. The S transformations corresponding to L-transformations (*I.10.27*) and (*I.10.28*) are given by

$$
\begin{aligned}
S_{(23)} &= S_1(\psi) = \exp\left[-\frac{i\psi}{2}\sigma_{23}\right] = \exp\left[-\frac{\psi}{2}\gamma_2\gamma_3\right] = \cos\frac{\psi}{2} - \gamma_2\gamma_3\sin\frac{\psi}{2},\\
S_{(31)} &= S_2(\phi) = \exp\left[-\frac{i\phi}{2}\sigma_{31}\right] = \exp\left[-\frac{\phi}{2}\gamma_3\gamma_1\right] = \cos\frac{\phi}{2} - \gamma_3\gamma_1\sin\frac{\phi}{2},\\
S_{(12)} &= S_3(\theta) = \exp\left[-\frac{i\theta}{2}\sigma_{12}\right] = \exp\left[-\frac{\theta}{2}\gamma_1\gamma_2\right] = \cos\frac{\theta}{2} - \gamma_1\gamma_2\sin\frac{\theta}{2}
\end{aligned}
\tag{VIII.5.56}
$$

as rotation transformations, and

$$
\begin{aligned}
S_{(14)} &= S(\lambda) = \exp\left[-\frac{i\lambda}{2}\sigma_{14}\right] = \exp\left[-\frac{\lambda}{2}\gamma_1\gamma_4\right] = \cosh\frac{\lambda}{2} - \gamma_1\gamma_4\sinh\frac{\lambda}{2},\\
S_{(24)} &= S(\epsilon) = \exp\left[-\frac{i\epsilon}{2}\sigma_{24}\right] = \exp\left[-\frac{\epsilon}{2}\gamma_2\gamma_4\right] = \cosh\frac{\epsilon}{2} - \gamma_2\gamma_4\sinh\frac{\epsilon}{2},\\
S_{(34)} &= S(\rho) = \exp\left[-\frac{i\rho}{2}\sigma_{34}\right] = \exp\left[-\frac{\rho}{2}\gamma_3\gamma_4\right] = \cosh\frac{\rho}{2} - \gamma_3\gamma_4\sinh\frac{\rho}{2}
\end{aligned}
\tag{VIII.5.57}
$$

as velocity transformations. It is interesting to observe that the generators of pure rotation (σ_i) transform like an axial vector, while the generators $-i\alpha_i$ of velocity transformation transform like a polar vector.

Finally we state the fundamental Lorentz-covariant quantities of spinor and Lorentz space:

(a) $\langle\psi|\beta|\psi\rangle = \langle\bar{\psi}|\psi\rangle$, a scalar,
(b) $\langle\bar{\psi}|\gamma_5|\psi\rangle$, a pseudoscalar,
(c) $\langle\bar{\psi}|\gamma_\mu|\psi\rangle$, a 4-vector,
(d) $\langle\bar{\psi}|\gamma_5\gamma_\mu|\psi\rangle$, a pseudovector
(e) $\langle\bar{\psi}|\sigma_{\mu\nu}|\psi\rangle$, an antisymmetric tensor.

VIII.6. Infinitesimal Lorentz Transformations

All possible motions of a rigid body in three-dimensional Euclidean space, one point of which is fixed, can be described by the three-dimensional orthogonal group. If we introduce a time coordinate as a group parameter, then the position of the body (or its orientation) at any time t can be obtained by the operation of an element of the group. It has been shown in Section I.7 that if $|a(t_0)\rangle$ is a vector specifying the orientation of a rigid body at time t_0, then its orientation at time t is obtained by operating on $|a(t_0)\rangle$ with

$$A(t, t_0) = P \exp \left[-i \int_{t_0}^{t} S(t_1)\, dt_1\right],$$

so $A(t, t_0)$ produces a continuous motion of the body from t_0 to t.

The form of $A(t, t_0)$ is such that the entire history of the motion can be followed by infinitesimal steps; that is, infinitesimal rotations sum up to finite rotations.

In relativistic theory the analogy with rigid body motion cannot be applied. The concept of rigidity cannot be reconciled with the fact that in relativity simultaneity of events does not have an invariant meaning. The rigidity of a body requires an instant transmission (that is, with infinite velocity of light) of any type of disturbance at one of its points to all others. This feature of special relativity does not imply a "point" description for elementary particles. Indeed, the "finiteness" or "point" nature of elementary particles cannot be given any physical meaning; this feature is not what is implied by special relativity theory. More precisely, special relativity implies a "field" description of physical phenomena.

An infinitesimal element of the Lorentz group can produce an infinitesimal change of "field points" that can only be connected by light signals. Such infinitesimal Lorentz motions of the four-dimensional events are generated by the operators $M_{(\mu\nu)}$ defined in (*I.10.22*) or, more generally, by those satisfying the commutation relations (*VIII.5.34*). All proper transformations can be generated from the infinitesimal elements $M = \Omega F$ [see (*I.10.20*)], where Ω is a small antisymmetric matrix [in the sense defined by (*I.5.D*)]. The knowledge of M at any proper time τ_0 allows us to construct by integration, as in Section I.7, the transformation at time τ as

$$L(\tau, \tau_0) = P \exp \left[-i \int_{\tau_0}^{\tau} \Omega(\tau_1) F\, d\tau_1\right]. \qquad (VIII.6.1)$$

The definition of $L(\tau, \tau_0)$ by (*VIII.6.1*) contains a certain restriction on the possible infinitesimal changes of field events: only those changes are allowed for which the positions of field events at an arbitrary proper time τ are obtained from their positions at a time τ_0 by a transformation $L(\tau_0, \tau)$, generated according to the infinitesimal steps implied in (*VIII.6.1*).

All infinitesimal Lorentz transformations lie in the "small" neighborhood of the unit element I_4 of the Lorentz group. For a time-independent generator $\Omega(\tau)$, an infinitesimal Lorentz matrix is given by

$$L - I_4 = -i(\tau - \tau_0)\Omega F$$

or, absorbing the factor $i(\tau - \tau_0)$ into Ω, we write

$$L = I_4 - \Sigma F, \qquad (VIII.6.2)$$

where Σ is a real 4×4 small antisymmetric matrix. In tensor notation we can write

$$L^\mu_\nu = \delta^\mu_\nu - \Sigma_{\nu\rho} a^{\rho\mu}, \qquad (VIII.6.3)$$

where $\Sigma_{\mu\nu} = -\Sigma_{\nu\mu}$. If we now put

$$\Sigma_{\mu\rho} a^{\rho\nu} = \omega^\nu_\mu,$$

and observe that the superscript ν in ω^ν_μ is to be regarded as the second index, we write (*VIII.6.3*) as

$$L^\mu_\nu = \delta^\mu_\nu - \omega^\mu_\nu. \qquad (VIII.6.4)$$

Hence infinitesimal Lorentz transformation of coordinates is given by $x'^\mu = L^\mu_\nu x^\nu$ or

$$x'^\mu = x^\mu - \omega^\mu_\nu x^\nu. \qquad (VIII.6.5)$$

VIII.6.A. Infinitesimal Complex Orthogonal Transformations

The derivation of a complex orthogonal operator describing finite rotations of a complex three-dimensional manifold, as a sum of infinitesimal rotations, is a straightforward generalization of the method discussed (Section I.7) for the real orthogonal group. It follows from equation (*VIII.1.19*) as

$$R = P \exp\left[-i \int_{\tau_0}^{\tau} Z(\tau_1)\, d\tau_1\right]. \qquad (VIII.6.6)$$

For a time-independent generator $Z(\tau_1)$, an infinitesimal complex Lorent transformation operator has the form

$$R = I - i(\tau - \tau_0)Z,$$

where Z is defined as in (*VIII.1.19*) with first-order quantities a^i and b^i. The factor $\tau - \tau_0$ can be absorbed into a^i and b^i, and we can rewrite it as

$$R = I - iZ. \qquad (VIII.6.7)$$

Hence, the infinitesimal complex orthogonal transformation of $|\chi\rangle$ is given by

$$|\chi'\rangle = R|\chi\rangle = |\chi\rangle - iZ|\chi\rangle. \qquad (VIII.6.8)$$

By using the transformation rules (*VIII.1.52*) relating R transformations to L transformations, we can express the coefficients a^i and b^i of the Z operator in terms of the infinitesimal Lorentz transformation coefficients $\omega_{\mu\nu}$. On substituting from (*VIII.6.7*) and (*VIII.6.4*) in (*VIII.1.52*) and neglecting second-order terms in Z, we obtain

$$Z^\dagger B_{\mu\nu} - B_{\mu\nu} Z = i(\omega_\mu^\rho B_{\rho\nu} + \omega_\nu^\rho B_{\mu\rho}). \qquad (VIII.6.9)$$

The condition det $R = 1$ on the proper complex orthogonal transformations implies

$$\operatorname{tr} Z = 0, \qquad (VIII.6.10)$$

so the most general form for Z is

$$Z = q^i K_i,$$

where the q^i are complex numbers. A simple calculation for $\mu = \nu = 4$ and for $\mu = i$ and $\nu = 4$ from $(VIII.6.9)$ yields

$$\epsilon_{ijk} K_j (q^k + \omega_k - i\omega_{4k}) = 0,$$

where

$$\omega_k = \tfrac{1}{2}\epsilon_{kij}\omega_{ij}. \qquad (VIII.6.11)$$

The expression for q^i can be satisfied by taking

$$q^k = i\omega_{4k} - \omega_k = i\epsilon_k - \omega_k,$$

where we take

$$\omega_{4k} = \epsilon_k.$$

Hence

$$-iZ = \boldsymbol{\epsilon}\cdot\boldsymbol{K} - i\boldsymbol{\omega}\cdot\boldsymbol{K}$$

and the change of $|\chi\rangle$ due to infinitesimal complex rotation is

$$|\chi'(x')\rangle - |\chi(x)\rangle = (\boldsymbol{\epsilon}\cdot\boldsymbol{K} - i\boldsymbol{\omega}\cdot\boldsymbol{K})|\chi\rangle. \qquad (VIII.6.12)$$

The total change of $|\chi\rangle$, however, is the combined effects of an "intrinsic" rotation (through the $\boldsymbol{K}$ degree of freedom of the field) and coordinate displacement. Therefore, we can further express $|\chi'(x')\rangle$ in the original coordinate system x_μ by

$$\begin{aligned} |\chi'(x')\rangle &= |\chi'(x^\mu - \omega_\nu^\mu x^\nu)\rangle \\ &= |\chi'(x)\rangle - \omega_\nu^\mu x^\nu \frac{\partial}{\partial x^\mu}|\chi'(x)\rangle + \cdots. \end{aligned} \qquad (VIII.6.13)$$

The ket $|\chi'(x)\rangle$ contains the effect of the infinitesimal transformation, so in its expansion the second term of $(VIII.6.13)$ is of the first order in the ω. Thus $(VIII.6.13)$ can be replaced by

$$|\chi'(x')\rangle = |\chi'(x)\rangle - \omega_\nu^\mu x^\nu \frac{\partial}{\partial x^\mu}|\chi(x)\rangle. \qquad (VIII.6.14)$$

The second term on the right is now expressed in terms of the original ket $|\chi(x)\rangle$, since higher terms in $|\chi'(x)\rangle$ contain terms in ω. Using the abbreviation

$$\frac{\partial}{\partial x^\mu} = \frac{i}{\hbar} p_\mu, \qquad (VIII.6.15)$$

the operator $\omega_\nu^\mu x^\nu \dfrac{\partial}{\partial x^\mu}$ can be expressed as

$$\omega_\nu^\mu x^\nu \frac{\partial}{\partial x^\mu} = \frac{i}{\hbar}\,[\epsilon_i(x^4 p_i + x^i p_4) - \boldsymbol{\omega}\cdot\boldsymbol{L}],$$

where $\boldsymbol{L} = \boldsymbol{r} \times \boldsymbol{p}$ is the quantum mechanical angular momentum operator.

With the above results, (*VIII.6.12*) becomes

$$\Delta|\chi\rangle = |\chi'(x)\rangle - |\chi(x)\rangle$$

$$= -\frac{i}{\hbar}(\boldsymbol{\omega}\cdot\boldsymbol{J})|\chi\rangle + \left[\boldsymbol{\epsilon}\cdot\boldsymbol{K} + \frac{i}{\hbar}(x^4\boldsymbol{\epsilon}\cdot\boldsymbol{p} + \boldsymbol{\epsilon}\cdot\boldsymbol{r}p_4)\right]|\chi\rangle, \qquad (VIII.6.16)$$

where

$$\boldsymbol{J} = \boldsymbol{L} + \hbar\boldsymbol{K} \qquad (VIII.6.17)$$

is the total angular momentum operator of the electromagnetic field.

The above discussion can easily be carried through for the two-valued representation of the complex group. In this case the infinitesimal transformation operator is given as

$$U = I - \tfrac{1}{2}i(i\boldsymbol{\epsilon}\cdot\boldsymbol{\sigma} + \boldsymbol{\omega}\cdot\boldsymbol{\sigma}). \qquad (VIII.6.18)$$

In deriving (*VIII.6.18*) we used (*VIII.2.7*) in (*VIII.2.11*), together with the definition of the infinitesimal R transformation by (*VIII.6.7*).

The change in the spinor $|u\rangle$, induced by (*VIII.6.9*) and the corresponding transformation of coordinates, is

$$\Delta|u\rangle = |u'(x)\rangle - |u(x)\rangle$$

$$= -\frac{i}{\hbar}(\boldsymbol{\omega}\cdot\boldsymbol{J})|u\rangle + \left[\tfrac{1}{2}\,\boldsymbol{\epsilon}\cdot\boldsymbol{\sigma} + \frac{i}{\hbar}(x^4\boldsymbol{\epsilon}\cdot\boldsymbol{p} + \boldsymbol{r}\cdot\boldsymbol{\epsilon}p_4)\right]|u\rangle, \qquad (VIII.6.19)$$

where

$$\boldsymbol{J} = \boldsymbol{L} + \tfrac{1}{2}\hbar\boldsymbol{\sigma} \qquad (VIII.6.20)$$

is the total angular momentum operator of a field of spin $\frac{1}{2}\hbar$.

VIII.6.B. The Infinitesimal Transformation of Four Dimensional Spinors

From the six spinor transformation operators (*VIII.5.56*) and (*VIII.5.57*) we can easily infer the operator

$$S = I + \tfrac{1}{2}iq^{\mu\nu}\sigma_{\mu\nu}$$

as the operator of infinitesimal transformation for a four-dimensional spinor space. The coefficients $q^{\mu\nu}$ are antisymmetric in μ and ν. Substitution of S in (*VIII.5.40*) for the transformation of the γ matrices provides the four equations

$$\tfrac{1}{2}iq^{\mu\nu}(\sigma_{\mu\nu}\gamma_\alpha - \gamma_\alpha\sigma_{\mu\nu}) = -\omega_\alpha^\nu\gamma_\nu.$$

If we use the commutation rules (*VIII.5.26*) for the γ and the σ we obtain

$$q^{\mu\nu}\gamma_\mu = \tfrac{1}{2}\omega^{\nu\mu}\gamma_\mu.$$

Hence

$$q_{\mu\nu} = -\tfrac{1}{2}\omega_{\mu\nu}.$$

Thus the required operator S for infinitesimal transformation of spinors is

$$S = I - \frac{i}{4}\omega^{\mu\nu}\sigma_{\mu\nu}. \qquad (VIII.6.21)$$

The change in the spinor $|\psi\rangle$, induced by S and the corresponding Lorentz transformation, is given by

$$\begin{aligned}\Delta|\psi\rangle &= |\psi'(x)\rangle - |\psi(x)\rangle \\ &= -\frac{i}{\hbar}(\boldsymbol{\omega}\cdot\boldsymbol{J})|\psi\rangle + \left[\frac{1}{2}\boldsymbol{\epsilon}\cdot\boldsymbol{\alpha} + \frac{i}{\hbar}(x^4\boldsymbol{\epsilon}\cdot\boldsymbol{p} + \boldsymbol{\epsilon}\cdot\boldsymbol{r}p_4)\right]|\psi\rangle, \qquad (VIII.6.22)\end{aligned}$$

where $\boldsymbol{J} = \boldsymbol{L} + \frac{1}{2}\hbar\boldsymbol{\sigma}$ and the second term on the right contains α matrices instead of σ, as occurred in (*VIII.6.19*).

VIII.6.C. Problems

1. Prove that the fourth-order group consisting of I, $-I$, F, $-F$ is homomorphic onto the eighth-order group $\pm I$, $\pm\beta$, $\pm\beta\gamma_5$, $\pm\gamma_5$. Show also that $\pm I$, $\pm\gamma_5$, $\pm\gamma_\mu$, $\pm\gamma_5\gamma_\mu$, $\pm\gamma_\mu\gamma_\nu$ form a group of order 32.

2. Prove the following properties of Dirac matrices:

(a) $\gamma^\nu\gamma_\mu\gamma_\nu = 2\gamma_\mu$,

(b) $\frac{1}{2}\sigma^{\mu\nu}F_{\mu\nu} = i(1 - i\gamma_5)(\boldsymbol{\sigma}\cdot\boldsymbol{\chi}^*)$, $\qquad (VIII.6.23)$

where $F_{\mu\nu} = f_{\mu\nu} + i\phi_{\mu\nu}$. [See (*VIII.1.9*).]

(c) If we set

$$T_\mu = \tfrac{1}{2}F_{\mu\nu}\gamma^\nu,$$

then

$$T^\mu T_\mu = (i\boldsymbol{\sigma}\cdot\boldsymbol{\chi})^2 = -(\Omega + 2i\Lambda)$$

and

$$\gamma^\mu T_\mu = i(1 - i\gamma_5)(\boldsymbol{\sigma}\cdot\boldsymbol{\chi}^*),$$
$$\tfrac{1}{4}(T^*_\mu)^2(T_\mu)^2 = c^2S_\mu S^\mu,$$

where S_μ is defined by (*VIII.1.33*).

(d) $(\frac{1}{2}\phi^{\mu\nu}\sigma_{\mu\nu})^2 = \Omega - 2\gamma_5\Lambda$.

(e) From the identity

$$\gamma_\mu = \gamma_5\gamma_\mu\gamma_5$$

it follows that

$$\operatorname{tr}(\gamma_\mu) = 0, \qquad \mu = 1, 2, 3, 4.$$

3. The determinant of the tensor $g_{\mu\nu} = a_{\mu\nu} + f_{\mu\nu}$ is given by

$$g = \det g_{\mu\nu} = -(1 + \Omega - \Lambda^2).$$

Show that the expression

$$\sqrt{-g} = \sqrt{(1 + \Omega - \Lambda^2)}$$

can be rationalized in terms of Dirac matrices either as

$$L_1 = c\gamma^\mu S_\mu + \tfrac{1}{2}i\gamma_5\Omega + i\gamma_5 \qquad (VIII.6.24)$$

or as

$$L_2 = c\gamma_5\gamma^\mu S_\mu + \tfrac{1}{2}i\gamma_5\Omega + i\gamma_5, \qquad (VIII.6.25)$$

where S_μ is defined by (*VIII.1.33*).

4. Discuss the transformation properties of the expressions

$$\langle \bar{\psi}|L_1|\psi\rangle, \qquad \langle \bar{\psi}|L_2|\psi\rangle,$$

where the operators L_1 and L_2 are defined by (*VIII.6.24*) and (*VIII.6.25*), respectively.

5. Show that Maxwell's equations can be written as

$$\Lambda^\mu \frac{\partial}{\partial x^\mu} |\eta\rangle = 0, \qquad (VIII.6.26)$$

where the 4×4 matrices are defined in terms of generators $M_{\mu\nu}$ of infinitesimal Lorentz transformations by

$$\begin{aligned} \Lambda^4 &= I_4, & \Lambda_1 &= -M_{(23)} + iM_{(14)}, \\ \Lambda_2 &= -M_{(31)} + iM_{(24)}, & \Lambda_3 &= -M_{(12)} + iM_{(34)}, \\ \Lambda_i\Lambda_j + \Lambda_j\Lambda_i &= 2\delta_{ij}, & \Lambda_i\Lambda_j - \Lambda_j\Lambda_i &= -2i\epsilon_{ijk}\Lambda_k \end{aligned} \qquad (VIII.6.27)$$

and the vector $|\eta\rangle$ is defined to be

$$|\eta\rangle = \begin{bmatrix} \chi_1 \\ \chi_2 \\ \chi_3 \\ \phi \end{bmatrix}. \qquad (VIII.6.28)$$

Prove that $\phi = 0$ corresponds to a free field. If we assume the electric current is derivable from a scalar function ϕ as

$$J_\mu = -\frac{1}{4\pi} \frac{\partial \phi}{\partial x^\mu}, \qquad (VIII.6.29)$$

then a complex ϕ would imply the existence of magnetic charges.

6. If $\Gamma_{\mu\nu}$ represents the generators of infinitesimal Lorentz transformations, then the operators $\frac{1}{2}\Gamma^{\mu\nu}\Gamma_{\nu\mu}$ and $\frac{1}{4}{}^*\Gamma^{\mu\nu}\Gamma_{\mu\nu}$ are called the invariants of the homogeneous group, where ${}^*\Gamma^{\mu\nu}$ is the dual tensor to $\Gamma_{\mu\nu}$. Show that for four-dimensional spin representation the corresponding group invariants are I_4 and γ_5. The corresponding transformation operators

$$S_0 = e^{i\lambda}, \qquad S_5 = e^{i\lambda\gamma_5} \qquad (VIII.6.30)$$

may be called "invariant gauge" transformation operators, where λ is an invariant function of space and time. Prove that (*VIII.5.38*) is invariant with respect to S_5 transformation only if the spinor $|\phi\rangle$ vanishes.

VIII.7. Representations of the Four-Dimensional Orthogonal Group

The invariant form of a four-dimensional Euclidean space is

$$\subset x|I_4|x\supset = x_1^2 + x_2^2 + x_3^2 + x_4^2, \qquad (VIII.7.1)$$

where the 4×4 unit matrix I_4 is the metric of the space. A transformation which leaves the form (*VIII.7.1*) unchanged constitutes a four-dimensional orthogonal group. The commutation relations for the six generators of infinitesimal rotations can be obtained from (*VIII.5.34*), by replacing the Lorentz metric $a_{\mu\nu}$ by $-\delta_{\mu\nu}$:

$$[E_{\mu\nu}, E_{\alpha\beta}] = i\delta_{\alpha\mu}E_{\nu\beta} + i\delta_{\mu\beta}E_{\alpha\nu} - i\delta_{\alpha\nu}E_{\mu\beta} - i\delta_{\beta\nu}E_{\alpha\mu}. \qquad (VIII.7.2)$$

As a special example, for $E_{\mu\nu}$ we shall take

$$E_{\mu\nu} = x_\mu S_\nu - x_\nu S_\mu, \qquad (VIII.7.3)$$

where

$$S_\mu = i\frac{\partial}{\partial x_\mu}, \qquad x^\mu = x_\mu,$$

and

$$[x_\mu, S_\nu] = -i\delta_{\mu\nu}. \qquad (VIII.7.4)$$

The operators $E_{\mu\nu}$ constitute a four-dimensional Euclidean angular momentum. By analogy with the three-dimensional case, we can construct the eigenfunctions of $(E_{\mu\nu})^2$. These eigenfunctions can form the basis for irreducible representations of the Lorentz group. In some cases one can obtain solutions of relativistic wave equations from the corresponding solutions of the Euclidean equation by means of an analytic continuation.

We introduce four-dimensional polar coordinates by

$$\begin{aligned} x_1 &= r\sin\theta\cos\phi, \\ x_2 &= r\sin\theta\sin\phi, \\ x_3 &= r\cos\theta, \\ x_4 &= R\cos\lambda, \\ r &= R\sin\lambda, \end{aligned} \qquad (VIII.7.5)$$

where

$$R^2 = x_1^2 + x_2^2 + x_3^2 + x_4^2.$$

In these coordinates we obtain

$$\begin{aligned} E_{23} &= -i\left(\sin\phi\frac{\partial}{\partial\theta} + \cos\phi\cot\theta\frac{\partial}{\partial\phi}\right), \\ E_{31} &= i\left(\cos\phi\frac{\partial}{\partial\theta} - \sin\phi\cot\theta\frac{\partial}{\partial\phi}\right), \\ E_{12} &= i\frac{\partial}{\partial\phi}, \\ E_{41} &= i\cot\lambda\left(\cos\theta\cos\phi\frac{\partial}{\partial\theta} - \frac{\sin\phi}{\sin\theta}\frac{\partial}{\partial\phi}\right) + \sin\theta\cos\phi\frac{\partial}{\partial\lambda}, \\ E_{42} &= i\cot\lambda\left(\cos\theta\sin\phi\frac{\partial}{\partial\phi} + \frac{\cos\phi}{\sin\theta}\frac{\partial}{\partial\phi}\right) + \sin\theta\sin\phi\frac{\partial}{\partial\lambda}, \\ E_{43} &= i\left(\cos\theta\frac{\partial}{\partial\lambda} - \sin\theta\cot\lambda\frac{\partial}{\partial\theta}\right). \end{aligned} \qquad (VIII.7.6)$$

Hence

$$E_{\mu\nu}^2 = \frac{\boldsymbol{L}^2}{\hbar^2 \sin^2 \lambda} - \frac{\partial^2}{\partial\lambda^2} - 2 \cot \lambda \frac{\partial}{\partial\lambda}, \qquad (VIII.7.7)$$

where $\boldsymbol{L}^2$ is the usual three-dimensional angular momentum operator in polar coordinates.

The eigenfunctions of $E_{\mu\nu}^2$, corresponding to its eigenvalues $2I_1$ (where I_1 is some integral number to be determined), are of the form

$$\Psi_{nlm}(\theta, \phi, \lambda) = Y_{lm}(\theta, \phi)\eta_{nl}(\lambda),$$

where $Y_{lm}(\theta, \phi)$ are eigenfunctions of $\boldsymbol{L}^2$. Thus we can write

$$2I_1 Y_{lm}\eta_{nl} = \left[\frac{l(l+1)}{\sin^2 \lambda} - \frac{\partial^2}{\partial\lambda^2} - 2 \cot \lambda \frac{\partial}{\partial\lambda}\right] Y_{lm}\eta_{nl}$$

or

$$2I_1 \eta_{nl} = \left[\frac{l(l+1)}{\sin^2 \lambda} - \frac{\partial^2}{\partial\lambda^2} - 2 \cot \lambda \frac{\partial}{\partial\lambda}\right] \eta_{nl}. \qquad (VIII.7.8)$$

Putting $x = \cos \lambda$, the eigenvalue equation (*VIII.7.8*) becomes

$$(1 - x^2) \frac{d^2\eta_{nl}}{dx^2} - 3x \frac{d\eta_{nl}}{dx} + \left[2I_1 - \frac{l(l+1)}{1 - x^2}\right]\eta_{nl} = 0. \qquad (VIII.7.9)$$

This can be solved by standard methods. We first make the substitution

$$\eta_{nl} = (x^2 - 1)^{(1/2)l} F_{nl} \qquad (VIII.7.10)$$

and obtain for F_{nl} the equation

$$(1 - x^2) \frac{d^2F_{nl}}{dx^2} - (2l + 3)x \frac{dF_{nl}}{dx} + [2I_1 - l(l + 2)]F_{nl} = 0. \qquad (VIII.7.11)$$

Now setting $l = 0$ in (*VIII.7.9*) and differentiating it l times, we find

$$(1 - x^2) \frac{d^2\eta_{n0}^{(l)}}{dx^2} - (2l + 3)x \frac{d\eta_{n0}^{(l)}}{dx} + [2I_1 - l(l + 2)]\eta_{n0}^{(l)} = 0, \qquad (VIII.7.12)$$

where

$$\eta_{n0}^{(l)} = \frac{d^l\eta_{n0}}{dx^l}.$$

Hence we infer that the required solutions for (*VIII.7.11*) are proportional to $\eta_{n0}^{(l)}$; that is,

$$F_{nl} = \gamma_{nl} \frac{d^l\eta_{n0}}{dx^l}. \qquad (VIII.7.13)$$

The equation for η_{n0},

$$(1 - x^2) \frac{d^2\eta_{n0}}{dx^2} - 3x \frac{d\eta_{n0}}{dx} + 2I_1\eta_{n0} = 0,$$

is solved by an ultraspherical polynomial,* $d/d(\cos \lambda)(\cos n\lambda)$, provided we

---

* G. Szegö, *Orthogonal Polynomials*, American Mathematical Society, Providence, 1939.

choose $2I_1 = n^2 - 1$. Hence the $\eta_{nl}(\lambda)$ are given by

$$\eta_{nl}(\lambda) = i^l \frac{(\sin \lambda)^l}{T_l} \frac{d^{l+1}(\cos n\lambda)}{d(\cos \lambda)^{l+1}}, \qquad (VIII.7.14)$$

where

$$T_l = [n^2(n^2 - 1^2)(n^2 - 2^2) \cdots (n^2 - l^2)]^{1/2}, \qquad (VIII.7.15)$$

for $n = 0, 1, 2, \cdots$.

The eigenfunctions

$$\Psi_{nlm} = i^l Y_{lm}(\theta, \phi) \frac{(\sin \lambda)^l}{T_l} \frac{d^{l+1}(\cos n\lambda)}{d(\cos \lambda)^{l+1}} \qquad (VIII.7.16)$$

are normalized according to

$$\int \Psi_{nlm}(\Omega) \Psi^*_{n'l'm'}(\Omega)\, d\Omega = \delta_{nn'}\delta_{mm'}\delta_{ll'}, \qquad (VIII.7.17)$$

where

$$d\Omega = \sin^2 \lambda \sin \theta \, d\lambda \, d\theta \, d\phi \qquad (VIII.7.18)$$

is the solid angle element of the four-dimensional space.

The expansion of the function $\exp (ik_\mu x_\mu)$ in terms of the eigenfunctions Ψ_{nlm}, like the expansion of a plane wave $\exp (i\boldsymbol{k} \cdot \boldsymbol{r})$ by (*IV.3.24*), can be carried through by using a procedure analogous to that used in Section *IV.3.A*. This can be done by first separating out the radial part of $(E_{\mu\nu})^2$. Thus we write

$$\begin{aligned} 2I_1 = E^2_{\mu\nu} &= (x_\mu S_\nu - x_\nu S_\mu)(x_\mu S_\nu - x_\nu S_\mu) \\ &= 2x_\mu S_\nu x_\mu S_\nu - 2x_\mu S_\nu x_\nu S_\mu. \end{aligned}$$

Using commutation relations (*VIII.7.4*) and $[S_R, R] = i$, we obtain

$$I_1 = R^2 S^2 + 3R \frac{\partial}{\partial R} + R^2 \frac{\partial^2}{\partial R^2}, \qquad (VIII.7.19)$$

where

$$RS_R = x_\mu S_\mu = iR \frac{\partial}{\partial R},$$

$$S^2 = -\left[\nabla^2 + \frac{1}{c^2} \frac{\partial^2}{\partial t^2}\right].$$

The operators S^2 and $(E_{\mu\nu})^2$ commute and the two together can form a complete commuting set of operators. If we assume that the eigenvalues of S^2 are given by k^2 $(= k_1^2 + k_2^2 + k_3^2 + k_4^2)$, then the radial eigenfunctions satisfy, as follows from (*VIII.7.19*), the equation

$$\frac{d^2 G_n}{dR^2} + \frac{3}{R} \frac{dG_n}{dR} + \left(k^2 - \frac{n^2 - 1}{R^2}\right) G_n = 0. \qquad (VIII.7.20)$$

This equation is solved by

$$G_n = \frac{1}{kR} J_n(kR) = \frac{1}{kR} J_{2j+1}(kR),$$

where we take $I_1 = 2j(j+1)$ and $n = 2j+1$. Hence the required expansion, following a method very similar to one used in deriving (*IV.3.24*), is given by

$$e^{ik_\mu x_\mu} = 8\pi \sum_{jlm} (-1)^j \frac{1}{kR} J_{2j+1}(kR) \Psi^*_{nlm}(\Lambda\Theta\Phi)\Psi_{nlm}(\lambda\theta\phi), \qquad (VIII.7.21)$$

where the angles Λ, Θ, Φ, and λ, θ, ϕ fix the directions of the four-dimensional vectors k_μ and x_μ, respectively. From the definition of polar coordinates by (*VIII.7.5*), it follows that $k_\mu x_\mu = |k|R \cos \omega$, where

$$\cos \omega = \cos \lambda \cos \Lambda + \sin \lambda \sin \Lambda \cos \gamma,$$
$$\cos \gamma = \cos \theta \cos \Theta + \sin \theta \sin \Theta \cos (\phi - \Phi).$$

The results obtained in this section will be found useful in the discussion of the infinite representations of the Lorentz group.

VIII.7.A. Group Invariants

If we put $E_{23} = M_1$, $E_{31} = M_2$, $E_{12} = M_3$, $E_{41} = N_1$, $E_{42} = N_2$, $E_{43} = N_3$, and use the commutation relations (*VIII.7.2*), we obtain

$$[M_i, M_j] = i\epsilon_{ijl}M_l, \qquad (VIII.7.22)$$
$$[N_i, N_j] = i\epsilon_{ijl}M_l, \qquad (VIII.7.23)$$
$$[M_i, N_j] = i\epsilon_{ijl}N_l. \qquad (VIII.7.24)$$

Hence we observe that the commutation relations between the M_i and N_j are the same as those between J_i and p_j of the three-dimensional inhomogeneous rotation group discussed in Chapter IV. In this case N_i correspond to p_i, except that the N_i do not commute among themselves as do the p_i.

The two invariants of the group are

$$I_1 = \tfrac{1}{2}(E_{\mu\nu})^2 = \tfrac{1}{2}(\boldsymbol{M}^2 + \boldsymbol{N}^2), \qquad (VIII.7.25)$$
$$I_2 = \boldsymbol{M}\cdot\boldsymbol{N} = \boldsymbol{N}\cdot\boldsymbol{M},$$

where M_i and N_i are regarded as three-dimensional vector operators. It is interesting to note that a particular choice for M_i and N_i is $M_i = K_i$ and $N_i = -K_i$. Specifically, the choices $M_i = (1/\hbar)J_i$ and $N_i = -(1/\hbar)J_i$ constitute a special solution for the commutation relations (*VIII.7.22*) and (*VIII.7.24*).

In order to establish a complete analogy with the three-dimensional inhomogeneous rotation group, we introduce the operators

$$\boldsymbol{Q} = \tfrac{1}{2}(\boldsymbol{M} + \boldsymbol{N}), \qquad \boldsymbol{Z} = \tfrac{1}{2}(\boldsymbol{M} - \boldsymbol{N})$$

and obtain the commutation relations

$$[Q_i, Z_j] = 0,$$
$$[Q_i, Q_j] = i\epsilon_{ijl}Q_l, \qquad (VIII.7.26)$$
$$[Z_i, Z_j] = i\epsilon_{ijl}Z_l.$$

Hence we see that the four-dimensional rotation group can be regarded as a direct product of the two homogeneous three-dimensional rotation groups. The eigenvalues of the Hermitian operators $\boldsymbol{Q}^2$ and $\boldsymbol{Z}^2$ are of the form

$$\boldsymbol{Q}^2 = l(l+1), \qquad \boldsymbol{Z}^2 = s(s+1), \qquad (VIII.7.27)$$

so the degree of the representation is $(2l+1)(2s+1)$. The eigenvalues of the group invariants

$$I_1 = \boldsymbol{Q}^2 + \boldsymbol{Z}^2 \quad \text{and} \quad I_2 = \boldsymbol{Q}^2 - \boldsymbol{Z}^2$$

are

$$I_1 = l(l+1) + s(s+1), \qquad I_2 = l(l+1) - s(s+1). \qquad (VIII.7.28)$$

Each representation may be labeled by the number pair (l, s). The reflection of spacial coordinates correspond to the mirror representations (l, s) and (s, l); the second one comes from changing the sign of N.

The operators $\boldsymbol{M}^2$, $\boldsymbol{N}^2$, and M_3 commute and they can form a complete commuting set of Hermitian operators. The eigenvalues of $\boldsymbol{M}^2$ and M_3 are known as $j(j+1)$ and m, respectively (with $-j \leqq m \leqq j$). We use the analogy between the present case and the inhomogeneous three-dimensional rotation group already discussed in Section IV.5. In place of the operators p_i we here have N_i. Therefore the diagonal matrix elements of $[N_+, N_-] = 2M_3$, as in $(IV.5.2)$, can be expressed, and we obtain the relation

$$\Phi(j+1) - \Phi(j) = -(2j+1) + \frac{I_2^2(2j+1)}{j^2(j+1)^2}, \qquad \text{for } j \neq 0, \qquad (VIII.7.29)$$

where $\Phi(j)$ is equal to the term $\phi(j-1)$ of $(IV.5.3)$, $\langle\gamma j|p|\gamma j\rangle$ is replaced by $\langle\gamma j|N|\gamma j\rangle$, and so on. In a similar way, for the invariants I_1 and I_2 we find

$$2I_1 = \boldsymbol{M}^2 + \boldsymbol{N}^2$$

$$= \Phi(j+1)\left(\frac{j+1}{2j+1}\right) + \Phi(j)\left[\frac{1}{j(j+1)}\right] + \frac{I_2^2}{j(j+1)} + j(j+1),$$

$$I_2 = \langle\gamma j|N|\gamma j\rangle j(j+1). \qquad (VIII.7.30)$$

Equation $(VIII.7.29)$ is solved by

$$\Phi(j) + \frac{I_2^2}{j^2} + j^2 = \text{constant}. \qquad (VIII.7.31)$$

Putting this result in $(VIII.7.30)$ we find that

$$2I_1 + 1 = \text{constant}. \qquad (VIII.7.32)$$

To find the possible forms of I_1 and the nature of the representations, we consider the following two cases.

(a) $I_2 = 0$: we have $\Phi(j) = \text{constant} - j^2$; since $\Phi(j)$ is nonnegative, j must assume a maximum value—$j = n$, say. Thus for $j = n + 1$ the function $\Phi(j)$ must vanish:

$$\Phi(n+1) = 0, \qquad 0 \leqq j \leqq n.$$

Hence constant $= (n+1)^2$ and

$$\Phi(j) = (n+1)^2 - j^2, \tag{VIII.7.33}$$

$$2I_1 + 1 = (n+1)^2. \tag{VIII.7.34}$$

This corresponds to a finite representation of the group.

(b) $I_2 \neq 0$: in this case, from

$$\Phi(j) = \text{constant} - \frac{I_2^2}{j^2} - j^2,$$

we see that j can assume a minimum value $j = j_0 \neq 0$, for which the right side does not become negative. Thus we must have

$$j_0 \leqq j \leqq n \tag{VIII.7.35}$$

and

$$\Phi(j_0) = \Phi(n+1) = 0. \tag{VIII.7.36}$$

Hence it follows that

$$(n+1)^2 + \frac{I_2^2}{(n+1)^2} = \frac{I_2^2}{j_0^2} + j_0^2 = 2I_1 + 1 \tag{VIII.7.37}$$

and

$$I_2^2\left[\frac{1}{j_0^2} - \frac{1}{(n+1)^2}\right] = (n+1)^2 - j_0^2. \tag{VIII.7.38}$$

These results yield the relations

$$I_2^2 = j_0^2(n+1)^2, \tag{VIII.7.39}$$

$$2I_1 = (n+1)^2 + j_0^2 - 1 = n(n+2) + j_0^2. \tag{VIII.7.40}$$

This representation is also finite and its degree is given by

$$\sum_{j=j_0}^{n} (2j+1) = (n+1)^2 - j_0^2 = (n+1+j_0)(n+1-j_0). \tag{VIII.7.41}$$

The degree of this representation, as defined by (*VIII.7.41*), must be equal to the degree $(2l+1)(2s+1)$ of the representation found previously. The same applies to the invariants of the group. Thus we have the equations

$$\begin{aligned}(2l+1)(2s+1) &= (n+1)^2 - j_0^2,\\ 2I_1 + 1 &= 2s(s+1) + 2l(l+1) = (n+1)^2 + j_0^2,\\ 2I_2 &= 2s(s+1) - 2l(l+1) = 2j_0^2(n+1)^2.\end{aligned} \tag{VIII.7.42}$$

Equations (*VIII.7.42*) are solved by

$$n = s + l, \qquad j_0 = |s - l| \tag{VIII.7.43}$$

From (*VIII.7.39*) we see that the finite representations just found can be classified according to the sign of the group invariant I_2. Thus we have three cases:

(a) $I_2 > 0$, so

$$s > l, \qquad s = \tfrac{1}{2}(n + j_0), \qquad l = \tfrac{1}{2}(n - j_0). \tag{VIII.7.44}$$

(b) $I_2 < 0$; in this case

$$s < l, \qquad s = \tfrac{1}{2}(n - j_0), \qquad l = \tfrac{1}{2}(n + j_0). \tag{VIII.7.45}$$

(c) $I_2 = 0$, where $j_0 = 0$,

$$s = l = \tfrac{1}{2}n. \tag{VIII.7.46}$$

The mirror representations (s, l) and (l, s) have different signs of I_2.

VIII.8. Infinite Representations of the Lorentz Group

VIII.8.A. The Homogeneous Group

The six generators of the infinitesimal Lorentz transformations, as shown in (*VIII.5*), satisfy the commutation relations

$$[J_{\mu\nu}, J_{\alpha\beta}] = i\hbar a_{\alpha\nu} J_{\mu\beta} - i\hbar a_{\mu\beta} J_{\alpha\nu} + i\hbar a_{\nu\beta} J_{\alpha\mu} - i\hbar a_{\alpha\mu} J_{\nu\beta}. \tag{VIII.8.1}$$

A particular case for the generators $J_{\mu\nu}$ is contained in

$$J_{\mu\nu} = L_{\mu\nu} = x_\mu p_\nu - x_\nu p_\mu. \tag{VIII.8.2}$$

This is the relativistic definition of orbital angular momentum. By analogy with (*IV.2.12*) the relativistic form of the orbital angular momentum tensor operator can be written as

$$L_{\mu\nu} = i\langle x|FM_{\mu\nu}|p\rangle, \tag{VIII.8.3}$$

where F is as defined by (*I.10.4*) and

$$|x\rangle = \begin{bmatrix} x_1 \\ x_2 \\ x_3 \\ x_4 \end{bmatrix}, \qquad |p\rangle = \begin{bmatrix} p_1 \\ p_2 \\ p_3 \\ p_4 \end{bmatrix}, \qquad [x_\mu, p_\nu] = i\hbar a_{\mu\nu}, \tag{VIII.8.4}$$

and the 4×4 matrices $M_{\mu\nu}$ are given by (*I.10.23*). As an interesting exercise the reader should show that $L_{\mu\nu}$, as defined by (*VIII.8.3*) and (*VIII.8.4*), satisfies the commutation relations (*VIII.8.1*). The form (*VIII.8.3*) of $L_{\mu\nu}$ will be used to develop a discussion of the Lorentz group, similar to the representation of J_i [see (*IV.2.14*)]. The basic difference between the four-dimensional orthogonal and the Lorentz groups arises mainly in the respective definition of E_{4i} and L_{4i}.

The commutation relations (*VIII.7.22*) and (*VIII.7.24*) are now replaced by

$$[L_i, L_j] = i\hbar\epsilon_{ijk} L_k, \tag{VIII.8.5}$$

$$[N_i, N_j] = -i\hbar\epsilon_{ijk} L_k, \tag{VIII.8.6}$$

$$[L_i, N_j] = i\hbar\epsilon_{ijk} N_k, \tag{VIII.8.7}$$

so in this case the change occurs only in the commutation relations between the components of N_i, where $L_1 = L_{23}$, $L_2 = L_{31}$, $L_3 = L_{12}$, $N_1 = L_{41}$, $N_2 = L_{42}$, $N_3 = L_{43}$. The group invariants are now of the form

$$2I_1 = \tfrac{1}{2}L_{\mu\nu}L^{\mu\nu} = \mathbf{L}^2 - \mathbf{N}^2, \tag{VIII.8.8}$$

$$I_2 = \mathbf{L}\cdot\mathbf{N}. \tag{VIII.8.9}$$

Now, because of the correspondence $N \longrightarrow iN$ between the orthogonal and the Lorentz groups, we replace $\Phi(j)$ and I_2, in (*VIII.7.31*), by $-\Psi(j)$ and iI_2, respectively. We obtain*

$$\Psi(j) + \frac{I_2^2}{j^2} - j^2 = -(2I_1 + 1), \tag{VIII.8.10}$$

where the nonnegative number $\Psi(j)$ is defined by

$$\Psi(j) = \langle\gamma j|N|\gamma j - 1\rangle\langle\gamma j - 1|N|\gamma j\rangle(2j-1)(2j+1) \tag{VIII.8.11}$$

and

$$I_2 = j(j+1)\langle\gamma j|N|\gamma j\rangle. \tag{VIII.8.12}$$

The expression (*VIII.8.10*) for $\Psi(j)$ shows that the requirement that $\Psi(j)$ be a nonnegative number does not limit the possible values of j. Therefore there is no upper limit for j and the representation for the case $I_2 \neq 0$ is infinite. Thus we have three cases to consider.

(a) $I_2 \neq 0$: because of definition (*VIII.8.12*) for I_2, j must have a minimum nonzero value j_0. For $j = j_0$, $\Psi(j)$ must vanish—$\Psi(j_0) = 0$. Hence we get

$$2I_1 = j_0^2 - 1 - \frac{I_2^2}{j_0^2} \tag{VIII.8.13}$$

and

$$\Psi(j) = j^2 - j_0^2 + I_2^2\left(\frac{1}{j_0^2} - \frac{1}{j^2}\right), \tag{VIII.8.14}$$

which is nonnegative for all $j \geqq j_0$.

(b) $I_2 = 0$, $j \geqq j_0 \geqq 0$. In this case also we must have $\Psi(j_0) = 0$, so

$$2I_1 = j_0^2 - 1, \qquad \Psi(j) = j^2 - j_0^2, \tag{VIII.8.15}$$

where j has no upper bound.

(c) $I_2 = 0$, $j \geqq 0$. In this case $\Psi(j)$ is always positive definite and $\Psi(j) = 0$ is not required as a condition. Thus we have $\Psi(j) > 0$ for $j = 1, 2, \cdots$, and $I_1 < 0$.

We may thus form a complete orthogonal set with

$$2I_1 = j_0^2 - 1 - \lambda^2, \qquad I_2 = j_0\lambda$$

for $j_0 = 0, 1, 2, 3, \cdots$ or $\frac{1}{2}, \frac{3}{2}, \cdots$, where λ is real. This series contains cases (a) and (b) above and also part of case (c).

---

* W. Pauli, *Continuous Groups in Quantum Mechanics*, *CERN* 56–31 (1956).

If we use the case $I_1 < 0$, we get $2I_1 = -1 + \eta^2$, with $I_2 = j_0 = 0$ and $0 < \eta < 1$. This representation is not used in physics. Further discussions of these points, to cite only a few, can be found in various interesting papers on the subject.*

VIII.8.B. Eigenfunctions of the Representation

We introduce polar coordinates by

$$\begin{aligned} x_1 &= r \sin\theta \cos\phi, \\ x_2 &= r \sin\theta \sin\phi, \\ x_3 &= r \cos\theta, \\ x_4 &= \begin{cases} R \cosh\lambda, \\ R \sinh\lambda, \end{cases} \\ r &= \begin{cases} R \sinh\lambda, \\ R \cosh\lambda, \end{cases} \end{aligned} \tag{VIII.8.16}$$

where the alternatives ($x_4 = R \cosh\lambda$, $r = R \sinh\lambda$) and ($x_4 = R \sinh\lambda$, $r = R \cosh\lambda$) correspond to timelike and spacelike intervals, respectively. Thus, for the first choice,

$$R^2 = x_4^2 - r^2 > 0$$

is a timelike interval. If we replace λ by $i\lambda$ in (*VIII.8.16*), both cases would lead to equivalent representations of the Euclidean group.

The eigenfunctions of the irreducible representations of the Lorentz group can be obtained from the irreducible representations of the four-dimensional orthogonal group. Thus if in equation (*VIII.7.16*) we simultaneously replace λ by $i\lambda$ and n by in, where $0 \leqq n \leqq \infty$, we obtain one of the infinite-dimensional representations of the Lorentz group. For the timelike intervals, (*VIII.7.16*) yields the eigenfunctions†

$$\Psi_{lnm}(\Omega) = \Psi_{nlm}(\lambda, \theta, \phi) = \Pi_l(n, \lambda) Y_{lm}(\theta, \phi), \tag{VIII.8.17}$$

where

$$\begin{aligned} \Pi_l(n, \lambda) &= \frac{(\sinh\lambda)^l}{Q_l} \frac{d^{l+1}(\cos n\lambda)}{d(\cosh\lambda)^{l+1}}, \\ Q_l &= [n^2(n^2 + 1^2)(n^2 + 2^2) \cdots (n^2 + l^2)]^{1/2}. \end{aligned} \tag{VIII.8.18}$$

---

* E. Wigner, *Ann. Math.* **40** (1939), 149–204.
Harish-Chandra, *Proc. Roy. Soc. London, A*, **189** (1947), 272–401.
V. Bargmann and B. Wigner, *Nat. Sci. Sci. Proc.*, **34** (1948), 211–230.
V. Bargmann, *Ann. Math.*, **48** (1947), 568–640.
H. Weyl, *The Classical Groups*, Princeton Univ. Press, Princeton, 1939.
I. Gelf and M. Neumark, *J. Phys. USSR*, **10** (1946), 93–94.
† A. Z. Dolginov and A. N. Moskalev, *Sov. Phys. JETP*, **37**, No. 6 (1960), 1202.
A. Z. Dolginov, *Sov. Phys. JETP*, **3**, No. 4 (1956).

The spacelike case follows from replacing λ by $\lambda + (i\pi/2)$ in (*VIII.8.18*). The functions $\Psi_{lnm}(\Omega)$ are normalized according to

$$\int \Psi_{nlm}(\Omega)\Psi_{n'l'm'}(\Omega)\, d\Omega = \frac{\pi}{2}\,\delta_{nn'}\delta_{ll'}\delta_{mm'}, \qquad (VIII.8.19)$$

where

$$d\Omega = \sinh^2\lambda \sin\theta\, d\lambda\, d\theta\, d\phi. \qquad (VIII.8.20)$$

A comparison with (*VIII.7.8*) shows that Ψ_{nlm} are eigenfunctions of the operator

$$L_{\mu\nu}L^{\mu\nu} = \frac{\partial^2}{\partial\lambda^2} + 2\coth\lambda\,\frac{\partial}{\partial\lambda} - \frac{l(l+1)}{\sinh^2\lambda}$$

for $R^2 > 0$, and of

$$L_{\mu\nu}L^{\mu\nu} = \frac{\partial}{\partial\lambda^2} + 2\tanh\lambda\,\frac{\partial}{\partial\lambda} + \frac{l(l+1)}{\cosh^2\lambda}$$

for $R^2 < 0$. In both cases we have

$$\frac{\partial^2}{c^2\partial t^2} - \nabla^2 = \frac{\partial^2}{\partial R^2} + \frac{3}{R}\frac{\partial}{\partial R} - \frac{l(l+1)}{R^2}.$$

The total volume of the Lorentz group is infinite, so it is not possible to carry out an operation of group integration using only finite-dimensional representations. (The parameter λ has its range from 0 to ∞.)

VIII.8.C. Rotation of the Eigenstates of the Representation

We shall base our discussion on the observation that the definition (*VIII.8.3*) of the angular momenta suggests a correspondence of the type discussed for the three-dimensional angular momentum in Section IV.2. This correspondence is the respresentation of $J_{\mu\nu}$ by

$$J_{\mu\nu} \longrightarrow \frac{i}{2}\,\langle s|\beta\sigma_{\mu\nu}|q\rangle, \qquad (VIII.8.21)$$

where the spinor operators s_α and q_α, for $\alpha = 1, 2, 3, 4$, are subject to the commutation relations

$$[s_\alpha, q_{\alpha'}] = i\hbar\beta_{\alpha\alpha'}, \qquad i\beta = \gamma_4, \qquad (VIII.8.22)$$

and where s_3 and s_4 are complex conjugates of s_1 and s_2, respectively. It is easy to show that $J_{\mu\nu}$, as represented by (*VIII.8.21*) and (*VIII.8.22*), satisfy the commutation relations (*VIII.8.1*). In this formalism the role of the Lorentz metric $(a_{\mu\nu}) = F$ is played by β, the metric of spinor space.

The operator $\mathfrak{m}$, corresponding to (*IV.2.18*), is defined by

$$\mathfrak{m} = \frac{i}{2\hbar}\,s_\alpha q_\alpha. \qquad (VIII.8.23)$$

The corresponding eigenstates, as in Section IV.2, must be of the form

$$|\gamma JjMm\rangle = A^{Jj}_{Mm} s_1^{J+M} s_2^{J-M} s_3^{j+m} s_4^{j-m}, \qquad (VIII.8.24)$$

where the coefficients A^{Jj}_{Mm} are given by

$$A^{Jj}_{Mm} = [(J+M)!(J-M)!]^{-1/2}[(j+m)!(j-m)!]^{-1/2}, \qquad (VIII.8.25)$$

where

$$-J \leqq M \leqq J \quad \text{and} \quad -j \leqq m \leqq j.$$

The representation is $(2J+1)(2j+1)$-dimensional. A "rotation" of the eigenstates $|\gamma JjMm\rangle$ can be affected by a transformation of the spinor s_k, for $k = 1, 2$. Since the representation refers to the Lorentz group, the relevant transformation can be obtained as a product of rotation and the Lorentz transformation operators for a two-dimensional spinor.

Thus, from the analogy with Section IV.2, we write

$$D(\lambda, \theta, \phi)|\gamma JjMm\rangle = \sum_{\substack{M'=-J \\ m'=-j}}^{J,j} D^{(Jj)}_{MM'mm'}(\psi, \theta, \phi)|\gamma JjM'm'\rangle$$

$$= A^{Jj}_{Mm}(s_1')^{J+M}(s_2')^{J-M}(s_3')^{j+m}(s_4')^{j-m}, \qquad (VIII.8.26)$$

where

$$s_k' = U_{kk'}s_{k'},$$

$$U = \begin{bmatrix} \cos\frac{\theta}{2}\, e^{-(1/2)(i\phi-\psi)} & i\sin\frac{\theta}{2}\, e^{-(1/2)(i\phi+\psi)} \\ i\sin\frac{\theta}{2}\, e^{(1/2)(i\phi+\psi)} & \cos\frac{\theta}{2}\, e^{(1/2)(i\phi-\psi)} \end{bmatrix} \qquad (VIII.8.27)$$

and $\tanh\psi = v$ is the velocity of the new reference frame. We note that s_3 and s_4 are to be transformed by the complex conjugate of U. Substituting from (*VIII.8.27*) in (*VIII.8.26*) we find that the representations $D^{(Jj)}$ of the Lorentz group are related to $D^{(J)}$ and $D^{(j)}$ of $(2J+1)$- and $(2j+1)$-dimensional representations of three-dimensional rotation groups by

$$D^{(Jj)}_{MM'mm'}\left(\psi, \theta, \phi - \frac{\pi}{2}\right)$$

$$= \left[D^{(J)}_{M'M}\left(-\frac{\pi}{2}, \theta, \phi\right)\right]^* D^{(j)}_{m'm}\left(-\frac{\pi}{2}, \theta, \phi\right) e^{(M'+m')\psi} \qquad (VIII.8.28)$$

where

$$D^{(J)}_{M'M}(\gamma, \theta, \phi) = \sum_l (-1)^l \frac{[(J+M)!(J-M)!(J+M')!(J-M')!]^{1/2}}{(J+M-l)!l!(M'-M+l)!(J-M'-l)!}$$

$$\times e^{iM\gamma}\left[\cos\frac{\theta}{2}\right]^{2J+M-M'-2l}\left[\sin\frac{\theta}{2}\right]^{2l-M-M'} e^{iM\phi}, \qquad (VIII.8.29)$$

$$[D^{(J)}_{M'M}(\gamma, \theta, \phi)]^* = (-1)^{M-M'} D^{(J)}_{-M',-M}(\gamma, \theta, \phi).$$

We shall not elaborate these representations any further. For more detailed treatment the reader should consult the papers by Dolginov and Moskalev. In recapitulation: *An irreducible representation of the Lorentz group may be characterized by two numbers, j_0 and η. The number j_0 determines the lowest dimension of the representations of the three-dimensional subgroup contained in the given representation of the Lorentz group. The number η may be an arbitrary complex number and is related to group invariants.*

VIII.8.D. The Inhomogeneous Group

The inhomogeneous group is a ten-parameter group. Its representations require the study of the commutation relations (*VIII.8.1*) together with the quantum form of the classical relations (*III.1.24*):

$$[J_{\mu\nu}, p_\rho] = i\hbar(a_{\rho\nu}p_\mu - a_{\mu\rho}p_\nu) \qquad (VIII.8\ 30)$$

and

$$[p_\mu, p_\nu] = 0, \qquad (VIII.8.31)$$

The invariants of the group—that is, the operators commuting with all the others—can be constructed in a simple way. By multiplying the commutation relations (*VIII.8.30*) from the left by p^ρ, repeating the same from the right, and adding the resulting expressions, we find that

$$[p^2, J_{\mu\nu}] = 0, \qquad (VIII.8.32)$$

where

$$p^2 = p_\mu p^\mu \qquad (VIII.8.33)$$

is the invariant of the group. To find the second invariant we use the commutation relations (*VIII.8.30*). By cyclic permutation of $\mu\nu\rho$ and the addition of the resulting expression, we obtain

$$I_{\mu\nu\rho} = J_{\mu\nu}p_\rho + J_{\nu\rho}p_\mu + J_{\rho\mu}p_\nu = p_\rho J_{\mu\nu} + p_\mu J_{\nu\rho} + p_\nu J_{\rho\mu}. \qquad (VIII.8.34)$$

Because of the complete antisymmetry in μ, ν, ρ, the quantities $I_{\mu\nu\rho}$ have only four nonvanishing components: I_{234}, I_{314}, I_{124}, I_{123}. The dual of the tensor $I_{\mu\nu\rho}$ defined by

$$\Lambda^\gamma = \frac{1}{3!}\epsilon^{\gamma\mu\nu\rho}I_{\mu\nu\rho} \qquad (VIII.8.35)$$

is a 4-vector.

From the commutation relations (*VIII.8.1*), denoting the right side by $S_{\mu\nu\alpha\beta}$, we have

$$p_\rho J_{\mu\nu}J_{\alpha\beta} - p_\rho J_{\alpha\beta}J_{\mu\nu} = p_\rho S_{\mu\nu\alpha\beta},$$
$$p_\mu J_{\nu\rho}J_{\alpha\beta} - p_\mu J_{\alpha\beta}J_{\nu\rho} = p_\mu S_{\nu\rho\alpha\beta},$$
$$p_\nu J_{\rho\mu}J_{\alpha\beta} - p_\nu J_{\alpha\beta}J_{\rho\mu} = p_\nu S_{\rho\mu\alpha\beta}.$$

If we use (*VIII.8.30*) to express $p_\rho J_{\alpha\beta}, \cdots$ in terms of $J_{\alpha\beta}p_\rho, \cdots$, add the resulting expressions and multiply through by $\epsilon^{\gamma\rho\mu\nu}$, we get

$$[J_{\mu\nu}, \Lambda_\rho] = i\hbar(a_{\rho\nu}\Lambda_\mu - a_{\mu\rho}\Lambda_\nu) \qquad (VIII.8.36)$$

and

$$[\Lambda_\mu, p_\nu] = 0. \qquad (VIII.8.37)$$

Hence the second invariant

$$\Lambda^2 = p_\mu p^\nu S^\mu_\nu, \qquad (VIII.8.38)$$

where the tensor operator

$$S^\mu_\nu = \tfrac{1}{2}\delta^\mu_\nu J^{\alpha\beta}J_{\alpha\beta} - J^{\alpha\mu}J_{\alpha\nu} \qquad (VIII.8.39)$$

is obtained from

$$\Lambda^2 = \left(\frac{1}{3!}\right)^2 \epsilon^{\delta\mu\nu\rho}\epsilon_{\delta\alpha\beta\gamma}I_{\mu\nu\rho}I^{\alpha\beta\gamma} = \frac{1}{36}\,\delta^{\mu\nu\rho}_{\alpha\beta\gamma}I_{\mu\nu\rho}I^{\alpha\beta\gamma}$$

$$= \frac{1}{36}\det\begin{vmatrix} \delta^\mu_\alpha & \delta^\mu_\beta & \delta^\mu_\gamma \\ \delta^\nu_\alpha & \delta^\nu_\beta & \delta^\nu_\gamma \\ \delta^\rho_\alpha & \delta^\rho_\beta & \delta^\rho_\gamma \end{vmatrix} I_{\mu\nu\rho}I^{\alpha\beta\gamma}$$

$$= \tfrac{1}{2}\, p^\alpha J^{\mu\nu}J_{\mu\nu}p_\alpha - p^\alpha J^{\beta\gamma}J_{\alpha\gamma}p_\beta.$$

By using the commutation relations (*VIII.8.36*) we obtain

$$p^\alpha J^{\mu\nu}J_{\mu\nu}p_\alpha = p^2 J_{\mu\nu}J^{\mu\nu} + 6\hbar^2 p^2,$$
$$p^\alpha J^{\beta\gamma}J_{\alpha\gamma}p_\beta = p^\mu p_\rho J^{\rho\nu}J_{\mu\nu} + 3\hbar^2 p^2,$$

and these lead to (*VIII.8.38*). The trace of S^μ_ν yields the first invariant of the homogeneous group:

$$\tfrac{1}{2}\,\mathrm{tr}\, S^\mu_\nu = \tfrac{1}{2}S^\mu_\mu = \tfrac{1}{2}J^{\mu\nu}J_{\mu\nu} = I_1. \qquad (VIII.8.40)$$

Because of the Lorentz invariance of the above operator relations it will be sufficient to consider their significance in the rest frame. In such a frame $p_i = 0$, where $i = 1, 2, 3$, and the first invariant is just p_4^2. For the second invariant, from (*VIII.8.38*), we get

$$\Lambda^2 = p_4^2 S^4_4,$$

where

$$S^4_4 = \tfrac{1}{2}J^{\mu\nu}J_{\mu\nu} - J^{\mu 4}J_{\mu 4} = \boldsymbol{M}^2 - \boldsymbol{N}^2 + \boldsymbol{N}^2 = \boldsymbol{M}^2.$$

Hence

$$\Lambda^2 = \boldsymbol{M}^2 p_4^2$$

or

$$\Lambda^2 = \hbar^2 s(s+1)p_4^2, \qquad (VIII.8.41)$$

where $\boldsymbol{M}$ is the three-dimensional angular momentum in the rest frame; therefore the eigenvalues $\hbar^2 s(s+1)$ of $\boldsymbol{M}^2$ is expressed in terms of spin s alone. From the definition of Λ_α we see that the component I_{123} vanishes in the rest frame and we are left with $I_{234}, I_{314}, I_{124}$ components, which yield

$$\Lambda_\alpha \equiv p_4[J_{23}, J_{31}, J_{12}, 0]. \qquad (VIII.8.42)$$

For a particle with mass there are, for a given momentum, $2s + 1$ states. The cases $s = 0$, $s = \frac{1}{2}$, and $s = 1$ correspond to the transformation properties of the wave equations (and therefore of the wave functions) of particles of spin 0, $\frac{1}{2}\hbar$, and $\hbar$. The corresponding wave functions of the particles are scalar (pseudoscalar), spinor, vector (pseudovector) quantities, respectively. We see that representations of the inhomogeneous group do not exclude particles with spin higher than $\hbar$.

For a massless free particle with integral spin, the number of states is not represented by $2s + 1$. For example, $s = 1$ for the photon, but the number of possible states is just 2 instead of 3 (see Section II.2). If $m = 0$, then for a free particle (not in the rest frame, of course) from

$$p^2 p^\nu S^\mu_\nu = \Lambda^2 p^\mu, \qquad (VIII.8.43)$$

we see that for $p^2 = 0$ we must have $\Lambda^2 = 0$. Using the identity

$$p^\gamma \Lambda_\gamma = 0 \qquad (VIII.8.44)$$

we infer that for $p^2 = 0$ we have

$$\Lambda_\gamma = a p_\gamma. \qquad (VIII.8.45)$$

From the definition of Λ_γ we have

$$\begin{aligned}
\Lambda_1 &= p_3 J_{42} - p_2 J_{43} + p_4 J_{23} = -(\boldsymbol{p} \times \boldsymbol{N})_1 + p_4 M_1, \\
\Lambda_2 &= p_1 J_{43} - p_3 J_{41} + p_4 J_{31} = -(\boldsymbol{p} \times \boldsymbol{N})_2 + p_4 M_2, \\
\Lambda_3 &= p_2 J_{41} - p_1 J_{42} + p_4 J_{12} = -(\boldsymbol{p} \times \boldsymbol{N})_3 + p_4 M_3, \\
\Lambda_4 &= p_1 J_{23} + p_2 J_{31} + p_2 J_{12} = \boldsymbol{p} \cdot \boldsymbol{M}.
\end{aligned}$$

Hence we write

$$\boldsymbol{\Lambda} = -(\boldsymbol{p} \times \boldsymbol{N}) + p_4 \boldsymbol{M} = a\boldsymbol{p}, \qquad \Lambda_4 = \boldsymbol{p} \cdot \boldsymbol{M} = ap, \qquad (VIII.8.46)$$

where $p_4 = \pm\sqrt{(p_1^2 + p_2^2 + p_3^2)} = \pm p$; therefore

$$a = \pm \frac{\boldsymbol{p} \cdot \boldsymbol{M}}{p}. \qquad (VIII.8.47)$$

Comparing this result with (*IV.5.12*) of the three-dimensional inhomogeneous group, we see that the quantity a in (*VIII.8.47*) is just the minimum j value possible in the given representation. Thus for a given momentum vector there are two possible independent states for $a \neq 0$, which correspond to two different states of polarization. For $a = 0$ there is only one state; it corresponds to the transformation properties of a spinless and massless particle. For nonzero spin we shall consider two particular cases.

(a) $\boldsymbol{M} = \boldsymbol{L} + \hbar\boldsymbol{K}$, the total angular momentum of the photon. We have

$$a = \pm \frac{\boldsymbol{p} \cdot \boldsymbol{L} + \hbar \boldsymbol{p} \cdot \boldsymbol{K}}{p}. \qquad (VIII.8.48)$$

In this case the two states can be transformed into one another by a space reflection; this holds also for higher spins. The two states remain unchanged under a time reflection.

(b) $\boldsymbol{M} = \boldsymbol{L} + \frac{1}{2}\hbar\boldsymbol{\sigma}$, the total angular momentum of the neutrino. We have

$$a = \pm\frac{\boldsymbol{p}\cdot\boldsymbol{L} + \frac{1}{2}\hbar\boldsymbol{\sigma}\cdot\boldsymbol{p}}{p}. \qquad (VIII.8.49)$$

Here it is not possible to transform one state into another under space reflection, but the two states remain unchanged under time reversal.

CHAPTER IX

SYMMETRIES OF MASSLESS PARTICLES

IX.1. Angular Momentum of the Photon

The photon is a vector particle and therefore we need a complete set of vectors to expand its wave function into its "multipoles." Such a complete set of eigenfunctions can be formed from the simultaneous eigenfunctions of $\boldsymbol{J}^2$ and J_z. The special class of eigenfunctions obtained by taking $j_1 = l$ and $j_2 = 1$ in the expansion formula (*IV.3.4*) are called "vector spherical harmonics":

$$|\gamma l 1 j M\rangle = \sum_{m=-l}^{l} \sum_{s=-1}^{1} C(l1j; msM)|\gamma l 1 m s\rangle. \tag{IX.1.1}$$

From the addition rule (*IV.3.8*) of two angular momenta, it follows that for $j_2 = 1$ there are three kinds of vector spherical harmonics corresponding to $j = l - 1, l, l + 1$ or $l = j + 1, j, j - 1$. For each value of j we have three different vector spherical harmonics.*

We shall write (*IX.1.1*) in the form

$$|Y_{jl1}^{M}(\theta, \phi)\rangle = \sum_{m=-l}^{l} \sum_{s=-1}^{1} C(l1j; msM) Y_{lm}(\theta, \phi)|s\rangle, \tag{IX.1.2}$$

where

$$M = m + s \tag{IX.1.3}$$

and where we use the correspondence

$$|\gamma l 1 j M\rangle = |Y_{jl1}^{M}(\theta, \phi)\rangle, \qquad |\gamma l 1 m s\rangle = Y_{lm}(\theta, \phi)|s\rangle.$$

The eigenvalue equations are

---

* J. Blatt and V. F. Weisskopf, *Theoretical Nuclear Physics*, Wiley, New York, 1952.

$$\begin{aligned} \boldsymbol{J}^2|Y^M_{jl1}(\theta, \phi)\rangle &= \hbar^2 j(j+1)|Y^M_{jl1}\rangle, \\ J_z|Y^M_{jl1}(\theta, \phi)\rangle &= \hbar M|Y^M_{jl1}\rangle. \end{aligned} \tag{IX.1.4}$$

The vectors $|s\rangle$, where $s = 0, 1, -1$, are eigenvectors of K_3 as defined in (*I.8.7*). The functions $Y_{lm}(\theta, \phi)$ are the usual scalar spherical harmonics. The vectors $|s\rangle$ are the spin wave functions of the photon; they span the "spin space" of spin 1.

For $j = 0$ there exists only one vector spherical harmonic. For $j = 0$ we have $l = 0$ and $m = 0$, and (*IX.1.2*) gives

$$\begin{aligned} |Y^0_{001}(\theta, \phi)\rangle &= C(010, 000) Y_{00}(\theta, \phi)|0\rangle \\ &= -\frac{1}{\sqrt{(4\pi)}}|0\rangle, \end{aligned}$$

which is in the radial direction opposite to the spin $\boldsymbol{s}$.

Because of the completeness of $Y_{lm}(\theta, \phi)$ and of $|s\rangle$ the vector spherical harmonics constitute a complete set. Since there are three kinds of vector spherical harmonics corresponding to $l = j, j-1, j+1$, the unit operator of the complete set is

$$I = \sum_{j=0}^{\infty} \sum_{M=-j}^{j} \sum_{s=-1}^{1} |Y^M_{j,j+s,1}\rangle\langle Y^M_{j,j+s,1}|, \tag{IX.1.5}$$

where, as follows from the definitions of Clebsch-Gordon coefficients and the properties of $|s\rangle$ and Y_{lm}, the vector spherical harmonics satisfy the orthogonality and normalization conditions:

$$\int_0^{2\pi} \int_0^{\pi} \langle Y^M_{jl1}(\theta, \phi)|Y^{M'}_{j'l'1}(\theta, \phi)\rangle \sin\theta \, d\theta \, d\phi = \delta_{jj'}\delta_{MM'}\delta_{ll'}. \tag{IX.1.6}$$

Any vector function $|\eta_0\rangle$ of x_1, x_2, x_3 can be expanded according to

$$|\eta_0\rangle = \sum_{j=0}^{\infty} \sum_{M=-j}^{j} \sum_{s=-1}^{1} A^M_{j,j+s,1}|Y^M_{j,j+s,1}\rangle, \tag{IX.1.7}$$

where the expansion coefficients $A^M_{j,j+s,1}$ are defined as

$$A^M_{j,j+s,1} = \langle Y^M_{j,j+s,1}|\eta_0\rangle. \tag{IX.1.8}$$

For $s = 0, 1, -1$ the expansion coefficients are three functions of the radial coordinate r, depending on the quantum numbers j and M.

It follows from (*IX.1.7*) that a photon state represented by a given j and M has a wave function consisting of linear combinations of three types of vector spherical waves ($l = j, j-1, j+1$):

$$|\eta^M_j\rangle = \sum_{s=-1}^{1} A^M_{j,j+s,1}|Y^M_{j,j+s,1}\rangle, \tag{IX.1.9}$$

subject to the conditions

$$\boldsymbol{p}\cdot\boldsymbol{\eta}^M_j = 0. \tag{IX.1.10}$$

Hence for a given j and M the state of the photon is obtained as a superposition of two states only.

The vector $|Y_{jj1}^{M}\rangle$ for $j = l$ can be generated from the scalar spherical harmonics Y_{lm}. By representing the vector operator $\boldsymbol{L}$ in the form of a column vector we can project it into the spin space [we use the unit operator (*I.8.8*)] by

$$|L\rangle = \sum_{s=-1}^{1} |s\rangle\langle s|L\rangle. \tag{IX.1.11}$$

Hence

$$\begin{aligned}|L\rangle Y_{lm} &= \sum_{s=-1}^{s} |s\rangle\langle s|L\rangle Y_{lm} \\ &= \frac{1}{\sqrt{2}}|1\rangle L_{-}Y_{lm} + \frac{1}{\sqrt{2}}|-1\rangle L_{+}Y_{lm} + |0\rangle L_3 Y_{lm} \\ &= \hbar|1\rangle\left[\frac{(l+m)(l-m+1)}{2}\right]^{1/2} Y_{lm-1} \\ &\qquad + \hbar|-1\rangle\left[\frac{(l-m)(l+m+1)}{2}\right]^{1/2} Y_{lm+1} + \hbar|0\rangle m Y_{lm}.\end{aligned}$$

By using the properties of spherical harmonics we can further write

$$|L\rangle Y_{lm} = \hbar\sqrt{[l(l+1)]}|Y_{ll1}^{M}\rangle. \tag{IX.1.12}$$

From this it follows that

$$\langle p|[F(r)|Y_{ll1}^{M}\rangle] = 0, \tag{IX.1.13}$$

where $F(r)$ is an arbitrary function of r and $\boldsymbol{p} = -i\hbar\boldsymbol{\nabla}$.

Application of the above method, together with the use of the properties of spherical harmonics Y_{lm}, enables us to obtain vector spherical harmonics of the form

$$|\hat{x}\rangle Y_{lm} = -\left[\frac{l+1}{2l+1}\right]^{1/2}|Y_{l,l+1,1}^{M}\rangle + \left[\frac{l}{2l+1}\right]^{1/2}|Y_{l,l-1,1}^{M}\rangle, \tag{IX.1.14}$$

where $|\hat{x}\rangle$ represents the unit vector $\boldsymbol{r}/r$.

We may also construct a vector spherical harmonic orthogonal to the momentum vector $\boldsymbol{p}$ and to $|Y_{ll1}^{M}\rangle$. It is given by

$$|X_{lM}^{1}\rangle = -\frac{i}{cp}H|Y_{ll1}^{M}\rangle. \tag{IX.1.15}$$

The vectors $|X_{lM}^{0}\rangle = |Y_{ll1}^{M}\rangle$ and $|X_{lM}^{1}\rangle$ are called transverse spherical vectors and they satisfy the normalization conditions

$$\int \langle X_{lM}^{\alpha}|X_{l'M'}^{\beta}\rangle\, d\Omega = \delta_{\alpha\beta}\delta_{ll'}\delta_{MM'}, \tag{IX.1.16}$$

where α, $\beta = 0, 1$.

IX.1.A. The Parity of the Photon

We may now use the transverse spherical vectors $|X^{\alpha}_{jM}\rangle$ to express the wave function $|\eta^M_j\rangle$ in the form

$$|\eta^M_j\rangle = \sum_{\alpha=0}^{1} F^{\alpha}_{jM}(r)|X^{\alpha}_{jM}\rangle, \qquad (IX.1.17)$$

where the functions F^{α}_{jM} are arbitrary. The complete wave function of the free photon can be written as

$$|\eta\rangle = \sum_{j=1}^{\infty} \sum_{M=-j}^{j} \sum_{\alpha=0}^{1} F^{(\alpha)}_{jM}(r)|X^{\alpha}_{jM}\rangle, \qquad (IX.1.18)$$

where the $j = 0$ state, as shown before, does not correspond to a transverse mode and is therefore excluded from the summations.

Because of the invariance of the electromagnetic field under parity operation we shall require the wave function (*IX.1.18*) to be an eigenstate of the parity operator $\mathcal{P}$. The latter requirement will impose a further restriction on the definition of the functions* F^{α}_{Mj}. Hence we infer that for a complete specification of the state of a photon we need to specify four quantum numbers referring to its energy E, its angular momentum quantum numbers j and M, and its parity.

From the parity relation

$$\mathcal{P}Y_{lm}(\theta, \phi) = Y_{lm}(\pi - \theta, \pi + \phi) = (-1)^l Y_{lm}(\theta, \phi)$$

and

$$[\mathcal{P}, L_i] = 0,$$

where the L_i are the components of angular momentum, it follows that

$$\mathcal{P}|X^0_{jM}\rangle = (-1)^{j+1}|X^0_{jM}\rangle \qquad (IX.1.19)$$

and

$$\mathcal{P}|X^1_{jM}\rangle = (-1)^{j}|X^1_{jM}\rangle. \qquad (IX.1.20)$$

We thus see that for a given j and M there exist two different parity states. In the expansion (*IX.1.18*) the states with $\alpha = 1$ and $\alpha = 0$ correspond to electric and magnetic states, respectively. The relation of electric and magnetic states to electric and magnetic dipole (or multipole) radiations will be considered in later chapters.

From the eigenfunctions $|\eta^M_j\rangle$ we can construct a probability function $\langle\eta^M_j|\eta^M_j\rangle$, determining the probability that the photon is moving in the direction of its spin with a polarization direction $|s\rangle$ (where $s = 1$ or -1) in an angular momentum state (j, M) and parity α. Because of the definitions of $|X^{\alpha}_{jM}\rangle$, the

---

* A. I. Akhiezer and V. B. Berestetsky, *Quantum Electrodynamics*, Part I, USAEC Technical Information Service Extension, 1957. Oak Ridge, Tennessee.

probability is independent of α and depends on vector spherical harmonics of the type $|Y_{jj1}^M\rangle$. Hence *the angular distribution of the photon is independent of its parity and depends only on its angular momentum.*

In the state $j = l$ we have

$$\boldsymbol{J}^2 A_{jj1}^M|Y_{jj1}^M\rangle = \boldsymbol{L}^2 A_{jj1}^M|Y_{jj1}^M\rangle = \hbar^2 j(j+1) A_{jj1}^M|Y_{jj1}^M\rangle. \qquad (IX.1.21)$$

By using $(IV.3.17)$ we can write

$$\boldsymbol{J}^2 = \boldsymbol{r}^2\boldsymbol{p}^2 - rp_r^2 r,$$

where the operator $\boldsymbol{p}^2$, because of transversality of the waves, can be replaced by the square of the photon Hamiltonian

$$\frac{1}{c^2}H^2 = \boldsymbol{p}^2 - \boldsymbol{pp}.$$

Hence $(IX.1.21)$ becomes

$$\hbar^2 j(j+1)\frac{1}{r}f_j = \left(r^2\frac{E^2}{c^2} + \hbar^2 r\frac{\partial^2}{\partial r^2}r\right)\frac{1}{r}f_j$$

or

$$\frac{d^2 f_j}{dr^2} - \frac{j(j+1)}{r^2}f_j + k^2 f_j = 0, \qquad (IX.1.22)$$

where we take $(1/r)f_j = A_{jj1}^M$ and $k = E/\hbar c = \omega/c$. The solutions of $(IX.1.22)$ representing outgoing waves* are asymptotically given by

$$u^{(+)}(r) \cong \exp\left[i(kr - \tfrac{1}{2}l\pi)\right], \qquad \text{for } kr \gg l, \qquad (IX.1.23)$$

which results from the combinations of the exact solutions

$$F_l(r) = \sqrt{\left(\frac{\pi kr}{2}\right)}\, J_{l+(1/2)}(kr),$$

$$G_l(r) = -\sqrt{\left(\frac{\pi kr}{2}\right)}\, N_{l+(1/2)}(kr).$$

Then the solutions of $(IX.1.22)$ are in the form

$$u_l^{(+)} = G_l(r) + iF_l(r), \qquad (IX.1.24)$$

where $J_{l+1/2}$ and $N_{l+1/2}$ are the Bessel and Neumann functions as defined in Jahnke-Emde.†

The complex conjugate function $u_l^{(-)}$ of $u_l^{(+)}$ corresponds to ingoing spherical waves. In accordance with the time-reversal operation of the electromagnetic field [see $(VIII.1.69)$], we deduce that ingoing and outgoing spherical waves are related by a time-reversal operation.

---

* Blatt and Weisskopf, *Theoretical Nuclear Physics*, Wiley, New York, 1952.

† E. Jahnke and F. Emde, *Funktionentafeln*, B. G. Teubner, Leipzig, 1933. [English edition (4th), Dover, New York, 1951.]

IX.1.B. The Partial Polarization of a Beam of Photons

A definite state of polarization for photons is represented by either (a) two plane polarized waves with the polarization planes orthogonal to one another, or (b) two right and left circularly polarized waves (Fig. 9.1). In terms of a density matrix [see (*VI.2.A*)], a state of polarization corresponds to a pure state (Fig. 9.1) represented by a plane wave,

$$|\Phi_k\rangle = u_1 e^{i\boldsymbol{k}\cdot\boldsymbol{r}} b_{1k}|1\rangle + u_2 e^{i\boldsymbol{k}\cdot\boldsymbol{r}} b_{2k}|-1\rangle, \qquad (IX.1.25)$$

where the vectors $|1\rangle$ and $|-1\rangle$ are orthogonal. Since there are only two states, the number of data required is $N^2 - 1 = 3$, and the density matrix is a 2×2 matrix. For a totally polarized beam of photons the density matrix can be calculated directly from (*VI.2.20*) and from the direction of the spin of the photon. The direction of the spin in terms of two complex numbers u_1 and u_2 in (*IX.1.25*) can be expressed by the definition of momentum of the wave, as given by (*VIII.4.26*). The spin of the photon is parallel (or antiparallel) to its momentum; therefore (*VIII.4.26*) yields

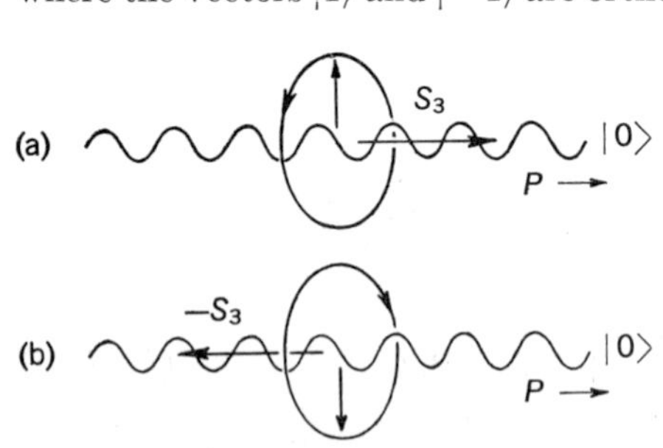

FIG. IX.1. *The pure state. (a) Right circular polarization. (b) Left circular polarization. Under space and time inversions (a) and (b) do not change.*

$$\boldsymbol{q} = \langle u|\boldsymbol{\tau}|u\rangle, \qquad (IX.1.26)$$

where we use $\boldsymbol{\tau}$ in place of Pauli matrices in order not to confuse them with the $\boldsymbol{\sigma}$ occurring in the density matrix (*VI.2.20*) and where

$$|u\rangle = \begin{bmatrix} u_1 \\ u_2 \end{bmatrix}, \qquad \boldsymbol{q}^2 = 1 = \langle u|u\rangle.$$

The normalization of $\boldsymbol{q}$ reduces the number of parameters from four to three. Hence, using (*VI.2.20*), the density matrix in a pure state assumes the form

$$\begin{aligned} \rho &= \tfrac{1}{2}(1 + \boldsymbol{\sigma}\cdot\boldsymbol{q}) \\ &= \tfrac{1}{2}\begin{bmatrix} 1 + q_3 & q_- \\ q_+ & 1 - q_3 \end{bmatrix} = \begin{bmatrix} |u_1|^2 & u_1 u_2^* \\ u_1^* u_2 & |u_2|^2 \end{bmatrix}. \end{aligned} \qquad (IX.1.27)$$

It can further be simplified into an operator form

$$\rho = |u\rangle\langle u|, \qquad (IX.1.28)$$

whose matrix representation with respect to eigenstates $|1\rangle$ and $|-1\rangle$ of σ_3 yields (*IX.1.27*). We see from the form of (*IX.1.28*) and the normalization condition $\langle u|u\rangle = 1$ that ρ is a projection operator:

$$\rho^2 = \rho. \qquad (IX.1.29)$$

Hence the density matrix of a pure state under a unitary transformation can be transformed (see Section I.5.B) into

$$\rho = \begin{bmatrix} 1 & 0 \\ 0 & 0 \end{bmatrix}, \qquad (IX.1.30)$$

where ρ is the density matrix for totally polarized beams.

For an ensemble of states the corresponding density matrix can be written as

$$\rho = \begin{bmatrix} \lambda_1 & 0 \\ 0 & \lambda_2 \end{bmatrix}, \qquad (IX.1.31)$$

where we can assume that $\lambda_1 \geqq \lambda_2 \geqq 0$. Using the condition $\operatorname{tr} \rho = 1$ for a density matrix and putting $\lambda_1 - \lambda_2 = P$, we can write* ρ as an incoherent superposition of two beams,

$$\rho = P \begin{bmatrix} 1 & 0 \\ 0 & 0 \end{bmatrix} + (1 - P) \begin{bmatrix} \frac{1}{2} & 0 \\ 0 & \frac{1}{2} \end{bmatrix}, \qquad (IX.1.32)$$

where the first and second terms represent a totally polarized beam with weight P, superposed incoherently to an unpolarized beam with weight $1 - P$, respectively. For $P = 1$ we again get the total polarization state. Hence P, with $0 \leqq P \leqq 1$, represents the degree of polarization.

In general, for a nonpure state (a mixture of states) the density matrix is of the form

$$\rho = \tfrac{1}{2}(1 + \boldsymbol{\sigma} \cdot \boldsymbol{q}), \qquad (IX.1.33)$$

where $\boldsymbol{q}$ is not a unit vector, but satisfies the inequality

$$|q| < 1. \qquad (IX.1.34)$$

By deriving an algebraic equation for ρ we can cast it as a diagonal matrix, since the same algebraic equation is also satisfied by the eigenvalues of ρ. From $(IX.1.33)$ it follows that the eigenvalues of ρ satisfy the equation $(2\rho' - 1)^2 = q^2$, where ρ' is the eigenvalue of ρ. Hence

$$\lambda_1 = \rho_1' = \tfrac{1}{2}(1 + |q|),$$
$$\lambda_2 = \rho_2' = \tfrac{1}{2}(1 - |q|),$$

so the degree of polarization is given by

$$P = \lambda_1 - \lambda_2 = |q|. \qquad (IX.1.35)$$

IX.2. The Two-Photon System

As a system of two noninteracting particles, the wave equation for two photons can be obtained by noting that the total Hamiltonian is the sum of

* H. A. Tolhoek, *Rev. Mod. Phys.*, **28** (1956), 278.

the Hamiltonians of the single photons. The Schrödinger equation for two photons is, therefore, given by

$$i\hbar \frac{\partial}{\partial t} |\eta_{ab}\rangle = H|\eta_{ab}\rangle, \tag{IX.2.1}$$

where

$$H = H_a + H_b,$$
$$H_a = c\mathbf{K}_a \cdot \boldsymbol{p}_a, \qquad \boldsymbol{p}_a = -i\hbar\nabla_a,$$
$$H_b = c\mathbf{K}_b \cdot \boldsymbol{p}_b, \qquad \boldsymbol{p}_b = -i\hbar\nabla_b,$$

and the ket $|\eta_{ab}\rangle$ represents the two-photon wave function. The wave equation (*IX.2.1*) must be supplemented by the two conditions of transversality of the photons:

$$\nabla_a \cdot \boldsymbol{\eta}_{ab} = 0, \qquad \nabla_b \cdot \boldsymbol{\eta}_{ab} = 0. \tag{IX.2.2}$$

The wave function of the two-photon system must be regarded as a tensor, so each transversality condition in (*IX.2.2*) corresponds to three equations. The physical interpretation of $|\eta_{ab}\rangle$ can be based on the quantity

$$\langle\eta_{ab}|\eta_{ab}\rangle,$$

which is the probability of finding one photon with a momentum $\boldsymbol{p}_a$ and polarization in the direction a and another photon with momentum $\boldsymbol{p}_b$ and polarization in the direction b. Condition (*IX.2.2*) eliminates the possibilities of polarizations of the first photon along the direction $\boldsymbol{p}_a$ and of the second photon along the direction $\boldsymbol{p}_b$, respectively. The wave function of the photons must further be qualified by the symmetry properties induced by the identity of the photons. The photons as particles of spin 1 obey the Bose-Einstein statistics and therefore the wave function $|\eta_{ab}\rangle$ must be symmetrical with respect to a, b and the momenta $\boldsymbol{p}_a$, $\boldsymbol{p}_b$.

The ordinary coordinate concept is not well defined for photons, as was pointed out before, but physically it is meaningful to introduce the total and relative momenta of two photons by

$$\boldsymbol{P} = \boldsymbol{p}_a + \boldsymbol{p}_b, \qquad \boldsymbol{p} = \tfrac{1}{2}(\boldsymbol{p}_a - \boldsymbol{p}_b), \tag{IX.2.3}$$

and write the Hamiltonian in the form

$$H = c[\tfrac{1}{2}\boldsymbol{S}\cdot\boldsymbol{P} + (\boldsymbol{K}_a - \boldsymbol{K}_b)\cdot\boldsymbol{p}], \tag{IX.2.4}$$

where $\boldsymbol{S}$ is the total spin of the two-photon system:

$$\boldsymbol{S} = \boldsymbol{K}_a + \boldsymbol{K}_b = \boldsymbol{K}. \tag{IX.2.5}$$

Hence it follows that the eigenstates of H are of the form

$$|\eta_{ab}\rangle = e^{(i/\hbar)\boldsymbol{R}\cdot\boldsymbol{P}}|\phi_{ab}(\boldsymbol{r}, t)\rangle,$$

which in momentum space can be written as

$$|\eta_{ab}\rangle = F(\boldsymbol{P})|\phi_{ab}(\boldsymbol{p})\rangle.$$

In this way "center of mass" motion is separated out. The transversality conditions (*IX.2.2*) become

$$\sum_{a=1}^{3} \boldsymbol{p}_a \cdot \boldsymbol{\phi}_{ab}(\boldsymbol{p}) = 0,$$

$$\sum_{b=1}^{3} \boldsymbol{p}_b \cdot \boldsymbol{\phi}_{ab}(\boldsymbol{p}) = 0,$$

or

$$\sum_{i=1}^{3} p_i \phi_{ij}(\boldsymbol{p}) = 0, \qquad \text{for } j = a, b,$$

where, because of the symmetry with respect to an interchange of the photons, we have

$$\boldsymbol{\phi}_{ab}(\boldsymbol{p}) = \boldsymbol{\phi}_{ba}(-\boldsymbol{p}). \qquad (IX.2.6)$$

A special coordinate system in momentum space is obtained by taking $\boldsymbol{p} = 0$ (provided $\boldsymbol{p}_a$ and $\boldsymbol{p}_b$ are not parallel). In this case the momenta of the two photons in the coordinate system where "center of mass" is at rest are represented by

$$\boldsymbol{p}_a = \boldsymbol{p}, \qquad \boldsymbol{p}_b = -\boldsymbol{p}. \qquad (IX.2.7)$$

IX.2.A. Spin Eigenstates and Parity of Two-Photon System

From the addition of angular momenta it follows that the total spin s, $[\boldsymbol{S}^2 = s(s+1)]$ in (*IX.2.5*), can assume the values 0, 1, and 2. The corresponding nine eigenfunctions are also eigenstates of the exchange operator

$$P_{ab} = \boldsymbol{K}_a \cdot \boldsymbol{K}_b \qquad (IX.2.8)$$

(see problem 4, Section IV.3.B). For the antisymmetric states ($s = 1$) the corresponding eigenvalue of P_{ab} is -1. The three antisymmetric spin states are

$$|\gamma_a\gamma_b, -1\rangle = \frac{1}{\sqrt{2}}[|\gamma_a, 0\rangle|\gamma_b, -1\rangle - |\gamma_a, -1\rangle|\gamma_b, 0\rangle],$$

$$|\gamma_a\gamma_b, 0\rangle = \frac{1}{\sqrt{2}}[|\gamma_a, 1\rangle|\gamma_b, -1\rangle - |\gamma_a, -1\rangle|\gamma_b, 1\rangle], \qquad (IX.2.9)$$

$$|\gamma_a\gamma_b, 1\rangle = \frac{1}{\sqrt{2}}[|\gamma_a, 1\rangle|\gamma_b, 0\rangle - |\gamma_a, 0\rangle|\gamma_b, 1\rangle].$$

For the five symmetric states ($s = 2$) the corresponding eigenvalue of P_{ab} is 1. The five symmetric spin states are

$$|\gamma_a\gamma_b, -2\rangle = |\gamma_a, -1\rangle|\gamma_b, -1\rangle,$$

$$|\gamma_a\gamma_b, -1\rangle = \frac{1}{\sqrt{2}}[|\gamma_a, 0\rangle|\gamma_b, -1\rangle + |\gamma_a, -1\rangle|\gamma_b, 0\rangle],$$

$$|\gamma_a\gamma_b, 0\rangle = \frac{1}{\sqrt{6}}[|\gamma_a, 1\rangle|\gamma_b, -1\rangle + |\gamma_a, -1\rangle|\gamma_b, 1\rangle + 2|\gamma_a, 0\rangle|\gamma_b, 0\rangle],$$

$$|\gamma_a\gamma_b, 1\rangle = \frac{1}{\sqrt{2}}[|\gamma_a, 1\rangle|\gamma_b, 0\rangle + |\gamma_a, 0\rangle|\gamma_b, 1\rangle],$$

$$|\gamma_a\gamma_b, 2\rangle = |\gamma_a, 1\rangle|\gamma_b, 1\rangle. \quad (IX.2.10)$$

Finally, the one symmetric state ($s = 0$) belongs to the eigenvalue -2 of P_{ab} and is given by

$$|\gamma_a\gamma_b, 0\rangle = \frac{1}{\sqrt{3}}[|\gamma_a, 1\rangle|\gamma_b, -1\rangle + |\gamma_a, -1\rangle|\gamma_b, 1\rangle + |\gamma_a, 0\rangle|\gamma_b, 0\rangle]. \quad (IX.2.11)$$

The above nine spin wave functions are simultaneous eigenstates of the total spin value $\boldsymbol{S}^2 = (\boldsymbol{K}_a + \boldsymbol{K}_b)^2$ and of $S_3 = K_{a3} + K_{b3}$. From the addition rule for angular momenta we find that the j values corresponding to

$$\boldsymbol{J} = \boldsymbol{L} + \hbar\boldsymbol{S} \quad (IX.2.12)$$

are given by

$$j = l \pm 1, l \qquad \text{for } s = 1, \quad (IX.2.13)$$
$$j = l \qquad \text{for } s = 0, \quad (IX.2.14)$$
$$j = l \pm 1, l \pm 2, l \qquad \text{for } s = 2, \quad (IX.2.15)$$

where $\boldsymbol{S} = \boldsymbol{K}_a + \boldsymbol{K}_b$, and $\boldsymbol{L}$ is the angular momentum of the "relative motion." From (*IX.2.12*) it follows that the wave function of two photons can be constructed as linear combinations of the products of $Y_{lm}(\theta, \phi)$, eigenfunctions of $\boldsymbol{L}^2$ and $\boldsymbol{L}_3$, and the spin eigenstates (*IX.2.9*) and (*IX.2.11*). The parity of the wave function will be determined from its orbital part. However, under Bose-Einstein statistics the symmetry

$$|\eta_{ab}(\boldsymbol{p}_a, \boldsymbol{p}_b)\rangle\rangle = |\eta_{ba}(\boldsymbol{p}_b, \boldsymbol{p}_a)\rangle\rangle$$

of the wave function in terms of relative momenta assumes the form

$$|\phi_{ab}(\boldsymbol{p})\rangle\rangle = |\phi_{ba}(-\boldsymbol{p})\rangle\rangle, \quad (IX.2.16)$$

and therefore it involves the symmetry properties of the spin wave functions. The statement (*IX.2.16*) means that

$$Y_{lm}(\theta, \phi)|\gamma_a\gamma_b M_s\rangle = Y_{lm}(\theta - \pi, \phi + \pi)|\gamma_b\gamma_a, M_s\rangle$$
$$= Y_{lm}(\theta, \phi)(-1)^l|\gamma_b\gamma_a, M_s\rangle.$$

Hence the parity of a state and the symmetry properties of spin states are related by

$$|\gamma_a\gamma_b, M_s\rangle = (-1)^l|\gamma_b\gamma_a, M_s\rangle, \quad (IX.2.17)$$

meaning that even states (even l) are symmetric with respect to spin variables and odd states (odd l) are antisymmetric. The only spin states that are possible for odd parity can be antisymmetric in spin variables. Such states are represented by (*IX.2.9*).

For the antisymmetric spin states (*IX.2.9*) to correspond to transverse waves they must also satisfy the transversality conditions. For the states (*IX.2.9*) we have $s = 1$, $l = j \pm 1$, j, so for odd l, j must be even, $j = 2n$, say; therefore $l = 2n \pm 1$. The case $j = l$ is not allowed, since l is odd. The states (*IX.2.9*) can be regarded as the components of an antisymmetric second-rank tensor in three dimensions. We set

$$A_{ij} = a_i b_j - a_j b_i, \qquad (IX.2.18)$$

where $i, j = -1, 0, 1$ labels the quantities a_i and b_j and where each a_i or b_i for a given i represents a ket vector (spin eigenfunction of the photon a or photon b). The tensor A_{ij} can represent an axial vector A_i, defined by

$$A_i = \tfrac{1}{2}\epsilon_{ijk}A_{jk}$$

[see (I.4.15)]. Hence

$$A_{ij} = \epsilon_{ijk}A_k.$$

The transversality condition of the wave function in the antisymmetric spin state (*IX.2.9*) can be expressed by

$$A_{ij}p_j = \epsilon_{ijk}p_jA_k = 0,$$

or, in ordinary vector notation,

$$\boldsymbol{p} \times \boldsymbol{A} = 0 \qquad (IX.2.19)$$

Hence for odd parity states of two photons the axial vector spin wave function must be parallel to the relative momentum $\boldsymbol{p}$—that is, the spin wave function must be longitudinal. For a given j and M, as follows from (*IX.1.14*), there is only one such state,

$$|\phi_j^M\rangle = F(\mathbf{p})|T_j^M\rangle, \qquad (IX.2.20)$$

where $F(\mathbf{p})$ is a function of $\boldsymbol{p}$ and

$$|T_j^M\rangle = -\left[\frac{j+1}{2j+1}\right]^{1/2}|Y_{j,j+1,1}^M\rangle + \left[\frac{j}{2j+1}\right]^{1/2}|Y_{j,j-1,1}^M\rangle,$$

with the two l values $l = j \pm 1 = 2n \pm 1$. Condition (*IX.2.19*), in the form

$$\boldsymbol{p} \times \boldsymbol{A} = \boldsymbol{p} \times (\boldsymbol{a} \times \boldsymbol{b}) = 0,$$

implies perpendicularity of the polarization states of the two photons. Thus, *two photons in odd parity state are polarized perpendicular to each other* (Fig. 9.2). For the spin state $s = 1$ of the photons, the only m_s value is $M_s = 0$ and the spins are antiparallel.

The antisymmetric superposition of (a) and (b) is the odd parity state of two photons. A π-meson as a pseudoscalar particle (that is, of odd parity) with spin zero can, in its rest frame, decay into the odd parity state of two photons.*

---

* H. A. Bethe and F. DeHoffmann, *Mesons and Fields*, Row, Peterson, Evanston, Ill., 1955, Vol. II, p. 12.

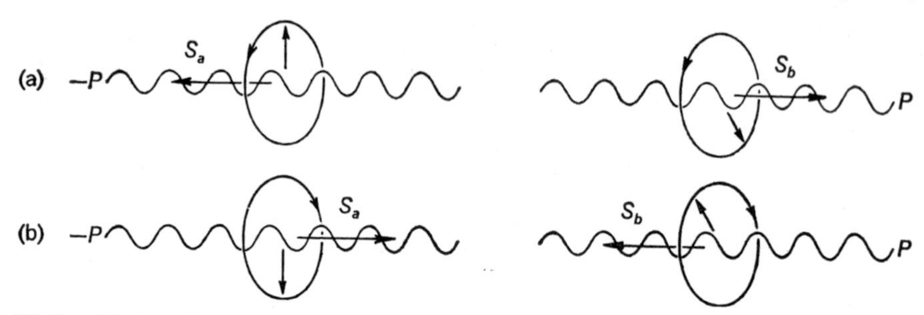

FIG. IX.2. *The odd parity state of two photons.* (*a*) *The two-photon state with total spin zero and right circular polarizations perpendicular to one another.* (*b*) *This state is obtained from* (*a*) *by spatial reflection and corresponds to perpendicular left circular polarization of the two photons.*

For even parity states the only possible total M_s values of spin are 0, 2, and -2. Other even parity states corresponding to $M_s = -1, 1$, with $s = 2$, and to $M_s = 0$, with $s = 0$, do not satisfy the transversality condition. The longitudinal nature of the vector spherical harmonics for $j = 0$ has been discussed in Section IX.1. *In general, there exist no even and odd parity states with* $j = 1$. *As a result, a two-photon system can never be in a state with unit angular momentum. We may also infer that a system with unit angular momentum cannot decay into two photons.*

Figure 9.3 illustrates the possible two-photon states with parallel polarization.

The three symmetric superpositions of the states in (a), (b), and (c) correspond to even parity states of two photons.

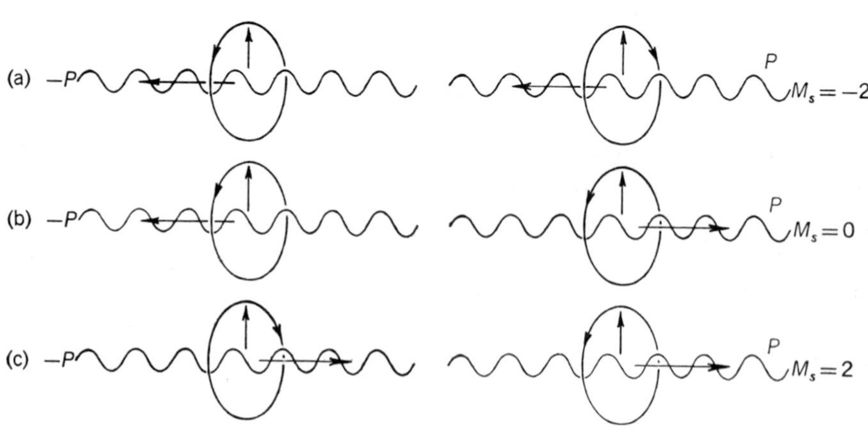

FIG. IX.3. *The even parity states of two photons.* (*a*) *The state where* a *and* b *are right and left circularly polarized.* (*b*) *Both* a *and* b *are right circularly polarized.* (*c*) *Obtained from* (*a*) *by space reflection.*

IX.2.B. Problems

1. The positronium atom is a bound state of electron and positron. It is known that in the singlet S state ($s = 0$, $l = 0$ spin state) the ground-state positronium can decay into two photons. What can one conclude from this fact on the parities of electron and positron?
2. Can a scalar π-meson decay into two photons?

IX.3. The Wave Equation of the Neutrino

The massless particle of spin $\frac{1}{2}$, described by the wave equation

$$i\hbar \frac{\partial}{\partial t} |\nu\rangle = H|\nu\rangle, \tag{IX.3.1}$$

is called a neutrino, where H, defined by $H = c\boldsymbol{\sigma}\cdot\boldsymbol{p}$ and $\boldsymbol{p} = -i\hbar\boldsymbol{\nabla}$, is the Hamiltonian and the two-component spinor $|\nu\rangle$ is the wave function of the neutrino. The derivation of the neutrino wave equation and its formal relation to photon theory has been discussed in Section VIII.4 from a group-theoretical point of view. In this chapter we shall discuss its physical implications.

Fourier series expansion of its wave function can be written as

$$|\nu\rangle = \frac{1}{\sqrt{V}} \sum_{\boldsymbol{k}} e^{i\boldsymbol{k}\cdot\boldsymbol{r}} |u_{\boldsymbol{k}}\rangle, \tag{IX.3.2}$$

where $|u_{\boldsymbol{k}}\rangle$ is a time-dependent two-component spinor and the wave number vector $\boldsymbol{k}$ is subject to the conditions (*II.1.33*) used for the photon. From the expansion (*IX.3.2*) and the wave equation (*IX.3.1*) we obtain

$$i\hbar \frac{\partial}{\partial t} |u_{\boldsymbol{k}}\rangle = H|u_{\boldsymbol{k}}\rangle, \tag{IX.3.3}$$

where $H = c\hbar\boldsymbol{k}\cdot\boldsymbol{\sigma}$.

In order to find the eigenvalues of the operator H we look for stationary-state solutions of (*IX.3.3*). We can posit

$$|u_{\boldsymbol{k}}\rangle = |v_{\boldsymbol{k}}\rangle e^{-(i/\hbar)Et},$$

and obtain from (*IX.3.3*) the result

$$E_{\boldsymbol{k}}|v_{\boldsymbol{k}}\rangle = H|v_{\boldsymbol{k}}\rangle.$$

Hence the eigenvalues for H follow as in the case of photon; for each $\boldsymbol{k}$,

$$E_{\boldsymbol{k}} = \pm\, \hbar c|\boldsymbol{k}|. \tag{IX.3.4}$$

The apparent negative-energy solution can be understood (like the situation for the photon polarization states) in terms of positive-energy solutions with opposite directions of spin. In other words, there are two positive-energy particles, which differ from one another only in having their spins pointing in opposite directions. We can say that both particles are polarized in the longitudinal direction, but that for each particle there is only one spin state. The two particles of this theory are distinguishable, since, as shown in Section VIII.4, the neutrino equation is not invariant under space inversion. Hence, *the neutrino or its antiparticle would not conserve parity. Space reflection for the photon is an invariant operation, so photons of opposite spins are not to be regarded as particle and antiparticle systems. For this reason we say that the photon has no* "handedness." *But a neutrino can be right- or left-handed, although one cannot be transformed into the other* (Figs. 9.4, 9.5). Neutrinos which appear in the β decay

$$n \rightarrow p + e + \bar{\nu}$$

are right-handed; from the conservation of lepton charge they will be called antineutrino.

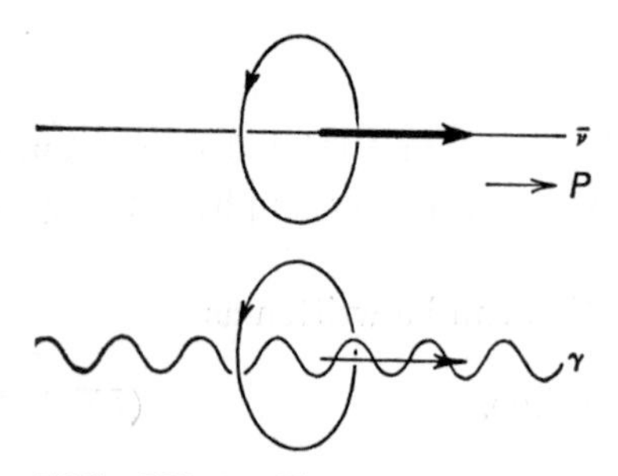

FIG. IX.4. *The antineutrino and right circularly polarized photon, where $\bar{\nu}$ is right-handed.*

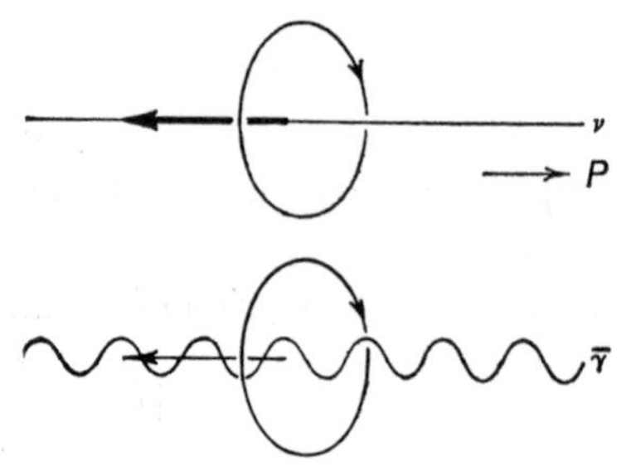

FIG. IX.5. *The neutrino and left circularly polarized photon, where ν is left-handed.*

There exists always a transformation S such that $\bar{\gamma}$ can be transformed into γ,

$$S^{-1}\bar{\gamma}S = \gamma,$$

but the same transformation does not exist for the neutrino and antineutrino; that is,

$$S^{-1}\bar{\nu}S \neq \nu. \qquad (IX.3.5)$$

Experiments on weak interactions prove that the neutrino is described by the two-component theory contained in equation (*IX.3.1*). After the breakdown of parity became evident, equation (*IX.3.1*) was proposed as a two-component theory of the neutrino, independently by Lee and Yang, by Salam, and by Landau.*

---

* T. D. Lee and C. N. Yang, *Phys. Rev.*, **105** (1957), 1671.
A. Salam, *Nuovo Cimento*, **5** (1957), 299.
L. Landau, *Nuclear Phys.*, **3** (1957), 127.

The states represented by Figs. 9.4 and 9.5 are the only possible neutrino states. If we replace a left-handed neutrino by its antiparticle we get a left-handed antineutrino, which does not exist in a two-component theory. Hence we say that *charge conjugation is not an invariant symmetry operation for the neutrino.* However, *charge conjugation together with parity operation is an invariant operation,* since in this case the left-handed antineutrino arising from the charge conjugation of the left-handed neutrino becomes, under space inversion, a right-handed antineutrino.

Theoretically the distinction between neutrino and antineutrino is based, essentially, on the validity of lepton charge conservation. The latter is, certainly, not independent of charge conjugation symmetry. But charge conjugation breaks down for interactions involving the neutrino. This situation is remedied for weak interactions by imposing a restriction on charge conjugation: it holds with reflection of charges provided that we interchange left and right as an additional symmetry operation. Thus the ordinary concept of charge conjugation for mass particles is replaced by the simultaneous operations of charge conjugation and space reflection, and vice versa. The normal law of parity conservation is replaced by the simultaneous operation of parity plus charge conjugation. If we represent charge conjugation operation by $\mathcal{C}$, then, in order to maintain our invariance principles on a universal basis, we may, in regard to the neutrino, drop our separate requirement of invariance under $\mathcal{C}$ and $\mathcal{P}$ operations and replace it by the invariance under the joint operation $\mathcal{CP}$. The symmetry operations $\mathcal{P}$, $\mathcal{C}$, $\mathcal{T}$ can, together with the unit operation I, form a finite group with the symmetry operations $\mathcal{PC}$, $\mathcal{PT}$, $\mathcal{PCT}$. Since $\mathcal{P}$ and $\mathcal{C}$ are not conserved for weak interactions we eliminate their separate existence as symmetry elements and introduce the discrete symmetry group,* comprising only the elements I, $\mathcal{T}$, $\mathcal{CP}$, $\mathcal{PCT}$.

Instead of saying that the laws of nature are invariant with respect to the group of discrete transformations affected by I, $\mathcal{C}$, $\mathcal{T}$, $\mathcal{P}$, $\mathcal{PC}$, $\mathcal{PT}$, $\mathcal{PCT}$ (where $\mathcal{PCT}$ is not equivalent to unit operation), we postulate the invariance with respect to a restricted group of discrete transformations affected by I, $\mathcal{CP}$, $\mathcal{T}$, $\mathcal{CPT}$. In this way the violation of parity and the conservation of charge conjugation by processes involving the neutrino do not appear as isolated phenomena that admit only a restricted transformation group; therefore these

---

* J. Schwinger, *Phys. Rev.*, **74** (1948), 1439.
H. A. Kramers, *Proc. Acad. Sci. Amsterdam*, **40** (1937), 814.
W. Pauli, *Niels Bohr and the Development of Physics*, Pergamon Press, London, 1955.
G. Lüders, *Z. Physik*, **133** (1952), 325.
G. Lüders, *Kgl. Danske Videnskab, Selskab Mat.-Fys. Medd.*, **28** (1954), 5.
E. P. Wigner, *Rev. Mod. Phys.*, **29** (1957), 255.

processes may be compared to the processes involving electromagnetic and strong nuclear interactions.*

It must be pointed out that the adherence to I, $\mathcal{CP}$, $\mathfrak{T}$, $\mathcal{PC}\mathfrak{T}$ operations as the universal symmetry principles does not necessarily solve the problem of distinguishing between the neutrino and its antiparticle, the antineutrino. Later in this chapter it will be shown that the methods of conventional Dirac theory for particles of spin $\frac{1}{2}$ allow for the possibility of describing ν and $\bar{\nu}$ as self-conjugate particles.

As a preliminary orientation we shall recapitulate some of the results obtained in Chapter VIII in connection with the discussion of the complex orthogonal group. The simple observation was made that for plane electromagnetic wave the invariant

$$\subset \chi | \chi \supset \; = \chi_1^2 + \chi_2^2 + \chi_3^2 = Q^2$$

vanishes everywhere, and this was interpreted as an invariant statement for a massless and chargeless field. All three stereographic projections of the complex sphere (*VIII.4.1*) reduce, in the case where $Q^2 = 0$, to projections on a single plane, where $|\mathcal{E}| = |\mathcal{H}|$ and $\mathcal{E} \cdot \mathcal{H} = 0$, which is the plane wave itself. If we regard the three possible stereographic projections (*VIII.4.21*) as representing three charge states (positive, negative, and zero), then we see that for $Q^2 = 0$ they are equivalent and lead to the transformations of the χ-field in the form (*VIII.4.25*). Since the transformation (*VIII.4.25*) yields, as shown, the neutrino equation (*VIII.4.29*), we infer that all three charge states satisfy the same neutrino equation. Hence a chargeless neutrino is described by a complex wave function $|\nu\rangle$ and not by a real wave function. A real wave function is self-conjugate and therefore corresponding particles are identical. We must, of course, make it clear that a complex wave function need not describe two distinct particles. For example, the photon wave function is complex, but the corresponding particles differ only in their direction of polarization.

The neutrino wave equation (*IX.3.1*) is not invariant with respect to antilinear transformations:

$$|\bar{\nu}'\rangle = \overline{C}|\bar{\nu}\rangle, \qquad \overline{C}\sigma_i\overline{C} = \sigma_i^L. \qquad (IX.3.6)$$

Hence the wave function $|\bar{\nu}\rangle$ for the antineutrino is not just a complex conjugate of $|\nu\rangle$, while for the photon $|\eta\rangle$ and $\overline{C}|\eta\rangle$ describe its states of opposite polarization. To obtain the wave equation for the antineutrino we must consider the projection of $|\chi^*\rangle$ onto the neutral plane $Q^2 = 0$. This may be regarded as a process of stereographic projection of the left circularly polar-

* However, future investigations, especially in the region of very high energy, may lead to further modifications of our presently well-established symmetry principles.

ized photon; from the point of view of projection we have the correspondence that the right-handed antineutrino $\bar{\nu}$ corresponds to the right circularly polarized photon, and the left-handed neutrino corresponds to the left circularly polarized photon; the photon itself has no handedness since both directions of polarizations can be transformed into one another.

It is important to point out that the acceptance of equation (*IX.3.1*) as a wave equation for the neutrino was a natural result of the unexpected hypotheses, advanced by T. D. Lee and C. N. Yang,* that nature, by way of weak interactions, can discriminate between left and right. One of its most interesting consequences has been that the electrons in weak decays are polarized. The first experimental test of the Lee-Yang hypothesis was carried out by Wu, Ambler, Hayward, Hoppes, and Hudson.†

The basic features of the experiment consist of the observation of the angular distribution of the electrons emitted by radioactive Co^{60} cooled to a very low temperature (0.01°K). The low temperature is required in order to eliminate possible thermal motions of nuclei. Under these circumstances the experimenters observed an isotropic emission of electrons. When the cobalt source was placed within a current carrying a solenoidal coil the electron emission had a higher intensity parallel to the axis of the coil than in the opposite direction, since the magnetic field aligned the spin vectors of the Co^{60} nuclei. Greater numbers of emitted electrons occured in the direction opposite to the spin direction of the Co^{60}. Under a space reflection the spins of nuclei and electrons remain unchanged but the current changes sign—there is reversing of the current. As a result, the intensity pattern of electron emission did not change; that is, the reversed and unreversed experiments maintained the same intensity and direction of electron emission.

In this experiment the main role of the neutrino, as one of the four fermions ($n \rightarrow p + e^- + \bar{\nu}$) partaking in the decay of the Co^{60} nucleus, was to provide the necessary balance of angular momenta for the polarization of the electrons. Since there is an electron-neutrino correlation, the neutrino emission also is not isotropic; this demonstrates the handedness property of the neutrino. In the same experiment it was observed that the γ radiation that follows the β decay of Co^{60} had complete left and right symmetry. Therefore no violation of parity occurs for electromagnetic interactions.

Parity nonconservation in weak interactions, other than nuclear β decay, has also been observed‡ in the decay of a muon (μ-meson).

The longitudinality of the neutrino will effect the decay of the spinless

* T. D. Lee and C. N. Yang, *Phys. Rev.*, **105** (1957), 1671.

† C. S. Wu, E. Ambler, R. W. Hayward, D. D. Hoppes, and R. P. Hudson, *Phys. Rev.*, **105** (1957), 1413.

‡ R. L. Garwin, L. M. Lederman, and M. Weinrich, *Phys. Rev.*, **105** (1957), 1415.

π^+-meson in the form of a polarization of its decay products μ^+ and ν; that is, $\pi^+ \rightarrow \mu^+ + \nu$. Conservation of spin for a π^+ decaying in its own rest frame requires that the decay products μ^+ and ν shall travel in opposite directions; thus the neutrino's spin angular momentum $\frac{1}{2}\hbar$ about its direction of motion will be balanced by a μ^+, also carrying a spin angular momentum $\frac{1}{2}\hbar$ about its direction of motion. This means that in π^+ decay the μ^+ is 100 percent polarized. The same applies for a μ^- in the decay of a π^-. The precise experimental measurements of μ^- polarization are made especially difficult because the muons can be depolarized before they decay. The *helicity* (*handedness or correlation of the direction of motion and direction of spin*) of a decay product in ordinary nuclear β decay and in weak decays of pions are the same. For example, μ^+ is found to be right-handed and μ^- left-handed.

IX.3.A. The Positive and Negative Energy States of the Neutrino

The neutrino, like the photon, is a purely relativistic particle. Because of the absence of mass, we cannot construct a nonrelativistic theory of the neutrino. The classical relativistic Hamiltonian of a neutrino can be formulated as

$$H = c\sqrt{(p_1^2 + p_2^2 + p_3^2)}. \qquad (IX.3.7)$$

By using the rules of quantum mechanics we can write down a corresponding wave equation for the neutrino, as

$$[cp_4 - c\sqrt{(p_1^2 + p_2^2 + p_3^2)}]|\nu\rangle = 0, \qquad (IX.3.8)$$

where the $\boldsymbol{p}$ are to be interpreted as operators, in accordance with the Schrödinger representation. Equation (*IX.3.8*) is unsymmetrical between p_4 and the momenta p_i, where $i = 1, 2, 3$. From the analogy with the photon we should expect that the equation for the neutrino ought to be a linear equation in the p, since it is linear in p_4. (The latter is also a natural relativistic requirement.) The only irreducible linearization (from the group-theoretical point of view) of (*IX.3.7*) can be obtained in terms of Pauli spin matrices. The result is the wave equation (*IX.3.1*), obtained from an entirely different point of view. However, there is some virtue in the present approach. The process of rationalization of (*IX.3.7*) could be avoided if we used the square of the relativistic relation,

$$p_4^2 = p_1^2 + p_2^2 + p_3^2,$$

and we could write down a second-order wave equation in place of a first-order one. The relativistic requirements are still satisfied, but the second-order wave equation is not equivalent to (*IX.3.8*): every solution of (*IX.3.8*) is also a solution of the second-order equation but the converse is not true; every solution of the second-order wave equation is not a solution of the first-order wave equation. Only those solutions of the second-order equation where $p_4 > 0$ are also solutions of (*IX.3.8*). Hence we see that the first-order wave equation for the neutrino will have twice as many solutions—one group of solutions with positive values and another group with negative values of the energy. In classical theory an initial positive energy will always remain a positive energy. *In quantum mechanics an initial positive energy state need not remain positive at all times. There is always a probability of transition to negative energy states.* However, for free particles, positive and negative energy states can be separated completely and no transitions between them can occur. In the presence of an interaction the positive and negative energy states cannot be separated and a transition between the states can occur.

The negative-energy solutions of the wave equations can be interpreted as referring to a different particle than the one described by the positive-energy solutions. According to Dirac's interpretation, "*nearly all the negative-energy states are occupied with one neutrino in each state in accordance with Pauli's exclusion principle.*" An unoccupied negative-energy state will appear as a particle with positive energy, since its disappearance requires the addition of a neutrino with negative energy. These unoccupied negative-energy states, which actually have positive energy, describe antineutrinos. *A state where all positive-energy states are unoccupied and all negative-energy states are occupied shall be called "vacuum state."* For a particle with electric charge, for example, vacuum is a state of zero "electric charge density." The electric field of a vacuum must satisfy the Maxwell equation $\nabla \cdot \mathcal{E} = 0$. For a neutrino we replace the concept of electric charge by the concept of lepton charge and define vacuum as the state of zero "lepton charge density," where the infinite distribution of negative-energy neutrinos does not contribute to a "field" produced by lepton charge density. However, we must note that the ordinary vacuum defined with respect to electric charge alone is also a state of zero lepton charge density. In general, any departure from the vacuum state will contribute to lepton charge density, and we shall find for each occupied state of positive energy a contribution $+1$ and for each unoccupied negative-energy state a contribution of -1 to lepton charge.

IX.3.B. The Velocity of the Neutrino

The velocity of a massless particle of spin $\frac{1}{2}\hbar$, described by the wave equation (*IX.3.1*), is obtained from Heisenberg's equations of motion, according to

$$\boldsymbol{V} = \frac{d\boldsymbol{r}}{dt} = \frac{1}{i\hbar}[\boldsymbol{r}, H] = c\boldsymbol{\sigma}. \qquad (IX.3.9)$$

Hence we see that the spin operator $\boldsymbol{\sigma}$ and velocity operator $\boldsymbol{V}$ are "parallel," so *for a fermion moving with the velocity of light there is a complete longitudinal polarization.* Under the time-reversal operation affected by $\mathfrak{J} = i\sigma_2\overline{C}$ the velocity changes its sign, but under parity operation, for reasons discussed previously, the transformation does not lead to the expected result—instead of reflection of the velocity operator we obtain $c\boldsymbol{\sigma}^L$, where the $c\boldsymbol{\sigma}^L$ are left-handed Pauli spin operators [see (*I.9.19*)]. All other results obtained for the velocity of photon can be extended to the present case.

IX.3.C. Angular Momentum Eigenstates of the Neutrino

The neutrino is a two-component spinor particle and therefore we need a complete set of spinors to expand its wave function into its "multipoles." The special class of eigenfunctions obtained by taking $J_1 = l$ and $J_2 = \frac{1}{2}$ in the expansion formula (*IV.3.4*) are called "spinor spherical harmonics." They are simultaneous eigenfunctions of $\boldsymbol{J}^2$ and J_3, where $\boldsymbol{J} = \boldsymbol{L} + \frac{1}{2}\hbar\boldsymbol{\sigma}$:

$$|\gamma l\tfrac{1}{2}jM\rangle = \sum_{m=-l}^{l} \sum_{s} C(l\tfrac{1}{2}j,\, m,\, \tfrac{1}{2}sM)|\gamma l\tfrac{1}{2}ms\rangle, \qquad (IX.3.10)$$

where $s = -1, 1$ and $M = m + \frac{1}{2}s$,

$$|\gamma l\tfrac{1}{2}ms\rangle = Y_{lm}(\theta, \phi)|s\rangle, \qquad |1\rangle = \begin{bmatrix}1\\0\end{bmatrix}, \qquad |-1\rangle = \begin{bmatrix}0\\1\end{bmatrix}.$$

The Clebsch-Gordon coefficients in the expansion (*IX.3.10*) are given for $j_1 = l$ in Table IV.2. We use the notation

$$|\gamma l\tfrac{1}{2}jM\rangle = |S_{lj}^M\rangle$$

and rewrite (*IX.3.10*) in the form

$$|S_{lj}^M\rangle = \sum_{m=-l}^{l} C(l\tfrac{1}{2}j,\, m,\, -\tfrac{1}{2},\, M)Y_l^m|-1\rangle + \sum_{m=-l}^{l} C(l\tfrac{1}{2}j,\, m,\, \tfrac{1}{2},\, M)Y_l^m|1\rangle, \qquad (IX.3.11)$$

where the only nonvanishing C coefficients on the right side refer to m values for which $M = m - \frac{1}{2}$ in the first sum and $M = m + \frac{1}{2}$ in the second sum. For $j_1 = l$ Table IV.2 can be reconstructed in the following form.

TABLE IX.1. The Clebsch-Gordon coefficients for $j_1 = l$ $C(l\frac{1}{2}j,\, mm_sM)$.

	$m_s = \frac{1}{2}$	$m_s = -\frac{1}{2}$
$j = l + \frac{1}{2}$	$\sqrt{\left[\frac{j+M}{2j}\right]}$	$\sqrt{\left[\frac{j-M}{2j}\right]}$
$j = l - \frac{1}{2}$	$-\sqrt{\left[\frac{j-M+1}{2(j+1)}\right]}$	$\sqrt{\left[\frac{j+M+1}{2(j+1)}\right]}$

For $l = 1$, $j = \frac{3}{2}$, $M = -\frac{3}{2}, -\frac{1}{2}, \frac{1}{2}, \frac{3}{2}$ values from (*IX.3.11*) and from Table IX.1, we obtain

$$|S_{1,3/2}^{-3/2}\rangle = Y_1^{-1}(\theta, \phi)|-1\rangle = \sqrt{\left(\frac{3}{8\pi}\right)} \sin\theta\, e^{-i\phi}|-1\rangle,$$

$$|S_{1,3/2}^{-1/2}\rangle = \frac{1}{\sqrt{3}} Y_1^{-1}(\theta, \phi)|1\rangle + \sqrt{\left(\tfrac{2}{3}\right)}\, Y_1^0(\theta, \phi)|-1\rangle$$

$$= \frac{1}{\sqrt{(8\pi)}} \sin\theta\, e^{-i\phi}|1\rangle + \frac{1}{\sqrt{(2\pi)}} \cos\theta|-1\rangle,$$

$$|S_{1,3/2}^{-1/2}\rangle = \sqrt{\left(\tfrac{2}{3}\right)}\, Y_1^0(\theta, \phi)|1\rangle + \frac{1}{\sqrt{3}} Y_1^1(\theta, \phi)|-1\rangle \qquad (IX.3.12)$$

$$= \frac{1}{\sqrt{(2\pi)}} \cos\theta|1\rangle - \frac{1}{\sqrt{(8\pi)}} \sin\theta\, e^{i\phi}|-1\rangle,$$

$$|S_{1,3/2}^{3/2}\rangle = Y_1^1(\theta, \phi)|1\rangle = -\sqrt{\frac{3}{(8\pi)}} \sin\theta\, e^{i\phi}|1\rangle.$$

For $l = 1$, $j = \frac{1}{2}$, $M = -\frac{1}{2}, \frac{1}{2}$ values, we obtain the total angular momentum wave functions:

$$|S_{1,1/2}^{-1/2}\rangle = \frac{1}{\sqrt{3}} Y_1^0(\theta, \phi)|-1\rangle - \sqrt{\left(\tfrac{2}{3}\right)}\, Y_1^{-1}(\theta, \phi)|1\rangle$$

$$= \frac{1}{\sqrt{(4\pi)}} \cos\theta|-1\rangle - \frac{1}{\sqrt{(4\pi)}} \sin\theta\, e^{-i\phi}|1\rangle, \qquad (IX.3.13)$$

$$|S_{1,1/2}^{1/2}\rangle = \sqrt{\left(\tfrac{2}{3}\right)}\, Y_1^1(\theta, \phi)|-1\rangle - \frac{1}{\sqrt{3}} Y_1^0(\theta, \phi)|1\rangle$$

$$= -\frac{1}{\sqrt{(4\pi)}} \sin\theta\, e^{i\phi}|-1\rangle - \frac{1}{\sqrt{(4\pi)}} \cos\theta|1\rangle.$$

We now give some further properties of spinor spherical harmonics. Consider the operator

$$\sigma_r = \frac{1}{r} \boldsymbol{r} \cdot \boldsymbol{\sigma}, \qquad (IX.3.14)$$

where $\sigma_r^2 = 1$. In polar coordinates it is given by

$$\sigma_r = \begin{bmatrix} \cos\theta & e^{-i\phi}\sin\theta \\ e^{i\phi}\sin\theta & -\cos\theta \end{bmatrix} = \sqrt{\left(\frac{8\pi}{3}\right)} \begin{bmatrix} \frac{1}{\sqrt{2}} Y_1^0 & Y_1^{-1} \\ -Y_1^1 & -\frac{1}{\sqrt{2}} Y_1^0 \end{bmatrix}.$$

The eigenfunctions of σ_r corresponding to its eigenvalues $+1$ and -1 are

$$|\sigma', 1\rangle = \begin{bmatrix} \cos\dfrac{\theta}{2} \\ e^{i\phi}\sin\dfrac{\theta}{2} \end{bmatrix}, \qquad |\sigma', -1\rangle = \begin{bmatrix} -e^{-i\phi}\sin\dfrac{\theta}{2} \\ \cos\dfrac{\theta}{2} \end{bmatrix}. \tag{IX.3.15}$$

On operating by σ_r on the spinor spherical harmonics $|S^M_{l,j}\rangle$, we obtain

$$\sigma_r|S^M_{l,j}\rangle = -\sqrt{(4\pi)}\sum_{m=-l}^{l} C(l\tfrac{1}{2}j,\, m,\, -\tfrac{1}{2},\, M)Y^m_l|S^{-1/2}_{1,1/2}\rangle$$

$$-\sqrt{(4\pi)}\sum_{m=-l}^{l} C(l\tfrac{1}{2}j,\, m,\, \tfrac{1}{2},\, M)Y^m_l|S^{1/2}_{1,1/2}\rangle.$$

Hence we obtain

$$\begin{aligned} \sigma_r|S^M_{j-(1/2),j}\rangle &= -|S^M_{j+1/2,j}\rangle, \\ \sigma_r|S^M_{j+1/2,j}\rangle &= -|S^M_{j-1/2,j}\rangle. \end{aligned} \tag{IX.3.16}$$

IX.3.D. The Neutrino Hamiltonian in Polar Coordinates

We begin with the operator relation

$$(\boldsymbol{\sigma}\cdot\boldsymbol{r})(\boldsymbol{\sigma}\cdot\boldsymbol{p}) = \sigma_i\sigma_j x_i p_j = (\delta_{ij} + i\epsilon_{ijs}\sigma_s)x_i p_j = \boldsymbol{r}\cdot\boldsymbol{p} + i\boldsymbol{\sigma}\cdot\boldsymbol{L}. \tag{IX.3.17}$$

Hence

$$\boldsymbol{\sigma}\cdot\boldsymbol{p} = \sigma_r p_r + \frac{i}{r}\sigma_r\boldsymbol{\sigma}\cdot\boldsymbol{L}, \tag{IX.3.18}$$

where

$$p_r = \frac{1}{r}\boldsymbol{r}\cdot\boldsymbol{p} = -i\hbar\frac{\partial}{\partial r}.$$

The Hamiltonian can now be written as

$$H = c\sigma_r p_r + \frac{ic}{r}\sigma_r\boldsymbol{\sigma}\cdot\boldsymbol{L}. \tag{IX.3.19}$$

In this form of H, angular momentum is not separated out. For this purpose consider the operators

$$\boldsymbol{J}^2 = (\boldsymbol{L} + \tfrac{1}{2}\hbar\boldsymbol{\sigma})^2 = \boldsymbol{L}^2 + \hbar\boldsymbol{\sigma}\cdot\boldsymbol{L} + \tfrac{3}{4}\hbar^2$$

and

$$(\boldsymbol{\sigma}\cdot\boldsymbol{L})^2 = \sigma_i\sigma_j L_i L_j = \boldsymbol{L}^2 - \hbar\boldsymbol{\sigma}\cdot\boldsymbol{L}.$$

Then we obtain

$$\zeta^2 = \boldsymbol{J}^2 + \tfrac{1}{4}\hbar^2, \tag{IX.3.20}$$

where

$$\zeta^2 = (\hbar + \boldsymbol{\sigma}\cdot\boldsymbol{L})^2 = \boldsymbol{L}^2 + \hbar\boldsymbol{\sigma}\cdot\boldsymbol{L} + \hbar^2. \tag{IX.3.21}$$

It is easy to show that the operator $\hbar + \boldsymbol{\sigma}\cdot\boldsymbol{L}$ anticommutes with H:

$$[H, \hbar + \boldsymbol{\sigma}\cdot\boldsymbol{L}]_+ = 0. \qquad (IX.3.22)$$

To obtain an operator that commutes with H and depends linearly on $\hbar + \boldsymbol{\sigma}\cdot\boldsymbol{L}$, we introduce a linear operator ϵ with the following properties:

$$\epsilon^2 = 1, \qquad (IX.3.23)$$

$$[\epsilon, H]_+ = 0, \qquad (IX.3.24)$$

$$[\epsilon, \hbar + \boldsymbol{\sigma}\cdot\boldsymbol{L}] = 0, \qquad (IX.3.25)$$

$$[\epsilon, \sigma_r]_+ = 0. \qquad (IX.3.26)$$

We may now define a linear Hermitian operator that commutes with the Hamiltonian. We can take

$$\zeta = \epsilon(\hbar + \boldsymbol{\sigma}\cdot\boldsymbol{L}), \qquad (IX.3.27)$$

where ζ now commutes with the Hamiltonian—just as its square ($IX.3.20$) does—and it is a constant of the motion. The operator ζ commutes also with σ_r, for

$$[\sigma_r, \zeta] = [\sigma_r, \epsilon(\hbar + \boldsymbol{\sigma}\cdot\boldsymbol{L})] = [\sigma_r, \epsilon](\hbar + \boldsymbol{\sigma}\cdot\boldsymbol{L}) + \epsilon[\sigma_r, \hbar + \boldsymbol{\sigma}\cdot\boldsymbol{L}]$$
$$= 2\sigma_r\zeta + \epsilon[\sigma_r, \boldsymbol{\sigma}\cdot\boldsymbol{L}].$$

The second term can be calculated:

$$[\sigma_r, \boldsymbol{\sigma}\cdot\boldsymbol{L}] = \left[\frac{1}{r}x_i\sigma_i, \sigma_j L_j\right] = \epsilon_{jks}\left[\frac{1}{r}x_i\sigma_i, \sigma_j x_k p_s\right]$$
$$= \frac{2i}{r}\boldsymbol{\sigma}\cdot(\boldsymbol{r}\times\boldsymbol{L}) + \frac{i\hbar}{r}\epsilon_{jki}\sigma_j\sigma_i x_k$$
$$= \frac{2i}{r}[(\boldsymbol{\sigma}\cdot\boldsymbol{r})(\boldsymbol{r}\cdot\boldsymbol{p}) - r^2(\boldsymbol{\sigma}\cdot\boldsymbol{p})] + 2\hbar\sigma_r.$$

Using ($IX.3.17$) we obtain

$$[\sigma_r, \boldsymbol{\sigma}\cdot\boldsymbol{L}] = 2\sigma_r(\hbar + \boldsymbol{\sigma}\cdot\boldsymbol{L}).$$

Hence it follows that

$$[\sigma_r, \zeta] = 0. \qquad (IX.3.28)$$

Furthermore, σ_r commutes also with $p_r - i\hbar/r$:

$$\left[\sigma_r, p_r - \frac{i\hbar}{r}\right] = 0. \qquad (IX.3.29)$$

The Hamiltonian ($IX.3.19$) can now be written as

$$H = c\left(p_r - \frac{i\hbar}{r}\right)\sigma_r + \frac{ic}{r}\sigma_r\epsilon\zeta. \qquad (IX.3.30)$$

The eigenvalues of ζ can be obtained from the eigenvalue equation

$$\zeta^2|S_{l,j}^M\rangle = (\boldsymbol{J}^2 + \tfrac{1}{4}\hbar^2)|S_{l,j}^M\rangle = [\hbar^2 j(j+1) + \tfrac{1}{4}\hbar^2]|S_{l,j}^M\rangle.$$

Hence

$$\zeta^2|S^M_{l,j}\rangle = \hbar^2(j + \tfrac{1}{2})^2|S^M_{l,j}\rangle \qquad (IX.3.31)$$

and

$$\zeta|S^M_{l,j}\rangle = \pm\hbar(j + \tfrac{1}{2})|S^M_{l,j}\rangle. \qquad (IX.3.32)$$

Thus the eigenvalues of ζ are all positive and negative integers, excluding zero. The anticommutation property (*IX.3.24*) can be written as

$$\epsilon H \epsilon^{-1} = -H \qquad (IX.3.33)$$

and it shows that ϵ is just the parity operator itself. The general state of the neutrino for a given j and M can be expressed as a linear combination of two possible spinor spherical harmonics:

$$|\nu_j^M\rangle = f^j_M(r)|S^M_{j-(1/2),j}\rangle + h^j_M(r)|S^M_{j+(1/2),j}\rangle. \qquad (IX.3.34)$$

The wave function of the neutrino is not an eigenstate of the parity (*since* H *depends on the parity*). The two states of polarization, one parallel and the other antiparallel to the direction of motion, correspond to two distinct particles. Furthermore, *the dependence of the Hamiltonian on the parity implies that the angular distribution of the neutrino will, in addition to angular momentum, depend on its parity; hence there will be some directional preference for neutrino emission.*

CHAPTER X

THE WAVE EQUATION OF PARTICLES OF SPIN $\frac{1}{2}\hbar$ WITH MASS

X.1. Dirac's Equation

In accordance with the four-dimensional irreducible spin representation of the Lorentz group, the wave function of a particle with mass and spin $\frac{1}{2}$ must transform as a four-component spinor. A particle with mass and spin can assume two spin states in opposite directions. To obtain the wave equation for a free particle of spin $\frac{1}{2}$ with mass we must use the relativistic definition of energy: $E = c\sqrt{(\boldsymbol{p}^2 + m^2c^2)}$. The arguments used in the derivation of the neutrino equation can be extended to particles with mass. In this case, however, because of the mass term in the square root, we cannot rationalize it by using Pauli spin matrices. For particles with mass, as follows from the discussion in (*VIII.5*), we must use four-dimensional Dirac matrices. Thus the relativistic Hamiltonian operator of a free particle is given by

$$H = c\boldsymbol{\alpha}\cdot\boldsymbol{p} + \beta mc^2, \tag{X.1.1}$$

where $\boldsymbol{\alpha}$ and β matrices are defined by (*VIII.5.10*). Hence, the Dirac wave equation for particles of spin $\frac{1}{2}$ is given by

$$i\hbar\frac{\partial}{\partial t}|\psi\rangle = H|\psi\rangle, \tag{X.1.2}$$

where the four-dimensional spinor $|\psi\rangle$ is as defined by (*VIII.5.37*).

Introducing γ matrices (*VIII.5.11*), we can write the Dirac equation in a manifestly covariant form as

$$(\gamma^\mu p_\mu - imc)|\psi\rangle = 0, \tag{X.1.3}$$

where the γ_μ satisfy the anticommutation relations (*VIII.5.13*) and

$$cp_4 = i\hbar \frac{\partial}{\partial t}, \qquad p_i = i\hbar \frac{\partial}{\partial x^i} = -i\hbar \frac{\partial}{\partial x_i}.$$

The Lorentz-covariance of the wave equation (*X.1.3*) has already been discussed in Section VIII.5.

The operator $\gamma^\mu p_\mu$ is not Hermitian and therefore the equation for the bra $\langle\psi|$ will not be the same as (*X.1.3*). We shall now show that the quantity $\langle\psi|\beta|\psi\rangle = \langle\bar{\psi}|\psi\rangle$, as the fundamental scalar of spinor space, implies that the bra $\langle\bar{\psi}|$ is the right spinor, satisfying the same equation as (*X.1.3*). If we take the Hermitian conjugate of (*X.1.3*) and multiply by β from the right, we obtain the wave equation

$$\langle\bar{\psi}|(\gamma^\mu p_\mu - imc) = 0, \tag{X.1.4}$$

where the differential operators p_μ are assumed to act on the bra $\langle\bar{\psi}|$ to their left.

We now use the wave equations (*X.1.3*) and (*X.1.4*) and derive a conservation law of probability and current. If we multiply (*X.1.3*) from the left with $\langle\bar{\psi}|$ and (*X.1.4*) from the right with $|\psi\rangle$, add the results, and recall that p_μ in (*X.1.3*) acts to the right and p_μ in (*X.1.4*) acts to the left, we obtain

$$\frac{\partial}{\partial x^\mu} \langle\bar{\psi}|\gamma^\mu|\psi\rangle = 0, \tag{X.1.5}$$

where the components of the current vector

$$J_\mu = -ie\langle\bar{\psi}|\gamma_\mu|\psi\rangle \tag{X.1.6}$$

are to be interpreted in accordance with probability interpretation of quantum mechanics. From

$$J_4 = -ie\langle\bar{\psi}|\gamma_4|\psi\rangle = e(|\psi_1|^2 + |\psi_2|^2 + |\psi_3|^2 + |\psi_4|^2), \tag{X.1.7}$$

we see that J_4 is a positive definite quantity and can therefore be interpreted as a probability density. Thus the quantity

$$\langle\psi|\psi\rangle\, d^3x \tag{X.1.8}$$

is the probability that at time t a particle or antiparticle can be found within the volume element d^3x with the spin of the particle or antiparticle pointing "up" or "down." The integral of (*X.1.8*) over the whole of space should be unity;

$$\int \langle\psi|\psi\rangle\, d^3x = 1. \tag{X.1.9}$$

Note that the probability density $\langle\psi|\psi\rangle$ is not the same as the scalar quantity $\langle\bar{\psi}|\psi\rangle$. The latter need not be positive definite. The result (*X.1.9*) can also be given in a manifestly Lorentz-covariant form by introducing a hypersurface element by

$$d\sigma_\mu \equiv [dx_2dx_3dx_4,\ dx_3dx_1dx_4,\ dx_1dx_2dx_4,\ dx_1dx_2dx_3]$$

and writing (*X.1.9*) in the form

$$-i \int_{\Sigma} \langle \bar{\psi} | \gamma_\mu | \psi \rangle \, d\sigma^\mu = 1, \qquad (X.1.10)$$

where the integration extends over the hypersurface x_4 = constant. The integral is the same regardless of the hypersurface x_4 = constant, over which we integrate.

X.1.A. Particle and Antiparticle States

The general solutions of the free particle Dirac wave equation are of considerable importance. We write equation (*X.1.3*) in the form

$$(-i\boldsymbol{\gamma}\cdot\boldsymbol{p} + mc)|\psi\rangle = \beta p_4 |\psi\rangle \qquad (X.1.11)$$

We introduce the anti-Hermitian operator

$$\gamma_p = -\frac{i}{p}\,\boldsymbol{\gamma}\cdot\boldsymbol{p}, \qquad (X.1.12)$$

where $\gamma_p^\dagger = -\gamma_p$ and

$$\gamma_p^2 = -1. \qquad (X.1.13)$$

We further introduce the transformation

$$p = mc \tan \lambda \qquad (X.1.14)$$

and write the wave equation (*X.1.11*) in the form

$$mc(1 + \gamma_p \tan \lambda)|\psi\rangle = \beta p_4 |\psi\rangle$$

or

$$\frac{mc}{\cos \lambda}(\cos \lambda + \gamma_p \sin \lambda)|\psi\rangle = \beta p_4 |\psi\rangle.$$

Because of (*X.1.13*), we can treat the operator γ_p as $i = \sqrt{-1}$ and write the relations

$$\cos \lambda + \gamma_p \sin \lambda = e^{\lambda\gamma_p}$$

and

$$\cos \lambda = \tfrac{1}{2}(e^{\lambda\gamma_p} + e^{-\lambda\gamma_p}).$$

Hence the wave equation becomes

$$\frac{2mce^{\lambda\gamma_p}}{e^{\lambda\gamma_p} + e^{-\lambda\gamma_p}}|\psi\rangle = \beta p_4 |\psi\rangle. \qquad (X.1.15)$$

From the relation

$$p_4 = \sqrt{(m^2c^2 + \boldsymbol{p}^2)}$$

and (*X.1.14*) we obtain

$$\frac{1}{\cos \lambda} = \frac{2}{e^{\lambda\gamma_p} + e^{-\lambda\gamma_p}} = \frac{p_4}{mc} = \frac{\sqrt{(\boldsymbol{p}^2 + m^2c^2)}}{mc}.$$

Hence the wave equation (*X.1.15*) becomes

$$\sqrt{(\mathbf{p}^2 + m^2c^2)}\, e^{\lambda\gamma}|\psi\rangle = \beta p_4|\psi\rangle. \qquad (X.1.16)$$

Let us now introduce the unitary transformations induced by

$$U = e^{-(1/2)\lambda\gamma_p}. \qquad (X.1.17)$$

We write

$$|\phi\rangle = e^{(1/2)\lambda\gamma_p}|\psi\rangle = U^\dagger|\psi\rangle \qquad (X.1.18)$$

and

$$p_4' = U^\dagger p_4 U = p_4 \qquad (X.1.19)$$

in the wave equation (*X.1.16*) and obtain

$$\sqrt{(\mathbf{p}^2 + m^2c^2)}|\phi\rangle = e^{-(1/2)\lambda\gamma_p}\beta e^{-(1/2)\lambda\gamma_p}p_4|\phi\rangle.$$

Hence, using the operator relation

$$\beta e^{-(1/2)\lambda\gamma_p} = e^{(1/2)\lambda\gamma_p}\beta,$$

we get finally the wave equation

$$i\hbar\frac{\partial}{\partial t}|\phi\rangle = \beta E_p|\phi\rangle, \qquad (X.1.20)$$

where

$$E_p = c\sqrt{(\mathbf{p}^2 + m^2c^2)}$$

and where we assume that a Fourier transformation in 3-dimensional momentum space has been carried out; that is,

$$|\phi(p, t)\rangle = \int e^{(i/\hbar)\mathbf{p}\cdot\mathbf{r}}|\phi(\mathbf{r}, t)\rangle\, d^3x.$$

By using the matrix form of β, equation (*X.1.20*) can be split up into two two-component spinor wave equations in the form

$$\begin{aligned} i\hbar\frac{\partial}{\partial t}|\phi_+\rangle &= E_p|\phi_+\rangle,\\ i\hbar\frac{\partial}{\partial t}|\phi_-\rangle &= -E_p|\phi_-\rangle, \end{aligned} \qquad (X.1.21)$$

where the two-component spinors are defined by

$$|\phi_+\rangle = \begin{bmatrix}\phi_1\\ \phi_2\end{bmatrix}, \qquad |\phi_-\rangle = \begin{bmatrix}\phi_3\\ \phi_4\end{bmatrix}.$$

A more convenient notation is to write

$$|\phi_+\rangle = \tfrac{1}{2}(1 + \beta)|\phi\rangle = \begin{bmatrix}\phi_1\\ \phi_2\\ 0\\ 0\end{bmatrix}, \qquad (X.1.22)$$

$$|\phi_-\rangle = \tfrac{1}{2}(1-\beta)|\phi\rangle = \begin{bmatrix} 0 \\ 0 \\ \phi_3 \\ \phi_4 \end{bmatrix}, \tag{X.1.23}$$

where

$$\Lambda \pm = \tfrac{1}{2}(1 \pm \beta) \tag{X.1.24}$$

are projection operators.

From (*X.1.21*) we see that the lower two components (ϕ_3 and ϕ_4) refer to the negative energy state. A set of special positive- and negative-energy solutions of (*X.1.21*) can be obtained from the representations (*X.1.22*) and (*X.1.23*) in the form

$$\begin{aligned} |\phi_+\uparrow\rangle &= |1\uparrow\rangle e^{-(i/\hbar)E_pt}, \\ |\phi_+\downarrow\rangle &= |1\downarrow\rangle e^{-(i/\hbar)E_pt}, \\ |\phi_-\uparrow\rangle &= |-1\uparrow\rangle e^{(i/\hbar)E_pt}, \\ |\phi_-\downarrow\rangle &= |-1\downarrow\rangle e^{(i/\hbar)E_pt}, \end{aligned} \tag{X.1.25}$$

where the spinors $|1\uparrow\rangle$, $|1\downarrow\rangle$, $|-1\uparrow\rangle$, $|-1\downarrow\rangle$ constitute an orthonormal set of the form

$$|1\uparrow\rangle = \begin{bmatrix} 1 \\ 0 \\ 0 \\ 0 \end{bmatrix}, \quad |1\downarrow\rangle = \begin{bmatrix} 0 \\ 1 \\ 0 \\ 0 \end{bmatrix}, \quad |-1\uparrow\rangle = \begin{bmatrix} 0 \\ 0 \\ 1 \\ 0 \end{bmatrix}, \quad |-1\downarrow\rangle = \begin{bmatrix} 0 \\ 0 \\ 0 \\ 1 \end{bmatrix}. \tag{X.1.26}$$

These four solutions can be expressed in the form of a 4×4 matrix

$$[\phi] = \begin{bmatrix} e^{-(i/\hbar)E_pt} & 0 & 0 & 0 \\ 0 & e^{-(i/\hbar)E_pt} & 0 & 0 \\ 0 & 0 & e^{(i/\hbar)E_pt} & 0 \\ 0 & 0 & 0 & e^{(i/\hbar)E_p t} \end{bmatrix}, \tag{X.1.27}$$

where the columns represent the solutions.

The most general solutions can now be obtained from (*X.1.18*) in the form of a 4×4 matrix,

$$[\psi] = U[\phi]. \tag{X.1.28}$$

The unitary matrix U can be expressed in a simple form. On writing

$$\sin \tfrac{1}{2}\lambda = \sin\left[\tfrac{1}{2}\tan^{-1}\left(\frac{p}{mc}\right)\right] = \sin\theta,$$

$$\theta = \tfrac{1}{2}\tan^{-1}\left(\frac{p}{mc}\right),$$

we find that

$$\sin\theta = \left[\frac{E_p - mc^2}{2E_p}\right]^{1/2}, \qquad \cos\theta = \left[\frac{E_p + mc^2}{2E_p}\right]^{1/2}.$$

Hence

$$U = \frac{(E_p + H\beta)}{\sqrt{[2E_p(E_p + mc^2)]}}, \qquad (X.1.29)$$

where U satisfies the equation

$$HU = E_p U\beta. \qquad (X.1.30)$$

The matrix form of U is

$$U = N\begin{bmatrix} E_p + mc^2 & 0 & -cp_3 & -cp_- \\ 0 & E_p + mc^2 & -cp_+ & cp_3 \\ cp_3 & cp_- & E_p + mc^2 & 0 \\ cp_+ & -cp_3 & 0 & E_p + mc^2 \end{bmatrix}, \qquad (X.1.31)$$

where

$$N = \frac{1}{\sqrt{[2E_p(E_p + mc^2)]}}.$$

In matrix form the Hamiltonian is

$$H = \begin{bmatrix} mc^2 & 0 & cp_3 & cp_- \\ 0 & mc^2 & cp_+ & -cp_3 \\ cp_3 & cp_- & -mc^2 & 0 \\ cp_+ & -cp_3 & 0 & -mc^2 \end{bmatrix}. \qquad (X.1.32)$$

We can show that the first two columns of U correspond to positive-energy $[E_p = c\sqrt{(\mathbf{p}^2 + m^2c^2)}]$ solutions of the Dirac equation. The last two columns are the negative-energy $[-E_p = -c\sqrt{(\mathbf{p}^2 + m^2c^2)}]$ solutions. All four solutions, as represented by the four columns of U, constitute an orthonormal system. In the rest frame of the particle ($p = 0$) the solutions represented by U reduce to the solutions (*X.1.26*).

Next consider a particle having its momentum $\mathbf{p}$ along the Z-axis. In this case we find that the spin operator

$$\mathbf{S} = \tfrac{1}{2}\hbar\begin{bmatrix} \boldsymbol{\sigma} & 0 \\ 0 & \boldsymbol{\sigma} \end{bmatrix} \qquad (X.1.33)$$

assumes the value $\frac{1}{2}\hbar$ with respect to states represented by the first and third columns of U and the value $-\frac{1}{2}\hbar$ with respect to states represented by the second and fourth columns of U. Hence we see that the four solutions of the Dirac equation refer to two positive energy states with "spin up" and "spin down" to two negative energy states with "spin up" and "spin down." These states will be represented by

$$|E_+, \tfrac{1}{2}\rangle = N\begin{bmatrix} E_p + mc^2 \\ 0 \\ cp_3 \\ cp_+ \end{bmatrix}, \qquad |E_+, -\tfrac{1}{2}\rangle = N\begin{bmatrix} 0 \\ E_p + mc^2 \\ cp_- \\ -cp_3 \end{bmatrix} \qquad (X.1.34)$$

for positive energy states and

$$|E_-, \tfrac{1}{2}\rangle = N\begin{bmatrix} -cp_3 \\ -cp_+ \\ E_p + mc^2 \\ 0 \end{bmatrix}, \qquad |E_-, -\tfrac{1}{2}\rangle = N\begin{bmatrix} -cp_- \\ cp_3 \\ 0 \\ E_p + mc^2 \end{bmatrix} \tag{X.1.35}$$

for negative energy states. The states represented by (*X.1.34*) and (*X.1.35*) constitute a complete orthonormal set and therefore we can form a unit operator of the spinor space spanned by these four spinors. Thus the unit operator is

$$I = |E_+, \tfrac{1}{2}\rangle\langle E_+, \tfrac{1}{2}| + |E_+, -\tfrac{1}{2}\rangle\langle E_+, -\tfrac{1}{2}| + |E_-, \tfrac{1}{2}\rangle\langle E_-, \tfrac{1}{2}| + |E_-, -\tfrac{1}{2}\rangle\langle E_-, -\tfrac{1}{2}|. \tag{X.1.36}$$

Any state represented by a spinor $|\psi\rangle$ can now be expanded as a superposition of four states

$$\begin{aligned} |\psi\rangle &= |E_+, \tfrac{1}{2}\rangle\langle E_+, \tfrac{1}{2}|\psi\rangle + |E_+, -\tfrac{1}{2}\rangle\langle E_+, -\tfrac{1}{2}|\psi\rangle \\ &\quad + |E_-, \tfrac{1}{2}\rangle\langle E_-, \tfrac{1}{2}|\psi\rangle + |E_-, -\tfrac{1}{2}\rangle\langle E_-, -\tfrac{1}{2}|\psi\rangle \\ &= a_+|E_+, \tfrac{1}{2}\rangle + b_+|E_+, -\tfrac{1}{2}\rangle + a_-|E_-, \tfrac{1}{2}\rangle + b_-|E_-, -\tfrac{1}{2}\rangle, \end{aligned} \tag{X.1.37}$$

where the expansion coefficients are probability amplitudes for the particle in the state $|\psi\rangle$ having positive or negative energy with spin up or spin down.

If $|\psi\rangle$ is a solution of Dirac's equation, then we can express it in the form

$$|\psi\rangle = \begin{bmatrix} |\psi_+\rangle \\ |\psi_-\rangle \end{bmatrix}, \tag{X.1.38}$$

where $|\psi_+\rangle$ and $|\psi_-\rangle$ are two two-component spinors formed from the upper and lower two components of $|\psi\rangle$. Thus from the Dirac equation (*X.1.3*) we obtain

$$\begin{aligned} (p_4 - mc)|\psi_+\rangle - (\boldsymbol{\sigma}\cdot\boldsymbol{p})|\psi_-\rangle &= 0, \\ (\boldsymbol{\sigma}\cdot\boldsymbol{p})|\psi_+\rangle - (p_4 + mc)|\psi_-\rangle &= 0, \end{aligned} \tag{X.1.39}$$

where $cp_4 = E$. From the second equation we obtain

$$|\psi_-\rangle = \frac{c\boldsymbol{\sigma}\cdot\boldsymbol{p}}{E + mc^2}\,|\psi_+\rangle. \tag{X.1.40}$$

For the positive energy E we can look for the nonrelativistic limit of (*X.1.40*). In the nonrelativistic limit we have $E \cong mc^2$ and $\boldsymbol{p} \cong m\boldsymbol{v}$; therefore

$$|\psi_-\rangle \cong \tfrac{1}{2}\,\frac{\boldsymbol{v}\cdot\boldsymbol{\sigma}}{c}\,|\psi_+\rangle. \tag{X.1.41}$$

This result shows that in the nonrelativistic sense we may regard $|\psi_+\rangle$ and $|\psi_-\rangle$ as large and small components, respectively, where $|\psi_+\rangle$ refers to positive energies and $|\psi_-\rangle$ refers to negative energies; $|\psi_-\rangle$ is of the order of $\boldsymbol{v}/c$ (in the nonrelativistic limit) compared to $|\psi_+\rangle$.

It is interesting to note that in the extreme relativistic approximation—

that is, for $E_p \cong cp$, where $mc/p \cong 0$—solutions (*X.1.34*) and (*X.1.35*) become

$$|E_+, \tfrac{1}{2}\rangle = \frac{p^{-1}}{\sqrt{2}}\begin{bmatrix} p \\ 0 \\ p_3 \\ p_+ \end{bmatrix}, \qquad |E_+, -\tfrac{1}{2}\rangle = \frac{p^{-1}}{\sqrt{2}}\begin{bmatrix} 0 \\ p \\ p_- \\ -p_3 \end{bmatrix},$$

$$|E_-, \tfrac{1}{2}\rangle = \frac{p^{-1}}{\sqrt{2}}\begin{bmatrix} -p_3 \\ -p_+ \\ p \\ 0 \end{bmatrix}, \qquad |E_-, \tfrac{1}{2}\rangle = \frac{p^{-1}}{\sqrt{2}}\begin{bmatrix} -p_- \\ p_3 \\ 0 \\ p \end{bmatrix}. \tag{X.1.42}$$

It is easy to show that in the extreme relativistic states the spin of the particle is practically parallel or antiparallel to its momentum.*

X.2. Charge Conjugation

The concept of charge conjugation as an important symmetry operation can be used to establish a relation between negative-energy solutions and antiparticle states with positive energy. It removes the association of antiparticles with negative energy states. For the sake of convenience we shall use Dirac's equation describing the motion of a particle in an external electromagnetic field. Such an equation follows from replacing the momenta p_μ by $p_\mu - (e/c)A_\mu$ and hence writing Dirac's equation for particles interacting with an external field A_μ in the form

$$\left[\gamma^\mu\left(p_\mu - \frac{e}{c}A_\mu\right) - imc\right]|\psi\rangle = 0. \tag{X.2.1}$$

A displacement of a particle in time multiplies its wave function by the factor $e^{-(i/\hbar)Et}$ and the complex conjugation operation changes the sign of the energy. It is natural to expect a relation between charge conjugation that is, replacing the charge e by $-e$, and sign of energy.

Theorem. *Charge-conjugate states of a particle of spin $\frac{1}{2}$ are related by an antiunitary transformation.*

Let $|\psi_c\rangle$ be the wave function of a particle satisfying the wave equation obtained from the wave equation for $|\psi\rangle$ by replacing the electric charge e by $-e$ Thus from (*X.2.1*) we write

---

* We note that the states (*X.1.42*) have resulted by setting $m = 0$ in the states (*X.1.34*) and (*X.1.35*). The zero mass here does not imply that the states (*X.1.42*) are the same as the neutrino states, since the neutrino is not described by a Dirac equation where $m = 0$.

$$\left[\gamma^{\mu}\left(p_{\mu}+\frac{e}{c}A_{\mu}\right)-imc\right]|\psi_c\rangle=0. \tag{X.2.2}$$

We shall write it in the form

$$\left[\gamma_4\left(p_4+\frac{e}{c}A_4\right)-\boldsymbol{\gamma}\cdot\left(\boldsymbol{p}+\frac{e}{c}\boldsymbol{A}\right)-imc\right]|\psi_c\rangle=0. \tag{X.2.3}$$

The complex conjugation of (*X.2.1*) reads as

$$\left[\gamma_4\left(p_4+\frac{e}{c}A_4\right)+\boldsymbol{\gamma}^*\cdot\left(\boldsymbol{p}+\frac{e}{c}\boldsymbol{A}\right)+imc\right]|\psi^*\rangle=0,$$

where

$$\boldsymbol{\gamma}^*=\overline{C}\boldsymbol{\gamma}\overline{C},\qquad |\psi^*\rangle=\overline{C}|\psi\rangle,$$

and according to the definition of the $\boldsymbol{\gamma}$ we may write

$$\boldsymbol{\gamma}^*=\begin{bmatrix}0 & -i\boldsymbol{\sigma}^L\\ i\boldsymbol{\sigma}^L & 0\end{bmatrix}.$$

From (*VIII.2.16*) it follows that

$$\begin{aligned}\boldsymbol{\gamma}^* &=\begin{bmatrix}0 & f^{-1}i\boldsymbol{\sigma}f\\ -f^{-1}i\boldsymbol{\sigma}f & 0\end{bmatrix}\\ &=\begin{bmatrix}0 & f\\ f & 0\end{bmatrix}\begin{bmatrix}0 & i\boldsymbol{\sigma}\\ -i\boldsymbol{\sigma} & 0\end{bmatrix}\begin{bmatrix}0 & f\\ f & 0\end{bmatrix},\end{aligned}$$

where $f=i\sigma_2$. Hence

$$\boldsymbol{\gamma}^*=\mathfrak{C}\boldsymbol{\gamma}\mathfrak{C}, \tag{X.2.4}$$

where $\mathfrak{C}$ is called the charge conjugation matrix and is of the form

$$\mathfrak{C}=\begin{bmatrix}0 & f\\ f & 0\end{bmatrix}=\begin{bmatrix}0 & i\sigma_2\\ i\sigma_2 & 0\end{bmatrix}=i\alpha_2 \tag{X.2.5}$$

or

$$\mathfrak{C}=\beta\gamma_2. \tag{X.2.6}$$

It has the properties of

(a) unitarity,

$$\mathfrak{C}^\dagger\mathfrak{C}=1, \tag{X.2.7}$$

(b) antisymmetry,

$$\tilde{\mathfrak{C}}=-\mathfrak{C}, \tag{X.2.8}$$

(c)

$$\mathfrak{C}^2=-1, \tag{X.2.9}$$

(d)

$$\mathfrak{C}^{-1}\gamma_\mu\mathfrak{C}=-\tilde{\gamma}_\mu. \tag{X.2.10}$$

Thus, using the expression (*X.2.4*) for $\boldsymbol{\gamma}^*$ in the complex conjugate equation, we obtain

$$\left[\gamma^4\left(p_4+\frac{e}{c}A_4\right)+\mathfrak{C}\boldsymbol{\gamma}\mathfrak{C}\cdot\left(\boldsymbol{p}+\frac{e}{c}\boldsymbol{A}\right)+imc\right]|\psi^*\rangle=0.$$

Multiplying through with $\mathfrak{C}$ and using $\mathfrak{C}\gamma_4\mathfrak{C} = \gamma_4$, we get

$$\left[\gamma_4\left(p_4 + \frac{e}{c}A_4\right) + \boldsymbol{\gamma}\cdot\left(\boldsymbol{p} + \frac{e}{c}\boldsymbol{A}\right) - imc\right]\mathfrak{C}|\psi^*\rangle = 0,$$

which differs from charge conjugate equation (*X.2.2*) in the positive sign of the second term. Multiplication with β and use of $\beta\mathfrak{C}|\psi^*\rangle$ in place of $\mathfrak{C}|\psi^*\rangle$ leads to the equation

$$\left[\gamma^4\left(p_4 + \frac{e}{c}A_4\right) - \boldsymbol{\gamma}\cdot\left(\boldsymbol{p} + \frac{e}{c}\boldsymbol{A}\right) - imc\right]\beta\mathfrak{C}|\psi^*\rangle = 0$$

or

$$\left[\gamma^\mu\left(p_\mu + \frac{e}{c}A_\mu\right) - imc\right]\beta\mathfrak{C}|\psi^*\rangle = 0. \qquad (X.2.11)$$

Comparing (*X.2.11*) and (*X.2.2*), we find that the charge conjugate states are related by

$$|\psi_c\rangle = \pm\beta\mathfrak{C}\overline{C}|\psi\rangle = \mathfrak{I}_e|\psi\rangle, \qquad (X.2.12)$$

where the "charge-reversal operator" $\mathfrak{I}_e$ is given by

$$\mathfrak{I}_e = \pm\beta\mathfrak{C}\overline{C}, \qquad (X.2.13)$$

and it is, like the time-reversal operator, an antiunitary operator; it satisfies the relation

$$\mathfrak{I}_e^2 = 1. \qquad (X.2.14)$$

The adjoint charge conjugate state $\langle\overline{\psi}_c| = \langle\psi_c|\beta$ is, as follows from (*X.2.12*), given by

$$\langle\overline{\psi}_c| = -\langle\overline{\psi}|\overline{C}_L\beta\mathfrak{C} = -\langle\overline{\psi}|\mathfrak{I}_{eL}, \qquad (X.2.15)$$

where

$$\mathfrak{I}_{eL} = \pm\overline{C}_L\beta\mathfrak{C}. \qquad (X.2.16)$$

By operating with $\mathfrak{I}_e$ on the negative energy states (*X.1.35*) we obtain

$$|E_+, \tfrac{1}{2}\rangle = \mathfrak{I}_e|E_-, -\tfrac{1}{2}\rangle, \qquad |E_+, -\tfrac{1}{2}\rangle = -\mathfrak{I}_e|E_-, \tfrac{1}{2}\rangle. \qquad (X.2.17)$$

Thus $\mathfrak{I}_e$ transforms a particle of negative energy with spin state down into a particle of positive energy with spin state up, and $-\mathfrak{I}_e$ transforms a particle of negative energy with spin state up into a particle of positive energy with spin state down. Hence negative energy states, actually, correspond to antiparticles of positive energy. The change of the sign of energy is expected also, because $\mathfrak{I}_e$ anticommutes with the Hamiltonian operator of a free particle:

$$[\mathfrak{I}_e, H]_+ = 0. \qquad (X.2.18)$$

The reversal of the spin is also a consequence of the anticommutation relations:

$$[\mathfrak{I}_e, \sigma_{\mu\nu}]_+ = 0. \qquad (X.2.19)$$

Furthermore, if the momentum eigenvalue of the state $|\psi\rangle$ is $\boldsymbol{p}$, then the momentum eigenvalue of the state $|\psi_c\rangle$ is $-\boldsymbol{p}$, since $\mathfrak{J}_e$ anticommutes with the momentum operator:

$$[\mathfrak{J}_e, \boldsymbol{p}]_+ = 0. \tag{X.2.20}$$

The "charge-reversal operator" anticommutes also with the time-reversal operator of Dirac theory. The time-reversal operator $\mathfrak{J}$, as defined by (*VIII.5.48*), together with $\mathfrak{J}_e$ yields the anticommutation relation:

$$[\mathfrak{J}_e\ \mathfrak{J}]_+ = 0. \tag{X.2.21}$$

This result implies that *particles and antiparticles can be described as moving in "opposite directions" in time.* However, $\mathfrak{J}_e$ commutes with the total reflection of the space and time symmetry operation:

$$\mathfrak{R} = \gamma_5 \overline{C},$$

or

$$[\mathfrak{J}_\nu, \mathfrak{R}] = 0. \tag{X.2.22}$$

The current defined by (*X.1.6*) remains unchanged under the $\mathfrak{J}_e$ operation:

$$J_\mu = -ie\langle\bar{\psi}|\gamma_\mu|\psi\rangle = -ie\langle\bar{\psi}_c|\gamma_\mu|\psi_c\rangle. \tag{X.2.23}$$

X.3. The Four-Component Neutrino Wave Equation

A description of the masslessness of the photon by a guage-invariant field should constitute an important guide to discover new gauge-invariance principles for the description of a massless fermion field. A detailed discussion of the relation of the complex orthogonal group to the neutrino field was given in Section VIII.4. The approach there was based on a three-dimensional representation. A four-dimensional representation of the complex group and its relation to Maxwell's equations have been discussed by Moses* and also by Lomont.† We shall not consider here a direct group-theoretical approach but will find it sufficient to base our arguments on simple isomorphisms of various representations of the Lorentz group. Such correspondences between representations of spin $\frac{1}{2}$ and spin 1 have already been established in the previous chapters.

We can begin with the four-dimensional form of Maxwell's equations, where it is not necessary to separate out the transversality condition of the electromagnetic waves. Thus we shall use the wave equation (*VIII.6.26*) of problem 5 in Section VIII.6.C.,

$$\Lambda^\mu \frac{\partial}{\partial x^\mu} |\eta\rangle = 0, \tag{X.3.1}$$

---

* H. E. Moses, *Nuovo Cimento, Suppl.* 7 (1958), 1.
† J. S. Lomont, *Phys. Rev.*, **111** (1958), 1710.

where the 4×4 matrices Λ_μ are given by

$$\Lambda_4 = I_4, \qquad \Lambda_1 = -M_{(23)} + iM_{(14)}, \tag{X.3.2}$$
$$\Lambda_2 = -M_{(31)} + iM_{(24)}, \quad \Lambda_3 = -M_{(12)} + iM_{(34)}.$$

The 4×4 matrices $M_{\mu\nu}$ are defined in (*I.10.23*); they are generators of infinitesimal Lorentz transformations. The ket $|\eta\rangle$ is the wave function of the photon as a four-component complex vector,

$$|\eta\rangle = \begin{bmatrix} \eta_1 \\ \eta_2 \\ \eta_3 \\ 0 \end{bmatrix}.$$

Equation (*X.3.1*), if written explicitly in terms of real and imaginary parts of $|\eta\rangle$ as electric and magnetic vectors, respectively, leads to Maxwell's equations for free fields, including the transversality condition $\nabla \cdot \boldsymbol{\eta} = 0$.

In order to obtain an equation for the massless field of spin $\frac{1}{2}$ we must use the correspondence between $M_{(\mu\nu)}$ matrices and $\sigma_{\mu\nu}$ matrices of spin $\frac{1}{2}$ representation. There is no other justification needed, since such a correspondence already exists between the Lorentz matrices (*I.10.27*), (*I.10.28*) and the transformation matrices (*VIII.5.56*), (*VIII.5.57*). Therefore, to the above Λ matrices, in spin $\frac{1}{2}$ representation, there will correspond the matrices

$$\begin{aligned} \Gamma_4 &= I_4, \\ \Gamma_1 &= -\tfrac{1}{2}\sigma_{23} + \tfrac{1}{2}i\sigma_{14} = -\sigma_1\tfrac{1}{2}(1 + i\gamma_5), \\ \Gamma_2 &= -\tfrac{1}{2}\sigma_{31} + \tfrac{1}{2}i\sigma_{24} = -\sigma_2\tfrac{1}{2}(1 + i\gamma_5), \\ \Gamma_3 &= -\tfrac{1}{2}\sigma_{12} + \tfrac{1}{2}i\sigma_{34} = -\sigma_3\tfrac{1}{2}(1 + i\gamma_5), \end{aligned} \tag{X.3.3}$$

where the $\boldsymbol{\sigma}$ commute with γ_5. [See the definition of spin matrices in (*VIII.5.23*) and (*VIII.5.24*).] The neutrino wave equation follows from the photon wave equation (*X.3.1*), replacing the Λ by the Γ and $|\eta\rangle$ by a four-component spinor $|\psi\rangle$. Hence we obtain

$$i\hbar \frac{\partial}{\partial t} |\psi\rangle = -i\hbar\boldsymbol{\sigma}\cdot\nabla\tfrac{1}{2}(1 + i\gamma_5)|\psi\rangle,$$

where $\frac{1}{2}(1 + i\gamma_5)$ is a projection operator; therefore the wave equation can be written as

$$i\hbar \frac{\partial}{\partial t} [\tfrac{1}{2}(1 + i\gamma_5)]|\psi\rangle = -i\hbar\boldsymbol{\sigma}\cdot\nabla[\tfrac{1}{2}(1 + i\gamma_5)]|\psi\rangle. \tag{X.3.4}$$

It is now easy to see that this four-component wave equation is equivalent to the two-component wave equation (*IX.3.1*). From the form of the projection operator,

$$\tfrac{1}{2}(1 + i\gamma_5) = \begin{bmatrix} I & -I \\ -I & I \end{bmatrix},$$

it follows that

$$\tfrac{1}{2}(1 + i\gamma_5)|\psi\rangle = \begin{bmatrix} \psi_1 - \psi_3 \\ \psi_2 - \psi_4 \\ -(\psi_1 - \psi_3) \\ -(\psi_2 - \psi_4) \end{bmatrix},$$

which can be written as

$$\tfrac{1}{2}(1 + i\gamma_5)|\psi\rangle = \begin{bmatrix} \nu_1 \\ \nu_2 \\ -\nu_1 \\ -\nu_2 \end{bmatrix}.$$

We thus see that the wave equation (*X.3.4*) is reducible to the wave equation (*IX.3.1*). There is some virtue in the above derivation of the neutrino equation. Most importantly, it leads to a new type of gauge-invariance principle for a massless fermion field. The masslessness of field corresponding to the wave equation is guaranteed from the method of derivation. The equation is left unchanged with respect to a gauge transformation

$$|\psi'\rangle = e^{i\lambda}i\gamma_5|\psi\rangle, \tag{X.3.5}$$

where λ is some fixed number. The Dirac equation, for example, is invariant under the gauge transformation (*X.3.5*), provided the mass $m = 0$. (The reader should show it for himself.) The above gauge-invariance requirement was the starting point of the two-component theory proposed by Lee and Yang, Salam, and Landau. However, the derivation given here gives a clear insight into why a gauge transformation of the type (*X.3.5*) associates a rigorous masslessness with the neutrino field.

By analogy with electromagnetic interactions we can say that the neutrino will interact with matter in a γ_5 gauge-invariant way; that is, the neutrino field will occur only in the combination $\frac{1}{2}(1 + i\gamma_5)|\nu\rangle$ and its Hermitian conjugate. This is the basis of vector and pseudovector interaction in weak interaction theory. As we have seen, the projection operator $\frac{1}{2}(1 + i\gamma_5)$ strikes out two of the four components and hence also one of the two spin states. Physically this means that the neutrino is produced or destroyed in one spin state only, and this, in turn, is the basis of the breakdown of parity conservation.

X.3.A. Problems

1. Show that the normalized eigenvectors of the projection operator $\frac{1}{2}(1 - i\gamma_5)$ constitute a complete set. Consider a wave equation of the form

$$[\gamma^\mu p_\mu - im\tfrac{1}{2}(1 - i\gamma_5)]|\psi\rangle = 0, \tag{X.3.6}$$

and expand the wave function $|\psi\rangle$ with respect to the complete set of eigenfunctions of $\frac{1}{2}(1 - i\gamma_5)$. By interpreting the four eigenstates obtained in this as mass and massless states of particles and antiparticles, discuss the solutions of (*X.3.6*). Compare the results with solutions of the Dirac equation with mass and also with the solutions of the neutrino equation.*

2. Show that the free particle Dirac wave equation is invariant with respect to gauge transformations of the form

$$|\psi'\rangle = e^{(i/\hbar)S}|\psi\rangle, \qquad (X.3.7)$$

where S is a real function of space and time and satisfies the relativistic Hamilton-Jacobi equation

$$(\nabla S)^2 - \left(\frac{\partial S}{c\partial t}\right)^2 + M^2c^2 = 0.$$

3. Show that the eigenvalues of the operator $\mathfrak{C}_e = \frac{1}{2}(\mathfrak{J}_e + \mathfrak{J}_{eL})$ are $+1$, -1, and 0.

X.4. Physical Interpretation of the Dirac Wave Equation

Besides its relativistic invariance property, the Dirac equation is gauge-invariant. By analogy with the gauge invariance of the classical relativistic Hamilton-Jacobi equation (*III.2.10*) [see (*III.2.11*)], the gauge transformation for the Dirac equation is defined by

$$A'_\mu = A_\mu + \frac{\partial G}{\partial x^\mu}, \qquad (X.4.1)$$

$$|\psi'\rangle = e^{-(ie/\hbar c)G}|\psi\rangle, \qquad (X.4.2)$$

where G is a function of space and time and is restricted as a solution of the equation

$$\nabla^2 G - \frac{1}{c^2}\frac{\partial^2 G}{\partial t^2} = 0. \qquad (X.4.3)$$

The restriction (*X.4.3*) is a consequence of the so-called Lorentz condition,

$$\frac{\partial A_\mu}{\partial x^\mu} = 0. \qquad (X.4.4)$$

The wave equation

$$[(\gamma^\mu \pi_\mu - imc)]|\psi\rangle = 0 \qquad (X.4.5)$$

is obviously invariant under the gauge transformations (*X.4.1*) and (*X.4.2*), where

$$\pi_\mu = p_\mu - \frac{e}{c}A_\mu. \qquad (X.4.6)$$

---

* B. Kurşunoğlu, *Nuovo Cimento*, **15** (1960), 729.

However, the preservation of gauge invariance in specific calculations has met with some difficulties. The requirement of gauge invariance is, of course, very important, since it implies a definite link between the two unobservables A_μ and $|\psi\rangle$ of electromagnetic field and matter waves. An important example of the consequence of manifestly gauge-invariant calculation has been discussed by Schwinger* in quantum field theory. The gauge group should be expected to have some relation to the Lorentz group and hence must play a basic role in determining the interactions of dynamical systems. Its significance lies at a much deeper level than is understood at present. A very interesting approach to the problem of gauge invariance connecting the Lorentz and gauge groups has been proposed by Salam and Ward.† It leads to a generalization of the electromagnetic field and to some possibility of a unified description of weak and electromagnetic interactions.

Further properties of the Dirac equation can be seen by comparing it with the Klein-Gordon equation, which for free fields follows from the discussion of the transformation function of a relativistic particle [see problem 2 (*V.5.65*)]. In the presence of fields it is given by

$$\left[\left(p_\mu - \frac{e}{c}A_\mu\right)\left(p^\mu - \frac{e}{c}A^\mu\right) - m^2c^2\right]|\phi\rangle = 0, \qquad (X.4.7)$$

where $|\phi\rangle$ is a scalar (or pseudoscalar) wave function. Let us first write down the easily derivable operational statements

$$[\pi_\mu, \pi_\nu] = \frac{ie\hbar}{c} f_{\mu\nu}, \qquad (X.4.8)$$

where the electromagnetic field tensor $f_{\mu\nu}$ is defined by

$$f_{\mu\nu} = \frac{\partial A_\nu}{\partial x^\mu} - \frac{\partial A_\mu}{\partial x^\nu}. \qquad (X.4.9)$$

We also have

$$\begin{aligned}\gamma^\mu\pi_\mu\gamma^\nu\pi_\nu &= \tfrac{1}{2}(\gamma^\mu\gamma^\nu + \gamma^\nu\gamma^\mu)\pi_\mu\pi_\nu + \tfrac{1}{2}(\gamma^\mu\gamma^\nu - \gamma^\nu\gamma^\mu)\pi_\mu\pi_\nu \\ &= -\pi^\mu\pi_\mu + i\sigma^{\mu\nu}\pi_\mu\pi_\nu = -\pi^\mu\pi_\mu - \frac{e\hbar}{2c}\sigma^{\mu\nu}f_{\mu\nu}. \qquad (X.4.10)\end{aligned}$$

Multiplying the Dirac equation on the left by the operator $(\gamma^\mu\pi_\mu + imc)$, we obtain

$$\left[\pi^\mu\pi_\mu - m^2c^2 + \frac{e\hbar}{2c}f^{\mu\nu}\sigma_{\mu\nu}\right]|\psi\rangle = 0. \qquad (X.4.11)$$

This equation differs from the Klein-Gordon equation (*X.4.7*) in the term

$$\frac{e\hbar}{2c}f^{\mu\nu}\sigma_{\mu\nu} = \frac{e\hbar}{c}\boldsymbol{\mathcal{H}}\cdot\boldsymbol{\sigma} + i\frac{e\hbar}{c}\boldsymbol{\alpha}\cdot\boldsymbol{\mathcal{E}}. \qquad (X.4.12)$$

---

* J. Schwinger, *Phys. Rev.*, **82** (1951), 664.
† A. Salam and J. C. Ward, *Nuovo Cimento*, **11** (1959), 568.

The physical meaning of the two terms in (*X.4.12*) will be discussed in the following section.

X.4.A. The Low-Energy Limit of the Dirac Equation

The study of the low-energy form of the Dirac equation is based on the assumption that the kinetic energy of the particle is small compared to its rest energy. This is equivalent to the expansion of the interaction energy and the wave function into a series in powers of the parameter p/mc. There are various methods* and almost all of them lead to the same results within the range of energies that are of practical interest.

The simplest way to study the low-energy approximation to Dirac's equation is to extend the free particle solutions (*X.1.17*) to the general case of interaction with an external field. We must first express the unitary operator (*X.1.17*) in a suitable form, one that allows the replacement of the momentum vector $\boldsymbol{p}$ by $\boldsymbol{\pi}$ and p_4 by π_4. The operator $\lambda\gamma_p$ in (*X.1.17*) can be written as

$$\gamma_p\lambda = \gamma_p \tan^{-1}\left(\frac{p}{mc}\right) = \gamma_p\left[\left(\frac{p}{mc}\right) - \frac{1}{3}\left(\frac{p}{mc}\right)^3 + \frac{1}{5}\left(\frac{p}{mc}\right)^5 - \cdots\right]$$

$$= \left(\frac{\gamma_p p}{mc}\right) + \frac{1}{3}\left(\frac{\gamma_p p}{mc}\right)^3 + \frac{1}{5}\left(\frac{\gamma_p p}{mc}\right)^5 + \cdots$$

$$= i\left[\left(\frac{-ip\gamma_p}{mc}\right) - \frac{1}{3}\left(\frac{-i\gamma_p p}{mc}\right)^3 + \frac{1}{5}\left(\frac{-i\gamma_p p}{mc}\right)^5\right] + \cdots = i \tan^{-1}\left(\frac{-ip\gamma_p}{mc}\right).$$

Using the definition of γ_p as given by (*X.1.12*), we obtain

$$\lambda\gamma_p = -i \tan^{-1}\left(\frac{\boldsymbol{\gamma}\cdot\boldsymbol{p}}{mc}\right). \tag{X.4.13}$$

Hence the unitary operator (*X.1.17*) becomes

$$U_{\text{free}} = \exp(iS_0),$$

where

$$S_0 = \tfrac{1}{2} \tan^{-1}\left(\frac{\boldsymbol{\gamma}\cdot\boldsymbol{p}}{mc}\right) \tag{X.4.14}$$

is a Hermitian operator. The form (*X.4.14*) of the generator of the unitary operator does not involve the magnitude of the momentum operator, as only the components of $\boldsymbol{p}$ appear in S_0. The corresponding unitary operator

---

* G. Breit, *Phys. Rev.*, **51** (1937), 248; *Phys. Rev.*, **51** (1937), 778; *Phys. Rev.*, **53** (1937), 153.

L. L. Foldy and S. A. Wouthuysen, *Phys. Rev.*, **78** (1950), 29.

G. Breit and R. M. Thaler, *Phys. Rev.*, **89** (1953), 1182.

B. Kurşunoğlu, *Phys. Rev.*, **101** (1956), 1419.

for a particle interacting with an external field can be inferred from (*X.4.14*) to have the form

$$U = \exp(iS), \tag{X.4.15}$$

where

$$S = \tfrac{1}{2}\tan^{-1}\left(\frac{\gamma\cdot\pi}{mc}\right). \tag{X.4.16}$$

The new wave function corresponding to (*X.1.18*) is

$$|\phi\rangle = U^\dagger|\psi\rangle. \tag{X.4.17}$$

If we write the wave equation in the form

$$(-i\gamma\cdot\pi + mc)|\psi\rangle = \beta\pi_4|\psi\rangle,$$

we can derive the corresponding equation (*X.1.15*) in the case of interaction in the form

$$2mc\beta(U^2 + U^{2\dagger})^{-1}|\phi\rangle = U^\dagger\pi_4 U|\phi\rangle, \tag{X.4.18}$$

where we use the transformation (*X.4.17*) and the operator property

$$\beta U = U^\dagger\beta. \tag{X.4.19}$$

To compare the approximation to be made with the nonrelativistic theory it is convenient to transform the equation (*X.4.18*) into two two-component wave equations, where the upper and lower components of $|\phi\rangle$ are separated. Thus, let us write equation (*X.4.18*) in the form

$$M|\phi\rangle = R|\phi\rangle + L|\phi\rangle, \tag{X.4.20}$$

where

$$\begin{aligned} M &= 2mc\beta(U^2 + U^{2\dagger})^{-1}, \\ R &= \tfrac{1}{2}(U^\dagger\pi_4 U + U\pi_4 U^\dagger), \\ L &= \tfrac{1}{2}(U^\dagger\pi_4 U - U\pi_4 U^\dagger). \end{aligned} \tag{X.4.21}$$

The operators M, R, and L are Hermitian. Under a change of sign of m the operator U changes to $U^\dagger$; therefore, while M and R remain unchanged, the operator L changes its sign. In order to see more explicitly the structure of M, R, and L for small p/mc, we can write

$$\begin{aligned} U^\dagger\pi_4 U &= \pi_4 + i[\pi_4, S] - \frac{1}{2!}\Big[[\pi_4, S], S\Big] \\ &\quad - \frac{1}{3!}\Big[\Big[[\pi_4, S], S\Big], S\Big] + \cdots. \end{aligned} \tag{X.4.22}$$

Hence

$$R = \pi_4 - \frac{1}{2!}\Big[[\pi_4, S], S\Big] + \cdots, \tag{X.4.23}$$

$$L = i[\pi_4, S] - \frac{1}{3!}\Big[\Big[[\pi_4, S], S\Big], S\Big] + \cdots. \tag{X.4.24}$$

The generator S is defined by

$$S = \frac{\boldsymbol{\gamma}\cdot\boldsymbol{\pi}}{2mc} - \frac{(\boldsymbol{\gamma}\cdot\boldsymbol{\pi})^3}{6m^3c^3} + \cdots. \tag{X.4.25}$$

It is now convenient to split up equation (*X.4.20*) into two coupled equations,

$$M|\phi_+\rangle = R|\phi_+\rangle + L|\phi_-\rangle, \qquad M|\phi_-\rangle = R|\phi_-\rangle + L|\phi_+\rangle.$$

Hence

$$(M - R)|\phi_+\rangle - L(M - R)^{-1}L|\phi_+\rangle = 0, \tag{X.4.26}$$

$$(M - R)|\phi_-\rangle - L(M - R)^{-1}L|\phi_-\rangle = 0, \tag{X.4.27}$$

where $|\phi_+\rangle$ and $|\phi_-\rangle$ are defined, as in (*X.1.22*) and (*X.1.23*), according to

$$|\phi_\pm\rangle = \tfrac{1}{2}(1 \pm \beta)|\phi\rangle. \tag{X.4.28}$$

Because of the unitary property of U the expectation values of the observables in both the old and the new representations are the same, provided the definition of an observable $\mathcal{O}$ in the old representation is replaced in the new representation by

$$\mathcal{O}' = U^\dagger \mathcal{O} U. \tag{X.4.29}$$

For example, the probability density $\langle\phi|\phi\rangle$ is conserved with a current density given by

$$\boldsymbol{J}' = \langle\phi|U^\dagger\boldsymbol{\alpha}U|\phi\rangle. \tag{X.4.30}$$

Thus the physical interpretation of the Dirac theory is still based on the use of a four-component wave function. For the exact theory, the functions $|\phi_+\rangle$ and $|\phi_-\rangle$ by themselves cannot be regarded as different wave functions, one describing the positive-energy and the other the negative-energy particle. The only probability that is conserved refers to the state

$$|\phi\rangle = |\phi_+\rangle + |\phi_-\rangle.$$

This means that the possibility of reducing the Dirac equation to two-component equations does not prevent transitions to negative energy states. The physical meaning of the functions $|\phi_+\rangle$ and $|\phi_-\rangle$ is now clear: (a) the sum of $|\phi_+\rangle$ and $|\phi_-\rangle$ is a probability amplitude of the same kind as Dirac's wave function $|\psi\rangle$; (b) in the nonrelativistic limit the function $|\phi_-\rangle$ refers to small components and the function $|\phi_+\rangle$ is a probability amplitude.

We may now carry out the required approximation for the low-energy limit. We shall retain only the terms proportional to $1/m^2c^2$. We shall need the following easily established relations:

$$[\pi_4, S] \cong \frac{ie\hbar}{2m^2c^2}\boldsymbol{\gamma}\cdot\boldsymbol{\mathcal{E}}, \tag{X.4.31}$$

$$[[\pi_4, S], S] \cong \frac{e\hbar^2}{4m^2c^3}\nabla\cdot\boldsymbol{\mathcal{E}} - \frac{e\hbar}{2m^2c^3}\boldsymbol{\sigma}\cdot(\boldsymbol{\mathcal{E}}\times\boldsymbol{\pi}) - \frac{ie\hbar^2}{4m^2c^3}\boldsymbol{\sigma}\cdot(\nabla\times\boldsymbol{\mathcal{E}}), \tag{X.4.32}$$

$$R \cong \pi_4 - \frac{e\hbar^2}{8m^2c^3}\nabla\cdot\mathcal{E} + \frac{e\hbar}{4m^2c^3}\boldsymbol{\sigma}\cdot(\mathcal{E}\times\boldsymbol{\pi}) + \frac{ie\hbar^2}{8m^2c^3}\boldsymbol{\sigma}\cdot(\nabla\times\mathcal{E}), \qquad (X.4.33)$$

$$L \cong -\frac{e\hbar}{2mc^2}\boldsymbol{\gamma}\cdot\mathcal{E}, \qquad (X.4.34)$$

$$U^2 = e^{2iS} \cong 1 + 2iS - 2S^2 + \cdots$$

$$\cong 1 + i\frac{\boldsymbol{\gamma}\cdot\boldsymbol{\pi}}{mc} + \frac{1}{2m^2c^2}\left(\pi^2 + \frac{e\hbar}{c}\boldsymbol{\sigma}\cdot\mathcal{H}\right), \qquad (X.4.35)$$

$$\beta M = 2mc(U^2 + U^{2\dagger})^{-1} \cong mc - \frac{\pi^2}{2mc} - \frac{e\hbar}{2mc^2}(\boldsymbol{\sigma}\cdot\mathcal{H}). \qquad (X.4.36)$$

Hence equation $(X.4.26)$ yields

$$\pi_4|\phi_+\rangle = \Big[-mc + \frac{\pi^2}{2mc} + \frac{e\hbar}{2mc^2}\boldsymbol{\sigma}\cdot\mathcal{H} + \frac{e\hbar^2}{8m^2c^3}\nabla\cdot\mathcal{E}$$
$$- \frac{e\hbar}{4m^2c^3}\boldsymbol{\sigma}\cdot(\mathcal{E}\times\boldsymbol{\pi}) - \frac{ie\hbar^2}{8m^2c^3}\boldsymbol{\sigma}\cdot(\nabla\times\mathcal{E})\Big]|\phi_+\rangle$$

or

$$i\hbar\frac{\partial}{\partial t}|\phi\rangle = H|\phi_+\rangle, \qquad (X.4.37)$$

where

$$H = \frac{\left(\boldsymbol{p} - \frac{e}{c}\boldsymbol{A}\right)^2}{2m} + eA_4 + \frac{e\hbar}{2mc}\boldsymbol{\sigma}\cdot\mathcal{H} - \frac{e\hbar}{4m^2c^2}\boldsymbol{\sigma}\cdot(\mathcal{E}\times\boldsymbol{\pi})$$
$$+ \frac{e\hbar^2}{8m^2c^2}\nabla\cdot\mathcal{E} - \frac{ie\hbar^2}{8m^2c^2}\boldsymbol{\sigma}\cdot(\nabla\times\mathcal{E}) - mc^2. \qquad (X.4.38)$$

The term $(e\hbar/2mc)\boldsymbol{\sigma}\cdot\mathcal{H}$ is an additional potential energy and it arises from the electron's magnetic moment,

$$\boldsymbol{\mu} = -\frac{e\hbar}{2mc}\boldsymbol{\sigma}. \qquad (X.4.39)$$

For a static field we set $\boldsymbol{A} = 0$. In this case the term $-(e\hbar/4m^2c^2)\boldsymbol{\sigma}\cdot(\mathcal{E}\times\boldsymbol{\pi})$ becomes $(e\hbar/4m^2c^2)\boldsymbol{\sigma}\cdot(\nabla A_4\times\boldsymbol{p})$, where the electric potential A_4 is a function of r alone, so

$$\frac{e\hbar}{4m^2c^2}\boldsymbol{\sigma}\cdot(\nabla A_4\times\boldsymbol{p}) = \frac{e\hbar}{4m^2c^2}\frac{1}{r}\frac{dA_4}{dr}\boldsymbol{\sigma}\cdot(\boldsymbol{r}\times\boldsymbol{p})$$
$$= \frac{e}{2m^2c^2}\frac{1}{r}\frac{dA_4}{dr}(\boldsymbol{s}\cdot\boldsymbol{L}) \qquad (X.4.40)$$

is the additional energy arising from "spin-orbit coupling." The remaining terms are small and need not be discussed in this connection.

X.4.B. Problems

1. Find the position, momentum, and angular momentum operators in a representation where the energy of a free Dirac particle is given by

$$H' = \beta c\sqrt{(\boldsymbol{p}^2 + m^2c^2)}.$$

Show that the group velocity of a particle of spin $\frac{1}{2}$ with mass m is given by

$$\boldsymbol{v} = \beta \frac{c\boldsymbol{p}}{\sqrt{(\boldsymbol{p}^2 + m^2c^2)}}.$$

The velocity in the original representation is $c\boldsymbol{\alpha}$. Under what conditions is the velocity of any particle independent of a representation?

2. Prove that the total angular momentum

$$\boldsymbol{J} = \boldsymbol{L} + \tfrac{1}{2}\hbar\begin{bmatrix} \boldsymbol{\sigma} & 0 \\ 0 & \boldsymbol{\sigma} \end{bmatrix}$$

of a Dirac particle with mass is a constant of the motion. Compare this result with the conservation of $\boldsymbol{J}' = U^{\dagger}\boldsymbol{J}U$, where each term is conserved by itself. The unitary operator U is defined by (*X.4.15*).

CHAPTER XI

QUANTIZATION OF MASSLESS FIELDS

XI.1. The Basic Formalism of Quantization

The explanation of the duality properties of matter as waves and particles is not completely achieved by the quantum theory we have discussed so far. We must ascribe particle features to fields; particles must be representable in terms of some kind of fields. This is done by "field quantization," where the amplitudes of the wave fields in ordinary space and time are replaced by operators. The idea of field quantization has first been discussed and applied by Jordan and Klein* and Jordan and Wigner.†

We shall be concerned in this book only with the quantization of massless fields. The quantization of fields with mass is outside its scope. We shall not discuss the phenomena that fall naturally within the territory of quantum electrodynamics. But quantization of the free electromagnetic field and also of the neutrino field is of basic importance for further understanding of the statistical and philosophical foundations of quantum theory.‡ (See also Chapters II and IV.)

We begin with an outline of the Lagrangian formulation of classical fields. We assume that the Lagrangian of a classical field is a function of field variables—for example electromagnetic potentials or electric and magnetic fields—and their first-order partial derivatives. Thus a Lagrangian is of the form

$$\mathfrak{L} = \mathfrak{L}\left(\eta_\alpha, \frac{\partial \eta_\alpha}{\partial x^\mu}\right)$$

where α and μ run through 1 to 4. The action function S corresponding to the "Langrangian density" $\mathfrak{L}$ is

---

* P. Jordan and O. Klein, *Z. Phys.* **45** (1927), 751.

† P. Jordan and E. Wigner, *Z. Phys.* **47** (1928), 631.

‡ A good account of modern quantum electrodynamics can be found in *Quantum Electrodynamics*, Dover, New York, 1958; edited by J Schwinger.

$$S(\Omega) = \int_\Omega \mathfrak{L}\left(\eta_\alpha, \frac{\partial \eta_\alpha}{\partial x^\mu}\right) d^4x, \qquad (XI.1.1)$$

where Ω is a four-dimensional region of integration. We envisage variations of field variables η_α of the form

$$\eta_\alpha + \delta\eta_\alpha,$$

such that the variations $\delta\eta_\alpha$ vanish on the surface bounding the region Ω. The stationary values of S for such variations satisfy the equation

$$\delta S = 0. \qquad (XI.1.2)$$

The boundary of the four-dimensional region Ω consists of physically independent space-time points; that is, points that are separated by spacelike intervals. The totality of such points constitute a spacelike surface σ. We may look upon Ω as spanned by two spacelike surfaces σ_1 and σ_2 at times t_1 and t_2. Thus (*XI.1.1*) can be written as

$$S(\Omega) = \int_{\sigma_1}^{\sigma_2} \mathfrak{L}\left(\eta_\alpha, \frac{\partial \eta_\alpha}{\partial x^\mu}\right) d^4x. \qquad (XI.1.3)$$

The change δF of an arbitrary function F entails two types of variations: (a) changing the field variables at each point by $\delta\eta_\alpha$, and (b) altering the region of integration by a displacement δx^μ of the points on the boundary surfaces. Hence

$$\delta S = \int_{\sigma_1}^{\sigma_2} (\delta_0 \mathfrak{L})\, d^4x + \int_{\sigma_1} \mathfrak{L}\,\delta x^\mu\, d\sigma_\mu - \int_{\sigma_2} \mathfrak{L}\,\delta x^\mu\, d\sigma_\mu, \qquad (XI.1.4)$$

where

$$\delta_0 \mathfrak{L} = \frac{\partial \mathfrak{L}}{\partial \eta_\alpha}\,\delta_0\eta_\alpha + \frac{\partial \mathfrak{L}}{\partial\left(\dfrac{\partial \eta_\alpha}{\partial x^\mu}\right)}\,\frac{\partial}{\partial x^\mu}(\delta_0\eta_\alpha)$$

$$= \left[\frac{\partial \mathfrak{L}}{\partial \eta_\alpha} - \frac{\partial}{\partial x^\mu}\left(\frac{\partial \mathfrak{L}}{\partial\left(\dfrac{\partial \eta_\alpha}{\partial x^\mu}\right)}\right)\right]\delta_0\eta_\alpha + \frac{\partial}{\partial x^\mu}\left[\frac{\partial \mathfrak{L}}{\partial\left(\dfrac{\partial \eta_\alpha}{\partial x^\mu}\right)}\,\delta_0\eta_\alpha\right]. \qquad (XI.1.5)$$

According to Gauss' theorem we have

$$\int_\Omega \frac{\partial}{\partial x^\mu}\left[\frac{\partial \mathfrak{L}}{\partial\left(\dfrac{\partial \eta_\alpha}{\partial x^\mu}\right)}\,\delta_0\eta_\alpha\right] d^4x = \int_{\sigma_1} \frac{\partial \mathfrak{L}}{\partial\left(\dfrac{\partial \eta_\alpha}{\partial x^\mu}\right)}\,\delta_0\eta_\alpha\, d\sigma_\mu - \int_{\sigma_2} \frac{\partial \mathfrak{L}}{\partial\left(\dfrac{\partial \eta_\alpha}{\partial x^\mu}\right)}\,\delta_0\eta_\alpha\, d\sigma_\mu\, d^4x.$$

Hence the variation of the action integral can be written as

$$\delta S = \int_\Omega \left[\frac{\partial \mathfrak{L}}{\partial \eta_\alpha} - \frac{\partial}{\partial x^\mu}\left(\frac{\partial \mathfrak{L}}{\partial\left(\dfrac{\partial \eta_\alpha}{\partial x^\mu}\right)}\right)\right]\delta_0\eta_\alpha\, d^4x$$

$$+ \int_{\sigma_1}\left[\mathfrak{L}\,\delta x^\mu + \frac{\partial \mathfrak{L}}{\partial\left(\dfrac{\partial \eta_\alpha}{\partial x^\mu}\right)}\,\delta\eta_\alpha\right] d\sigma_\mu - \int_{\sigma_2}\left[\mathfrak{L}\,\delta x^\mu + \frac{\partial \mathfrak{L}}{\partial\left(\dfrac{\partial \eta_\alpha}{\partial x^\mu}\right)}\,\delta_0\eta_\alpha\right] d\sigma_\mu. \qquad (XI.1.6)$$

From Hamilton's principle (*XI.1.2*) the equations of motion follow as

$$\frac{\partial \mathfrak{L}}{\partial \eta_\alpha} - \frac{\partial}{\partial x^\mu}\left(\frac{\partial \mathfrak{L}}{\partial\left(\frac{\partial \eta_\alpha}{\partial x^\mu}\right)}\right) = 0 \tag{XI.1.7}$$

and

$$\int_{\sigma_1}\left[\mathfrak{L}\delta x^\mu + \frac{\partial \mathfrak{L}}{\partial\left(\frac{\partial \eta_\alpha}{\partial x^\mu}\right)}\delta_0\eta_\alpha\right]d\sigma_\mu = \int_{\sigma_2}\left[\mathfrak{L}\delta x^\mu + \frac{\partial \mathfrak{L}}{\partial\left(\frac{\partial \eta_\alpha}{\partial x^\mu}\right)}\delta_0\eta_\alpha\right]d\sigma_\mu. \tag{XI.1.8}$$

Equations (*XI.1.7*) are the field equations and (*XI.1.8*) lead to the laws of conservation.* We shall be concerned only with the field equations. Since the Lagrangian is a Lorentz-invariant quantity, the corresponding field equations are, of course, Lorentz-covariant.

In order to establish a correspondence between field and particle we must try to make a transition from a continuously infinite degree of freedom of fields to a discrete infinite degree of freedom. This can be done, at a fixed time t, by decomposing the three dimensional coordinate space into small cells of volume $\delta V^{(s)}$, for $s = 1, 2, \cdots$. The corresponding field variable in each volume $\delta V^{(s)}$ will be designated by $\eta_\alpha(r_s, t)$. At a given time t the Lagrangian can be defined by

$$\mathfrak{L}'(t) = \sum_s \delta V^{(s)}\mathfrak{L}^{(s)}, \tag{XI.1.9}$$

where $\mathfrak{L}^{(s)}$ refers to the value of $\mathfrak{L}$ in the sth cell. We can set up a correspondence with the Hamiltonian dynamics by

$$\begin{aligned} q_\alpha^s &= \eta_\alpha(\boldsymbol{r}_s, t),\\ p_\alpha^s &= \frac{\partial \mathfrak{L}'}{\partial \dot{q}_\alpha^s} = \frac{\partial \mathfrak{L}'}{\partial \dot{\eta}_\alpha(\boldsymbol{r}_s, t)} = \frac{\partial \mathfrak{L}^{(s)}}{\partial \dot{\eta}_\alpha(\boldsymbol{r}_s, t)}\delta V^{(s)}, \end{aligned} \tag{XI.1.10}$$

where $\dot{\eta}_\alpha = \partial\eta_\alpha/\partial t$.

The Hamiltonian can now be defined by

$$\boldsymbol{H} = \sum_s p_\alpha^s \dot{q}_\alpha^s - \mathfrak{L}'.$$

In the limit of zero volume of the cells we can write

$$\pi^\alpha = \frac{\partial \mathfrak{L}}{\partial \dot{\eta}_\alpha} \tag{XI.1.11}$$

as the canonically conjugate variable to η_α, so (*XI.1.10*) yields

$$p_\alpha^s = \pi_\alpha(\boldsymbol{r}_s, t)\delta V^{(s)},$$

and we also obtain

$$\boldsymbol{H} = \sum_s [\pi^\alpha(\boldsymbol{r}_s, t)\dot{\eta}_\alpha(\boldsymbol{r}_s, t) - \mathfrak{L}^{(s)}]\delta V^{(s)}.$$

---

* J. Schwinger, *Phys. Rev.*, **82** (1951), 914.

In the limit $\delta V^{(s)} \longrightarrow 0$ we have

$$H(t) = \int \boldsymbol{H}(\boldsymbol{r}, t)\, d^3x, \tag{XI.1.12}$$

where the Hamiltonian density $\boldsymbol{H}(\boldsymbol{r}, t)$ is

$$\boldsymbol{H}(\boldsymbol{r}, t) = \pi^{\alpha}\dot{\eta}_{\alpha} - \mathfrak{L}. \tag{XI.1.13}$$

Quantization of a field consists of regarding the canonically conjugate variables η_α and π_α as field operators and deriving, from analogy with particle dynamics, the corresponding commutation rules. From the above definitions and quantum postulates (*III.4.2*) it follows that the commutation rules for field operators are

$$\begin{aligned} [\eta_\alpha(\boldsymbol{r}_s, t),\ \eta_\beta(\boldsymbol{r}'_s, t)] &= 0, \\ [\pi_\alpha(\boldsymbol{r}_s, t),\ \pi_\beta(\boldsymbol{r}'_s, t)] &= 0, \\ [\eta_\alpha(\boldsymbol{r}_s, t),\ \pi_\beta(\boldsymbol{r}'_s, t)] &= i\hbar\delta_{\alpha\beta}\frac{\delta_{ss'}}{\delta V^{(s)}}. \end{aligned}$$

Since the time development of the dynamical system is not specified, we can work with Schrödinger's picture, where the operators are time-independent. In the limit $\delta V^{(s)} \longrightarrow 0$ we have

$$\lim \frac{\delta_{ss'}}{\delta V^{(s)}} = \delta(\boldsymbol{r} - \boldsymbol{r}'),$$

so the commutation relations are given by*

$$\begin{aligned} &[\eta_\alpha(\boldsymbol{r}),\ \eta_\beta(\boldsymbol{r}')] = 0, \qquad [\pi_\alpha(\boldsymbol{r}),\ \pi_\beta(\boldsymbol{r}')] = 0, \\ &[\eta_\alpha(\boldsymbol{r}),\ \pi_\beta(\boldsymbol{r}')] = i\hbar\delta_{\alpha\beta}\delta(\boldsymbol{r} - \boldsymbol{r}'). \end{aligned} \tag{XI.1.14}$$

The Hamiltonian (*XI.1.13*) can be employed to write Heisenberg's equations of motion for the field operators η_α and π_α:

$$i\hbar\frac{d\eta_\alpha}{dt} = [\eta_\alpha, \mathrm{H}], \qquad i\hbar\frac{d\pi_\alpha}{dt} = [\pi_\alpha, \mathrm{H}]. \tag{XI.1.15}$$

By using the commutation relations (*XI.1.14*), the equations of motion (*XI.1.15*) can be written as

$$i\hbar\frac{\delta \mathrm{H}}{\delta\pi_\alpha} = [\eta^\alpha, \mathrm{H}], \qquad i\hbar\frac{\delta \mathrm{H}}{\delta\eta_\alpha} = -[\pi^\alpha, \mathrm{H}], \tag{XI.1.16}$$

where the functional derivatives at a fixed time are defined as

$$\frac{\delta\eta_\alpha(x)}{\delta\eta_\beta(x')} = \delta_{\alpha\beta}\delta(x - x'). \tag{XI.1.17}$$

The state of a quantized field is described by a state vector $|\boldsymbol{\Psi}\rangle$ satisfying Schrödinger's equation,

$$i\hbar\frac{d}{dt}|\boldsymbol{\Psi}\rangle = H|\boldsymbol{\Psi}\rangle, \tag{XI.1.18}$$

where $|\boldsymbol{\Psi}\rangle$ describes the state of a system of any number of field quanta—photons, neutrinos, and so on.

The time-dependent field operators are defined by

$$\begin{aligned} \eta_\alpha(\boldsymbol{r}, t) &= e^{(it/\hbar)H}\eta_\alpha(\boldsymbol{r})e^{-(it/\hbar)H}, \\ \pi_\alpha(\boldsymbol{r}, t) &= e^{(it/\hbar)H}\pi_\alpha e^{-(it/\hbar)H}, \end{aligned} \qquad (XI.1.19)$$

where H does not contain time explicitly. Hence

$$\begin{aligned} i\hbar\frac{\partial\eta_\alpha(\boldsymbol{r}, t)}{\partial t} &= [\eta_\alpha(\boldsymbol{r}, t), H], \\ i\hbar\frac{\partial\pi_\alpha(\boldsymbol{r}, t)}{\partial t} &= [\pi_\alpha(\boldsymbol{r}, t), H]. \end{aligned} \qquad (XI.1.20)$$

In this way we have established a complete analogy between Hamiltonian particle dynamics and field quantization.

XI.2. The Photon Field

The square of the Hamiltonian operator of the free Dirac particle is of the same form as the classical expression for the square of the energy. For example, the squares of $H_\nu = c\boldsymbol{\sigma}\cdot\boldsymbol{p}$ and $H = c\boldsymbol{\alpha}\cdot\boldsymbol{p} + \beta mc^2$ are $c^2\boldsymbol{p}^2$, and $c^2\boldsymbol{p}^2 + m^2c^2$ respectively. As will be seen below, the same property could be possessed by the Hamiltonian operator of the photon. Thus, in the expression

$$(c\boldsymbol{K}\cdot\boldsymbol{p})^2 = c^2\boldsymbol{p}^2 - c^2\boldsymbol{pp},$$

the second term on the right (the longitudinal part of the energy) can be eliminated without using the transversality condition. The first term, $c^2\boldsymbol{p}^2$, is the square of the photon energy and it can be expressed as

$$c^2\boldsymbol{p}^2 = (c\boldsymbol{K}\cdot\boldsymbol{p})^2 + c^2\boldsymbol{pp} = \left(c\boldsymbol{K}\cdot\boldsymbol{p} + \frac{c}{p}\boldsymbol{pp}\right)^2.$$

Hence we can choose

$$H_e = c\boldsymbol{K}\cdot\boldsymbol{p} + \frac{c}{p}\boldsymbol{pp} \qquad (XI.2.1)$$

as the "effective Hamiltonian operator" of a single-photon theory, discussed previously (see Chapter II). It operates on $|\eta\rangle$ in the same way as does $c\boldsymbol{K}\cdot\boldsymbol{p}$ and it leads to the same results. However, the determinantal equation (see Chapter II) is now replaced by

$$\det(H_e - E) = -(E - cp)^2(E + cp) = 0. \qquad (XI.2.2)$$

The root $E = -cp$, because of the transversality condition, cannot occur. The repeated root $E = cp$ corresponds to the energy of the two states of polarization.

The Lagrangian density of the electromagnetic field can now be given by

$$\mathfrak{L} = \langle\eta| \left(i\hbar \frac{\partial}{\partial t} - H_e \right) |\eta\rangle = i\hbar\eta_i^\dagger\dot{\eta}_i - \eta_i^\dagger(H_e)_{ij}\eta_j, \qquad (XI.2.3)$$

summed for repeated indices, $i, j = 1, 2, 3$. The field is quantized according to the commutation rules

$$[\eta_i(\boldsymbol{r}, t), \eta_j(\boldsymbol{r}', t)] = 0, \qquad [\pi_i(\boldsymbol{r}, t), \pi_j(\boldsymbol{r}', t)] = 0,$$
$$[\eta_i(\boldsymbol{r}, t), \pi_j(\boldsymbol{r}', t)] = i\hbar\delta_{ij}\delta(\boldsymbol{r} - \boldsymbol{r}'), \qquad (XI.2.4)$$

where

$$\pi_i = \frac{\partial\mathfrak{L}}{\partial\dot{\eta}_i} = i\hbar\eta_i^\dagger, \qquad (XI.2.5)$$

so we may also write

$$[\eta_i(\boldsymbol{r}, t), \eta_j^\dagger(\boldsymbol{r}', t)] = \delta_{ij}\delta(\boldsymbol{r} - \boldsymbol{r}'). \qquad (XI.2.6)$$

From definition (*XI.1.13*) it follows that the Hamiltonian density of the field is given by

$$\mathbf{H} = \eta_i^\dagger(H_e)_{ij}\eta_j. \qquad (XI.2.7)$$

The state $|\boldsymbol{\Psi}\rangle$ of the electromagnetic field is a solution of the Schrödinger equation for the quantized field,

$$i\hbar \frac{d}{dt} |\boldsymbol{\Psi}\rangle = H|\boldsymbol{\Psi}\rangle, \qquad (XI.2.8)$$

where

$$H = \int \eta_i^\dagger(H_e)_{ij}\eta_j \, d^3x. \qquad (XI.2.9)$$

The field equation $\boldsymbol{\nabla}\cdot\boldsymbol{\eta} = 0$ is not consistent with the commutation rules (*XI.2.6*). This difficulty is removed by replacing the operator equation $\boldsymbol{\nabla}\cdot\boldsymbol{\eta} = 0$ by a subsidiary condition,

$$(\boldsymbol{\nabla}\cdot\boldsymbol{\eta})|\boldsymbol{\Psi}\rangle = 0, \qquad (XI.2.10)$$

which is a further restriction on the state vector $|\boldsymbol{\Psi}\rangle$ of the field.

From the Hamiltonian (*XI.2.9*) and the commutation rules we obtain

$$i\hbar \frac{\partial}{\partial t} \eta_i = [\eta_i, H] = (H_e)_{ij}\eta_j \qquad (XI.2.11)$$

as the quantized photon wave equation.

In order to appreciate the significance of the above quantization process it is convenient to use spatial periodic boundary conditions, as in (*II.1.34*), and expand the field operators as a superposition of states of the form (*II.1.45*):

$$\eta_i(\boldsymbol{r}, t) = \sum_n \sum_\lambda a_{\lambda n} u_n(\boldsymbol{r}) e_{\lambda i}^{(n)} e^{-(i/\hbar)E_n t},$$
$$\eta_i^\dagger(\boldsymbol{r}, t) = \sum_n \sum_\lambda a_{\lambda n}^\dagger u_n^*(\boldsymbol{r}) e_{\lambda i}^{*(n)} e^{(i/\hbar)E_n t}, \qquad (XI.2.12)$$

where λ assumes the values 1 and -1, corresponding to two states of polarization. The polarization directions are specified by the vectors $e_{\lambda i}^{(n)}$ and they are of the type $|1\rangle$ and $|-1\rangle$ used in (*II.1.45*). They satisfy the relations

$$e_{\lambda i}^{(n)} e_{\lambda j}^{*(n)} = \delta_{ij}, \qquad e_{\lambda i}^{(n)} e_{\mu i}^{(n)*} = \delta_{\lambda\mu}. \tag{XI.2.13}$$

The functions

$$f_{\lambda i}^{(n)} = u_n e_{\lambda i}^{(n)}$$

are eigenfunctions of H_e, given by

$$(H_e)_{ij} f_{\lambda j}^{(n)} = E_n f_{\lambda i}^{(n)}, \tag{XI.2.14}$$

and the functions $u_n(\mathbf{r})$ are normalized according to

$$\int_V u_n^*(\mathbf{r}) u_{n'}(\mathbf{r})\, d^3x = \delta_{nn'}. \tag{XI.2.15}$$

To satisfy the commutation relations (*XI.2.4*) or (*XI.2.6*) the operators $a_{\lambda n}$ and $a_{\lambda n}^\dagger$ must obey the commutation rules

$$\begin{aligned} [a_{\lambda n}, a_{\lambda' n'}] &= [a_{\lambda n}^\dagger, a_{\lambda' n'}^\dagger] = 0, \\ [a_{\lambda n}, a_{\lambda' n'}^\dagger] &= \delta_{nn'}\delta_{\lambda\lambda'}, \end{aligned} \tag{XI.2.16}$$

where we used the completeness relation of the eigenfunctions

$$\sum_n u_n(\mathbf{r}) u_n^*(\mathbf{r}') = \delta(\mathbf{r} - \mathbf{r}'). \tag{XI.2.17}$$

From the above definitions it follows that the Hamiltonian (*XI.2.9*) of the field is given by

$$H = \sum_s \sum_\lambda E_s N_{\lambda s}, \tag{XI.2.18}$$

where the occupation number operator $N_{\lambda s}$ is defined by

$$N_{\lambda s} = a_{\lambda s}^\dagger a_{\lambda s} \tag{XI.2.19}$$

and

$$E_s = \hbar\omega_s.$$

The eigenvalues of $N_{\lambda s}$ are integral numbers $n_{\lambda s}$ so that the total energy of the field is given as a sum of the energies of two independent integers n_{1s} and n_{-1s}, corresponding respectively to the numbers of light quanta with right and left circular polarizations (or two possibilities of spin orientation). Thus

$$E = \sum_s \hbar\omega_s (n_{1s} + n_{-1s}). \tag{XI.2.20}$$

The stationary states of the field satisfy the Schrödinger equation of the quantized field, as

$$\left(\sum_s \hbar\omega_s n_s\right) |n\rangle = E|n\rangle, \tag{XI.2.21}$$

where

$$|\Psi\rangle = e^{-(it/\hbar)E}|n\rangle, \qquad n_s = n_{-1s} + n_{1s}. \tag{XI.2.22}$$

We have in this way obtained a description of the electromagnetic field as a field of radiation oscillators [see (*VII.1.41*)]. Each oscillator has an energy which is an integral multiple of $\hbar\omega_s$. A general solution of (*XI.2.21*) can be constructed in the form

$$|n\rangle = \sum_{n_1 n_2 \cdots n_s \cdots} C_{n_1 n_2 \cdots n_s \cdots} |n_1\rangle |n_2\rangle \cdots |n_s\rangle \cdots, \qquad (XI.2.23)$$

where $|C_{n_1 n_2 \cdots n_s \cdots}|^2$ is the probability of finding n_1 photons of type 1, n_2 photons of type 2, and so on. Each $|n_s\rangle$ satisfies

$$H_s|n_s\rangle = n_s\hbar\omega_s|n_s\rangle, \qquad H_s = N_s\hbar\omega_s, \qquad N_s = N_{-1s} + N_{1s}. \qquad (XI.2.24)$$

The total momentum operator of the field [see (*II.2.6*)] can be expressed as

$$P_r = \frac{1}{c}\int \langle\eta|K_r H_e|\eta\rangle\, d^3x = \frac{i\hbar}{c}\int \eta_i^\dagger K_r^{ij}\eta_j\, d^3x. \qquad (XI.2.25)$$

It yields

$$P_r = -\frac{i}{c}\sum_s \sum_{\lambda\lambda'} E_s a_{\lambda s}^\dagger a_{\lambda' s}[\boldsymbol{e}_\lambda^{*(s)} \times \boldsymbol{e}_{\lambda'}^{(s)}]_r$$

or, in vector notation,

$$\boldsymbol{P} = \sum_s \sum_\lambda \hbar \boldsymbol{k}_s N_{\lambda s}, \qquad (XI.2.26)$$

where we used the relations

$$K_r^{ij} = -i\epsilon_{rij}, \qquad (XI.2.27)$$

$$\boldsymbol{e}_\lambda^{*(s)} \times \boldsymbol{e}_{\lambda'}^{(s)} = i\delta_{\lambda\lambda'}\hat{\boldsymbol{k}}_s, \qquad (XI.2.28)$$

where $\hat{\boldsymbol{k}}_s$ is the unit vector in the direction of propagation $\boldsymbol{k}_s$, and

$$\boldsymbol{k}_s = \frac{1}{c}\,\omega_s\hat{\boldsymbol{k}}_s. \qquad (XI.2.29)$$

The momentum operator $\boldsymbol{P}$ operates on the stationary states according to

$$\boldsymbol{P}|n\rangle = \left(\sum_s \boldsymbol{p}_s\right)|n\rangle, \qquad (XI.2.30)$$

where

$$\boldsymbol{p}_s = \frac{\hbar\omega_s}{c}\, n_s\hat{\boldsymbol{k}}_s. \qquad (XI.2.31)$$

Hence the photon as a particle of zero mass satisfies the relation

$$\boldsymbol{p}_s^2 - \frac{1}{c^2}E_s^2 = 0. \qquad (XI.2.32)$$

The electromagnetic field quantized according to the commutation rules (*XI.2.4*) reduces, for $\hbar = 0$, to the classical field theory and the particle features disappear. The occupation number operator $N_{\lambda s}$ for fixed λ and s has integral eigenvalues, so the number of quanta attached to each radiation oscillator is not limited. Each radiation oscillator contains any number of identical particles in the same state. Hence we infer that *photons obey Bose-Einstein statistics.* The latter fact makes it possible for the quantized field to reduce to the classical field for $\hbar = 0$. *Only Bose-Einstein statistics for light quanta will lead to Planck's distribution law.* (See problem 6 of Chapter VII, p. 207.)

Finally, we note the following important properties of the operators a_s and $a_s^\dagger$,

$$\begin{aligned} a_s|n\rangle &= a_s|n_1 \cdots n_s\rangle = \sqrt{(n_s+1)}|n_1 \cdots n_s + 1, \cdots\rangle, \\ a_s^\dagger|n\rangle &= a_s^\dagger|n_1 \cdots n_s \cdots\rangle = \sqrt{n_s}|n_1 \cdots n_s - 1, \cdots\rangle, \end{aligned} \qquad (XI.2.33)$$

which follow from (*VII.1.55*) and (*VII.1.56*). The operators a_s and $a_s^\dagger$ are called "creation and annihilation operators," respectively. The operator a_s increases the occupation number in the sth state by one and the operator $a_s^\dagger$ decreases it in the same state by one. All other occupation number states are left unchanged.

XI.2.A. The Propagator of the Free Photon

The quantization procedures used in the above have been carried out at a fixed instant of time in terms of time-independent operators. The time development of the system requires the use of time-dependent operators and time-dependent commutators of the field variables, for which we need to know the commutators of field operators at two different instants. To obtain time-dependent commutation rules, we use the expansions (*XI.2.12*) in

$$[\eta_i(\mathbf{r}, t), \eta_j^\dagger(\mathbf{r}', t')] = F_{ij},$$

where F_{ij} is the commutator, and calculate the "propagator of the free photon." Substituting from (*XI.2.12*) we get

$$\begin{aligned} F_{ij} &= \sum_{nn'} \sum_{\lambda\lambda'} [a_{\lambda n} u_n(\mathbf{r}) e_{\lambda i}^{(n)} e^{-(i/\hbar)E_n t}, a_{\lambda' n'}^\dagger u_{n'}^*(\mathbf{r}') e_{\lambda' j}^{(n')} e^{(i/\hbar)E_n' t'}] \\ &= \sum_n \sum_\lambda e^{(i/\hbar)E_n(t'-t)} u_n(\mathbf{r}) u_n^*(\mathbf{r}') e_{\lambda i}^{(n)} e_{\lambda j}^{*(n)} \\ &= \delta_{ij} \sum_n e^{-(i/\hbar)E_n(t-t')} u_n(\mathbf{r}) u_n^*(\mathbf{r}'), \end{aligned} \qquad (XI.2.34)$$

where, because of the invariance under translation, F_{ij} depends only on the coordinate differences.

If we now set $t = t'$ in (*XI.2.34*) and use the commutation relation (*XI.2.6*), we find that

$$\sum_n u_n(\mathbf{r}) u_n^*(\mathbf{r}') = \delta(\mathbf{r} - \mathbf{r}').$$

Hence

$$(F_{ij})_{t=t'} = \delta_{ij} \delta(\mathbf{r} - \mathbf{r}').$$

From (*XI.2.14*) we can write (*XI.2.34*) in the form

$$F_{ij} = [e^{-(i/\hbar)(t-t')H_e}]_{ij}\delta(\mathbf{r} - \mathbf{r}'). \qquad (XI.2.35)$$

The operator $\exp[-(i/\hbar)(t - t')H_e]$ can be cast as

$$e^{-(i/\hbar)(t-t')H_e} = \cos\left[\frac{cp(t-t')}{\hbar}\right] - \frac{i}{cp}H_e \sin\left[\frac{cp(t-t')}{\hbar}\right], \qquad (XI.2.36)$$

where

$$p = \sqrt{(-\hbar^2\nabla^2)}.$$

Replacing the δ function by its Fourier representation

$$\delta(\mathbf{r} - \mathbf{r}') = \left(\frac{1}{2\pi\hbar}\right)^3 \int e^{(i/\hbar)\mathbf{q}\cdot(\mathbf{r}-\mathbf{r}')}\, d^3q$$

and using (*XI.2.30*), we can write (*XI.2.35*) in the form

$$F_{ij} = -i\left(i\hbar\frac{\partial}{\partial t} + H_e\right)\left(\frac{1}{2\pi}\right)^3 \int \frac{1}{c\hbar k}\sin[ck(t-t')]e^{i\mathbf{k}\cdot(\mathbf{r}-\mathbf{r}')}\, d^3k. \qquad (XI.2.37)$$

The integral in (*XI.2.37*) can be put into a manifestly covariant form. For that we introduce a function $D(x)$ such that it equals $-\delta(x_4^2 - r^2)$ on the future part of the light cone ($x_4 > 0$) and to $\delta(x_4^2 - r^2)$ on the past part of the light cone ($x_4 < 0$). Hence it has the form

$$D(x) = \frac{1}{4\pi r}[\delta(x_4 - r) - \delta(x_4 + r)]. \qquad (XI.2.38)$$

The Fourier transform of the D function is

$$\begin{aligned}\int D(x)e^{ik_\mu x^\mu}\, d^4x &= \int \frac{1}{4\pi r}[e^{ik_4 r} - e^{-ik_4 r}]e^{-ikr}\, d^3x \\ &= \frac{1}{4\pi}\int [e^{ik_4 r} - e^{-ik_4 r}]e^{-ikr\cos\theta}\, r\sin\theta\, d\theta\, d\phi\, d\mathbf{r} \\ &= 2\pi i D(k).\end{aligned}$$

Hence

$$D(x - x') = \frac{1}{8\pi^3}\int \frac{\sin kc(t-t')}{k}\, e^{i\mathbf{k}\cdot(\mathbf{r}-\mathbf{r}')}\, d^3\mathbf{k}$$

and

$$F_{ij} = -\frac{i}{c\hbar}\left(i\hbar\frac{\partial}{\partial t} + H_e\right)D(x - x') \qquad (XI.2.39)$$

The commutation relations for time-dependent field variables now become

$$[\eta_i(\mathbf{r}, t), \eta_j^\dagger(\mathbf{r}', t')] = \frac{i}{c\hbar}\left(i\hbar\frac{\partial}{\partial t} + H_e\right)D. \qquad (XI.2.40)$$

Hence the propagator of the photon is defined by

$$S_p(x - x') = \frac{1}{c\hbar}\left(i\hbar\frac{\partial}{\partial t} + H_e\right)D(x - x'), \qquad (XI.2.41)$$

where $x - x'$ represents the relative space-time coordinates.*
From the definition of the D function we have

$$\left(\nabla^2 - \frac{\partial^2}{c^2\partial t^2}\right)D = 0, \qquad D(\boldsymbol{r}, 0) = 0, \qquad \left[\frac{\partial D}{\partial ct}\right]_{t=0} = \delta(\boldsymbol{r}), \qquad (XI.2.42)$$

so the photon propagator satisfies the equation

$$\left(i\hbar\frac{\partial}{\partial t} - H_e\right)S_p = 0. \qquad (XI.2.43)$$

XI.2.B. Problems

1. Discuss the quantization of the four-dimensional form of Maxwell's equations [wave equation (*X.3.1*)] and point out its advantages and disadvantages as compared to the quantization carried out in the text.

2. Find the total angular momentum of the quantized electromagnetic field. Then show that the photon is a particle of spin $\hbar$ that aligns itself parallel or antiparallel to the propagation direction $\boldsymbol{k}$, where the eigenvalues of N_{1s} and N_{-1s} represent the number of spins oriented parallel or antiparallel, respectively.

3. Let ϕ_s be the phase of an electromagnetic wave consisting of n_s light quanta. Prove that N_s and ϕ_s are canonically conjugate and satisfy the commutation relation

$$N_s\phi_s - \phi_s N_s = i.$$

Hence show that the number of light quanta of a wave and its phase cannot be determined simultaneously with an arbitrary accuracy. The measure of spread in these quantities satisfies

$$\Delta\phi_s \Delta N_s \geqq 1.$$

4. Prove the relations (*XI.2.28*) used in the text. From using the expression (*XI.2.27*) discuss the symmetry properties of the photon spin under time-reversal and space-reflection operations.

5. Show that total number of photons in the field can be written as

$$N = \sum_s \sum_\lambda N_{\lambda s}.$$

6. Show that the operators $T_i = \int \langle\eta|K_i|\eta\rangle\, d^3\boldsymbol{x}$ satisfy the commutation rules for angular momentum.

---

* The usual theory, in which one quantizes electromagnetic field in terms of its potentials, uses D alone in the corresponding commutation relations.

XI.3. The Quantization of the Neutrino Field

Neutrino as a particle of spin $\frac{1}{2}\hbar$ must be quantized according to the Fermi-Dirac statistics. The Lagrangian of a neutrino field is given by

$$\mathfrak{L} = \langle\phi| \left(i\hbar \frac{\partial}{\partial t} - H_\nu\right) |\phi\rangle = i\hbar\phi_\alpha^\dagger\dot{\phi}_\alpha - \phi_\alpha^\dagger(H_\nu)_{\alpha\beta}\phi_\beta, \qquad (XI.3.1)$$

where $H_\nu = c\boldsymbol{\sigma}\cdot\boldsymbol{p}$ and $\alpha, \beta = 1, 2$.

In accordance with the exclusion principle the occupation number operator of the neutrino field must assume the eigenvalues 0 and 1. Therefore the canonical commutation rules used for the quantization of the electromagnetic field are not suitable for the quantization of the neutrino field, since the rules do not put an upper limit to the eigenvalues of the occupation number operator. An operator with eigenvalues 0 and 1 is a projection operator and can be represented by a diagonal matrix with diagonal elements 0 and 1 [see Section I.3.8 and (*VII.1.45*)]. For fields quantized according to the Fermi-Dirac statistics there is no physical limit reducing the quantized field into a classical field. Therefore all particles of spin $\frac{1}{2}\hbar$ belong to nonclassical fields, having no counterparts in the classical domain.

The anticommutation rules of the neutrino field are

$$\begin{aligned} &[\phi_\alpha(\boldsymbol{r}, t), \phi_\beta(\boldsymbol{r}', t)]_+ = 0, \qquad [\pi_\alpha(\boldsymbol{r}, t), \pi_\beta(\boldsymbol{r}', t)]_+ = 0, \\ &[\phi_\alpha(\boldsymbol{r}, t), \pi_\beta(\boldsymbol{r}', t)]_+ = i\hbar\delta_{\alpha\beta}\delta(\boldsymbol{r}' - \boldsymbol{r}), \end{aligned} \qquad (XI.3.2)$$

where

$$\pi_\alpha = \frac{\partial\mathfrak{L}}{\partial\dot{\phi}_\alpha} = i\hbar\phi_\alpha^\dagger, \qquad (XI.3.3)$$

so we may also write

$$[\phi_\alpha(\boldsymbol{r}, t), \phi_\beta^\dagger(\boldsymbol{r}', t)]_+ = \delta_{\alpha\beta}\delta(\boldsymbol{r} - \boldsymbol{r}'). \qquad (XI.3.4)$$

The Hamiltonian density of the neutrino field is

$$\mathbf{H} = \phi_\alpha^\dagger(c\boldsymbol{\sigma}\cdot\boldsymbol{p})_{\alpha\beta}\phi_\beta. \qquad (XI.3.5)$$

The state vector $|\boldsymbol{\Psi}\rangle$ of the neutrino field satisfies the Schrödinger equation of the quantized field,

$$i\hbar \frac{d}{dt} |\boldsymbol{\Psi}\rangle = H|\boldsymbol{\Psi}\rangle, \qquad (XI.3.6)$$

where the total Hamiltonian H is defined by

$$H = \int \phi_\alpha^\dagger(c\boldsymbol{\sigma}\cdot\boldsymbol{p})_{\alpha\beta}\phi_\beta \, d^3\boldsymbol{x}. \qquad (XI.3.7)$$

We shall use periodic boundary conditions and expand the neutrino field operators according to

$$\phi_\alpha(\boldsymbol{r}, t) = \sum_n \sum_\mu a_{\mu n} u_{\alpha n}^{(\mu)} e^{-(i/\hbar)\mu E_n^{(\mu)} t}, \qquad (XI.3.8)$$

$$\phi_\alpha^\dagger(\boldsymbol{r}, t) = \sum_n \sum_\mu a_{\mu n}^\dagger u_{\alpha n}^{*(\mu)} e^{(i/\hbar)\mu E_n^{(\mu)} t}, \qquad (XI.3.9)$$

where $\mu = 1$ and $\mu = -1$ now correspond to particle and antiparticle states, respectively. The spinor functions $u_{\alpha n}^{(\mu)}$ are eigenfunctions of H_ν,

$$(H_\nu)_{\alpha\beta} u_{\beta n}^{(\mu)} = \mu E_n^{(\mu)} u_{\alpha n}^{(\mu)}, \qquad (XI.3.10)$$

where $E_n^{(\mu)} = |E_n|$, for $\mu = 1$, and $E_n^{(\mu)} = -|E_n|$, for $\mu = -1$. The eigenfunctions are normalized according to

$$\sum_{\alpha=1}^{2} \int_V u_{\alpha n}^{*(\mu)}(\boldsymbol{r}) u_{\alpha n'}^{(\mu')}(r)\, d^3\boldsymbol{x} = \delta_{nn'}\delta_{\mu\mu'}. \qquad (XI.3.11)$$

The above eigenfunction and eigenvalue assignments are equivalent to Dirac's hole theory. We may, if we wish, regard the number μ as the "lepton charge content" of the neutrinos, with $\mu = 1$ and $\mu = -1$ corresponding to neutrino and antineutrino charge. We are assuming that the lepton charge is conserved. In this way negative energies are associated with particles having negative lepton charge. However, the resultant energy of the field, as will be shown below, is positive.

To satisfy the anticommutation relations (*XI.3.2*), the operators $a_{\mu n}$ and $a_{\mu n}^\dagger$ must obey the anticommutation rules

$$[a_{\mu n}, a_{\mu' n'}]_+ = 0, \qquad [a_{\mu n}^\dagger, a_{\mu' n'}^\dagger]_+ = 0, \qquad [a_{\mu n}, a_{\mu' n'}^\dagger]_+ = \delta_{nn'}\delta_{\mu\mu'},$$

where we used the completeness relation of the eigenfunctions

$$\sum_n \sum_\mu u_{\alpha n}^{(\mu)}(\boldsymbol{r}) u_{\beta n}^{*(\mu)}(\boldsymbol{r}') = \delta_{\alpha\beta}\delta(\boldsymbol{r} - \boldsymbol{r}'). \qquad (XI.3.13)$$

The total Hamiltonian of the field can now be obtained as

$$H = \sum_s \sum_\mu |E_s| N_{\mu s}, \qquad (XI.3.14)$$

where the occupation number operators $N_{\mu s}$ are defined by

$$N_{\mu s} = a_{\mu s}^\dagger a_{\mu s}. \qquad (XI.3.15)$$

Using the anticommutation relations for $n = n'$ and $\mu = \mu'$, we find that

$$(a_{\mu n})^2 = (a_{\mu n}^\dagger)^2 = 0; \qquad (XI.3.16)$$

therefore

$$N_{\mu s}^2 = N_{\mu s}. \qquad (XI.3.17)$$

Hence the occupation number operator $N_{\mu s}$ is a projection operator, as discussed in Section VII.1. This is the only quantization procedure consistent with Pauli's exclusion principle. The total energy eigenvalue of the field, as follows from (*XI.3.14*),

$$E = \sum_s |E_s|(n_{1s} + n_{-1s}), \qquad (XI.3.18)$$

is the sum of positive energies of particles and antiparticles.

The vacuum state, as in Section VII.1, is defined by

$$N_{\mu s}|\boldsymbol{\Psi}_0\rangle = 0. \qquad (XI.3.19)$$

Hence

$$N_{\mu s}|\boldsymbol{\Psi}_1\rangle = |\boldsymbol{\Psi}_0\rangle, \qquad (XI.3.20)$$

where the one-particle state $|\boldsymbol{\Psi}_1\rangle$ is defined by

$$|\boldsymbol{\Psi}_1\rangle = a_{\mu s}^{\dagger}|\boldsymbol{\Psi}_0\rangle. \qquad (XI.3.21)$$

Thus $a_{\mu s}^{\dagger}$ and $a_{\mu s}$ are creation and annihilation operators of particles ($\mu = 1$) and antiparticles ($\mu = -1$), respectively. For example, the field operators $a_{\mu s}$ can act on a one-particle state according to

$$\begin{aligned} a_{\mu s}|\boldsymbol{\Psi}_1\rangle &= a_{\mu s}a_{\mu s}^{\dagger}|\boldsymbol{\Psi}_0\rangle = |\boldsymbol{\Psi}_0\rangle - a_{\mu s}^{\dagger}a_{\mu s}|\boldsymbol{\Psi}_0\rangle \\ &= |\boldsymbol{\Psi}_0\rangle - N_{\mu s}|\boldsymbol{\Psi}_0\rangle = |\boldsymbol{\Psi}_0\rangle. \end{aligned} \qquad (XI.3.22)$$

We thus see that $a_{\mu s}$, when it acts on a one-particle state $|\boldsymbol{\Psi}_1\rangle$, reduces it to the vacuum state. A particular n-particle state is represented by

$$|\psi_{12}^{(\mu)} \cdots {}_n\rangle = a_{\mu 1}^{\dagger}a_{\mu 2}^{\dagger} \cdots a_{\mu n}^{\dagger}|\boldsymbol{\Psi}_0\rangle, \qquad (XI.3.23)$$

which for $\mu = 1$ and $\mu = -1$ corresponds to n-particle and n-antiparticle states, respectively. The most general n-particle state can be expressed as in (*VII.1.52*).

For the spin component of the neutrino field we have

$$S_3 = \tfrac{1}{2}\hbar \int \phi_{\alpha}^{\dagger}(\sigma_3)_{\alpha\beta}\phi_{\beta}\, d^3\boldsymbol{x}.$$

If we assume a coordinate system where $p_1 = p_2 = 0$, then we can write

$$S_3 = \tfrac{1}{2}\hbar \int \phi_{\alpha}^{\dagger}\frac{(H_{\nu})_{\alpha\beta}}{cp_3}\phi_{\beta}\, d^3\boldsymbol{x},$$

where $H_{\nu} = cp_3\sigma_3$.

Using the expansions (*XI.3.8*) and (*XI.3.9*) we obtain

$$S_3 = \tfrac{1}{2}\hbar \sum_{nn'}\sum_{\mu\mu'} a_{\mu n}^{\dagger}a_{\mu' n'} \exp\left[\frac{i}{\hbar}(\mu E_n^{(\mu)} - \mu' E_{n'}^{(\mu')})t\right] \times \sum_{\alpha=1}^{2}\int u_{\alpha n}^{*(\mu)}(\boldsymbol{r})\frac{\mu' E_{n'}^{(\mu')}}{cp_3}u_{\alpha n'}^{(\mu')}(\boldsymbol{r})\, d^3\boldsymbol{x},$$

where $E_{n'}^{(\mu')} = cp_3$; using the normalization conditions, we obtain

$$S_3 = \tfrac{1}{2}\hbar \sum_{n}\sum_{\mu} a_{\mu n}^{\dagger}a_{\mu n}\mu$$

or

$$S_3 = \tfrac{1}{2}\hbar \sum_{s}(N_{1s} - N_{-1s}). \qquad (XI.3.24)$$

Hence we see that spin projections of particles and antiparticles are opposite to one another and both particles and antiparticles are completely polarized in the longitudinal directions. For a one-particle state the projection operators N_{1s} for a fixed s will assume the eigenvalue zero and N_{-1s} the eigenvalue 1. For a one-antiparticle state the eigenvalue 1 for N_{1s} and zero for N_{-1s} occurs. Thus the particles have their spin antiparallel to their momenta and antiparticles occur with parallel spin and momenta. Hence the neutrino and antineutrino are left- and right-handed, respectively. We see that the neutrino and antineutrino are created in single spin states alone instead of two spin states, as in the case of particles with mass. Moreover, a given state of polarization (left- or right-handedness) cannot be transformed into an opposite state of polarization. Contrary to the case with photons, it is not possible to reflect the neutrino and change its direction of polarization. These results are in accord with the experimental facts on parity nonconservation in weak interactions. For example, the decay of a π^+ at rest into a μ^+ and a neutrino (with spins as well as momenta antiparallel) is followed by the decay of a μ^+ into a neutrino and antineutrino plus positron, where the spins of ν and $\bar{\nu}$ are antiparallel; the μ^+ is therefore essentially polarized and e^+ is emitted in the direction opposite to the μ^+ momentum. For the decay of a π^- into a μ^- and $\bar{\nu}$, the polarization of the μ^- is in the same direction as its momentum and therefore the μ^- must be right-handed.

XI.3.A. The Propagator of the Neutrino

We follow the same procedure as that used in deriving the photon propagator. For the neutrino propagator we obtain the expression

$$F_{\alpha\beta} = \sum_n \sum_\mu u_{\alpha n}^{(\mu)}(\mathbf{r}) u_{\beta n}^{*(\mu)}(\mathbf{r}') \exp\left[-\frac{i}{\hbar}\mu E_n^{(\mu)}(t-t')\right]. \qquad (XI.3.25)$$

This can be written as

$$F_{\alpha\beta} = [e^{-(i/\hbar)(t-t')H_\nu}]_{\alpha\beta}\delta(\mathbf{r}-\mathbf{r}'). \qquad (XI.3.26)$$

Hence

$$[\phi_\alpha(\mathbf{r},t), \phi_\beta^\dagger(\mathbf{r}',t')]_+ = \frac{i}{c\hbar}\left(i\hbar\frac{\partial}{\partial t} + H_\nu\right) D(x-x'). \qquad (XI.3.27)$$

Thus the propagator of the neutrino is given by

$$S_\nu(x-x') = \frac{1}{c\hbar}\left(i\hbar\frac{\partial}{\partial t} + H_\nu\right) D(x-x'), \qquad (XI.3.28)$$

and it satisfies the equation

$$\left(i\hbar\frac{\partial}{\partial t} - H_\nu\right) S_\nu = 0. \qquad (XI.3.29)$$

XI.4. Gauge Invariance

The conservation law (*II.1.20*) of the electromagnetic field can be replaced by

$$\frac{\partial}{c\partial t}\langle\eta|H|\eta\rangle + \nabla\cdot(\langle\eta|c\boldsymbol{p}|\eta\rangle) = 0. \tag{XI.4.1}$$

This conservation law implies a more general interpretation of $|\eta\rangle$ than the one given in Chapter II. According to (*XI.4.1*) the photon energy density is conserved with its momentum flux density. In the latter sense the quantity $\langle\eta|\eta\rangle$ should be regarded as the expected photon density so the integral $N = \int \langle\eta|\eta\rangle\, d^3\boldsymbol{r}$ is the number of photons in the field. The total number of photons, as shown in the previous section, can further be split up into the sum of left and right circularly polarized photon numbers, $N = N_+ + N_-$, where

$$\begin{aligned} N_+ &= \int |\eta_+|^2\, d^3\boldsymbol{r}, & N_- &= \int |\eta_-|^2\, d^3\boldsymbol{r}, \\ \eta_+ &= \langle\eta|1\rangle, & \eta_- &= \langle\eta|-1\rangle. \end{aligned} \tag{XI.4.2}$$

The form of the conservation law (*XI.4.1*) suggests the existence of a gauge transformation group under which (*XI.4.1*) remains unchanged. The gauge transformation is of the form

$$|\eta'\rangle = e^{(i/\hbar)S}|\eta\rangle, \tag{XI.4.3}$$

where S is an arbitrary real function of space and time. The transformations of the type (*XI.4.3*) are called "gauge transformations of the first kind" * as compared to "gauge transformations of the second kind," which are applied, for example, to the potentials of electromagnetic field.

The transformation (*XI.4.3*) corresponds to a rotation of the state vector $|\eta\rangle$ at a given space-time point. The conservation law (*XI.4.1*) is invariant under the transformation (*XI.4.3*). All observables of a dynamical system are gauge-invariant. This is a law of nature. Gauge invariance will impose certain restrictions on the possible course of physical phenomena. For example, according to the principle of gauge invariance the potentials of the electromagnetic field and the wave functions of elementary particles are arbitrary up to a gauge transformation. Therefore potentials and wave functions are not observable elements of a dynamical system. Gauge transformations are applied onto the unobservables of a dynamical system. Gauge invariance sets up definite relations between the unobservables.

In order to study the gauge transformation properties of the photon wave equation let us operate on both sides of (*XI.4.3*) with the operator $i\hbar\tilde{K}^\mu(\partial/\partial x^\mu)$ and obtain

---

* W. Pauli, *Rev. Mod. Phys.*, **13** (1941), 203–232.

$$i\hbar\tilde{K}^{\mu}\frac{\partial}{\partial x^{\mu}}|\eta'\rangle = -\tilde{K}^{\mu}\frac{\partial S}{\partial x^{\mu}}|\eta'\rangle + e^{(i/\hbar)S}i\hbar\tilde{K}^{\mu}\frac{\partial}{\partial x^{\mu}}|\eta\rangle.$$

For the wave equation to remain invariant under the gauge transformation we must have

$$i\hbar\tilde{K}^{\mu}\frac{\partial}{\partial x^{\mu}}|\eta'\rangle = i\hbar e^{(i/\hbar)S}K^{\mu}\frac{\partial}{\partial x^{\mu}}|\eta\rangle = 0,$$

and hence the gauge function S must be restricted according to

$$\tilde{K}^{\mu}\frac{\partial S}{\partial x^{\mu}}|\eta'\rangle = 0. \tag{XI.4.4}$$

If we write the matrix form of this equation and apply the same method as used in calculating the eigenvalues of H, we get

$$\frac{\partial S}{c\partial t}\left[\left(\frac{\partial S}{c\partial t}\right)^2 - (\nabla S)^2\right] = 0.$$

The transverse condition $\boldsymbol{p}\cdot\boldsymbol{\eta} = 0$ does not allow the solution $\partial S/\partial t = 0$. Thus the gauge transformation of a free photon is restricted according to

$$\left(\frac{\partial S}{c\partial t}\right)^2 - (\nabla S)^2 = 0, \tag{XI.4.5}$$

which resembles the classical eikonal equation of geometrical optics. The restriction (*XI.4.5*) on the gauge transformation can be removed completely only for a wave equation that allows the application of the gauge transformation to at least another set of unobservables. For example, a wave equation of the type

$$K^{\mu}\left[\frac{\partial}{\partial x^{\mu}} - \frac{i}{\hbar}a_{\mu}\right]|\psi\rangle = 0 \tag{XI.4.6}$$

is invariant under the gauge transformations

$$|\psi'\rangle = e^{(i/\hbar)S}|\psi\rangle, \qquad a'_{\mu} = a_{\mu} + \frac{\partial S}{\partial x^{\mu}} \tag{XI.4.7}$$

of the first and second kind, respectively. In this case the gauge function S, depending on the type of equation satisfied by the field a_{μ}, is restricted less than the gauge function of a free photon. Hence we infer that the requirement of gauge invariance without restriction involves an interaction of dynamical systems.

In general an enlargement of a gauge transformation group—for example many-parameter gauge transformations—will require the introduction of various dynamical degrees of freedom and the corresponding interactions between them. Thus a dynamical system with a restricted gauge group is, essentially, a free system and therefore not observed.

In general we may now postulate the invariance of the Lagrangian with respect to gauge transformations (*XI.4.3*) and investigate its implications with regard to conservation laws of the field. If the Lagrangian does not change under (*XI.4.3*), we then have

$$\left[\frac{d\mathfrak{L}}{dS}\right]_{S=0} = 0. \qquad (XI.4.8)$$

We shall show that (*XI.4.8*) is a conservation law. Since conserved quantities are represented by Hermitian operators, it is necessary to symmetrize the Lagrangian with respect to η (or ϕ) and $\eta^\dagger$. In this case $\mathfrak{L}$ becomes a function of η, $\eta^\dagger$, and their partial derivatives. Hence

$$\frac{1}{i}\left[\frac{d\mathfrak{L}}{dS}\right]_{S=0} = \frac{\partial\mathfrak{L}}{\partial\eta_i}\eta_i + \frac{\partial\mathfrak{L}}{\partial\left(\dfrac{\partial\eta_i}{\partial x^\mu}\right)}\frac{\partial\eta_i}{\partial x^\mu} - \frac{\partial\mathfrak{L}}{\partial\eta_i^+}\eta_i^\dagger - \frac{\partial\mathfrak{L}}{\partial\left(\dfrac{\partial\eta_i^\dagger}{\partial x^\mu}\right)}\frac{\partial\eta_i^\dagger}{\partial x^\mu} = 0, \qquad (XI.4.9)$$

which can be written as

$$\frac{\partial\Lambda_\mu}{\partial x^\mu} = 0, \qquad (XI.4.10)$$

where

$$\Lambda_\mu = i\left[\frac{\partial\mathfrak{L}}{\partial\left(\dfrac{\partial\eta_i}{\partial x^\mu}\right)}\eta_i - \eta_i^\dagger\frac{\partial\mathfrak{L}}{\partial\left(\dfrac{\partial\eta_i^\dagger}{\partial x^\mu}\right)}\right]. \qquad (XI.4.11)$$

For particles with charge, Λ_μ is interpreted as the charge-current density of the field and its conservation is connected with gauge invariance.

For photon and neutrino fields, symmetrized Lagrangians are given by

$$\mathfrak{L}_p = \frac{i\hbar c}{2}\left[\frac{\partial\eta_i^\dagger}{\partial x^\mu}K_{ij}^\mu\eta_j - \eta_i^\dagger K_{ij}^\mu\frac{\partial\eta_j}{\partial x^\mu}\right] \qquad (XI.4.12)$$

and

$$\mathfrak{L}_\nu = \frac{i\hbar c}{2}\left[\frac{\partial\phi_\alpha^\dagger}{\partial x^\mu}\sigma_{\alpha\beta}^\mu\phi_\beta - \phi_\alpha^\dagger\sigma_{\alpha\beta}^\mu\frac{\partial\phi_\beta}{\partial x^\mu}\right]. \qquad (XI.4.13)$$

The corresponding Λ are

$$\Lambda_\mu^{(p)} = \hbar c\eta_i^\dagger(K_\mu)_{ij}\eta_j, \qquad (XI.4.14)$$

$$\Lambda_\mu^{(\nu)} = \hbar c\phi_\alpha^\dagger(\sigma_\mu)_{\alpha\beta}\phi_\beta. \qquad (XI.4.15)$$

These are energy and momentum densities of the photon and neutrino fields, respectively.

XI.4.A. Problems

1. Prove that under the simultaneous operation of charge conjugation and parity a left-handed neutrino goes over into a right-handed antineutrino. Hence show that the decays $\pi^+ \longrightarrow \mu^+ + \nu$ and $\pi^- \longrightarrow \mu^- + \bar{\nu}$ are related by a $\mathcal{P}\mathfrak{I}_c$ [see (*X.2.13*)] symmetry operation.

2. Consider the reactions

$$X + \bar{\nu} \longrightarrow Y + e^-, \qquad Y + e^- \longrightarrow X + \nu,$$

where X and Y are some nuclei. Show that the two reactions cannot take place unless $\nu \equiv \bar{\nu}$. Thus, if we take $Y = \gamma$ and $X = n$, we have

$$p + e^- \longrightarrow n + \nu$$

and

$$n + \bar{\nu} \longrightarrow p + e^-,$$

where the second reaction is forbidden by lepton charge conservation. Therefore $\bar{\nu}$ is absorbable by protons but not by neutrons. In the same way ν can be absorbed by neutrons but not by protons. Apply these arguments to $\pi^{\pm}$ and $\mu^{\pm}$.

3. Consider the derivation of a four-component neutrino wave equation from the complex conjugate of the photon wave equation (*X.3.1*). Does the resulting wave equation describe the neutrino and antineutrino pairs discussed in the text or do these particles correspond to a different pair of neutrinos?

4. Discuss the differences between a very high-energy Dirac particle with mass negligible compared to its kinetic energy and a massless Dirac particle.

5. Construct the wave equation for a Majorana neutrino [see (*VIII.5.35*)], where $\nu \equiv \bar{\nu}$. What is the status of lepton charge conservation in a Majorana representation? What are the differences between the Dirac, the Majorana, and the two-component neutrino?

6. Discuss discrete transformation properties of neutrino and photon fields. Prove that the two states of photon polarization have the same intrinsic parities.

7. Show that the operators $\tau_i = \frac{1}{2}\int \langle\nu|\sigma_i|\nu\rangle\, d^3x$ satisfy angular momentum commutation relations.

XI.5. Spin and Statistics

The spin degree of freedom of elementary, atomic, and nuclear systems is entirely of relativistic origin. The concept of statistics (Bose-Einstein and Fermi-Dirac distributions) belongs to quantum mechanics. The methods used for the quantization of the electromagnetic and neutrino fields suggest a definite connection between spin and statistics. The quanta of integral and half-integral spin fields have different statistical distributions. The requirement of Lorentz invariance of the physical laws, together with the wave equations and corresponding representations of the Lorentz group, implies certain statistics for elementary systems. Therefore spin and statistics are two basic concepts where relativity and quantum theory find a definite and indispensable unification. This fact was first observed by Pauli* and he has given a rigorous proof for the case of free fields. Pauli's theory has recently been extended to interacting fields by Lüders and Zumino.†

We shall give a summary of the general proof of the connection between spin and statistics for the case of massless fields. In order to follow the basic arguments it will be necessary to use the two-dimensional complex linear transformations and their relations to the representations of the Lorentz group. It has been shown in Section VIII.8.C that the eigenfunctions of the representation have the general form

$$f_{ab} = u_1^{a-k}(u_1^*)^{a'-k'}u_2^k(u_2^*)^{k'}, \qquad (XI.5.1)$$

where k and k' are integers and satisfy the relations

$$0 \leqq k \leqq a, \qquad 0 \leqq k' \leqq a'.$$

For a given a and a' there are $(a + 1)(a' + 1)$ eigenfunctions of the type (*XI.5.1*), so they can span an $(a + 1)(a' + 1)$-dimensional space. Following Pauli we introduce the notation

$$j = \tfrac{1}{2}a, \qquad j' = \tfrac{1}{2}a',$$

and denote the corresponding representations of the Lorentz group by $D^{(jj')}$. The numbers j and j' assume integral or half-integral values. Thus the representation is $(2j + 1)(2j' + 1)$-dimensional and is, of course, irreducible. All finite irreducible representations of the Lorentz group can be characterized by two numbers, j and j'. A quantity $F(j, j')$, characterized by (j, j'), has $(a + 1)(a' + 1) = (2j + 1)(2j' + 1)$ independent components. Thus, to $(0, 0)$ corresponds the scalar, to $(\frac{1}{2}, \frac{1}{2})$ the vector, to $(1, 0)$ the self-dual antisymmetric tensor (such as $\mathfrak{E} + i\mathfrak{H}$), to $(0, 1)$ its complex conjugate $(\mathfrak{E} - i\mathfrak{H})$, to $(1, 1)$ the symmetrical tensor with vanishing trace, to $(\frac{3}{2}, \frac{3}{2})$ a nonsymmetric tensor with sixteen components, and so on.

The photon and neutrino fields transform irreducibly under the groups characterized by $(1, 0)$ and $(\frac{1}{2}, 0)$, respectively. In both cases (where $j \neq j'$) the transformation matrices are complex.

The product of two quantities, $F_1(j_1j_1')F_2(j_2j_2')$, can be decomposed into several $F(j, j')$, according to the usual addition of two angular momenta: $j = j_1 + j_2, \cdots |j_1 - j_2|$ and $j' = j_1' + j_2', \cdots |j_1' - j_2'|$. The spin value of the massless particles belonging to a given field must be determined by noting that for a photon $s = 1$; therefore $j = 0$ is not possible. For a neutrino $s = \frac{1}{2}$ and therefore $j = 0$ is not possible. Hence in both cases the total angular

---

* W. Pauli, *Phys. Rev.* **58** (1940), 716.

† G. Lüders and B. Zumino, *Phys. Rev.* **110** (1958). See also N. Burgoyne, *Nuovo Cimento*, **8** (1952), 607.

momentum j begins with a certain minimum value* s and takes then the values s, $s + 1$, $\cdots$.

In general (where $m \neq 0$) the statements $j + j' =$ an integer and $j + j' =$ a half-integer correspond to fields with integral and half-integral spin. Hence there can at most be four types of quantities that can occur in the field-theoretical description of particles.

(a) $j =$ an integer, $j' =$ an integer. The field variables and their adjoints have an odd number of components and belong to the representations $D^{(jj')}$ and $D^{(j'j)}$, respectively.

(b) $j =$ a half-integer, $j' =$ a half-integer. The field variables have an even number of components.

(c) $j =$ a half-integer, $j' =$ an integer. The field variables have an even number of components.

(d) $j =$ an integer, $j' =$ a half-integer. The field variables have an even number of components.

The classes (a) and (b) belong to an integral spin field, and (c) and (d) belong to a half-integral spin field.

XI.5.A. Remarks on the Observables of Massless Fields

The total energy for the unquantized neutrino field is not positive definite but the probability density $\phi_\alpha^\dagger \phi_\alpha$, as the fourth component of the current

$$s_\mu = \phi_\alpha^\dagger (\sigma_\mu)_{\alpha\beta} \phi_\beta, \qquad (XI.5.2)$$

for $\mu = 1, 2, 3, 4$, is positive definite, where

$$\frac{\partial s_\mu}{\partial x^\mu} = 0 \qquad (XI.5.3)$$

The total energy for the unquantized photon field is positive definite but the possibility of a third solution with negative energy is not excluded. The current vector

$$s_\mu = \eta_i^\dagger (K_\mu)_{ij} \eta_j \qquad (XI.5.4)$$

is conserved; that is,

$$\frac{\partial s_\mu}{\partial x^\mu} = 0. \qquad (XI.5.5)$$

The probability density $s_4 = \eta_i^\dagger \eta_i$ is positive definite.

The photon field variables η_i transform irreducibly under the representa-

* M. Fierz, *Helv. Phys. Acta*, **13** (1940), 45.

tions belonging to class (a) above. Both of the representations $D^{(10)}$ and $D^{(01)}$ belong to the covariance group of the photon and the two states of polarizations transform according to $D^{(10)}$ or $D^{(01)}$.

The neutrino field variables ϕ_α transform irreducibly under the representations belonging to class (c), corresponding to $D^{(1/2\ 0)}$. There is only one polarization state. The representation $D^{(0\ 1/2)}$ will transform the complex conjugate of the neutrino wave function. The complex conjugate of the neutrino wave equation is

$$i\hbar \frac{\partial}{\partial t} \phi_\alpha^* = (c\boldsymbol{\sigma}^L \cdot \boldsymbol{p})_{\alpha\beta}\phi_\beta^*, \tag{XI.5.6}$$

so $c\boldsymbol{\sigma}^L \cdot \boldsymbol{p}$ is not the same as $c\boldsymbol{\sigma} \cdot \boldsymbol{p}$. Hence the representation $D^{(0\ 1/2)}$ does not belong to the transformation group of the neutrino. However, if we were to assume the existence of another pair of neutrinos, then the representation $D^{(0\ 1/2)}$ could correspond to a group of physical transformations. The latter type of neutrinos may be involved in reactions of the type

$$\overline{n} + \overline{\nu}' \longrightarrow p + e^+, \qquad \overline{n} \longrightarrow \overline{p} + e^+ + \nu', \tag{XI.5.7}$$

where ν' and $\overline{\nu}'$ are the new neutrino and antineutrino, respectively. Thus $\overline{\nu}$ can be absorbed only by the antineutron and ν' only by the antiproton.

XI.5.B. Field Quantization According to Commutators and Anticommutators

The negative-energy eigenstate for a neutrino field does not arise if it is quantized in accordance with the exclusion principle. In this case, as has been shown before, all negative energy states are filled and positive energy states are empty, so no transitions to negative energy states can occur. This is a consequence of using anticommutators for the quantization of the neutrino field. The anticommutator or the propagator

$$S_\nu = \sigma^\mu \frac{\partial}{\partial x^\mu} [D(x - x')] \tag{XI.5.8}$$

of the neutrino field belongs to the class where j and j' assume half-integral values. The same type of transformation property for S_ν could be obtained even if we used the commutators, instead of the anticommutators, for the quantization of the neutrino field. However, the energy would not then be positive definite. Hence it is necessary, in connection with Dirac's hole theory, to apply the exclusion principle and quantize according to Fermi-Dirac statistics.

For the photon field the propagator (or commutator) S_p is of the form

$$S_p = K^\mu \frac{\partial}{\partial x^\mu} [D(x - x')] \tag{XI.5.9}$$

and it belongs to a class where both j and j' assume integral values. If we replace (*II.1.29*) by $\chi = \sqrt{(8\pi H_e)}\boldsymbol{\eta}$, then the commutator for the variables χ_i consists of an even number of derivatives of the function D. The D function, as seen from (*XI.2.38*), is even in space coordinates and odd in the time coordinate. Thus, the expression

$$X = [\chi_i(x'), \chi_i^\dagger(x'')] + [\chi_i(x''), \chi_i^\dagger(x')],$$

symmetrical in x' and x'', is equal to an even number of spacelike derivatives times an odd number of timelike derivatives of D. Therefore, X falls into the same class as the propagator of the neutrino field. This result is in contradiction with the property of the commutator of χ and $\chi^\dagger$. The consistency requires X to vanish. In particular, for $x' = x''$, the requirement $X = 0$ cannot be satisfied with an anticommutator, since $\chi_i\chi_i^\dagger + \chi_i^\dagger\chi_i$ is a positive quantity. Hence we infer that quantization of the photon field according to the exclusion principle is not possible. In general, all integral spin fields must be quantized according to Bose-Einstein statistics.

XI.5.C. Problems

1. Prove that Bose-Einstein quantization of the neutrino field implies an energy without a lower bound.

2. Give a proof different than the one in the text that Fermi-Dirac quantization of the photon field leads to an algebraic contradiction with the commutativity of physical events separated by a spacelike interval.

3. Discuss the transformation of the quantities

$$\int \langle\eta|K_\mu|\eta\rangle\, d\Sigma^\mu$$

and

$$\int \langle\phi|\sigma_\mu|\phi\rangle\, d\Sigma^\mu,$$

where the $d\Sigma^\mu$ are four-dimensional surface elements, under reflection of time. Hence show that time reflection interchanges the states of polarization.

4. Consider the spin matrices

$$\sigma_{AB} = -\tfrac{1}{2}i(\gamma_A\gamma_B - \gamma_B\gamma_A), \qquad (XI.5.10)$$

where subscripts A and B run through 1 to 5. Show that time-reflection transformation of a Dirac spinor can be obtained with a rotation through the angle π in (45)-plane; that is,

$$\mathfrak{J} = \exp\,(i\pi\tfrac{1}{2}\sigma_{45}) = i\sigma_{45}.$$

Hence show that

$$\langle\bar{\Psi}'|\Psi'\rangle = -\langle\bar{\Psi}|\Psi\rangle$$

where

$$|\Psi'\rangle = i\sigma_{45}|\Psi\rangle.$$

A spinor of rank n contains fields of spin $\frac{1}{2}n\hbar$, $(\frac{1}{2}n - 1)\hbar$ $\cdots$. For such a spinor we have the expression

$$\langle\bar{\psi}|\psi\rangle = \langle\psi|\prod_{i=1}^{n}\beta^{(i)}|\psi\rangle$$

as the basic invariant. Show that the time-reversal operator is given by

$$\mathfrak{J} = \prod_{s=1}^{n} i\sigma_{45}^{(s)}$$

and that

$$\langle\bar{\psi}'|\psi'\rangle = (-1)^n\langle\bar{\psi}|\psi\rangle.$$

5. Prove that a Dirac spinor with four components can be decomposed into two irreducible parts with two components each, characterized by $(\frac{1}{2}, 0)$ and $(0, \frac{1}{2})$, corresponding to the diagonalization* of the matrix γ_5 with its eigenvalues 1 and -1. Hence show that when applied to Dirac spinors the transformation

$$|\psi'\rangle = \gamma_5|\psi\rangle,$$

for the irreducible quantities $u_\alpha(\frac{1}{2}, 0)$ and $v_\alpha(0, \frac{1}{2})$, yields the forms

$$u'_\alpha(\tfrac{1}{2}, 0) = u_\alpha(\tfrac{1}{2}, 0), \qquad v'_\alpha(0, \tfrac{1}{2}) = -v_\alpha(0, \tfrac{1}{2}).$$

Discuss the significance of the above for the neutrino field.

6. Show that the results of the previous problem can be generalized by

$$u_\alpha(j, j') = (-1)^{2j'}u_\alpha(j, j').$$

Since for a vector $j = j' = \frac{1}{2}$, then the above transformation changes the sign of every vector.

7. Construct the expectation value of the energy momentum vectors of the quantized electromagnetic field in the form

$$\langle P_\mu\rangle = \frac{1}{c}\int \langle T_{\mu\nu}\rangle\, d\Sigma^\nu$$

and discuss its transformation properties under space- and time-reflection transformations.

8. Compare the reactions

$$n \longrightarrow p + e^- + \bar{\nu}, \qquad \bar{n} \longrightarrow \bar{p} + e^+ + \nu',$$

and show their relations to the representations $(\frac{1}{2}, 0)$ and $(0, \frac{1}{2})$ of the Lorentz group. Are these reactions charge conjugates of one another?

9. Are there any relations between invariance under time reflection and connection between spin and statistics?

---

* W. Pauli, *Niels Bohr and the Development of Physics*, Pergamon, London, 1955.

10. Derive the photon and neutrino propagators by solving the equations

$$\left(i\hbar \frac{\partial}{\partial t} - H_e\right) S_p(x - x') = 2i\delta(x - x')$$

and

$$\left(i\hbar \frac{\partial}{\partial t} - H_\nu\right) S_\nu(x - x') = 2i\delta(x - x'),$$

where H_e and H_ν are the photon and neutrino Hamiltonians, respectively. Prove that apart from the D function there is just one more function satisfying the equation

$$\Box D_{(1)}(x - x') = 2i\delta(x - x'),$$

and that it is an even function of space and time coordinates. What would be the consequence of using the $D_{(1)}$ function in place of the D function in the quantization of the photon and neutrino fields? Can one maintain that quantization of integral spin fields according to the exclusion principle is not possible?

11. Prove that

$$D(\mathbf{r}, 0) = 0, \qquad \left[\frac{\partial D}{\partial t}\right]_{t=0} = \delta(\mathbf{r}).$$

12. How would you interpret the massless spin $\frac{1}{2}\hbar$ wave equation obtained through stereographic projection of the complex conjugate of the photon wave equation? (Use a complex orthogonal representation of the Lorentz group.)

13. Can one regard the two possible states of polarization of the photon field as its indefinite observables? Does a single state of polarization of the neutrino imply a definite observable for the field?

14. Is there any way to differentiate between the two reactions

$$e^+ + e^- \longrightarrow \nu + \bar{\nu}, \qquad e^+ + e^- \longrightarrow \nu' + \bar{\nu}',$$

where ν' and $\bar{\nu}'$ are the second pair of neutrinos discussed in the text?

15. By using the connection of spin and statistics, prove that it is not possible to combine two neutrinos to obtain a photon, and vice versa.

16. Using the Fermi-Dirac distribution, discuss the differences between neutrino gases obeying the equations

$$\gamma^\mu p_\mu|\psi\rangle = 0$$

and

$$\sigma^\mu p_\mu|\psi\rangle = 0.$$

17. Show that the expectation values of the creation and annihilation operators of the photons are given by

$$\langle a_\lambda^\dagger\rangle = \sqrt{\langle N_{\lambda s} e\rangle}^{i\alpha_s}, \qquad \langle a_{\lambda s}\rangle = \sqrt{\langle N_{\lambda s}\rangle} e^{-i\alpha_s},$$

where $N_{\lambda s}$ represents the average number of photons of mode λ and s.

18. Assuming that the radiation field is built up by emission processes which are statistically independent events, show that the actual number $N_{\lambda s}$ of photons in different modes are distributed around the averages $\langle \mathrm{N}_{\lambda s} \rangle$ according to the Poisson formula

$$P(N_{\lambda s}) = (N_{\lambda s}!)^{-1}(\langle N_{\lambda s} \rangle)^{N_{\lambda s}} e^{-\langle N_{\lambda s} \rangle}.$$

19. It is known that in a strong gravitational field deflection of light from its path is an observable fact. Using the equation (*XI.4.6*) for a photon in a Newtonian gravitational field, where $a_4 = GM/r$, $a_i = 0$, and $i = 1, 2, 3$, and also the expansion of a photon wave function (as in Chapter IX), show that the resulting deflection is one-half of the value obtained in the general theory of relativity.

CHAPTER XII

PROBABILITY IN CLASSICAL AND QUANTUM PHYSICS

XII.1. The J.W.K.B. Method and Dependence of the Wave Function on h

If for the solutions ψ of a wave equation where the integral

$$\int |\psi|^2 \, d^3x$$

taken over the whole of space is finite or equal to unity, then we interpret $|\psi|^2$ as a probability density. The wave functions that do not satisfy the normalizability condition are also possible solutions of a wave equation and describe a possible physical process. In experiments with beams of particles extended over a long time interval, where the physical situation does not change with time, the quantity $|\psi|^2$ is to be interpreted as the average number of particles per unit volume (assuming that the interactions between the particles are negligible). In this case the current vector $\boldsymbol{J}$ in the conservation equation (obtained from Schrödinger's equation),

$$\frac{\partial}{\partial t}\rho + \nabla \cdot \boldsymbol{J} = 0, \tag{XII.1.1}$$

is to be interpreted as the average number of particles crossing a unit area perpendicular to $\boldsymbol{J}$ per unit time, where

$$\rho = |\psi|^2, \qquad \boldsymbol{J} = \frac{\hbar}{2mi}(\psi^* \nabla \psi - \psi \nabla \psi^*). \tag{XII.1.2}$$

We can, for example, observe electrons either as particles causing a flash on a screen, a kick of a counter, or so on, or as waves producing a diffraction pattern. We use a wave function to get the probability of finding some electrons in a given volume or the probable number of electrons crossing a unit area per unit time. If dV is a volume element at a point $\boldsymbol{r}$, then the probability of finding an electron in dV at time t is $|\psi|^2\, dV$. We may also speak of finding the average number of electrons in a certain volume V by calculating the quantity

$$\int_V |\psi|^2\, dV. \qquad (XII.1.3)$$

Let us consider a stationary state of a beam of particles. In a stationary state we have a definite energy of the system, satisfying the statement $E = T + V =$ constant total energy, where $T =$ kinetic energy, $V =$ potential energy. In the stationary state

$$\psi(\boldsymbol{r}, t) = \psi_0(\boldsymbol{r})e^{-(i/\hbar)Et}$$

the phase factor $e^{-(i/\hbar)Et}$ depends on the product Et of energy and time and therefore it cannot be measured experimentally. Furthermore, the potential energy $V = T_0 - T$ at a point $\boldsymbol{r}$ can not be determined experimentally. This is because the kinetic energy $\boldsymbol{p}^2/2m$ will be uncertain if we try to measure the position. But a measurement of potential energy in a sufficiently large region is, of course, possible. The quantity $E = T_0 = T + V$ can, however, be measured at a given point.

A beam of particles of infinite breadth in the z direction can be represented by a plane wave $\psi = A \exp\,[ikz - (i/\hbar)Et]$, where

$$k = \sqrt{\left[\frac{2Em}{\hbar}\right]}.$$

If the wave function is normalized in a volume V, then we have

$$\int_V |\psi|^2\, dV = |A|^2 V = 1.$$

Hence $|A|^2 = 1/V$. Thus $|A|^2$ can be regarded as the average number of particles per unit volume. The average number of particles crossing a unit area perpendicular to the z direction, per unit time, is given by $|A|^2 v$, where v is obtained from $E = (\frac{1}{2})mv^2$. The probability of finding one electron in a volume element dV at time t is

$$|\psi|^2\, dV = |A|^2\, dV = \frac{dV}{V}. \qquad (XII.1.4)$$

The number of particles crossing a given area per unit time is given by the normal component of the current vector with respect to the area. If $\boldsymbol{J}$ is the current vector and dS is the surface area, then the probability that a particle will cross an element dS of area in the time dt is

$$\boldsymbol{J}\cdot d\boldsymbol{S}\, dt, \qquad (XII.1.5)$$

where $\boldsymbol{J}$ is given by $(XII.1.2)$. For a plane wave of the form

$$\psi = Ae^{(i/\hbar)\boldsymbol{p}\cdot\boldsymbol{r}}e^{-(i/\hbar)Et},$$

the probability (*XII.1.5*) is given by $|A|^2\boldsymbol{v}\cdot d\boldsymbol{S}\,dt$.

For a beam of electrons or protons, $\boldsymbol{J}$ can be measured by measuring the charge falling on a collector. If we have many streams of electrons, say, they can be represented by a superposition of plane waves

$$\psi = \sum_n A_n e^{(i/\hbar)\boldsymbol{r}\cdot\boldsymbol{p}_n}e^{-(i/\hbar)tE_n}. \qquad (XII.1.6)$$

The interference of the waves would not affect the number of electrons. If the beams originate from different sources the wave function is

$$\psi = \sum_n A_n e^{i\phi_n}e^{(i/\hbar)\boldsymbol{r}\cdot\boldsymbol{p}_n}e^{-(i/\hbar)E_n t}, \qquad (XII.1.7)$$

where ϕ_n are arbitrary phases.

The average number of electrons moving into a volume V is, in a stationary-state beam, equal to the number moving out. This fact is expressed by

$$\nabla\cdot\boldsymbol{J} = 0. \qquad (XII.1.8)$$

For a nonstationary state we use the conservation law (*XII.1.1*).

XII.1.A. The Connection Between Classical and Quantum Mechanical Description

The time development of a wave packet is fixed by Schrödinger's equation. Thus a wave packet approximation may be regarded as the nearest analogue to a classical description. A wave packet must, on the average, have the properties of a classical system with long lifetime and must move according to classical laws. In accordance with our discussion of Schrödinger's equation, let us assume that a time-dependent wave function in Schrödinger's picture is given by

$$\psi(\boldsymbol{r}, t) = ae^{(i/\hbar)S}, \qquad (XII.1.9)$$

where a and S are real functions of $\boldsymbol{r}$ and t. An example of the form is provided by the transformation functions discussed in Chapter V. Let us assume that a and S are slowly varying functions of their arguments. This assumption is equivalent to saying that the change of potential energy within a de Broglie wavelength $\lambda = \hbar/p$ is small compared to kinetic energy, so the quantum features arising from the wave character of particles will not show up; therefore the corresponding description will be a good approximation to a classical picture.

Now, in analogy to a harmonic oscillator state [see (*VII.1.17*)], let us define the state of a dynamical system by

$$|\psi, t\rangle = \boldsymbol{\Psi}(t)|0\rangle, \qquad (XII.1.10)$$

where $|0\rangle$ will be called the constant state of zero energy and $\boldsymbol{\Psi}(t)$ is an operator satisfying Schrödinger's equation. Thus, if we write

$$\psi(r, t) = \langle \boldsymbol{r}, t|\boldsymbol{\Psi}(t)|0\rangle, \qquad (XII.1.11)$$

then it follows from (*XII.1.9*) and (*XII.1.10*) that

$$\boldsymbol{\Psi}(t) = e^{(i/\hbar)S}, \qquad (XII.1.12)$$

where now S is an operator function of the position operator $\boldsymbol{q}$ and time t, and

$$a = \langle \boldsymbol{r}t|0\rangle. \qquad (XII.1.13)$$

Hence

$$-\frac{\partial S}{\partial t}\, e^{(i/\hbar)S} = He^{(i/\hbar)S}$$

or

$$-\frac{\partial S}{\partial t} = e^{-(i/\hbar)S}He^{(i/\hbar)S}. \qquad (XII.1.14)$$

Using the relation

$$e^{-(i/\hbar)S}\boldsymbol{p}e^{(i/\hbar)S} = \boldsymbol{p} + \frac{\partial S}{\partial \boldsymbol{q}},$$

we obtain

$$e^{-(i/\hbar)S}He^{(i/\hbar)S} = H\left(\boldsymbol{q}, \boldsymbol{p} + \frac{\partial S}{\partial \boldsymbol{q}}\right)$$

and

$$-\frac{\partial S}{\partial t} = H\left(\boldsymbol{q}, \boldsymbol{p} + \frac{\partial S}{\partial \boldsymbol{q}}\right). \qquad (XII.1.15)$$

If we neglect the terms involving $\hbar$ we obtain

$$-\frac{\partial S_c}{\partial t} = H_c\left(\boldsymbol{q}, \frac{\partial S_c}{\partial \boldsymbol{q}}\right),$$

which is Hamilton-Jacobi equation.

Let us now assume that S can be expanded into a power series of the form

$$S = S_0 + \frac{\hbar}{i}\, S_1 + \left(\frac{\hbar}{i}\right)^2 S_2 + \cdots. \qquad (XII.1.16)$$

The Hamiltonian for an electron in an external electromagnetic field is

$$H\left(\boldsymbol{q}, \boldsymbol{\pi} + \frac{\partial S}{\partial \boldsymbol{q}}\right) = \frac{\boldsymbol{p}^2}{2m} + \frac{1}{2m}\left(\frac{\partial S}{\partial \boldsymbol{q}} - \frac{e}{c}\boldsymbol{A}\right)^2 + V(\boldsymbol{q})$$
$$+ \frac{1}{2m}\left[\boldsymbol{p}\cdot\frac{\partial S}{\partial \boldsymbol{q}} + \frac{\partial S}{\partial \boldsymbol{q}}\cdot\boldsymbol{p} - \frac{e}{c}(\boldsymbol{A}\cdot\boldsymbol{p} + \boldsymbol{p}\cdot\boldsymbol{A})\right]. \qquad (XII.1.17)$$

It can, up to the first order in $\hbar$, be written as

$$H\left(\boldsymbol{q}, \boldsymbol{\pi} + \frac{\partial S}{\partial \boldsymbol{q}}\right) = \frac{1}{2m}\left(\frac{\partial S_0}{\partial \boldsymbol{q}} - \frac{e}{c}\boldsymbol{A}\right)^2 + V(\boldsymbol{q})$$
$$+ \frac{\hbar}{m}\frac{\partial S_1}{\partial \boldsymbol{q}}\cdot\left(\frac{\partial S_0}{\partial \boldsymbol{q}} - \frac{e}{c}\boldsymbol{A}\right) \qquad (XII.1.18)$$
$$+ \frac{1}{2m}\left[\left(\boldsymbol{p}\cdot\frac{\partial S_0}{\partial \boldsymbol{q}} + \frac{\partial S_0}{\partial \boldsymbol{q}}\cdot\boldsymbol{p}\right) - \frac{e}{c}(\boldsymbol{A}\cdot\boldsymbol{p} + \boldsymbol{p}\cdot\boldsymbol{A})\right].$$

Using the commutation relations

$$\left[p_i, \frac{\partial S_0}{\partial q_j}\right] = -i\hbar \frac{\partial}{\partial q_i}\left[\frac{\partial S_0}{\partial q_j}\right], \qquad [p_i, A_j] = -i\hbar \frac{\partial}{\partial q_i}(A_j),$$

we can write (*XII.1.18*)

$$H = \frac{\pi_0^2}{2m} + V(q) + \frac{\hbar}{m}\frac{\partial S_1}{\partial \boldsymbol{q}} \cdot \boldsymbol{\pi}_0 + \frac{1}{m}(\boldsymbol{\pi}_0 \cdot \boldsymbol{p}) - \frac{i\hbar}{2m}\frac{\partial \pi_{0i}}{\partial q_i}, \tag{XII.1.19}$$

where

$$\pi_{0i} = \frac{\partial S_0}{\partial q_i} - \frac{e}{c}A_i. \tag{XII.1.20}$$

Substituting (*XII.1.19*) and (*XII.1.16*) in (*XII.1.15*) we obtain the equations

$$-\frac{\partial S_0}{\partial t} = \frac{\pi_0^2}{2m} + V(\boldsymbol{q}), \tag{XII.1.21}$$

$$-\frac{\partial S_1}{\partial t} = \frac{1}{m}\frac{\partial S_1}{\partial \boldsymbol{q}} \cdot \boldsymbol{\pi}_0 + \frac{1}{2m}\nabla_q \cdot \boldsymbol{\pi}_0, \tag{XII.1.22}$$

where, in obtaining (*XII.1.22*), we used the equation

$$\boldsymbol{p}|0\rangle = 0. \tag{XII.1.23}$$

That is, $|0\rangle$ is a state of zero momentum so the term involving $\boldsymbol{p}$ in (*XII.1.19*) can be dropped. Equation (*XII.1.21*) leads to the classical Hamilton-Jacobi equation. Equation (*XII.1.22*) can be written as

$$-\frac{\partial}{\partial t}(e^{2S_1}) = \nabla_q \cdot \left(\frac{1}{m}\boldsymbol{\pi}_0 e^{2S_1}\right). \tag{XII.1.24}$$

The wave function to the first order in $\hbar$ is

$$\psi(\boldsymbol{r}, t) = \langle \boldsymbol{r}, t|\boldsymbol{\Psi}(t)|0\rangle = \langle \boldsymbol{r}, t|e^{(i/\hbar)[S_0 + (\hbar/i)S_1]}|0\rangle = e^{(i/\hbar)S_0}e^{S_1},$$

where S_0 and S_1 are now functions of $\boldsymbol{r}$ and t. The probability density to the first order in $\hbar$ is therefore

$$\rho = |\psi|^2 = e^{2S_1}, \tag{XII.1.25}$$

so equation (*XII.1.24*) is just the conservation equation for the probability density e^{2S_1} and the current density,

$$\boldsymbol{J} = \frac{1}{m}\boldsymbol{\pi}_0 e^{2S_1}. \tag{XII.1.26}$$

From Heisenberg's equations of motion we have

$$\boldsymbol{v} = \frac{\partial H}{\partial \boldsymbol{p}} = \frac{1}{m}\boldsymbol{\pi}_0, \tag{XII.1.27}$$

and hence

$$\boldsymbol{J} = \rho \boldsymbol{v} \tag{XII.1.28}$$

proves that (*XII.1.24*) is the conservation law. Therefore, to the first order in $\hbar$, the expression e^{S_1} is the amplitude of the wave function ψ. The motion can be pictured in terms of a fluid, of density e^{2S_1} at any point and time, moving in the space of variables $\boldsymbol{r}$ with a velocity $\boldsymbol{v} = (1/m)\boldsymbol{\pi}_0$. Here equation (*XII.1.24*), written in the form

$$\frac{\partial \rho}{\partial t} + \nabla \cdot (\boldsymbol{v}\rho) = 0,$$

expresses the conservation of current density for such a fluid.

From the above argument it follows that

$$\boldsymbol{\Psi}^\dagger(t)\boldsymbol{\Psi}(t) = \boldsymbol{\Psi}(t)\boldsymbol{\Psi}^\dagger(t) = e^{(i/\hbar)(S-S^\dagger)}$$

is the operator statement of the fluid density, where we assume that

$$[S, S^\dagger] = 0.$$

Writing

$$S = S_R - i\hbar S_I,$$

we obtain

$$\boldsymbol{\Psi}^\dagger(t)\boldsymbol{\Psi}(t) = e^{2S_I}, \qquad (XII.1.29)$$

where $\boldsymbol{\Psi}^\dagger\boldsymbol{\Psi}(t)$ now corresponds to the operator form of the amplitude a in (*XII.1.9*).

XII.2. Probability and Waves

The basic difference between classical and quantum mechanical probabilities arises because in quantum mechanics probabilities are calculated in terms of wave functions satisfying Schrödinger s equation. The wave function is a probability amplitude. In classical mechanics—for example, statistical mechanics—we calculate directly the probability itself.

For an illustration of the quantum probability consider the penetration of a particle through a hole in a diaphragm placed at some distance from a photographic plate.

Classically if the particle is recorded at one point A of the plate then it would be impossible to observe an effect of the particle at another point B; that is, there could be no correlation between the two events at A and at B. In Fig. 12.1 the vertical parallel lines represent plane waves constituting a one-particle state moving toward the diaphragm with a momentum $\boldsymbol{p} = \hbar\boldsymbol{k}$. Quantum mechanically the plane waves representing the particle will be diffracted at the hole and will emerge to the right in the form of spherical waves having a limited radial extension. The aperture θ of the waves is given by $\theta \cong \lambda/a$. The spread Δq in position of the particle is equal to the radius a of the diaphragm. Hence $\Delta p \cong \theta p = (\lambda/a)p = \hbar/a = \hbar/\Delta q$ or $\Delta p\Delta q = \hbar$. Also, if we imagine a shutter on the hole, then during the time Δt when the shutter is open, the number of harmonic components present in the waves after they emerge from the hole is $\Delta\nu \cong 1/\Delta t = \Delta E/\hbar$ or $\Delta t\Delta E = \hbar$.

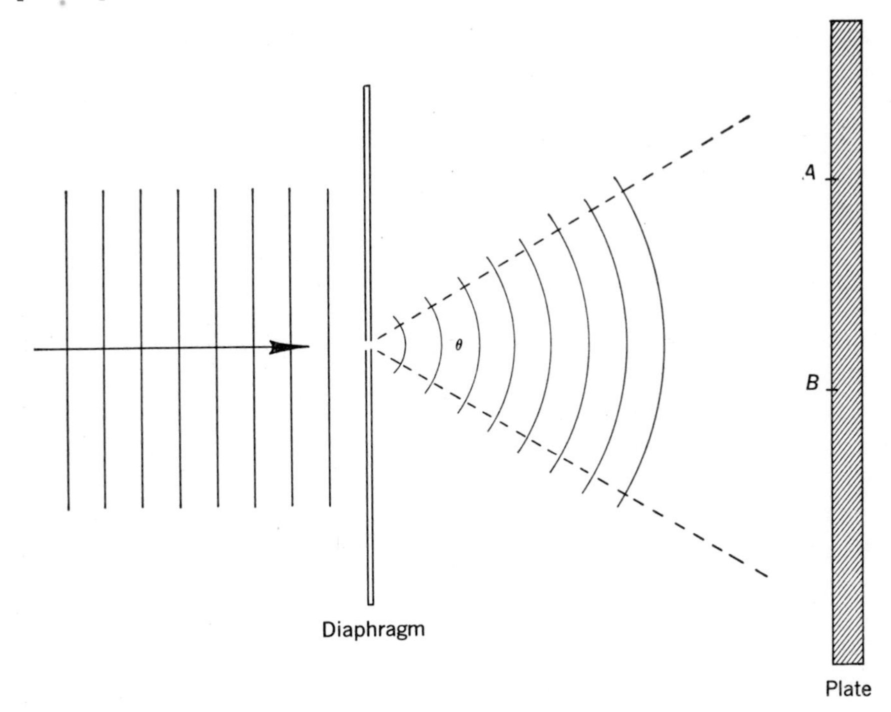

FIG. XII.1. *Penetration of a particle through a hole in a diaphragm placed at some distance from a photographic plate.*

According to quantum description the spreads ΔE, Δq, Δp result from interactions—that is, exchange of energy and momentum—with the diaphragm and also with the shutter. These interactions take place in accordance with the conservation of energy and momentum. The shutter, which leaves the hole opened for a time Δt, moves with a velocity $v \cong a/\Delta t$ and therefore a momentum transfer Δp between the particle and the diaphragm will cause an energy exchange with the particle, amounting to

$$v\Delta p \cong \frac{a}{\Delta t}\,\Delta p \cong \frac{1}{\Delta t}\,\Delta q\Delta p \cong \frac{\hbar}{\Delta t},$$

which is of the same order of magnitude as the energy spread ΔE. Hence a balance of energy and momentum is possible.*

Here we have assumed that the diaphragm and shutter are sufficiently heavy. We might be interested to know the momentum and energy of shutter

* This problem has formed the basis of interesting and detailed discussions between Einstein and Bohr. Einstein was not convinced of the limitation on a control of momentum and energy transfer involved in the passage of the particle through the hole and subsequent specification of the state of a particle. See the article by N. Bohr in P. A. Schilpp (Ed.), *Albert Einstein: Philosopher-Scientist,* Harper, New York, 1959, Vol. 1.

and diaphragm. Sufficiently accurate knowledge should allow us to control the momentum and energy exchange between the particle and shutter or diaphragm. But here we would expect a conflict with physical reality, since in accordance with uncertainty relations the location of the shutter in space and time, for example, becomes indeterminate. This uncertainty was the question raised by Einstein. It means that the state of the particle after it emerges from the hole is not specified correctly. However, the argument given in the above for the energy and momentum balance is based on the assumption that the diaphragm and the photographic plate have fixed positions in space and that, within the quantum mechanical description, it is not possible to predict *exactly* where the particle will be recorded.

The photoelectric effect or the Compton effect furnish good examples of situations where the diaphragm can be replaced by a particle. In both cases there is a large latitude in the knowledge of the position of the particle and it is then possible to predict, by means of an experiment, the direction in which an electron or a photon is scattered. The balance of energy and momentum is, then, clearly understood. For further illustration let us consider a diaphragm with two parallel slits, as shown in Fig. 12.2, where S is a source of electrons with the same energy.

The arrangement can be used for two different experiments. We can try to discover the electron (a) as a particle going through one of the slits (or holes) or (b) as a wave going through both holes at the same time. The electron will behave either as a particle or as a wave, depending on what we are interested to find out about it.

Under the usual conditions the beam of electrons will produce on the detector an interference pattern. If the beam is sufficiently intense, then the interference pattern will consist of a large number of small spots on the detector. Before the arrival of the electron at A, the wave function of the beam covers both slits 1 and 2. After the interaction with the slits 1 and 2, the plane waves must interfere destructively and form wave packets of widths Δ_1 and Δ_2, the sizes of the slits.

We can compute the probability of finding the electrons near 1 and 2. The corresponding wave functions, being wave packets, represent single electrons. An analogy exists between this situation and classical optics, and the propagation of electron waves can be described by means of a Huygen principle. If we know the value of the wave function on a given wave front, then we can express its value elsewhere as "the sum of contributions from different elements of the wave front." It implies that the probability amplitude as a function of time arises from the entire motion of the particle.

If $|\psi_1, t\rangle$ and $|\psi_2, t\rangle$ are the states corresponding to the passage of the parti-

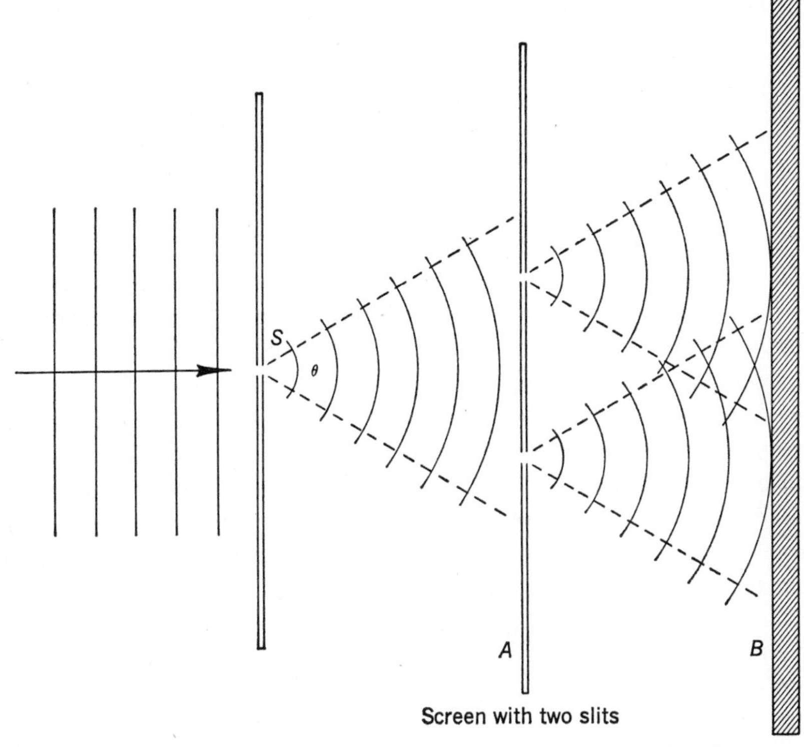

FIG. XII.2. *Penetration of a particle through two parallel slits in a diaphragm placed at some distance from a photographic plate.*

cles through slits 1 and 2, respectively, then the overall state corresponding to the two slits taken together is the sum of the two states:

$$|\Psi, t\rangle = |\Psi_1, t\rangle + |\Psi_2, t\rangle. \qquad (XII.2.1)$$

The wave function at an arbitrary point $\boldsymbol{r}$ to the right of the slits is

$$\psi(\boldsymbol{r}, t) = \psi_1(\boldsymbol{r}, t) + \psi_2(\boldsymbol{r}t), \qquad (XII.2.2)$$

where $\psi_1(\boldsymbol{r}, t)$ represents that part of the wave reaching the point $\boldsymbol{r}$ that has come from slit 1, and $\psi_2(\boldsymbol{r}, t)$ represents that part which has come from slit 2. The calculation of probabilities proceeds as follows:

(a) If only slit 1 is open, then the probability that an electron reaches the point $\boldsymbol{r}$ is

$$P_1(\boldsymbol{r}, t) = |\psi_1(\boldsymbol{r}, t)|^2.$$

(b) If only slit 2 is open, then the probability in question is

$$P_2(\boldsymbol{r}, t) = |\psi_2(\boldsymbol{r}, t)|^2.$$

(c) If both slits are open, then

$$P(\mathbf{r}, t) = |\psi_1 + \psi_2|^2 = P_1 + P_2 + \psi_1^*\psi_2 + \psi_1\psi_2^*.$$

Thus the Laplacian rule for the probabilities is modified by the appearance of the interference terms $\psi_1^*\psi_2 + \psi_1\psi_2^*$. These terms arise from the wave properties of the electrons.

When the position of an electron is observed, the interaction process involved in an observation will not change the probability but the wave function will change in an unpredictable and uncontrollable way. This kind of change in the wave function can be fitted into the mathematical scheme of quantum mechanics in the form of phase factors. We know that a state $|\Psi, t\rangle$ is completely determined, except for a phase factor, when its scalar product with every vector of a quantum frame of reference is known. Thus in an act of observation each part of the wave function corresponding to a definite position of the electron is changed during the course of interaction between the electron and the observing apparatus in such a way that the state is undetermined by an unpredictable and uncontrollable phase factor, $e^{i\gamma}$. In this case the total probability amplitude is

$$\psi'(\mathbf{r}, t) = e^{i\gamma_1(\mathbf{r})}\psi_1(\mathbf{r}, t) + e^{i\gamma_2(\mathbf{r})}\psi_2(\mathbf{r}, t), \qquad (XII.2.3)$$

where γ_1 and γ_2 are functions of position. The probability is

$$P = P_1 + P_2 + \psi_1^*\psi_2 e^{i(\gamma_2-\gamma_1)} + \psi_1\psi_2^* e^{-i(\gamma_2-\gamma_1)}. \qquad (XII.2.4)$$

We see that the interaction arising from the act of observation has changed the interference terms. At slits, before the waves actually do interfere, the phases γ_1 and γ_2 are equal. Outside the slits, $\gamma_1 \neq \gamma_2$. Therefore the statistical distribution of particles is affected by the phase through the interference terms.

To continue with the second double-slit experiment, let us suppose that the intensity of the source S is very low, so the detector at B (such as a Geiger counter) will record pulses representing the arrival of a particle, separated by gaps in time during which nothing arrives. If nothing else is done to disturb the above state of affairs, then we say that we are carrying out an observation to find out if the electrons are particles. The result is that in this case the electrons are actually particles.*

If the whole of screen B is covered with detectors, with a very weak source S, only one detector should respond; then after a small time interval another detector or the same one should record the arrival of an electron. For various

---

* R. P. Feynman, *Proceedings of the Second Berkley Symposium on Mathematical Statistics and Probability*, edited by J. Neyman, Univ. of California Press, Berkeley and Los Angeles, 1951.

positions $\boldsymbol{r}$ of the detector we shall measure the number of pulses per second. This is equivalent to determining the relative probability P that an electron passes from S to $\boldsymbol{r}$ as a function of $\boldsymbol{r}$. Qualitatively, this probability is illustrated in Figs. 12.3 to 12.6.

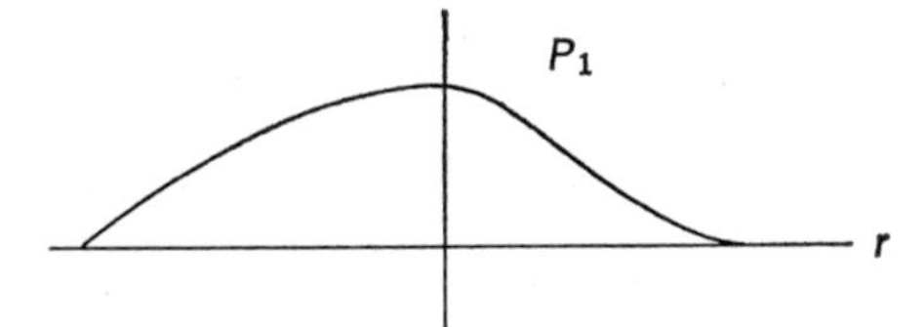

FIG. XII.3. *The probability distribution for the case of slit 2 closed.*

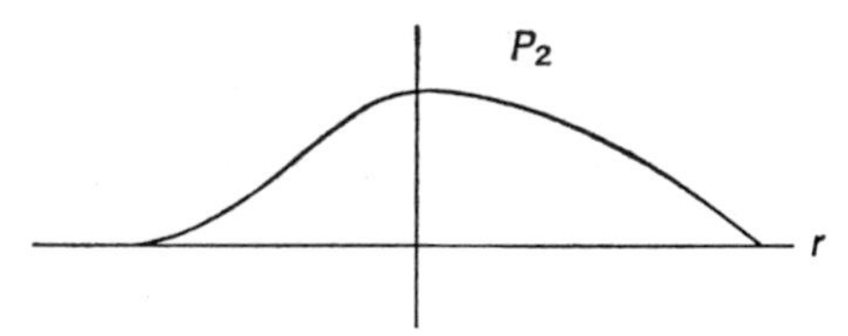

FIG. XII.4. *The probability distribution for the case of slit 1 closed.*

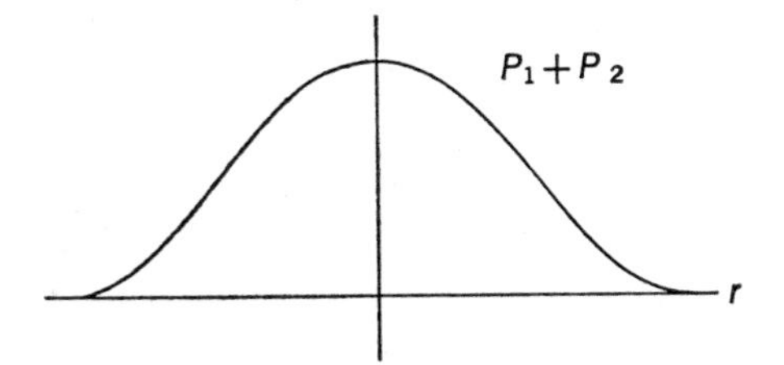

FIG. XII.5. *The classical probability that if both slits are open the particle goes through one hole or the other. The probability P of arrival of the particles at a point C on the detector is the sum of the probability P_1 of those coming from slit 1 and probability P_2 of those coming from slit 2.*

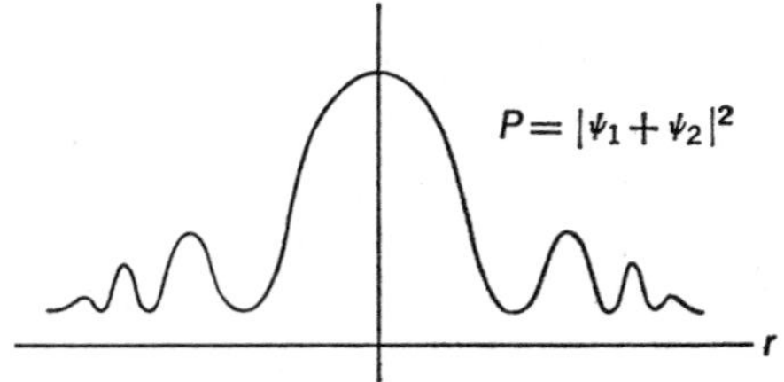

FIG. XII.6. *The quantum probability that it is not true that the electron passes from slit 1 or slit 2. The passage of the particle from one of the slits is not independent of its passage from the other slit. The waves will interfere and hence the Laplacian rule of addition of probabilities $P_1 + P_2$ will be replaced by the quantum rule $P = P_1 + P_2 +$ interference terms.*

For each electron there is a probability of going through slit 1 or 2, so the chance of arrival at $\boldsymbol{r}$, when no interference is possible through their wave nature, should be the sum P_1, the chance of arrival through slit 1, and P_2, the chance of arrival through slit 2. The probabilities P_1 and P_2 can be determined separately by closing one of the slits corresponding to the arrival of electrons from that particular slit. The sum of the two probabilities P_1 and P_2 is the classical distribution of the electrons and is represented in Fig. 12.5. However, this is not what one observes experimentally. The result $P = P_1 + P_2$ is obtained, because the electrons coming through slits 1 and 2 were particles alone, without wave properties. Therefore, this kind of statistical interpretation does not take into account the destructive interference brought about by the interaction between the electron and the observing apparatus. The interference arises from the wave nature of the electrons. The wave and particle properties of the electron—and consequently the destructive interference effect—can only be included within the quantum mechanical description. The chance of arrival at $\boldsymbol{r}$ with both slits open is not the sum of the chance with slit 1 alone open plus the chance with slit 2 alone open. The intensity of distribution in the interference pattern must be derived from the probability amplitudes and not from the probabilities themselves. The resulting probability P must be derived from a probability amplitude of arrival at $\boldsymbol{r}$ as a square of its modulus. The total probability amplitude is to be defined as the sum of two probability amplitudes.

Since $P \neq P_1 + P_2$, then it is not true that the electron passes through slit 1 or slit 2. But if we "watch" the electrons to see through which slit they pass, then they will pass either through slit 1 or through slit 2. The amplitude at $\boldsymbol{r}$ results from an incoherent superposition of the amplitudes ψ_1 and ψ_2; that is, after we interact the light used in locating the position of the electron, for example, with the electron, the total amplitude at $\boldsymbol{r}$ is $\psi = \psi_1 e^{i\gamma_1} + \psi_2 e^{i\gamma_2}$. Because of the unknown amount of disturbance of the electrons caused by "watching" them, the functions γ_1 and γ_2 can change in such a way that the interference between ψ_1 and ψ_2 will be destroyed. Consequently the probability that a particle can be found at the point $\boldsymbol{r}$ becomes $P = P_1 + P_2$. If we do not try to see through which slit the electrons pass, then the probability that an electron can be found at the point $\boldsymbol{r}$ is $P = |\psi_1 + \psi_2|^2$.

It is to be understood that if we try to see through which slit an electron passes, we change the chance of the electron's arrival at $\boldsymbol{r}$. The use of a weak intensity or low energy for the light to locate the electron will not help to reduce the disturbance of the electron. The photon's nature of light implies an exchange of a whole energy $h\nu$. One might think that with the use of light of long wavelength λ, the momentum $\hbar/\lambda$ can be made small. But this has its limitations also, since now we shall not be able to tell whether it was scattered from behind slit 1 or slit 2. In accordance with photon theory and the uncertainty principle, a source of light of wavelength λ cannot be located in space with a precision greater than that of the order of λ.

Thus the act of observation must produce enough disturbance to alter the distribution from Fig. 12.5 to Fig. 12.6. According to the uncertainty principle no apparatus exists or can be designed to determine through which hole the electron passes. Whenever we try to separate an observer and observed—or, to put it more objectively, when we do not attempt to determine through which hole the electron passes—we are not in a position to say that it will pass through one hole or the other.

For the occurrence of successive events, the calculation of probability is based on the knowledge of a probability amplitude

$$\psi = \psi_{S1}\psi_{R1}, \qquad (XII.2.5)$$

where ψ_{S1} is the amplitude to go from S to the hole at 1, and ψ_{R1} is the amplitude to go from the hole at 1 to R. For a hole that is large compared to the wavelength of the electron we have to consider each differential of the area of the hole, calculate the amplitude of going from S to this area times the amplitude of going from this area to R, and sum these amplitudes over the total area of the hole. Each differential area constitutes an alternative. Despite the indeterministic interpretation, the probability amplitude is obtained from a completely deterministic equation (Schrödinger's equation). A knowledge of ψ at $t = 0$ implies its knowledge at all subsequent times. The indeterministic trend in quantum mechanics arising from the finite value of Planck's constant h is not an entirely settled question.*

XII.2.A. The Quantum Mechanical Path of an Electron

A cloud chamber track of a particle is an experimentally determined path of the particle. The track has quite large dimensions compared to the possible size of the electron. The track of the particle is made visible through the formation of drops around every positive and negative ion by condensation of a vapor admixed to the gas of the chamber.

In order to form a quantum mechanical path of a particle for every position measurement one has to cause further disturbance of the system. A quantum mechanical path is, therefore, built up by a series of experiments. If the electron at time t_1, starts from, say, position $\mathbf{r}_1$, and later is found at position $\mathbf{r}_3$, it need not have had a definite position $\mathbf{r}_2$ at time t_2 in order to have a position $\mathbf{r}_3$ at a later time t_3. The fact is that $\mathbf{r}_1$ and $\mathbf{r}_3$ exist as a result of measurements carried out at times t_1 and t_3. But what were the positions of the electron between $\mathbf{r}_1$ and $\mathbf{r}_3$ corresponding to times $t_1 < t_2 < t_3$? The answer depends on the position measurements carried out between the times t_1 and t_3.

---

* A. Einstein, B. Podolski, and N. Rosen, *Phys. Rev.*, **47** (1935), 777.
N. Bohr, *Phys. Rev.*, **47** (1935), 676.
D. Bohm and Y. Aharonov, *Phys. Rev.*, **108** (1957), 1070.
A. Peres and P. Singer, *Nuovo Cimento*, **15** (1960), 902.
D. Bohm and Y. Aharonov, *Nuovo Cimento*, **17** (1960), 964.
D. Bohm, *Phys. Rev.*, **85** (1952), 166, 180.
L. de Broglie, *C. R. Acad. Sci. Paris*, **233** (1951), 641.
L. de Broglie and J. P. Vigier, *C. R. Acad. Sci. Paris*, **233** (1951), 1031, **234** (1952), 265.

Classically, a measurement between t_1 and t_3 could be made and a number $\mathbf{r}_2$ could be found such that the electron's position at time t_3 would still be $\mathbf{r}_3$. This statement in quantum mechanics is not true, since the number $\mathbf{r}_3$ found at time t_3 is $\mathbf{r}_3$ because of not measuring $\mathbf{r}_2$ at time t_2. The position of the electron need not have a specified value $\mathbf{r}_2$ at time t_2 in order for it to have the measured value $\mathbf{r}_3$ at time t_3.

In the classical case the probabilities are not subject to Heisenberg's uncertainty principle, while a quantum probability has to comply with its requirements.

If we let P_{ab} be the probability that if the measurement A—for example the position at time t_a—gave the result a, then measurement B will give the result b. Similarly we can define P_{bc}, P_{abc}, $\cdots$, $P_{abc\cdots e}$. If the events between a and b are independent of those between b and c, then

$$P_{abc} = P_{ab}P_{bc}. \qquad (XII.2.6)$$

If the statement that B is b is a complete specification of the state, then (*XII.2.6*) is also true in quantum mechanics. In general, we have the probability law

$$P_{ac} = \sum_b P_{abc}. \qquad (XII.2.7)$$

The summation over b means that the quantity B must have had some value at the time intermediate to A and C. We can say that it had the value b; since we are dealing directly with the probabilities themselves, no other quantity is needed to calculate the probability.

However, in quantum mechanics we first calculate the probability amplitudes. Accordingly we replace the law

$$P_{ac} = \sum_b P_{ab}P_{bc} \qquad (XII.2.8)$$

by

$$\phi_{ac} = \sum_b \phi_{ab}\phi_{bc}, \qquad (XII.2.9)$$

where the ϕ are probability amplitudes,

$$P_{ab} = |\phi_{ab}|^2, \qquad P_{bc} = |\phi_{bc}|^2, \qquad P_{ac}^q = |\phi_{ac}|^2,$$

so

$$P_{ac}^q \neq P_{ac}. \qquad (XII.2.10)$$

Statement (*XII.2.10*), as discussed before, contains the fundamental difference between the calculation of probabilities in classical and quantum physics. Why $P_{ac}^q \neq P_{ac}$ is clear. For the particle to go from a to c classically, it had to go through a condition such that B had to have some definite value b. The law of composition of probabilities as given by (*XII.2.8*) holds only where an attempt is made to measure B between the experiments A and C and where this measurement did not effect the result c found later by measuring

C. The statement that B had some value, even if one made no attempt to measure it, is a meaningless statement in quantum mechanics. The laws (*XII.2.8*) and (*XII.2.9*) are to be used in accordance with our decision whether we do or do not attempt to measure B. Of course, a measurement of B cannot escape the limitations imposed by the principle of uncertainty. The attempt to measure B must disturb the system, at least enough to replace the law (*XII.2.8*) by the law (*XII.2.9*).

Now let $q(t_a)$ and $q(t_b)$ be the position operators corresponding to the times t_a and t_b, and let $|q_a', t_a\rangle$ and $|q_b'', t_b\rangle$ be the eigenstates of $q(t_a)$ and $q(t_b)$, respectively. The amplitude ϕ_{ab} is an element of the unitary operator transforming $|q_a', t_a\rangle$ to $|q_b'', t_b\rangle$,

$$|q_b', t_b\rangle = U(t_b t_a)|q_a', t_a\rangle, \qquad (XII.2.11)$$

where $q_a' = q_b'$. The transformation function ϕ_{ab} is given by

$$\phi_{ab} = \langle q_a' t_a | q_b'' t_b\rangle = \langle q_a' t_a | U(t_b, t_a)|q_a'', t_a\rangle. \qquad (XII.2.12)$$

This is a transformation from a representation in which $q(t_a)$ is diagonal to one in which $q(t_b)$ is diagonal. If we choose a time t_b in the interval (t_a, t_c) we can write the usual relation

$$\phi_{ac} = \int \langle q_a' t_a | q_b''' t_b\rangle \, dq_b''' \, \langle q_b''' t_b | q_c'' t_c\rangle,$$

so

$$\phi_{ac} = \int \phi_{ab}\phi_{bc} \, dq_b'''. \qquad (XII.2.13)$$

Since the probability calculated from (*XII.2.13*) leads to interference terms, we can say that it is a typical representation of the wave nature of matter.

When measurements disturb the system the effect of this disturbance can be taken into account by means of phase factors. Therefore, if (*XII.2.13*) is the transformation function before a measurement, then, after the measurement, the system being disturbed by an unknown and unpredictable amount, the transformation function is

$$\phi_{ac} = \int e^{i\gamma(q'_b)}\phi_{ab}\phi_{bc} \, dq_b'. \qquad (XII.2.14)$$

If we measure $q(t_b)$, the phases $\gamma(q_b')$ must remain unknown, so the resulting probability is the square of the modulus of ϕ_{ac} averaged over all phases. This gives

$$P_{ac} = \int P_{ab}P_{bc} \, dq_b'. \qquad (XII.2.15)$$

Thus the electron acts as a wave if we do not attempt to verify that it is a particle. If we attempt to find its path, as if it were a particle, then we find that it behaves as a particle, and (*XII.2.15*) holds.*

---

* R. P. Feynman, *Rev. Mod. Phys.*, **20** (1948), 267. This paper contains Feynman's formulation of nonrelativistic quantum mechanics.

In order to construct a path we shall need more general forms of (*XII.2.13*) and (*XII.2.15*), given by

$$P_{abcd\cdots} = |\phi_{abcd\cdots}|^2. \qquad (XII.2.16)$$

The probability of the results a, c, k, for example, to occur if b, d, $\cdots$ are measured, is the classical formula

$$P_{ack} = \sum_{bd\cdots} P_{abcd\cdots k}. \qquad (XII.2.17)$$

If no attempt is made to measure the sequence of events between a and c and between c and k, then the probability that sequence a, c, k will occur is

$$P^q_{ack} = |\sum_{bd\cdots} \phi_{abcd\cdots}|^2 \qquad (XII.2.18)$$

or

$$P^q_{ack} = |\int dq'_b dq'_d \cdots dq'_k \, \phi_{ab}\phi_{bc}\phi_{cd} \cdots \phi_{lk}|^2. \qquad (XII.2.19)$$

XII.3. Definition of a Probability Amplitude for a Space-Time Path

Let $q(t)$ be an observable referring to the position of a particle, and let $q(t_i)$, for $i = 1, 2, \cdots$, be the operators corresponding to position measurements at times $t_i = t_{i-1} + \epsilon$, where ϵ is a small positive time interval. The operators $q(t_1), q(t_2), \cdots, q(t_n), \cdots$ can be used to define a quantum mechanical path. The quantum frames of references corresponding to $q(t_i)$ are constructed in terms of the eigenstates $|q'_1, t_1\rangle, |q'_2, t_2\rangle, \cdots, |q'_n, t_n\rangle, \cdots$ of $q(t_i)$, for $i = 1, 2, \cdots$, each defining a representation at time t_i.

From a classical point of view the successive values of the observables $q_1, q_2, \cdots, q_n, \cdots$ define a path $q'(t)$. In the limit $\epsilon \longrightarrow 0$ the above path is a continuous one. The probability that such a path will occur is a function of $q'_1 \cdots q'_n$, $P(\cdots, q'_1, \cdots, q'_i, \cdots, q'_{i+1}, \cdots)$, let us say. If we integrate $P(\cdots q'_1, \cdots, q'_{i+1}, \cdots)$ over a particular region R, we obtain the probability of a path going through the q which lie in the region R. The probability that q'_i lies between a_i and b_i and q'_{i+1} lies between a_{i+1} and b_{i+1}, and so on, is

$$\cdots \int_{a_i}^{b_i} \int_{a_{i+1}}^{b_{i+1}} P(\cdots, q'_i, q'_{i+1}, \cdots) \cdots dq'_i dq'_{i+1}$$

$$= \int_R P(\cdots, q'_i, q'_{i+1}, \cdots) \cdots dq'_i dq'_{i+1} \cdots. \qquad (XII.3.1)$$

The symbol R means that the integration is to be taken over those ranges of the variables which lie within the region R. If all the $q_1, q_2, \cdots$ were actually measured, and only those lying in the region R were taken, then the law (*XII.3.1*) would also be correct quantum mechanically. If no such detailed measurements were available, then the number of interest is the probability amplitude for the region R given by

$$\phi(R) = \lim_{\epsilon \to 0} \int_R \Phi(\cdots, q'_i, q'_{i+1}, \cdots) \cdots dq'_i dq'_{i+1} \cdots \qquad (XII.3.2)$$

The complex number $\phi(R)$ is a function of the variables defining the path. In the limit $\epsilon \longrightarrow 0$ the function Φ will depend on the entire path $q'(t)$ rather than just on the values of q_i at the particular times t_i. In this case we call $\Phi[q'(t)]$ the probability amplitude functional of the paths $q'(t)$.

We may now state Feynman's first postulate.

"*(I) If an ideal measurement is performed to determine whether a particle has a path lying in a region of space-time, then the probability that the result will be affirmative is the absolute square of a sum of complex contributions, one from each path in the region.*"

Feynman's second postulate gives a prescription for the computation of the probability amplitude function Φ of the paths $q'(t)$.

"*(II) The paths contribute equally in magnitude, but the phase of their contribution is the classical action S (in units $\hbar$), i.e. the time integral of the Lagrangian taken along the path.*"

The contribution $\Phi[q'(t)]$ from a given path $q'(t)$ is proportional to $\exp\{(i/\hbar)S[q'(t)]\}$, where the action S is given by

$$S[q'(t)] = \int_{t_0}^{t} L[\dot{q}'(t), q'(t)]\, dt \qquad (XII.3.3)$$

and L is the classical Lagrangian. The action $S[q'(t)]$ must be computed for all possible paths $q'(t)$ and not just for one point $q'(t)$. The action integral (*XII.3.3*) is a minimum for a classical path (see Section III.2.A). This suggests that we can write the action S as the sum of the actions corresponding to the time intervals (t_i, t_{i+1}):

$$S = \sum_i S(q'_{i+1}, q'_i), \qquad (XII.3.4)$$

where

$$S(q'_{i+1}, q'_i) = \min \int_{t_i}^{t_{i+1}} L[q'(t), q'(t)]\, dt. \qquad (XII.3.5)$$

In Feynman's formulation of quantum mechanics the use of the correspondence principle in taking over the classical Lagrangian differs from Schwinger's formulation in that it does not make use of a Lagrangian operator corresponding to a given classical Lagrangian. Feynman's theory deals directly with the transformation functions and not with their differential characterizations. The latter procedure is the main starting point in Schwinger's action principle, which we have already discussed in some detail (see Section V.5.B).

Because of the infinite extent of time the sum in (*XII.3.4*) is infinite and hence meaningless. This, however, is not an important obstacle and will be clarified as we proceed. For the present let us restrict ourselves to a finite, but arbitrarily long, time interval. Interesting and detailed discussions of various problems raised by Feynman's formulation have been given in the literature.*

Feynman's postulates (*I*) and (*II*) together with (*XII.3.4*) can be combined into the statement that

$$\phi(R) = \lim_{\epsilon \to 0} \int_R \exp\left[\frac{i}{\hbar}\sum_i S(q'_{i+1}, q'_i)\right] \cdots \frac{dq'_{i+1}}{A}\frac{dq'_i}{A}\cdots, \qquad (XII.3.6)$$

where the $1/A$ are normalization factors for the transformation functions corresponding to the time intervals $(t_{i+1} - t_i = \epsilon)$, so each transformation is weighed equally. The constant A will be determined later on. The integration in (*XII.3.6*) is taken over all values $\cdots, q'_i, q'_{i+1}, \cdots$ lying in the region R. Equation (*XII.3.6*) and definition (*XII.3.5*), coupled with the physical interpretation that $|\phi(R)|^2$ is the probability that the particle will be found in R, constitute Feynman's formulation of quantum mechanics.

XII.3.A. Feynman's Definition of the Wave Function

A quantum version of the principle of least action with "fixed end points" cannot be understood in the manner it is used in classical mechanics. However, following Dirac, for a finite time interval (t_a, t_b) we can write

$$exp\left[i/\hbar\int_{t_a}^{t_b} L(t)\,dt\right] = e^{(i/\hbar)S(t_b,t_a)} = B(t_b, t_a),$$

so $B(t_b, t_a)$ corresponds to $\langle q't_b|q''t_a\rangle$ in quantum theory. The numbers q' and q'' correspond to the eigenvalues of the operators $q(t_a)$ and $q(t_b)$ at times t_a and t_b, respectively.

Let us now divide the time interval (t_a, t_b) into a large number of time intervals $t_{i+1} - t_i = \epsilon$. Then we may write $B(t, t_0)$ as

---

* Y. Nambu, *Prog. Theor. Phys., Japan*, 7 (1952), 131.
W. Tobacman, *Nuovo Cimento*, **10** (1956), 3, 1213.
K. Symanzik, *Z. Naturforsch*, **9a** (1954), 809.
K. Goto, *Nuovo Cimento*, **10** (1956), 3, 533.
F. Coester, *Phys. Rev.*, **95** (1954), 1318.
J. M. Jauch, *Helv. Phys. Acta*, **29** (1954), 287.
G. Wick, *Phys. Rev.*, **80** (1950), 268.
L. Van Hove, *Physica*, **18** (1952), 145.
W. Thirring, *Ann. Phys.*, **3** (1958), 91.

$$B(t, t_0) = B(t, t_m)B(t_m, t_{m-1}) \cdots B(t_2, t_1)B(t_1, t_0). \qquad (XII.3.8)$$

The corresponding quantum equation is in terms of transformation functions:

$$\langle q't|q''t_0\rangle = \int \cdots \int \langle q', t|q^{(m)}, t_m\rangle\, dq^{(m)} \langle q^{(m)}, t_m| \\ |q^{(m-1)}, t_{m-1}\rangle\, dq^{(m-1)} \cdots \langle q^{(2)}, t_2|q^{(1)}t_1\rangle\, dq^{(1)} \langle q^{(1)}t_1|q^{(0)}t_0\rangle. \qquad (XII.3.9)$$

Each B in (*XII.3.8*) must be regarded as a function of the q at the two ends of the time interval to which it refers. This makes the right side of (*XII.3.8*) a function of all the intermediate q. Since the small variations of the q leave $B(t, t_0)$ stationary, the quantum analogue of the action principle is contained in the composition law of the transformation function given by (*XII.3.9*). This relationship has first been pointed out by Dirac. Feynman has extended the above procedure to a time interval of infinite extent.

The quantity Φ can be written as an infinite product of contributions arising from successive sections of the path. By making $\epsilon = t_{i+1} - t_i$ tend to zero, we obtain a continuously infinite product of transformation functions generating a "quantum path." This method can be used to define a quantity having the properties of a wave function.

A more abstract definition of a Feynman path can be based on the unitary transformations of quantum mechanics. The composition property of the unitary operator $U(tt')$, referring to a time interval (t, t'), is expressed by

$$U(tt') = U(tt_1)U(t_1t_2) \cdots U(t_{n-1}t'), \qquad (XII.3.10)$$

which can be generalized into

$$U(tt') = \prod_{n=1}^{\infty} U(\epsilon_n), \qquad (XII.3.11)$$

where

$$\epsilon_n = t_n - t_{n-1}, \qquad \lim_{n\to\infty} t_n = t'.$$

The transformation function can be expressed, therefore, as

$$\langle q'|U(tt')|q'\rangle = \lim_{n\to\infty} \int \cdots \int \langle q'|U(tt_1)|q_1\rangle\, dq_1 \langle q_1|U(t_1t_2)|q_2\rangle \\ dq_2 \langle q_2|U(t_2t_3)|q_3\rangle \cdots dq_{n-1} \langle q_{n-1}|U(t_{n-1}t_n|q_n\rangle. \qquad (XII.3.12)$$

This method is suitable for further formal developments of Feynman's ideas.

To continue with our discussion of Feynman's postulates (I) and (II), we choose a particular time t with respect to which the region R consists of three parts: (a) a region R' lying earlier in time than some $t'(t' < t)$; (b) a region R'' lying later in time than some $t''(t'' > t)$; (c) the region between t' and t'' in which all the values of q' coordinates are unrestricted (Fig. 12.7).

We have $|\phi(R', R'')|^2$ as the probability that the path occupies R' and R''.

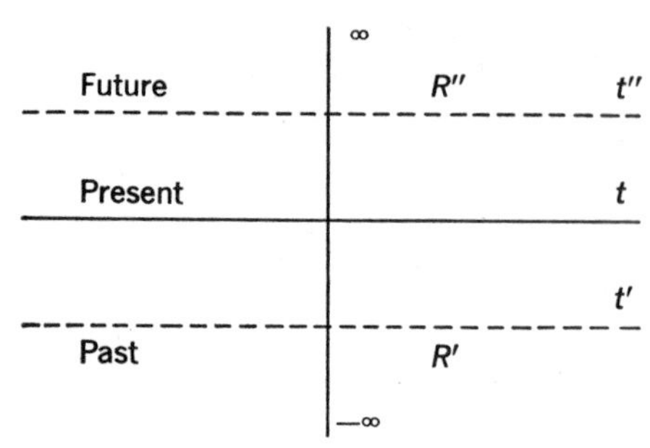

FIG. XII.7. *Schematic diagram of region R.*

The probability can be interpreted to mean that if the path has been in R', then it will be found in R''. Thus $|\phi(R', R'')|^2$, if properly normalized, is the relative probability that if the system was in region R', it will be found later in R''. If we assume that the particular time t corresponds to one particular point k of the subdivision of time into steps ϵ—that is, if we take $t = t_k$, where the index k depends on the subdivision t—then the exponential in the integrand of (*XII.3.6*) can be split up into a product of two factors,

$$\exp\left[\frac{i}{\hbar}\sum_{i=k}^{\infty} S(q'_{i+1}, q'_i)\right]\exp\left[\frac{i}{\hbar}\sum_{-\infty}^{k-1} S(q'_{i+1}, q'_i)\right]. \qquad (XII.3.13)$$

The first factor contains coordinates with index k or higher, while the second contains only coordinates with index k or lower. The integration in (*XII.3.6*) over all q'_i, for $i > k$, can be performed on the first factor, and it results in a function of q'_k (times the second factor). Next we integrate the second factor over all variables q'_i, for $i < k$. This results in a function of q'_k. The final form of (*XII.3.6*) is

$$\phi(R', R'') = \int \chi^*(q', t)\psi(q', t)\, dq', \qquad (XII.3.14)$$

where

$$\psi(q', t) = \lim_{\epsilon\to 0}\int_{R'} \exp\left[\frac{i}{\hbar}\sum_{i=-\infty}^{k-1} S(q'_{i+1}, q'_i)\right]\frac{dq'_{k-1}}{A}\frac{dq'_{k-2}}{A}\cdots, \qquad (XII.3.15)$$

$$\chi^*(q', t) = \lim_{\epsilon\to 0}\int_{R''} \exp\left[\frac{i}{\hbar}\sum_{i=k}^{\infty} S(q'_{i+1}, q'_i)\right]\frac{1}{A}\frac{dq'_{k+1}}{A}\frac{dq'_{k+2}}{A}\cdots. \qquad (XII.3.16)$$

The asterisk (on χ^*) denotes the complex conjugate of χ. The function ψ depends only upon the region R' previous to t, and it is completely defined if that region is known. It is independent of the future of the system with respect to the time t. The information for the future of the system is contained in χ. The ψ and χ, defined in the above manner, serve to separate past and future experiences of the system. Thus the function ψ completely determines the past state of the system, and the description is a causal one.

The function ψ can be used to predict future probabilities. This is done in the following sense: we could choose a time different from t, and we could have corresponding past and future regions r' and r''. Then, according to (*XII.3.14*), the probability of the path ending in any region R'' would be the same for R' as for r', because all that we have done is to shift the strip between t'' and t'. This means that future measurements will not distinguish whether the system had occupied R' or r'. In this sense the wave function ψ is sufficient to define those attributes that are left from past history which determine future behavior. We must remember that the wave function determines future probabilities only, and it does not contain deterministic information about future events. Regardless of the preparation of state ψ, equation (*XII.3.14*) asserts that the chance of finding the system in R'' is always the same as finding it in r''.

Finally, the probability that a transition from state ψ to state χ will take place is

$$\left|\int \chi^*(q't)\psi(q't)\,dq'\right|^2. \qquad (XII.3.17)$$

XII.3.B. Feynman's Derivation of Schrödinger's Equation

In the following it will be assumed that the Lagrangian L of the dynamical system is quadratic in the velocities. Since the wave equation describes the time development of the wave function, it is natural to expect that for a finite time difference ϵ, equation (*XII.3.15*) will permit the development of a simple recursive relation. At the time $t + \epsilon$ the equation corresponding to (*XII.3.15*) is

$$\psi(q'_{k+1}, t + \epsilon) = \int_{R'} \exp\left[\frac{i}{\hbar}\sum_{i=-\infty}^{k} S(q'_{i+1}, q'_i)\right]\frac{dq'_k}{A}\frac{dq'_{k-1}}{A}\cdots, \qquad (XII.3.18)$$

which can be written as

$$\psi(q'_{k+1}, t + \epsilon) = \int \exp\left[\frac{i}{\hbar}\sum_{i=-\infty}^{k-1} S(q'_{i+1}, q'_i)\right]\exp\left[\frac{i}{\hbar}S(q'_{k+1}, q'_k)\right]\frac{dq'_k}{A}\frac{dq'_{k-1}}{A}\cdots$$

$$= \int \exp\left[\frac{i}{\hbar}S(q'_{k+1}, q'_k)\right]\psi(q'_k, t)\,\frac{dq'_k}{A}.$$

Hence

$$\psi(q'_{k+1}, t + \epsilon) = \int \exp\left[\frac{i}{\hbar}S(q'_{k+1}, q'_k)\right]\psi(q'_k, t)\,\frac{dq'_k}{A}. \qquad (XII.3.19)$$

This gives the time development of the wave function $\psi(q', t)$. By a suitable choice of A, equation (*XII.3.19*) must lead to Schrödinger's equation. Equation (*XII.3.19*) is not exact, but is only true in the limit $\epsilon \longrightarrow 0$. We can, therefore, make ϵ as small as we please. Assumption of the validity of (*XII.3.19*) to the first order in ϵ is sufficient for the derivation of Schrödinger's equation.

We will consider a one-dimensional problem in which a single particle is acted upon by a potential $V(q')$. In Cartesian coordinates the path of a free particle is a "straight line." The integral (*XII.3.5*) can be taken along a straight line, and to the first order in ϵ we may use the procedure used in the classical theory (*III.2.14*) and write

$$S(q'_{i+1}, q'_i) = \tfrac{1}{2}\epsilon L\left(\frac{q'_{i+1} - q'_i}{\epsilon}, q'_{i+1}\right) + \tfrac{1}{2}\epsilon L\left(\frac{q'_{i+1} - q'_i}{\epsilon}, q'_i\right). \qquad (XII.3.20)$$

This is the same as

$$S(q'_{i+1}, q'_i) = \epsilon L\left(\frac{q'_{i+1} - q'_i}{\epsilon}, \frac{q'_{i+1} + q'_i}{2}\right). \qquad (XII.3.21)$$

In the absence of a vector potential and other terms we can, as in (*III.2.14*), write

$$S(q'_{i+1}, q'_i) = \tfrac{1}{2}m\epsilon\left(\frac{q'_{i+1} - q'_i}{\epsilon}\right)^2 - \epsilon V(q'_{i+1}). \qquad (XII.3.22)$$

Hence (*XII.3.19*) becomes

$$\psi(q'_{k+1}, t + \epsilon) = \int \exp\left\{\frac{i\epsilon}{\hbar}\left[\frac{m}{2}\left(\frac{q'_{k+1} - q'_k}{\epsilon}\right)^2 - V(q'_{k+1})\right]\right\}\psi(q'_k, t)\,\frac{dq'_k}{A}. \qquad (XII.3.23)$$

Let $q'_{k+1} = q'$ and $q'_{k+1} - q'_k = \xi$, so $q'_k = q' - \xi$. Then (*XII.3.23*) leads to

$$\psi(q', t + \epsilon) = \int \exp\left(\frac{im\xi^2}{2\hbar}\right)\exp\left[\frac{-i\epsilon V(q')}{\hbar}\right]\psi(q' - \xi, t)\,\frac{d\xi}{A}. \qquad (XII.3.24)$$

The appropriate boundary condition on $\psi(q', t)$ can be imposed by requiring that the integral (*XII.3.24*) converge. This means that $\psi(q', t)$ must fall off sufficiently for large q'. In the integration over ξ, since ϵ is very small, $\exp(im\xi^2/2\hbar)$ oscillates extremely rapidly, except in the region about $\xi = 0$. Thus it is only a small ξ that contributes effectively to the integral, for ξ is of the order $(\hbar\epsilon/m)^{1/2}$. We can expand $\psi(q' - \xi, t)$ as a Taylor series. Hence

$$\psi(q', t + \epsilon) = \exp\left[\frac{-i\epsilon V(q')}{\hbar}\right]\int \exp\left(\frac{im\xi^2}{2\hbar}\right)$$
$$\left[\psi(q', t) - \xi\frac{\partial\psi(q', t)}{\partial q'} + \frac{\xi^2}{2}\frac{\partial^2\psi(q', t)}{\partial q'^2}\cdots\right]\frac{d\xi}{A}. \qquad (XII.3.25)$$

We shall now use the relations

$$\int_{-\infty}^{\infty} \exp\left(\frac{im\xi^2}{2\hbar\epsilon}\right) d\xi = \left(\frac{2\pi\hbar i\epsilon}{m}\right)^{1/2}, \qquad (XII.3.26)$$

$$\int_{-\infty}^{\infty} \exp\left(\frac{im\xi^2}{2\hbar\epsilon}\right) \xi\, d\xi = 0, \qquad (XII.3.27)$$

$$\int_{-\infty}^{\infty} \exp\left(\frac{im\xi^2}{2\hbar\epsilon}\right) \xi^2\, d\xi = \left(\frac{\hbar i\epsilon}{m}\right)\left(\frac{2\pi\hbar\epsilon i}{m}\right)^{1/2}. \qquad (XII.3.28)$$

Expanding the left side of (*XII.3.25*) to the first order in ϵ, we get

$$\psi(q', t) + \epsilon \frac{\partial \psi(q', t)}{\partial t} + \cdots = \exp\left[\frac{-i\epsilon V(q')}{\hbar}\right]\left(\frac{2\pi\hbar\epsilon}{m}\right)^{1/2}\frac{1}{A}$$

$$\left[\psi(q', t) + \frac{\hbar\epsilon i}{m}\frac{\partial^2\psi(q', t)}{\partial q'^2} + \cdots\right]. \qquad (XII.3.29)$$

To have both sides agree to zero order in ϵ we must set

$$A = \left[\frac{2\pi\hbar\epsilon i}{m}\right]^{1/2}. \qquad (XII.3.30)$$

Hence, expanding the exponential containing $V(q')$, we obtain

$$i\hbar\frac{\partial\psi}{\partial t} = \frac{1}{2m}\left(-i\hbar\frac{\partial}{\partial q'}\right)^2\psi + V\psi, \qquad (XII.3.31)$$

which is Schrödinger's equation for a one-dimensional system.

Equation (*XII.3.19*) gives the time development of the wave function during a small time interval ϵ. We can compare it with Huygen's principle in optics, and regard it as Huygen's principle for matter waves: "*If the amplitude of the wave is known on a given surface the amplitude at a nearby point can be considered as a sum of contributions from all points of the surface. Each contribution is delayed in phase by an amount proportional to the time it would take the light to get from the surface to the point along the ray of least time in geometrical optics.*"

For a time-independent Hamiltonian the Schrödinger equation

$$i\hbar\frac{d}{dt}|\boldsymbol{\Psi}, t\rangle = H|\boldsymbol{\Psi}, t\rangle$$

can be solved by

$$|\boldsymbol{\Psi}, t\rangle = e^{-(i/\hbar)(t-t_0)H}|\boldsymbol{\Psi}, t_0\rangle.$$

Putting $t - t_0 = \epsilon$, we can write it as

$$|\boldsymbol{\Psi}, t + \epsilon\rangle = e^{-(i/\hbar)\epsilon H}|\boldsymbol{\Psi}, t\rangle. \qquad (XII.3.32)$$

Hence

$$\langle q'|\boldsymbol{\Psi}, t + \epsilon\rangle = \int \langle q'|e^{-(i/\hbar)\epsilon H}|q''\rangle\, dq''\, \langle q''|\boldsymbol{\Psi}, t\rangle$$

or

$$\psi(q', t + \epsilon) = \int \langle q'|e^{-(i/\hbar)\epsilon H}|q''\rangle\psi(q'', t)\, dq''. \qquad (XII.3.33)$$

A comparison of this equation with (*XII.3.19*) shows that it expresses the quantity $\langle q'|e^{-(i/\hbar)\epsilon H}|q''\rangle$ by an approximate integral operator for small ϵ.

But $\exp[(-i/\hbar)\epsilon H]$ is a unitary operator and therefore we can construct an ϵ-dependent position operator:

$$q(\epsilon) = e^{(i\epsilon/\hbar)H}q_0e^{-(i\epsilon/\hbar)H}.$$

Equation (*XII.3.33*) asserts that the wave function $\psi(q', t + \epsilon)$ at time

$t + \epsilon$ representing a state in which $q(\epsilon)$ is diagonal, is related to a wave function representing a state in which q corresponding to time t is diagonal, through a transformation function,

$$\langle q'|e^{-(i\epsilon/\hbar)H}|q''\rangle = \frac{1}{A}\, e^{(i/\hbar)S(q',q'')}. \qquad (XII.3.34)$$

For further discussion and applications of Feynman's formulation the reader should consult the papers by Polkinghorne* and by Mathews and Salam.†

---

* J. G. Polkinghorne, *Proc. Roy. Soc. London, A,* **230** (1955), 272.
† P. T. Mathews and A. Salam, *Nuovo Cimento,* **10** (1955), 2, 120.

CHAPTER XIII

ENERGY LEVELS AND SYMMETRIES OF SIMPLE SYSTEMS

XIII.1. The Hydrogen Atom

The hydrogen atom, like a harmonic oscillator, is another physical system that can be treated exactly both in nonrelativistic and relativistic quantum theory. Historically, it has always been a "test atom" for the new theories in physics, and every new attempt for its study gave rise to further observations and interesting discoveries about the interaction of matter and radiation. It is therefore worthwhile to devote to the hydrogen atom a fairly complete discussion. The hydrogen atom has, essentially, a simple spectrum, but its observation requires very high experimental precision. The basic characteristics of the atomic hydrogen spectrum are found to be in the visible region. A strong red line called H_α has a wavelength 6563 Å and appears in the solar absorption spectrum as a Fraunhofer line (usually called Fraunhofer C line). Besides the red H_α line there are strong blue H_β lines and violet H_γ lines; their respective wavelengths are 4861 Å and 4340 Å, and they correspond to Fraunhofer F and G lines. A further line falling into the visible region is the H_δ line, with wavelength 4101 Å. These lines are observed in the spectra of stars and they can be produced in the laboratory by electric discharges in a hydrogen gas.

The most recent experiments on the hydrogen spectrum have used the method of electron bombardment. In this method the hydrogen gas is excited by a controlled beam of electrons, which produce excited atomic states in hydrogen. In this way the fine structures of various atomic spectra have been studied exhaustively.

XIII.1.A. Relativistic Treatment

The nonrelativistic theory of the hydrogen atom can be deduced as the limiting case of the relativistic theory. The Hamiltonian, for the case where the effects arising from the finite electron and proton mass ratio are negligible, is given by

$$H = c\boldsymbol{\alpha}\cdot\boldsymbol{p} + \beta mc^2 + V(r), \qquad (XIII.1.1)$$

where $V(r)$ is the potential energy of the electron. Separation of the total angular momentum part of H can proceed as in the neutrino Hamiltonian (*IX.3.30*). The parity operator $\mathcal{P}$ is now to be replaced by the corresponding parity operator β of the four-dimensional representation [see (*VIII.5.42*)]. Hence the constant of the motion corresponding to (*IX.3.27*) of the neutrino is in the present case given as

$$\zeta = \beta(\hbar + \boldsymbol{\sigma}\cdot\boldsymbol{\mathfrak{L}}), \qquad (XIII.1.2)$$

which of course commutes with the Hamiltonian (*XIII.1.1*). The operator σ_r in (*IX.3.28*) is replaced by

$$\alpha_r = \frac{1}{r}\,\boldsymbol{\alpha}\cdot\boldsymbol{r}. \qquad (XIII.1.3)$$

Thus the Hamiltonian of the hydrogen atom in polar coordinates takes the form

$$H = c\alpha_r\left(p_r - \frac{i\hbar}{r}\right) + \beta mc^2 + \frac{i\alpha_r c}{r}\beta\zeta + V(r), \qquad (XIII.1.4)$$

where the operators α_r and β anticommute with the rest of the operators in H. The eigenvalues ζ' of Dirac's ζ operator replace the quantum numbers l and j. The eigenfunctions of H are of the form (*IX.3.34*), except that the spin vectors $|1\rangle$ and $|-1\rangle$ are now four-dimensional spinors. However, the spherical symmetry allows the reduction into two sets of two-component equations with the same structure. For example, because of spherical symmetry we can set $x_1 = x_2 = 0$ and $x_3 = r$ and obtain $\alpha_r = \alpha_3$. In this case we may replace the anticommuting operators α_3 and β by the anticommuting operators σ_2 and σ_3, respectively. The Hamiltonian becomes

$$H = c\left(p_r - \frac{i\hbar}{r}\right)\sigma_2 + \sigma_3 mc^2 - \frac{c}{r}\sigma_1\zeta + V(r). \qquad (XIII.1.5)$$

Hence the eigenvalue equation $H|\psi\rangle = E|\psi\rangle$ can be written as

$$\begin{bmatrix} mc^2 + V - E & -\frac{c}{r}\zeta' - \frac{\hbar c}{r} - icp_r \\ -\frac{c}{r}\zeta' + \frac{\hbar c}{r} + icp_r & -mc^2 + V - E \end{bmatrix}\begin{bmatrix} f^j_M \\ g^j_M \end{bmatrix} = 0.$$

Dropping the indices j and M, we finally have the equations

$$\left(\frac{1}{a_-} + \frac{1}{\hbar c} V\right) f - \left[\frac{q+1}{r} + \frac{\partial}{\partial r}\right] g = 0,$$
$$\left(\frac{1}{a_+} - \frac{1}{\hbar c} V\right) g - \left[-\frac{q-1}{r} + \frac{\partial}{\partial r}\right] f = 0, \qquad (XIII.1.6)$$

where

$$\frac{1}{a_-} = \frac{1}{\hbar c}(mc^2 - E), \qquad \frac{1}{a_+} = \frac{1}{\hbar c}(mc^2 + E), \qquad (XIII.1.7)$$

$$\hbar |q| = \zeta' = \hbar(j + \tfrac{1}{2}). \qquad (XIII.1.8)$$

For the attractive coulomb force the potential energy is $V(r) = -e^2/r$ and equations (*XIII.1.6*) become

$$\left[\frac{1}{a_-} - \frac{\alpha}{r}\right] u - \left[\frac{\partial}{\partial r} - \frac{1}{a} + \frac{q}{r}\right] v = 0,$$
$$\left[\frac{1}{a_+} + \frac{\alpha}{r}\right] v - \left[\frac{\partial}{\partial r} - \frac{1}{a} - \frac{q}{r}\right] u = 0, \qquad (XIII.1.9)$$

where we have used the substitutions

$$f = \frac{1}{r} e^{-r/a} u, \qquad g = \frac{1}{r} e^{-r/a} v, \qquad a = \sqrt{(a_+ a_-)} \qquad (XIII.1.10)$$

that are suitable for the discussion of a bound-state problem. The constant

$$\alpha = \frac{e^2}{\hbar c} \qquad (XIII.1.11)$$

is the Sommerfeld fine structure constant. The number q assumes the values

$$q = \begin{cases} -1, -2, -3, \cdots & \text{for } j = l - \frac{1}{2}, \\ 1, 2, 3, \cdots & \text{for } j = l + \frac{1}{2}. \end{cases} \qquad (XIII.1.12)$$

Equations (*XIII.1.12*) correspond to a selection rule imposed by the conservation of parity.

The most general solutions of equations (*XIII.1.6*) have been discussed by Darwin.* Dirac has solved equations (*XIII.1.9*) for the hydrogen atom.†

To find the nonrelativistic limit of (*XIII.1.6*) we put $E = mc^2 + T$, $(1/c)f = F$, and $g = G$, and obtain the exact equations

$$\left[\frac{2m}{\hbar} + \frac{T - V}{\hbar c^2}\right] G = \left[\frac{\partial}{\partial r} - \frac{q-1}{r}\right] F,$$
$$\frac{T - V}{\hbar} F = -\left[\frac{\partial}{\partial r} + \frac{q+1}{r}\right] G. \qquad (XIII.1.13)$$

---

* C. G. Darwin, *Proc. Roy. Soc. London, A*, **118** (1928), 654.

† P. A. M. Dirac, *Principles of Quantum Mechanics*, Oxford Univ. Press, Oxford, 1960.

The second term on the left side of the first equation is negligible compared to $2m/\hbar$, and so we get the approximate equations

$$G = \frac{\hbar}{2m}\left[\frac{\partial}{\partial r} - \frac{q-1}{r}\right]F \qquad (XIII.1.14)$$

$$(T - V)\,F = -\hbar\left[\frac{\partial}{\partial r} + \frac{q+1}{r}\right]G. \qquad (XIII.1.15)$$

Eliminating G, we obtain

$$(T - V)F = -\frac{\hbar^2}{2m}\left[\frac{1}{r}\frac{\partial^2}{\partial r^2}(rF) - \frac{l(l+1)}{r^2}\right]F, \qquad (XIII.1.16)$$

where we use the relation $q(q-1) = l(l+1)$, as follows from (*XIII.1.12*).

To solve equations (*XIII.1.9*) we apply a power series expansion method. We first cast the equations in the form

$$\begin{aligned} \frac{\alpha}{r}u + \frac{\partial v}{\partial r} + \frac{q}{r}v &= \frac{u}{a_-} + \frac{v}{a}, \\ -\frac{\alpha}{r}v + \frac{\partial u}{\partial r} - \frac{q}{r}u &= \frac{v}{a_+} + \frac{u}{a}, \end{aligned} \qquad (XIII.1.17)$$

where we observe that the definition of the constant a by $a^2 = a_+a_-$ is the same as the vanishing of the determinant of

$$\begin{bmatrix} \frac{1}{a_-} & \frac{1}{a} \\ \frac{1}{a} & \frac{1}{a_+} \end{bmatrix}. \qquad (XIII.1.18)$$

For the power series solution let us assume that

$$u = \sum_s c_s r^s, \qquad v = \sum_s d_s r^s, \qquad (XIII.1.19)$$

where the exponent s begins with an initial value s_0 and runs through the values $s_0, s_0 + 1, s_0 + 2, \cdots$. Substitution of (*XIII.1.19*) in equations (*XIII.1.17*) yields the recursion formulas

$$\begin{aligned} \alpha c_s + (s+q)d_s &= \frac{d_{s-1}}{a} + \frac{c_{s-1}}{a_-}, \\ -\alpha d_s + (s-q)c_s &= \frac{d_{s-1}}{a_+} + \frac{c_{s-1}}{a}. \end{aligned} \qquad (XIII.1.20)$$

From the vanishing of the determinant of (*XIII.1.18*), it follows that the determinant of the coefficients d_s and c_s on the left of (*XIII.1.20*) must also vanish. Thus the initial value of the exponent s is given by

$$s_0 = \sqrt{(q^2 - \alpha^2)}, \qquad (XIII.1.21)$$

where the negative value is discarded; otherwise it would lead to an infinite probability of finding the particle at the origin.

If we now multiply the first of (*XIII.1.20*) by a and the second by a_+ and subtract the results, we obtain

$$[\alpha a - (s - q)a_+]c_s + [\alpha a_+ + (s + q)a]d_s = 0. \qquad (XIII.1.22)$$

The probability of finding the particle at the origin must vanish. This boundary condition can be incorporated by requiring that rf and rg must tend to zero with $r \longrightarrow 0$. The existence of discrete energy eigenvalues depends on the convergence of the series (*XIII.1.19*). For large s the second of equations (*XIII.1.20*) and equation (*XIII.1.22*) yield

$$sc_s = \frac{c_{s-1}}{a} + \frac{d_{s-1}}{a_+}, \qquad a_+c_s = ad_s.$$

Hence

$$\frac{c_s}{c_{s-1}} = \frac{2}{as} = \frac{d_s}{d_{s-1}},$$

so the series converges:

$$\sum_s \frac{1}{s!}\left(\frac{2r}{a}\right)^s = e^{2r/a}.$$

If $E > mc^2$, then a is pure imaginary and therefore it does not correspond to a bound state. If $E < mc^2$, then for positive a the series must break off on the side of large s; otherwise we would get an infinite probability of finding the particle at large distances. Suppose that the series (*XIII.1.19*) terminates with the terms whose coefficients are c_s and d_s. In this case we must have $c_{s+1} = 0$ and $d_{s+1} = 0$; then equations (*XIII.1.20*) yield

$$\frac{d_s}{a} + \frac{c_s}{a_-} = 0, \qquad \frac{d_s}{a_+} + \frac{c_s}{a} = 0.$$

Using (*XIII.1.22*) to eliminate d_s we get

$$a_-[a\alpha - a_+(s - q)] = a[a_+\alpha + a(s + q)].$$

Hence the energy eigenvalues are

$$E = mc^2\left(1 + \frac{\alpha^2}{s^2}\right)^{-1/2}, \qquad (XIII.1.23)$$

where s differs from s_0 by an integer $n \geqq 0$. Thus

$$s = s_0 + n = \sqrt{(q^2 - \alpha^2)} + n.$$

The corresponding wave function is of the form

$$e^{-r/a}(r)^{\sqrt{(q^2-\alpha^2)}} \times \text{polynomial of degree } n.$$

If we neglect $\alpha^2 = (1/137)^2$, compared to q^2, then the energy E, effectively, depends on $n + |q|$. The states with quantum numbers (n, q) and $(n, -q)$

have the same energy eigenvalues or the two spectral lines with the same j, for which $l = j \pm \frac{1}{2}$ exactly coincide.

Formula (*XIII.1.23*) was first derived by Sommerfeld by the use of Bohr's orbit theory. Its expansion in powers of α^2 leads to

$$E - mc^2 = -\frac{R}{(n+q)^2}\left[1 + \frac{\alpha^2}{n+q}\left[\frac{1}{q} - \frac{3}{4(n+q)}\right] + \cdots\right], \qquad (XIII.1.24)$$

where R is the so-called "Rydberg constant," defined by $R = \frac{1}{2}e^4m/\hbar^2$. The first term in (*XIII.1.24*) corresponds to what we obtain both from Bohr's orbit theory and from the nonrelativistic theory. The principal quantum number of the nonrelativistic theory, $N = n + |q| = n + l + 1$, with l ranging from 0 to $N - 1$, is replaced in the relativistic theory by

$$N^2 = \tfrac{1}{2}\sqrt{(a^2 + s^2)}[s + \sqrt{(a^2 + s^2)}]. \qquad (XIII.1.25)$$

In the nonrelativistic limit, where $\alpha \longrightarrow 0$ and $s \longrightarrow n + |q|$, we obtain $N^2 = (n + |q|)^2$. The corresponding energy level formula and eigenfunctions are

$$E_N = -\frac{Z^2me^4}{2\hbar^2N^2} \qquad (XIII.1.26)$$

and

$$F_{nlm} = R_{nl}(r)Y_{lm}(\theta, \phi),$$

where the radial part of the wave function is defined in terms of Laguerre functions* by

$$R_{nl} = -\left[\frac{(n-l-1)!}{[(n+l)!]^3 2n}\right]^{1/2}\left[\frac{2Z}{n}\right]^{3/2} e^{-Zr/n} L_{n+l}^{2l+1}\left[\frac{2Zr}{n}\right], \qquad (XIII.1.27)$$

where the Laguerre function $L_\nu^\mu(\rho)$ is defined by

$$L_\nu^\mu(\rho) = \frac{d^\mu}{d\rho^\mu} L_\nu(\rho), \qquad L_\nu(\rho) = e^\rho \frac{d^\nu}{d\rho^\nu}(e^{-\rho}\rho^\nu).$$

They are normalized according to

$$\int_0^\infty (R_{nl})^2 r^2\, dr = 1.$$

XIII.2. Accidental Degeneracy and the Momentum-Space Description of Bound States

Because of the spherical symmetry of the potential energy there exist many states for the hydrogen atom with different magnetic quantum number

---

* In this book we shall not be concerned with the details of the eigenfunctions. A complete discussion of the relativistic and nonrelativistic eigenfunctions of the hydrogen atom is contained in H. A. Bethe and E. E. Salpeter, *Quantum Mechanics of One- and Two-Electron Atoms,* Academic, New York, 1957.

$L_3 = m\hbar$, which have the same total angular momentum l and the same energy. This corresponds to a degeneracy in the hydrogen atomic levels and it is a consequence of the invariance of potential energy with respect to the three-dimensional rotation group. Thus invariance under the operation of the elements of a symmetry group, together with certain conservation laws, leads to some kind of forced degeneracy of the system. In the following we shall show that a symmetry group in a given representation—for example configuration space or q representation—need not be the only one pertaining to a given system in another representation—momentum-space representation or p representation. In some quantum mechanical systems a certain symmetry that does not occur in a representation may reveal itself by going to another representation. This is a "hidden symmetry" of a dynamical system and can only arise from the invariance of the system under a different group of transformations.

Historically, a symmetry of the above type was observed by Fock* in the spectrum of the hydrogen atom. It was found that for a given principal quantum number n, angular momentum l, and the z component of the angular momentum, m, there were n^2 degenerate states—instead of $(2l + 1)$—with l ranging from 0 to $n - 1$ and m values from $-l$ to l. This "accidental degeneracy" was due to a higher symmetry in the system. Such accidental degeneracies are connected with the existence of further constants of the motion than can be recognized in a particular representation with a definite symmetry group. The latter was observed in the early stages of quantum mechanics by Pauli.† Such symmetries were later investigated for various systems by others.‡ An elementary discussion of the accidental degeneracy is summarized by McIntosh.§ A general formulation for Kepler-type problems has recently been discussed by Alliluev.||

We shall try to give a fairly comprehensive account of accidental degeneracy for the hydrogen atom from a group-theoretical point of view. But for this purpose we must first give a momentum-space representation of a bound state.

---

* V. Fock, *Z. Phys.*, **98** (1935), 145.
† W. Pauli, *Z. Phys.*, **36** (1926), 336.
‡ O. Laporte, *Phys. Rev.*, **50** (1936), 400 (A).
V. Bargmann, *Z. Phys.*, **99** (1936), 576.
O. Laporte and G. Y. Rainich, *Trans. Amer. Math. Soc.*, **39** (1936), 154.
A. W. Saenz, unpublished Ph.D. thesis, University of Michigan, 1949.
J. M. Jauch, *Phys. Rev.*, **55** (1940), 1132 (A).
J. M. Jauch and E. L. Hill, *Phys. Rev.*, **57** (1940), 641.
§ H. V. McIntosh, *Am. J. Phys.*, **27** (1959), 620.
|| S. P. Alliluev, *Soviet Phys. JETP*, **6** (1958), 156.

XIII.2.A. The Momentum-Space Description of Bound States

For the stationary state with energy E the momentum-space wave function $\phi(\boldsymbol{p}, t)$ in the wave equation (*V.2.30*) has the form

$$\phi(\boldsymbol{p}, t) = \phi(\boldsymbol{p})e^{-(i/\hbar)Et}.$$

In this case the wave equation (*V.2.30*) becomes an integral equation,

$$\left(E - \frac{\boldsymbol{p}^2}{2m}\right)\phi(\boldsymbol{p}) = \int V(\boldsymbol{p} - \boldsymbol{p}')\phi(\boldsymbol{p}')\, d^3\boldsymbol{p}', \qquad (XIII.2.1)$$

where $V(\boldsymbol{p} - \boldsymbol{p}')$ for Coulomb potential energy $V(r) = -Ze^2/r$ is given by [see (*V.2.31*)]

$$V(\boldsymbol{p} - \boldsymbol{p}') = \frac{-1}{(2\pi\hbar)^3} \int e^{(i/\hbar)\boldsymbol{r}\cdot(\boldsymbol{p}-\boldsymbol{p}')}\left(\frac{-Ze^2}{r}\right) d^3\boldsymbol{x}.$$

The integral on the right can easily be performed. To simplify the calculation we introduce a "screening" factor $e^{-\epsilon r}$, where ϵ is a positive small number.

Introducing polar coordinates with the polar axis in the direction of the $\boldsymbol{k}$-axis, we obtain

$$V(\boldsymbol{p} - \boldsymbol{p}') = -\frac{2\pi Ze^2}{(2\pi\hbar)^3} \int re^{ikr\cos\theta} \sin\theta\, d\theta\, dr,$$

where $\boldsymbol{k} = (1/\hbar)(\boldsymbol{p} - \boldsymbol{p}')$.
The θ integration leads to

$$V(\boldsymbol{p} - \boldsymbol{p}') = -\frac{2\pi iZe^2}{(2\pi\hbar)^3}\frac{1}{k} \int_0^\infty (e^{-(ik+\epsilon)r} - e^{(ik-\epsilon)r})\, dr.$$

Hence the Fourier transform of $V(r)$ is

$$V(\boldsymbol{p} - \boldsymbol{p}') = -\frac{Ze^2}{2\pi^2\hbar}\frac{1}{|\boldsymbol{p} - \boldsymbol{p}'|^2}. \qquad (XIII.2.2)$$

The integral equation (*XIII.2.1*) becomes

$$\left(E - \frac{\boldsymbol{p}^2}{2m}\right)\phi(\boldsymbol{p}) = -\frac{Ze^2}{2\pi^2\hbar} \int \frac{1}{|\boldsymbol{p} - \boldsymbol{p}'|^2}\phi(\boldsymbol{p}')\, d^3\boldsymbol{p}'. \qquad (XIII.2.3)$$

For bound-state solutions we write $E = -W$, where $W > 0$, and impose the condition that for $|\boldsymbol{p}| \longrightarrow \infty$ the function $\phi(\boldsymbol{p})$ must tend to zero; this is equivalent to saying that the probability of finding the particle at the origin must vanish. Furthermore, $\phi(\boldsymbol{p})$ must be zero or finite for $|\boldsymbol{p}| = 0$, which is the same as the vanishing of the probability of finding the particle at infinity. Thus the integral equation for bound states is

$$\phi(\boldsymbol{p}) = \frac{Ze^2}{2\pi^2\hbar}\frac{1}{W + \dfrac{\boldsymbol{p}^2}{2m}} \int \frac{d^3\boldsymbol{p}'}{|\boldsymbol{p} - \boldsymbol{p}'|^2}\phi(\boldsymbol{p}'). \qquad (XIII.2.4)$$

The wave function satisfies the normalization condition

$$\int |\phi(\boldsymbol{p})|^2 \, d^3\boldsymbol{p} = 1. \qquad (XIII.2.5)$$

If we put $\boldsymbol{p}' = \boldsymbol{p} + \boldsymbol{q}$ and assume that (q, Θ, Φ) are the polar coordinates of $\boldsymbol{q}$ and (p, θ, ϕ) those of $\boldsymbol{p}$, with respect to a fixed direction, we can write

$$\begin{aligned} \phi(\boldsymbol{p}') &= \phi(\boldsymbol{p} + \boldsymbol{q}) = e^{\boldsymbol{p}\cdot\nabla_q}\phi(\boldsymbol{q}), \\ \phi(\boldsymbol{p}) &= f_l(p) Y_{lm}(\theta, \phi), \\ \phi(\boldsymbol{q}) &= f_l(q) Y_{lm}(\Theta, \Phi), \end{aligned} \qquad (XIII.2.6)$$

where $f(p)$ [or $f(q)$] is a function of $|\boldsymbol{p}|$ [or $(\boldsymbol{q})$]. The angle between $\boldsymbol{p}$ and $\boldsymbol{q}$ is given by

$$\cos\alpha = \cos\theta\cos\Theta + \sin\theta\sin\Theta\cos(\phi - \Phi). \qquad (XIII.2.7)$$

Hence, the integral equation (*XIII.2.4*) becomes

$$f_l(p) Y_{lm}(\theta, \phi) = \frac{Ze^2}{2\hbar\pi^2} \frac{1}{W + \dfrac{\boldsymbol{p}^2}{2m}} \int \sin\Theta \, d\Theta \, d\Phi \, dq \, e^{\boldsymbol{p}\cdot\nabla_q} f_l(q) Y_{lm}(\Theta, \Phi). \qquad (XIII.2.8)$$

By using the addition theorem and the orthogonality property of spherical harmonics the integral equation (*XIII.2.8*) can be reduced to a one-dimensional integral equation of the form

$$f_l(p) = \frac{Ze^2}{\hbar\pi p} \frac{1}{W + \dfrac{\boldsymbol{p}^2}{2m}} \int_0^\infty dq \, q Q_l \left[\frac{\boldsymbol{p}^2 + \boldsymbol{q}^2}{2qp}\right] f_l(q), \qquad (XIII.2.9)$$

where the Legendre function of the second kind, Q_l, is related to the Legendre function of the first kind, P_l, by

$$Q_l(x) = \tfrac{1}{2} \int_{-1}^{1} \frac{P_l(u)}{x - u} \, du. \qquad (XIII.2.10)$$

The integral equation (*XIII.2.9*) can be solved exactly.

The discrete eigenvalues correspond to the energy levels of the hydrogen atom as obtained from solving the Schrödinger equation in the configuration space. The bound-state radial momentum space eigenfunctions for hydrogen are

$$f_{nl}(p) = \left[\frac{2(n - l - 1)!}{\pi(n + l)!}\right]^{1/2} n^2 2^{2(l+1)} l! \frac{n^l p^l}{(n^2p^2 + 1)^{l+2}} C_{n-l-1}^{l+1} \left[\frac{n^2p^2 - 1}{n^2p^2 + 1}\right],$$

where C_μ^λ is a Gegenbauer function, defined as the coefficient of a^μ in the expansion of $(1 - 2ax + a^2)^{-\lambda}$:

$$(1 - 2ax + a^2)^{-\lambda} = \sum_{n=0}^{\infty} C_n^\lambda(x) a^n.$$

The Gegenbauer function* is a solution of the hypergeometric equation

$$(1 - x^2)\frac{d^2G}{dx^2} - (2\lambda + 1)x\frac{dG}{dx} + n(n + 2\lambda)G = 0.$$

[Compare this with (*VIII.7.12*).]

Now, putting $p_4^2 = -2mE$ in (*XIII.2.3*), we can rewrite equation (*XIII.2.4*) for bound states in the form

$$(\mathbf{p}^2 + p_4^2)\phi(\mathbf{p}) = \frac{Zme^2}{\pi^2\hbar}\int\frac{\phi(\mathbf{p}')}{|\mathbf{p} - \mathbf{p}'|^2}\,d^3\mathbf{p}'. \qquad (XIII.2.11)$$

The Hamiltonian in configuration space is invariant under the transformations of the three-dimensional rotation group. These transformations are irreducible. But, as written in the form (*XIII.2.11*), the bound-state problem in momentum space exhibits a symmetry of the four-dimensional orthogonal group. This higher symmetry of the system can be represented by all possible motions of a hypersphere of unit radius in four-dimensional Euclidean space. The latter can in turn be represented by orthogonal transformations in the equatorial plane consisting of the stereographic projections of the points of the hypersphere. This means that the corresponding symmetry group is reducible and one speaks of "accidental degeneracy."

By analogy with the three-dimensional stereographic projections discussed in Section (VIII.4, we may regard the vector p_i/p_4, for $i = 1, 2, 3$, as the stereographic projections on the equatorial plane of a point q_1, q_2, q_3, q_4 on the hypersphere

$$q_1^2 + q_2^2 + q_3^2 + q_4^2 = 1. \qquad (XIII.2.12)$$

Thus we can write

$$q_1 = \frac{2p_1p_4}{\mathbf{p}^2 + p_4^2}, \qquad q_2 = \frac{2p_2p_4}{\mathbf{p}^2 + p_4^2},$$
$$q_3 = \frac{2p_3p_4}{\mathbf{p}^2 + p_4^2}, \qquad q_4 = \frac{p_4^2 - \mathbf{p}^2}{\mathbf{p}^2 + p_4^2}, \qquad (XIII.2.13)$$
$$\mathbf{p}^2 = p_1^2 + p_2^2 + p_3^2.$$

Hence, solving for the p, we get

$$p_1 = \frac{p_4}{1 + q_4}q_1, \qquad p_2 = \frac{p_4}{1 + q_4}q_2, \qquad p_3 = \frac{p_4}{1 + q_4}q_3, \qquad (XIII.2.14)$$

where

$$\mathbf{p}^2 + p_4^2 = \frac{p_4^2}{q^2}, \qquad q^2 = q_1^2 + q_2^2 + q_3^2.$$

From (*XIII.2.14*) we obtain

* W. Magnus and F. Oberhettinger, *Formulas and Theories for the Special Functions of Mathematical Physics*, Chelsea, London, 1949.

$$|\boldsymbol{p} - \boldsymbol{p}'|^2 = p_4^2 \left| \frac{\boldsymbol{q}}{1 + q_4} - \frac{\boldsymbol{q}'}{1 + q_4'} \right|^2$$
$$= \frac{2p_4^2}{(1 + q_4)(1 + q_4')} (1 - \cos \omega), \qquad (XIII.2.15)$$

where ω is the "angle" between two points Q and Q' of the hypersphere and is given by $q_\mu q_\mu' = \cos \omega$, with

$$\cos \omega = \cos \lambda \cos \lambda' + \sin \lambda \sin \lambda' \cos \gamma,$$
$$\cos \gamma = \cos \theta \cos \theta' + \sin \theta \sin \theta' \cos (\phi - \phi').$$

The polar coordinates for the q are defined by

$$q_1 = \sin \theta \cos \phi \sin \lambda, \qquad q_2 = \sin \theta \sin \phi \sin \lambda,$$
$$q_3 = \cos \theta \sin \lambda, \qquad q_4 = \cos \lambda.$$

By regarding q_4 as a function of q_1, q_2, q_3, the Jacobian for the transformation from the $\boldsymbol{p}$ to the $\boldsymbol{q}$ can easily be calculated. Thus we have

$$d^3\boldsymbol{p} = \frac{p_4^2}{q_4(1 + q_4)^3} d^3\boldsymbol{q},$$

where in polar coordinates we have

$$d\Omega = \frac{d^3\boldsymbol{q}}{q_4} = \frac{\sin^2 \lambda \, d (\sin \lambda) \sin \theta \, d\theta \, d\phi}{\cos \lambda} = \sin^2 \lambda \sin \theta \, d\theta \, d\lambda \, d\phi.$$

Hence the projected wave equation (*XIII.2.11*) becomes

$$\Psi(Q) = \frac{Zme^2}{4\pi^2 \hbar p_4} \int \frac{\Psi(Q')}{1 - \cos \omega} d\Omega', \qquad (XIII.2.16)$$

where we use the substitution

$$\phi = A(1 + q_4)^2 \Psi, \qquad (XIII.2.17)$$

A being a constant. Equation (*XIII.2.16*), as can be seen from the manner of its derivation, is invariant with respect to the group of four-dimensional orthogonal transformations. The latter is the hidden symmetry group of the bound-state problem for the hydrogen atom.

The eigenvalue of the integral equation (*XIII.2.16*) is $Zme^2/\hbar p_4$, expressed by $Zme^2/\hbar p_4 = n + 1$ or

$$E_n = -\frac{Z^2 me^4}{2\hbar^2 (n + 1)^2}. \qquad (XIII.2.18)$$

[Compare this with (*XIII.1.26*).]

As an interesting exercise the reader should show that the integral equation (*XIII.2.16*) can be replaced by the differential equation (*VIII.7.8*) for the four-dimensional orthogonal group. In this way we observe that the solutions of (*XIII.2.16*) are just hyperspherical functions defined by (*VIII.7.16*). These functions provide an irreducible representation of the group.

XIII.2.B. Accidental Degeneracy and Motion in a Constant Magnetic Field

The nonrelativistic theory has been discussed by Kennard, Darwin, Landau, Page, and Uhlenbeck and Young.* A more detailed discussion, involving various symmetries of the problem, has been given by Johnson and Lippmann.† Here we shall begin by establishing a complete analogy with the one-dimensional harmonic oscillator discussed in detail in Chapter VII. We shall assume a constant magnetic field in the z direction in space. The Hamiltonian for an electron in a magnetic field is given by

$$H = \frac{1}{2m}\boldsymbol{\pi}^2, \qquad (XIII.2.19)$$

where $\boldsymbol{\pi} = \boldsymbol{p} + (e/c)\boldsymbol{A}$ satisfies the commutation relations [see (X.4.8)]:

$$[\pi_i, \pi_j] = -\frac{ie\hbar}{c} f_{ij}, \qquad f_{ij} = \epsilon_{ijl}\mathcal{H}_l. \qquad (XIII.2.20)$$

From Heisenberg's equations of motion, $i\hbar(d\boldsymbol{\pi}/dt) = [\boldsymbol{\pi}, H]$, we obtain

$$\frac{d\pi_1}{dt} = -\omega_c\pi_2, \qquad \frac{d\pi_2}{dt} = \omega_c\pi_1, \qquad \frac{d\pi_3}{dt} = 0, \qquad (XIII.2.21)$$

where ω_c is the Larmor frequency $\omega_c = \dfrac{|e|\mathcal{H}}{mc}$.

The third equation of (*XIII.2.21*) yields the constant of the motion, $\pi_3 = \pi_{03}$. Using the equation $\boldsymbol{\mathcal{H}} = \nabla \times \boldsymbol{A}$, we easily infer that the vector potential $\boldsymbol{A}$ for a constant magnetic field in the z direction is given by

$$\boldsymbol{A} = \tfrac{1}{2}(\boldsymbol{\mathcal{H}} \times \boldsymbol{r}) \equiv (-\tfrac{1}{2}x_2\mathcal{H}, \tfrac{1}{2}x_1\mathcal{H}, 0),$$

so the constant of the motion π_3 is just

$$p_3 = p_{03} = \text{constant}. \qquad (XIII.2.22)$$

The first two equations in (*XIII.2.21*) can readily be solved by

$$\pi_+ = e^{i\omega_c t}\pi_+^0, \qquad \pi_- = e^{-i\omega_c t}\pi_-^0, \qquad (XIII.2.23)$$

where

$$\pi_\pm = \pi_1 \pm i\pi_2.$$

These solutions are quite similar to those of the one-dimensional classical harmonic oscillator represented by (*III.1.35*).

---

* E. H. Kennard, *Z. Phys.*, **44** (1927), 326.
G. C. Darwin, *Proc. Roy. Soc. London*, **117** (1928), 258.
L. Landau, *Z. Phys.*, **64** (1930), 629.
L. Page, *Phys. Rev.*, **36** (1930), 444.
Uhlenbeck and Young, *Phys. Rev.*, **36** (1930), 1721.

† M. H. Johnson and B. A. Lippmann, *Phys. Rev.*, **76** (1949), 828; **77** (1950), 702; **78** (1950), 329 (A).

By introducing the operators a_+ and a_-,

$$a_+ = \frac{1}{\sqrt{(2m\hbar\omega_c)}}\,\pi_+, \qquad a_- = \frac{1}{\sqrt{(2m\hbar\omega_c)}}\,\pi_-,$$

the Hamiltonian (*XIII.2.19*) can be rewritten as

$$H = \hbar\omega_c\left(N + \frac{1}{2}\right) + \frac{1}{2m}\,\pi_3^2, \tag{XIII.2.24}$$

where the occupation number operator N is defined by $N = a_+a_-$ and has the same properties as the one introduced by (*VII.1.13*). The operators a_+ and a_- satisfy the commutation relation $[a_-, a_+] = 1$.

From (*XIII.2.22*) and the form (*XIII.2.24*) of the Hamiltonian we see that the transverse and longitudinal motions of the electron are independent of one another—as in classical theory. The motion along the magnetic field is that of a free particle. The eigenvalues of the motion, as follows from the form of the Hamiltonian, are given by

$$E = \hbar\omega_c\left(n + \frac{1}{2}\right) + \frac{1}{2m}\,p_3^2, \tag{XIII.2.25}$$

where the first term refers to the eigenvalues of the transverse motion and the second term to the continuous eigenvalues of the free motion along the magnetic field.

Heisenberg's equations of motion, $i\hbar(dx_i/dt) = [x_i, H]$, yield

$$\frac{dx_1}{dt} = \frac{1}{m}\,\pi_1, \qquad \frac{dx_2}{dt} = \frac{1}{m}\,\pi_2, \qquad \frac{dx_3}{dt} = \frac{1}{m}\,\pi_3$$

for the position of the electron hence we easily obtain

$$x_3 = \frac{1}{m}\,p_3 + x_3^0$$

and

$$x_\pm^0 = x_\pm \pm i\sqrt{\left(\frac{2\hbar}{m\omega_c}\right)}\,a_\pm, \tag{XIII.2.26}$$

where $x_\pm = x_1 \pm ix_2$. The commutation relation $[x_-^0, x_+^0] = -2\hbar/m\omega_c$ gives the result

$$[x_1^0, m\omega_c x_2^0] = i\hbar. \tag{XIII.2.27}$$

Hence we infer that the canonically conjugate observables x_1^0 and $m\omega_c x_2^0$ obey the uncertainty relation

$$\Delta x_1^0 \Delta x_2^0 \geqq \frac{1}{2}\,\frac{\hbar}{m\omega_c}. \tag{XIII.2.28}$$

Therefore it is not possible initially to locate the center of the "orbit" of the particle exactly. However, at a later time t it is possible to measure the center of the orbit, by a simultaneous determination of the transverse coordinates and momenta, which are subject to the uncertainty relations

$$\Delta x_1 \Delta p_1 \geqq \tfrac{1}{2}\hbar, \qquad \Delta x_2 \Delta p_2 \geqq \tfrac{1}{2}\hbar.$$

Finally, we note that because of the commutation relations (*XIII.2.27*) the eigenvalues of x_1^0 and x_2^0 will coincide with the continuum of real numbers. Since x_1^0 and x_2^0 commute with the Hamiltonian, then to each energy will correspond an infinite number of eigenfunctions. Hence it follows that the energy is infinitely degenerate.

The hidden symmetry of the motion can be seen by writing the Hamiltonian (*XIII.2.19*) in the form

$$H = \frac{1}{2m}(p_1^2 + p_2^2) + \frac{1}{2} m\omega^2(x_1^2 + x_2^2) + H_L, \qquad (XIII.2.29)$$

where $\omega = \frac{1}{2}\omega_c$, $H_L = (1/2m)p_3^2 + \frac{1}{2}\omega_c L_3$, and $L_3 = x_1p_2 - x_2p_1$. The first part of the Hamiltonian H refers to the Hamiltonian of a two-dimensional isotropic harmonic oscillator. Furthermore, H_L commutes with H and L_3 commutes with p_3. The transverse part of the Hamiltonian can be written in the form

$$H_{\text{tr}} = \hbar\omega(N_1 + N_2 + 1) = \hbar\omega(a_1^+a_1^- + a_2^+a_2^-) + \hbar\omega, \qquad (XIII.2.30)$$

where the operators $a_\alpha^\pm$, for $\alpha = 1, 2$, defined by

$$a_\alpha^\pm = \frac{1}{\sqrt{(2m\omega\hbar)}}(p_\alpha \pm im\omega x_\alpha),$$

satisfy the commutation relations

$$[a_\alpha^-, a_\beta^+] = \delta_{\alpha\beta}. \qquad (XIII.2.31)$$

The eigenvalues of the motion are now given by

$$E = \frac{1}{2}\hbar\omega_c(n_1 + n_2 + 1) + \frac{1}{2m}p_3^2 + \frac{1}{2}\hbar m\omega_c, \qquad (XIII.2.32)$$

where n_1 and n_2 are eigenvalues of the occupation number operators $N_\alpha = a_\alpha^+a_\alpha^-$, for $\alpha = 1, 2$. The degeneracy arising in the transverse part of the motion is of the type discussed for the three-dimensional isotropic harmonic oscillator. Hence there is $(n + 1)$-fold degeneracy, where $n = n_1 + n_2$.

If we regard the operators $a_1^\pm$, $a_2^\pm$ as the components of a "spinor" in a two-dimensional space, then the Hamiltonian H_{tr} as given by (*XIII.2.30*) is invariant with respect to the group of unitary transformations

$$a_\alpha'^\pm = U_{\alpha\beta}a_\beta^\pm, \qquad (XIII.2.33)$$

where the infinitesimal generators of U transformations are Pauli spin matrices σ_i. The group of unitary transformations (*XIII.2.33*) is isomorphic to the three-dimensional rotation group. The latter is the hidden symmetry of the oscillator and is the cause of the accidental degeneracy of the eigenvalues of H.

Accidental degeneracy for simple relativistic systems has been discussed by Johnson and Lippmann. However, investigations on the hidden symmetries of bound states have not been pushed far enough to let us know if the concept of accidental degeneracy can find some applications in elementary particle physics.

XIII.2.C. Problems

1. Is there any relation between the symmetry group of the two-dimensional harmonic oscillator and the theory of angular momentum?

2. The non-Hermitian operator $a_1^- a_2^+$ is, for the Hamiltonian (*XIII.2.25*), a constant of the motion. Show that it represents the annihilation of one quantum of energy ($\hbar\omega_c$) from one coordinate, leaving it in an eigenstate, and the creation of the same energy in the other coordinate, which is also left in an eigenstate. What changes have taken place in the oscillator in its energy or its eigenstate? Is this related to accidental degeneracy of the oscillator?

XIII.3. The Zeeman Effect and the Lamb Shift

The splitting of the energy levels of an atom (with a one-valence electron) in an external magnetic field is called the Zeeman effect. These displacements of the energy levels arise from the interaction of the external field with electron spin and orbital angular momentum.

We know, in accordance with the hypothesis of spin, that an electron in the presence of an external field has a magnetic moment of magnitude $\mu = \mp e\hbar/2mc$ in the direction in which the electron spin is $\mp\frac{1}{2}\hbar$. The corresponding energy is $-\boldsymbol{\mu}\cdot\boldsymbol{\mathfrak{H}} = (e\hbar/2mc)\boldsymbol{\sigma}\cdot\boldsymbol{\mathfrak{H}}$. The effect of the magnetic field $\boldsymbol{\mathfrak{H}}$ on the orbital motion of the electron can be exhibited by writing the Hamiltonian for an electron in an external field $\boldsymbol{\mathfrak{H}}$. The Hamiltonian of a spinless electron—that is, regarding the electron as a Klein-Gordon particle—as follows from (*X.4.7*), is given by

$$H = eA_4 + c\sqrt{\left[\left(\boldsymbol{p} - \frac{e}{c}\boldsymbol{A}\right)^2 + m^2c^2\right]}, \qquad (XIII.3.1)$$

where e is the electron's charge. We shall be interested in the nonrelativistic limit of H; we shall neglect also the term $(e^2/2mc^2)\boldsymbol{A}^2$. The latter is responsible for the diamagnetism of helium, whose ground state is characterized by $s = 0$ and $L = 0$ and therefore there can be no Zeeman splitting in this case.

Thus the Hamiltonian is

$$H = \frac{\boldsymbol{p}^2}{2m} + \frac{e}{mc}\boldsymbol{A}\cdot\boldsymbol{P} + eA_4, \qquad (XIII.3.2)$$

where we use $\boldsymbol{A}\cdot\boldsymbol{p} = \boldsymbol{p}\cdot\boldsymbol{A}$, which follows from the commutation relation $[A_i, p_j] = i\hbar(\partial A_i/\partial x^j)$ and the Lorentz condition $\nabla\cdot\boldsymbol{A} = 0$.

In a uniform magnetic field we have

$$\boldsymbol{p}\cdot\boldsymbol{A} = \boldsymbol{A}\cdot\boldsymbol{p} = \tfrac{1}{2}\boldsymbol{\mathcal{H}}\cdot(\boldsymbol{r}\times\boldsymbol{p}) = \tfrac{1}{2}\boldsymbol{\mathcal{H}}\cdot\boldsymbol{L}. \qquad (XIII.3.3)$$

Taking the z-axis in the direction of $\boldsymbol{\mathcal{H}}$, we obtain

$$\boldsymbol{p}\cdot\boldsymbol{A} = \tfrac{1}{2}\mathcal{H}L_3$$

and

$$H = \frac{\boldsymbol{p}^2}{2m} + \frac{e\mathcal{H}}{2mc}L_3 + eA_4 \qquad (XIII.3.4)$$

or

$$H = \frac{\boldsymbol{p}^2}{2m} + V + \omega L_3, \qquad (XIII.3.5)$$

where V is the potential energy of the electron and $\omega = e\mathcal{H}/2mc = \frac{1}{2}\omega_c$ is the angular frequency of the Larmor precession. Hence we see that the external magnetic field effects the orbital motion of the electron by ωL_3. Thus the total effect of $\mathcal{H}$ is

$$H' = \omega L_3 + \mu\sigma_3\mathcal{H}. \qquad (XIII.3.6)$$

The interaction energy commutes with the Hamiltonian and is, therefore, a constant of the motion. The eigenstates of $\boldsymbol{p}^2/2m + V$ are also eigenstates of L_3; hence the energy eigenvalues of H as defined in $(XIII.3.5)$ are given by

$$E = E_0 + \hbar\omega m, \qquad (XIII.3.7)$$

where E_0 is the energy eigenvalue in the absence of a magnetic field. The first term in H' can be regarded as a magnetic moment energy arising from the orbital motion of the electron. Therefore the corresponding energy eigenvalues $\hbar\omega m$ do not depend on the quantum numbers n and l. Result $(XIII.3.7)$ implies that the eigenvalues in a magnetic field are split up. The corresponding splitting of spectral lines is given by

$$\nu_{mm'} = \frac{1}{h}(E - E') = \frac{1}{h}(E_0 - E_0') + \frac{\omega}{2\pi}(m - m')$$

$$= \nu_0 + \frac{\omega}{2\pi}(m - m'). \qquad (XIII.3.8)$$

If the emitted light is linearly polarized parallel to the magnetic field, then the magnetic quantum number does not change and the selection rule $(IV.4.14)$ holds. In this case the frequency of line does not change:

$$\nu_{mm} = \nu_0. \qquad (XIII.3.9)$$

However, if the emitted light is linearly polarized perpendicular to the direction of the magnetic field, then the selection rule (*IV.4.13*) holds. The corresponding line frequencies are given by

$$\nu_{m,m\pm1} = \nu_0 \pm \frac{\omega}{2\pi}, \qquad (XIII.3.10)$$

where ν_0 corresponds to the frequency of the unperturbed line. If the emitted light is viewed in a direction perpendicular to the magnetic field, in place of every unperturbed line of the atom there will appear a triplet of three equidistant lines, with the two components $\nu_0 + \omega/2\pi$ and $\nu_0 - \omega/2\pi$ polarized in a direction perpendicular to the field and the ν_0 component polarized parallel to the field. When a particular line is observed in a direction parallel to the field, only the components $\nu_0 + \omega/2\pi$ and $\nu_0 - \omega/2\pi$ appear with circular polarization about the axis of $\mathfrak{H}$. The two outer components of the triplet are separated by

$$\frac{1}{c}(\nu_{m,m+1} - \nu_{m,m-1}) = \frac{\omega}{\pi c} = \frac{e}{2\pi mc^2}\mathfrak{H} = \frac{\mathfrak{H}}{10710}\ \mathrm{cm}^{-1},$$

where $\mathfrak{H}$ is measured in gauss units.

A more general theory must treat the electrons as Dirac particles and hence the effect of the external field on the energy must be included. In this case the perturbing energy H' as given by (*XIII.3.6*) can be written as

$$H' = \mu\mathfrak{H}\cdot(\boldsymbol{L} + g_s\boldsymbol{S}), \qquad (XIII.3.11)$$

where, for Dirac theory, $\boldsymbol{S} = \frac{1}{2}\hbar\boldsymbol{\sigma}$ and $g_s = 2$. In terms of the total angular momentum we write it as

$$H' = \mu\mathfrak{H}\cdot[\boldsymbol{J} + (g_s - 1)\boldsymbol{S}]. \qquad (XIII.3.12)$$

The complete interaction energy must include the spin-orbit coupling term

$$H_{so} = \frac{e^2}{2m^2c^2}\frac{1}{r^3}\boldsymbol{S}\cdot\boldsymbol{L}.$$

Thus the complete energy is

$$H_{\mathrm{I}} = H' + H_{so}. \qquad (XIII.3.13)$$

A detailed calculation by Bethe* gives the perturbed level formula

$$E_{nljm} = (H_{so})_{nlj} + \mathfrak{H}\mu gm, \qquad (XIII.3.14)$$

where m is the eigenvalue of J_3, and

$$g = 1 + (g_s - 1)\left[\frac{j(j+1) + s(s+1) - l(l+1)}{2j(j+1)}\right] \qquad (XIII.3.15)$$

is the "Lande splitting factor." The quantity $(H_{so})_{nlj}$ represents the eigenvalue of H_{so}. The splitting of the spectral lines in a magnetic field in this case

---

* H. A. Bethe and E. E. Salpeter, *Quantum Mechanics of One- and Two-Electron Systems*, Academic, New York, 1957.

is more complicated; it is called the "anomalous Zeeman effect." The Lande g factor above comes from the expectation value of the spin $\boldsymbol{S}$ with respect to the simultaneous eigenstates of $\boldsymbol{L}^2$, $\boldsymbol{S}^2$, and $\boldsymbol{J}^2$. From (*IV.4.3*) and (*IV.4.4*), with $\boldsymbol{\kappa}$ replaced by $\boldsymbol{S}$, we obtain

$$\tfrac{1}{4}[\boldsymbol{J}^2, [\boldsymbol{J}^2, \boldsymbol{S}]] = \tfrac{1}{2}\hbar^2(\boldsymbol{J}^2\boldsymbol{S} + \boldsymbol{S}\boldsymbol{J}^2) - \hbar^2\boldsymbol{J}(\boldsymbol{J}\cdot\boldsymbol{S}). \qquad (XIII.3.16)$$

The average value of the left side is zero and therefore the right side yields

$$\langle \boldsymbol{S} \rangle = \left\langle \frac{\boldsymbol{J}\cdot\boldsymbol{S}}{\boldsymbol{J}^2} \right\rangle_{lsj} \langle \boldsymbol{J} \rangle = \left\langle \frac{\boldsymbol{J}^2 + \boldsymbol{S}^2 - \boldsymbol{L}^2}{2\boldsymbol{J}^2} \right\rangle_{lsj} \langle \boldsymbol{J} \rangle$$

$$= \frac{j(j+1) + s(s+1) - l(l+1)}{2j(j+1)} \langle \boldsymbol{J} \rangle, \qquad (XIII.3.17)$$

In the derivation of the energy formula (*XIII.3.14*) it was assumed that H' is a small perturbation to the spin-orbit coupling energy H_{so}. The second term in (*XIII.3.14*) is a first-order term obtained from calculating the average value of H' with respect to the eigenstates of H_{so}. The case where H_{so} is small compared to H' (strong magnetic field) is called the "complete Pashen-Back effect." In this case one calculates the average value of H_{so} with respect to the eigenstates of H', corresponding to its eigenvalues

$$\mu\mathcal{H}(m_j + s), \qquad (XIII.3.18)$$

with $s = \pm\frac{1}{2}$ and $m_j = m + s$. The average value of H_{so} is

$$\langle H_{so} \rangle = ms\frac{\Delta E}{l + \frac{1}{2}}, \qquad (XIII.3.19)$$

where

$$\Delta E = E_{j=l+1/2} - E_{j=l-1/2} = \frac{e^2}{2m^2c^2}\left\langle \frac{1}{r^3} \right\rangle \langle \boldsymbol{S}\cdot\boldsymbol{L} \rangle$$

$$= \frac{e^2}{2m^2c^2}\left\langle \frac{1}{r^3} \right\rangle \begin{cases} l & \text{if } l < \frac{1}{2}, \\ l + \frac{1}{2} & \text{if } l > \frac{1}{2}. \end{cases}$$

Hence the total energy of the atom is

$$E = \mu\mathcal{H}(m_j + s) + ms\frac{\Delta E}{l + \frac{1}{2}} + E_0. \qquad (XIII.3.20)$$

The recent microwave techniques used in the measurements of the anomalous Zeeman effect have provided greater precision and have led to observable discrepancies between Dirac theory and experimental observation when g_s differs slightly from 2 (attributed to an anomalous magnetic moment of the electron).

The same experimental techniques have been used for the measurements in the absence of a magnetic field. The experiments of Lamb and Retherford*

---

* W. E. Lamb and R. C. Retherford, *Phys. Rev.* **79** (1950), 549; **81** (1951), 222; **86** (1951), 1014. See also W. E. Lamb, *Rep. Prog. Phys.*, **14** (1951), 19.

have shown that for any n there is a shift in the S state of about 10% of the fine structure separation between the levels $j = \frac{1}{2}$ and $\frac{3}{2}$. This shift is zero in Dirac's theory. Because of the metastability of $2S$ states ($n = 2$), Lamb's experiments on these states have been carried out without much difficulty. The experiments prove that there is a Lamb shift in the hydrogen energy levels; that is, the energy by which the $2S_{1/2}$ state lies higher than $2P_{1/2}$.

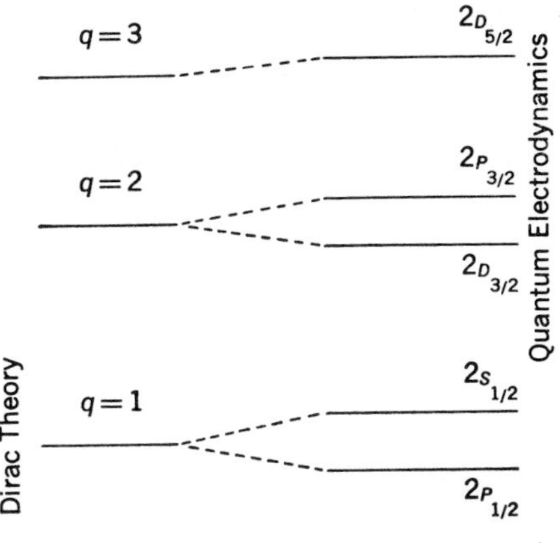

FIG. XIII.1. *The states with $n = 3$ in hydrogen.*

The experimental results for the separations $2S_{1/2} - 2P_{1/2}$ and $2S_{1/2} - 2P_{3/2}$ give also a very accurate experimental value for the fine structure separation $2P_{1/2} - 2P_{3/2}$.

According to Dirac's theory the levels having the same radial quantum number n and total angular momentum j are degenerate. This is shown for $n = 2$ in Fig. 13.2.

A further splitting of levels comes from the electron's interaction with the nuclear magnetic moment. The nuclear magnetic moment is, roughly, of the order of $e\hbar/Mc$, where M is the nucleon mass, being smaller than the electron's magnetic moment by a factor of one thousand. Therefore, the electron's interaction with the nuclear moment will be smaller than the ordinary fine structure splitting by a factor of the same order. The most closely adjacent energy levels of atomic states differ in the relative orientation of orbital and electron spin angular momenta. In a closer examination of the fine structure it is found that each spectral line of the fine structure can in turn be resolved into further lines or "hyperfine structure." This arises from the interaction of the magnetic moment of the nucleus with the orbital motion of the electron.

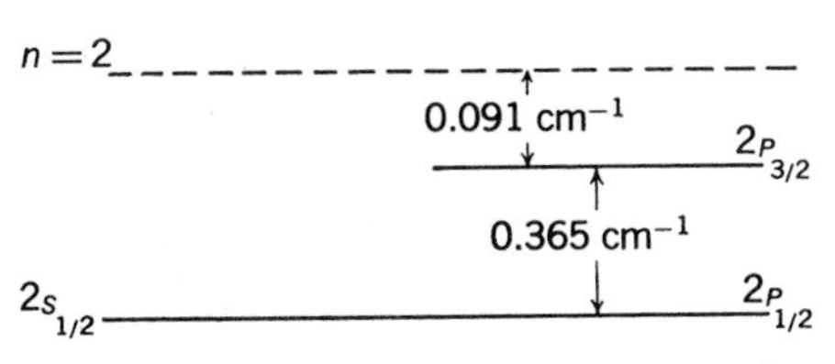

FIG. XIII.2. *The fine structure of $n = 2$ levels in Dirac's theory.*

The Lamb shift, $2S_{1/2} - 2P_{1/2}$, is completely accounted for by an improved formulation of quantum electrodynamics.*

* J. M. Jauch and F. Rohrlich, *Theory of Photons and Electrons*, Addison-Wesley, Reading, Mass., 1955. This book discusses the subject matter in detail and contains also a complete list of references to the papers by R. P. Feynman, J. Schwinger, and F. J. Dyson.

The separations of some of the Zeeman components of the states $2S_{1/2}$, $2P_{1/2}$, and $2P_{3/2}$ were the main results of the Lamb-Retherford experiment. See Figs. XIII.3, XIII.4, and XIII.5.

The experimental results of Lamb and Retherford are displaced by about

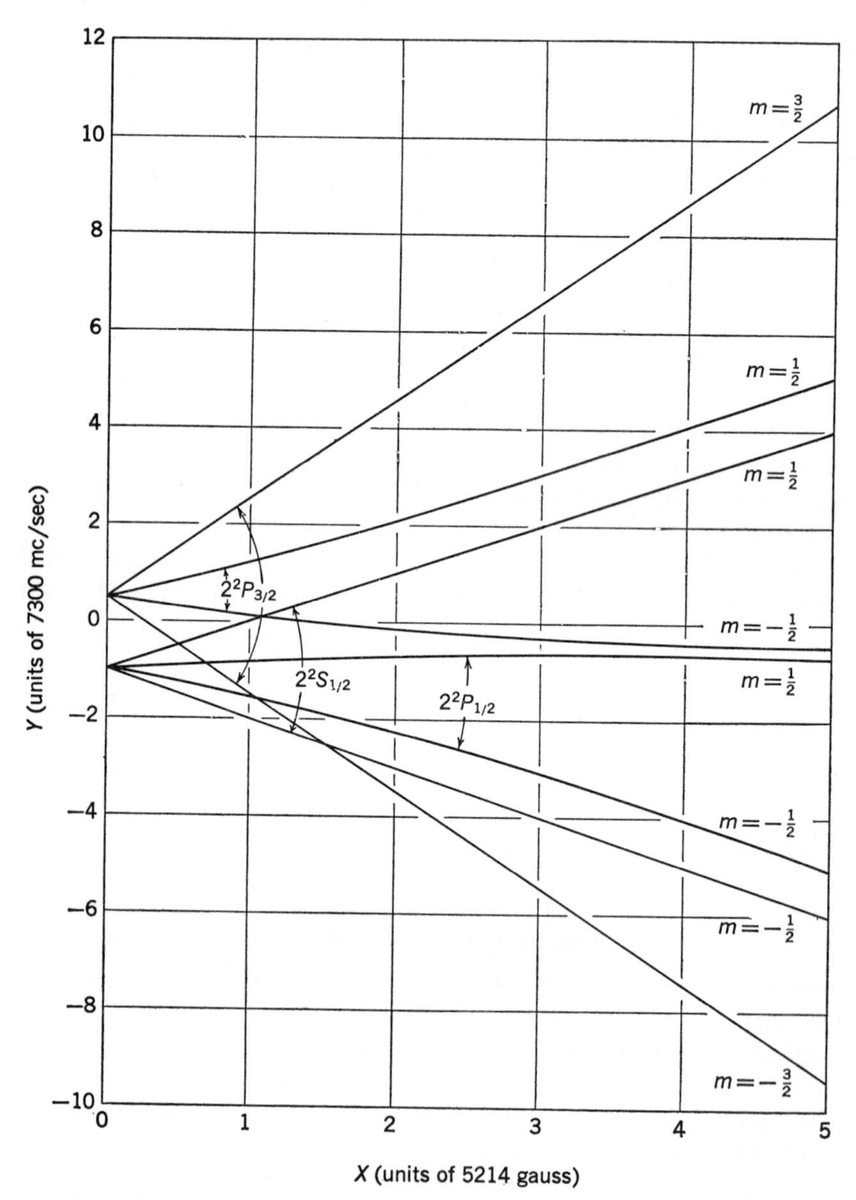

FIG. XIII.3. *Zeeman component energy levels for $n = 2$ in hydrogen, calculated from Dirac's theory.*

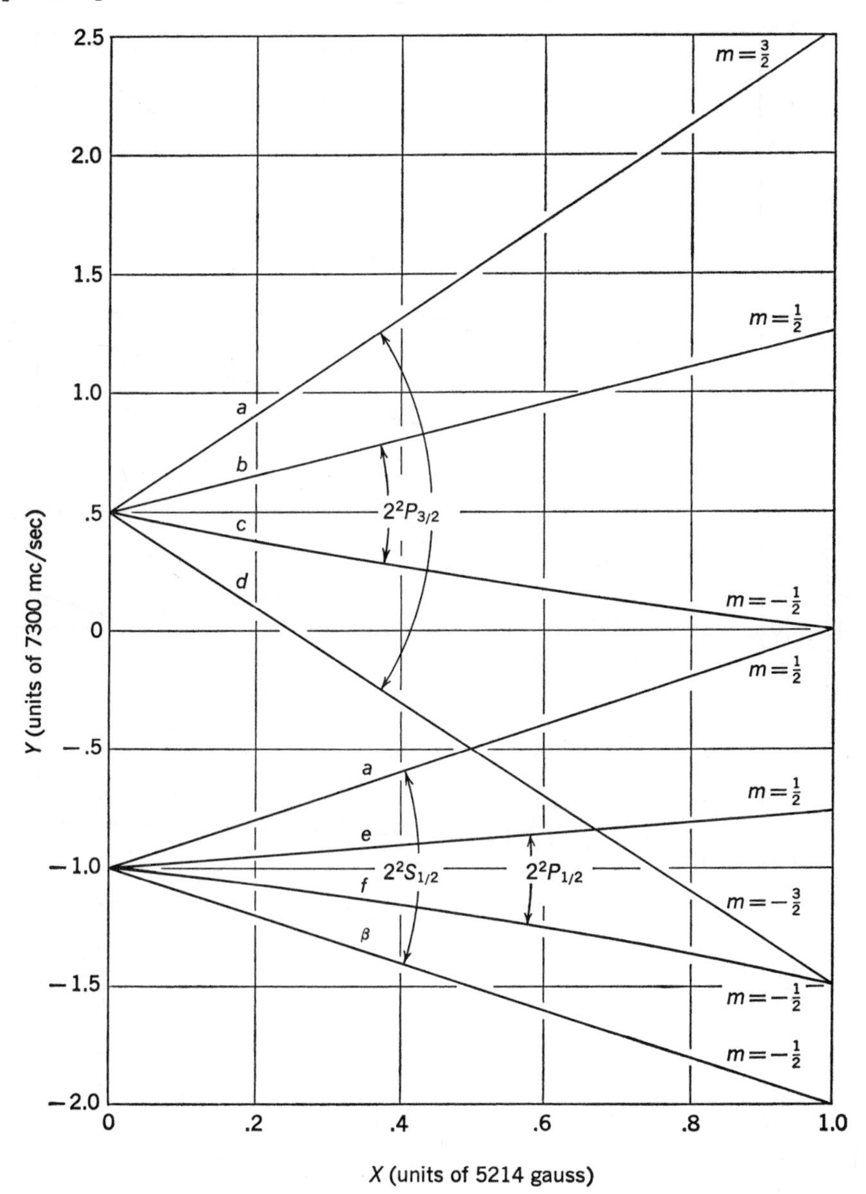

FIG. XIII.4. *Enlargement of Fig. XIII.3.*

1000 Mc/sec. The degeneracy in the $2S_{1/2}$, and $2P_{1/2}$ levels is removed contrary to Dirac's theory. The relativistic theory does not predict any upward displacement of $2S_{1/2}$ compared to $2P_{1/2}$ in the zero magnetic field, where these levels coincide.

The selection rules for electric dipole radiation in the anomalous Zeeman

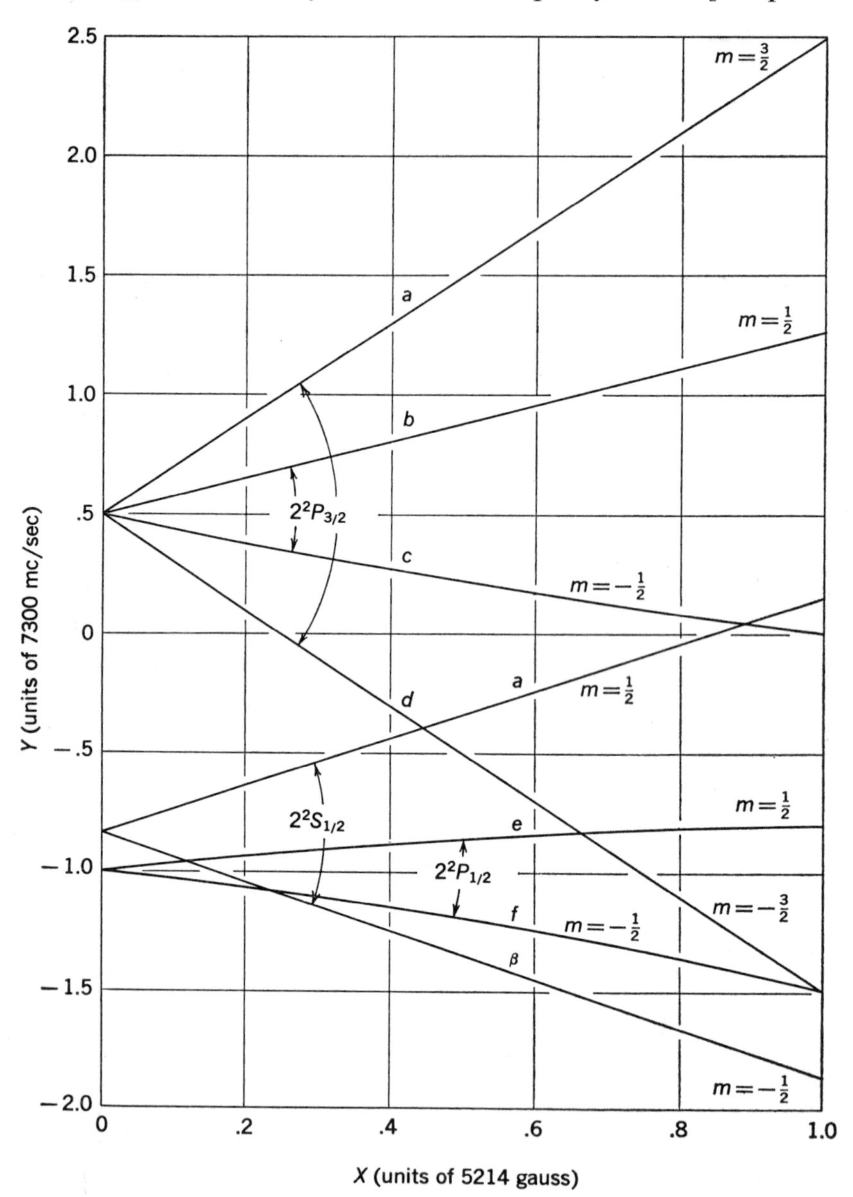

FIG. XIII.5. *Zeeman component energy levels for $n = 2$ in hydrogen calculated from quantum electrodynamics.*

region are $m_j'' = m_j'$, for the electric vector of radio waves polarized parallel to the magnetic field. The radio waves are used to induce transitions among the states $n = 2$ corresponding to the doublet separation $k = 0.365\ \text{cm}^{-1}$ or a wavelength $\lambda = 2.74$ cm and frequency 10,950 Mc/sec. For perpendicular polarization the selection rule is $m_j'' - m_j' = \pm 1$. For parallel polarization the allowed transitions are

$$\begin{aligned}
(2S_{1/2},\ s_3' &= \tfrac{1}{2}\hbar) \longrightarrow (2P_{3/2},\ m_j = \tfrac{1}{2}),\\
(2S_{1/2},\ s_3' &= \tfrac{1}{2}\hbar) \longrightarrow (2P_{1/2},\ m_j = \tfrac{1}{2}),\\
(2S_{1/2},\ s_3' &= -\tfrac{1}{2}\hbar) \longrightarrow (2P_{3/2},\ m_j = -\tfrac{1}{2}),\\
(2S_{1/2},\ s_3' &= -\tfrac{1}{2}\hbar) \longrightarrow (2P_{1/2},\ m_j = -\tfrac{1}{2}),
\end{aligned}$$

while for perpendicular polarizations the allowed transitions are

$$\begin{aligned}
(2S_{1/2},\ s_3' &= \tfrac{1}{2}\hbar) \longrightarrow (2P_{3/2},\ m_j = \tfrac{3}{2}),\\
(2S_{1/2},\ s_3' &= \tfrac{1}{2}\hbar) \longrightarrow (2P_{3/2},\ m_j = -\tfrac{1}{2}),\\
(2S_{1/2},\ s_3' &= \tfrac{1}{2}\hbar) \longrightarrow (2P_{1/2},\ m_j = -\tfrac{1}{2}),\\
(2S_{1/2},\ s_3' &= -\tfrac{1}{2}\hbar) \longrightarrow (2P_{3/2},\ m_j = \tfrac{1}{2}),\\
(2S_{1/2},\ s_3' &= -\tfrac{1}{2}\hbar) \longrightarrow (2P_{3/2},\ m_j = -\tfrac{3}{2}),\\
(2S_{1/2},\ s_3' &= -\tfrac{1}{2}\hbar) \longrightarrow (2P_{1/2},\ m_j = \tfrac{1}{2}).
\end{aligned}$$

XIII.3.A. Mesic Atoms, Muonium, Positronium

Negative mesons (such as π^- and K^-) and the negative muon μ^- can come to rest in matter and can form bound states by capture processes. Such states are called "mesic atoms." Since orbit size is inversely proportional to the mass of the particle, the mesic atoms have smaller orbits. In general, these particles will quickly cascade through successive orbits down to the nucleus and cause various nuclear reactions. These reactions in most cases (by way of radiation of the charged fragments) produce radiating tracks in emulsions referred to as a star. The fundamental difference between captures by μ^- and by π^- and K^- is that μ^- does not interact with the nucleus strongly, while π^- and K^- are involved in strong capture reactions. Typical examples are capture processes in deuteron and hydrogen,

$$\begin{aligned}
\pi^- + D &\longrightarrow n + n,\\
\pi^- + H &\longrightarrow n + \pi^0.
\end{aligned}$$

The second reaction competes with

$$\pi^- + H \longrightarrow n + \gamma.$$

In the case of the negative kaon (K^-) we can have

$$\begin{aligned}
K^- + p &\longrightarrow \Sigma^- + \pi^+,\\
K^- + p &\longrightarrow \Lambda + \pi^0,
\end{aligned}$$

and

$$\begin{aligned}
K^- + n &\longrightarrow \Sigma^- + \pi^0,\\
K^- + n &\longrightarrow \Lambda + \pi^-,
\end{aligned}$$

where Σ^- and Λ are baryons with strangeness -1. The strange meson K^- also has strangeness -1. Hence the above reactions are strangeness-conserving reactions.

When a muon is stopped the formation of a star takes place via weak interaction:

$$\mu^- + p \longrightarrow n + \nu.$$

Being a slow capture process, the muon tends to spend most of its lifetime in the ground state before undergoing a decay or nuclear capture. The energy of bound states for a muon is given by the Dirac energy level formula (*XIII.1.23*), where m is to be replaced by 206.77 m, the mass of the muon.

Muonium is a bound state of an electron and a positive muon, μ^+. Apart from the effect of larger magnetic moment and smaller mass of μ^+ compared to the proton, the energy level scheme is similar to a hydrogen atom. So far there is no experimental evidence for it, but theoretically it is considered as a possibility.

Positronium is a bound state of an electron and a positron. It is a hydrogen-like atom and can be formed when positron is slowed down in a hydrogen gas. Its formation is essentially through a radiative capture process. The reduced mass of the atom is $m_R = (m_1m_2)/(m_1 + m_2) = \frac{1}{2}m$, where m is the mass of the electron or positron. In the nonrelativistic theory, therefore, the energy levels of the positronium are exactly half of the hydrogen energy levels. The two spin states $S = 1$ and $S = 0$ correspond to triplet and singlet S states. In the singlet S state two-γ-ray annihilation of the positronium is possible, since zero total angular momentum is a possible two-γ-ray state. The fact that a two-photon system can never be in a state with unit total angular momentum (see Section IX.2.A) implies that a triplet positronium state cannot decay into two photons. However, a three-photon annihilation of the triplet S state of positronium is an allowed transition. According to quantum electrodynamics the mean lifetimes* for annihilation of a singlet and a triplet S state of positronium are

$$t_{\text{singlet}} = 1.25 \times 10^{-10}\, n^3 \text{ sec},$$
$$t_{\text{triplet}} = 1.4 \times 10^{-7}\, n^3 \text{ sec},$$

where n is the radial quantum number. The total energy separation between the triplet and singlet S states with the same value of n is (in frequency units) given by

$$\Delta E_0 = \frac{1}{n^3}\, 2.044 \times 10^5 \text{ Mc/sec}.$$

Corrections to ΔE arising from the Lamb shift and other effects originating

---

* A. Ore and J. Powell, *Phys. Rev.*, **75** (1953), 1696, 1963.
S. DeBenedetti and H. C. Corben, *Ann. Rev. Nuc. Sci.*, **4** (1954), 191.
J. Pirenne, *Arch. Sci. Phys. Nat.*, **29** (1947), 121, 207, 265.
V. Berestetski and L. Landau, *J. Exp. Theor. Phys. USSR.*, **19** (1949), 673, 1130.
R. A. Ferrell, *Phys. Rev.*, **84** (1951), 858.

from quantum electrodynamics have been calculated by Karplus and Klein.* The total theoretical value with $n = 1$ is

$$\Delta E = 2.0337 \times 10^5 \text{ Mc/sec.}$$

The experimental value for the splitting between singlet and triplet components of the positronium ground state† is

$$\Delta E_{\text{exp}} = (2.0338 \pm 0.0004) \times 10^5 \text{ Mc/sec,}$$

in good agreement with the theoretical result. Further discussions of the Lamb shift and hydrogenlike atoms will be given in Chapter XV, Section XV.4.

XIII.3.B. Parity Selection Rules and Parity of the Levels

Consider the electric dipole moment of a system of electric charges,

$$\boldsymbol{D} = -e \sum_i \boldsymbol{q}_{(i)}. \tag{XIII.3.21}$$

The operator $\boldsymbol{D}$ anticommutes with the parity operator $\mathcal{P}$. Thus from $[\mathcal{P}, D]_+ = 0$, taking representatives, we obtain

$$\int \langle \boldsymbol{r}|\mathcal{P}|\boldsymbol{r}'\rangle \, d^3x' \, \langle \boldsymbol{r}'|\boldsymbol{D}|\boldsymbol{r}''\rangle + \int \langle \boldsymbol{r}|\boldsymbol{D}|\boldsymbol{r}'\rangle \, d^3x' \, \langle \boldsymbol{r}'|\mathcal{P}|\boldsymbol{r}''\rangle = 0.$$

Using $\mathcal{P}|\boldsymbol{r}'\rangle = \mathcal{P}'|\boldsymbol{r}'\rangle$, where $\mathcal{P}' = \pm 1$, we obtain

$$\int \delta(\boldsymbol{r} - \boldsymbol{r}')\mathcal{P}' \, d^3x' \, \langle \boldsymbol{r}'|\boldsymbol{D}|\boldsymbol{r}''\rangle + \int \delta(\boldsymbol{r}' - \boldsymbol{r}'')\mathcal{P}'' \, d^3x' \, \langle \boldsymbol{r}|\boldsymbol{D}|\boldsymbol{r}'\rangle = 0.$$

Hence

$$(\mathcal{P}' + \mathcal{P}'')\langle \boldsymbol{r}|\boldsymbol{D}|\boldsymbol{r}''\rangle = 0, \tag{XIII.3.22}$$

so the only nonvanishing representative of $\boldsymbol{D}$ comes from

$$\mathcal{P}'' = -\mathcal{P}', \tag{XIII.3.23}$$

or opposite parity. This is a "parity selection rule," which means that all spectral lines due to electric dipole radiation arise from transitions between states of opposite parity. A parity selection rule is of particular importance for systems in which no angular momentum selection rule exists.

If in (*IV.4.4*) we take $\boldsymbol{D}$ for the operator $\boldsymbol{\kappa}$, we obtain another restriction on the dipole radiation, arising from taking representatives with respect to states involving orbital angular momenta. In this case the selection rule (*IV.4.9*) is replaced by

$$|\Delta l| = 1 \tag{XIII.3.24}$$

where $\Delta l = l'' - l'$.

---

* R. Karplus and A. Klein, *Phys. Rev.*, **87** (1952), 848. See also T. Fulton and P. Martin, *Phys. Rev.*, **95** (1954), 811, for similar calculation on the excited states of positronium.

† R. Weinstein, M. Deutsch, and S. Brown, *Phys. Rev.*, **98** (1955), 223.

The selection rule (*IV.4.9*) may be expected to be valid for all quantum numbers of angular momentum type. For example, it is observed that for strongly interacting particles, such as baryons and mesons, the weak interactions can induce decays that violate conservation of strangeness and, therefore, of isotopic spin. The following decays of the strange particles Ξ, $\Sigma^{\pm}$, K^{+}, K^{-} can provide possible selection rules.* Thus

$$\Xi \longrightarrow \Lambda + \pi, \qquad \Sigma^{\pm} \longrightarrow \text{nucleon} + \text{pion}, \qquad K \longrightarrow 2\pi (\text{or } 3\pi). \qquad (XIII.3.25)$$

If we assume that there is a selection rule

$$\Delta S = \pm 1 \qquad (XIII.3.26)$$

for strangeness quantum number S, then, as follows from (*VI.3.16*), one has the selection rule

$$\Delta T_3 = \pm \tfrac{1}{2}. \qquad (XIII.3.27)$$

However, the recent observation of the reactions $K_0 \longrightarrow \pi^- + \mu^+ + \nu$ and $K_0 \longrightarrow \pi^+ + \mu^- + \bar{\nu}$ do not agree with (*XIII.3.27*).

By analogy with (*IV.4.9*), it has been suggested† that there may exist a further I spin selection rule for the total I spin,

$$|\Delta T| = \tfrac{1}{2}. \qquad (XIII.3.28)$$

Because of the nonconservation of the total I spin by electromagnetic interactions, the rule (*XIII.3.28*) is subject to electromagnetic corrections.

The concept of parity plays an important role in the classification of atomic spectra. We shall give a brief discussion of the application of parity to atomic energy levels.

For an atom with N electrons the Hamiltonian is of the form $H = H_0 + H'$, where

$$H = \sum_{i=1}^{N} \left[\frac{\boldsymbol{p}_i^2}{2m} - \frac{Ze^2}{r_1} \right], \qquad H' = \tfrac{1}{2} \sum_{i \neq j} \frac{e^2}{|r_i - r_j|}.$$

The term H' represents mutual repulsion of the electrons. If we neglect H', then the electrons will move in the field of the nucleus alone. In the latter case the Schrödinger equation

$$\sum_{i=1}^{N} \left[\frac{\boldsymbol{p}_i^2}{2m} - \frac{Ze^2}{r_i} \right] \Psi(1, 2, \cdots, N) = E\Psi(1, 2, \cdots, N) \qquad (XIII.3.29)$$

can be solved exactly, where the numbers $1, 2, \cdots, N$ in the argument of the wave function refer to the coordinates of the electrons. The wave function Ψ can be expressed as a product of the individual electron wave functions

---

* M. Gell-Mann and A. H. Rosenfeld, *Annual Review of Nuclear Science*, Vol. 7, Annual Reviews, Palo Alto, 1957, p. 413.

† M. Gell-Mann and A. Pais, *Proceedings of the International Conference on High-Energy Physics*, Pergamon Press, London, 1955.

$$\Psi = \prod_{s=1}^{N} \psi_{n_s l_s m_s}(s), \tag{XIII.3.30}$$

where n_s, l_s, m_s for $s = 1, 2, \cdots, N$ are principal, orbital, and magnetic quantum numbers of the sth electron. Each $\psi_{n_s l_s m_s}$ satisfies the wave equation

$$\left[\frac{p_s^2}{2m} - \frac{Ze^2}{r_s}\right] \psi_{n_s l_s m_s} = E_{n_s} \psi_{n_s l_s m_s}, \tag{XIII.3.31}$$

where $l_s = 1, 2, \cdots, N_s - 1$ and $m_s = -l_s, -l_s + 1, \cdots, l_s$. Thus for a given n_s or for a given energy eigenvalue E_{n_s} there can be various quantum numbers and therefore various states. Furthermore, for a given set of n_s, the interchange of the electrons among themselves does not affect the corresponding energy eigenvalue. There is thus a degeneracy of the levels. The inclusion of H_s in the Hamiltonian will remove the degeneracy only partially. The complete removal of degeneracy—and hence the splitting of the levels—requires a relativistic treatment of the N-electron atom. In principle such an approach to the problem under certain approximations is possible. However, this aspect of the problem will not be considered here.

If L is the total angular momentum of the atom, then it can assume the values $L = 0, 1, 2, \cdots$, corresponding to $S, P, D, F, \cdots$ levels. The total magnetic quantum number M runs through $2L + 1$ values $(-L, -L + 1, \cdots, L)$, so a level with quantum number L has $2L + 1$ eigenfunctions. These eigenfunctions are distinguished by their magnetic quantum numbers. In this section we are using capital letters to represent quantum numbers and quantum states, to distinguish them from the corresponding quantum numbers and quantum states for which we used small letters before. From the discussion of the representation of the rotation group it follows that the eigenvalues $L = 0, 1, 2, \cdots$ belong to the representations $D^{(l)}$ of the rotation group. The levels corresponding to $L = 0, 1, 2, \cdots$ are designated as $S, P, D, F \cdots$ levels, with one, three, five, seven, $\cdots$ eigenfunctions, respectively. Besides the rotational symmetry (characterized by the quantum number L) we also have a reflection symmetry of a level. The latter refers to the "parity of a level." Therefore, from a parity point of view the classification of a level must be based on the representation of the reflection group which consists of the identity I_3 and the reflection $-I_3$. Every orthogonal matrix can be obtained from a rotation matrix by multiplication with I_3 or $-I_3$. Thus two representations of the rotation-reflection group can be obtained from every representation $D^{(l)}$ of the pure rotation group by combining $D^{(l)}$ with I_3 and with $-I_3$. The two irreducible representations of the three-dimensional rotation-reflection group are $(2l + 1)$-dimensional. The matrix $D^{(l)}$ corresponds both to a rotation matrix A and to a rotation-reflection matrix $-A$ in the "identical representation" of the reflection group. The matrix $-D^{(l)}$ corresponds to $-A$ in the "negative representation" of the reflection group.*

The even parity levels of the N-electron atom belong to the identical representation of the reflection group. The odd parity levels belong to negative representation of the reflection group. We incorporate the parity of the level to its angular momentum state with the subscripts + and −, corresponding to even and odd parity states, by writing S_+, S_-, P_+, P_-, $\cdots$. Spectroscopic analysis shows that S_+, P_-, D_+, F_-, $\cdots$ are the most common levels.

XIII.3.C. Multiplet Structure of the Levels

In an N-electron atom the electrostatic interactions can couple the orbital angular momenta $\boldsymbol{L}_{(i)}$, for $i = 1, 2, \cdots, N$, into the resultant orbital angular momentum $\boldsymbol{L}$ and spin angular momentum $\boldsymbol{S}$, respectively. The magnetic interaction between $\boldsymbol{L}$ and $\boldsymbol{S}$ leads to a quantized $\boldsymbol{J} = \boldsymbol{L} + \boldsymbol{S}$. A given $\boldsymbol{L}$ and $\boldsymbol{S}$ correspond to a certain multiplet. From the addition rule of two angular momenta,

$$J = L + S, L + S - 1, \cdots, |L - S| + 1, |L - S|,$$

it follows that for $L > S$ there are $2S + 1$ relative orientations of L and S and for $L < S$ there are $2L + 1$ relative orientations. Where $L > S$ there are $2S + 1$ different J values corresponding to the multiplet; the number $2S + 1$ is called the multiplicity. A level with $L = 1$ and $S = \frac{1}{2}$ has a multiplicity of 2. In spectroscopic notation they are indicated as ${}^2P_{1/2}$ and ${}^2P_{3/2}$, where the subscripts $\frac{1}{2}$ and $\frac{3}{2}$ correspond to J values. The levels ${}^2P_{1/2}$ and ${}^2P_{3/2}$ are $(2J + 1 = 2)$ and $(2J + 1 = 4)$-fold degenerate, corresponding to the magnetic quantum numbers $M = L_3 + S_3$. Hence in the absence of magnetic interactions all $(2S + 1)(2L + 1)$ sublevels of a multiplet are degenerate and each multiplet corresponding to different J values differs in the corresponding energy eigenvalue. The magnetic coupling removes the degeneracy in the sublevels of different J values. A complete removal of degeneracy is produced by an external magnetic field which splits different M values.

For a two-electron atom we have parallel or antiparallel spin states, represented by the values $S = 1$ and $S = 0$. For $L = 0$ the two levels are ${}^3S$ and ${}^1S$ (triplet and singlet spin states). Since S is greater than L, the corresponding number of levels is $2L + 1 = 1$.

In general, for an N-electron atom the quantity S can assume the values $0, 1, 2, \cdots$, if N is even, and the values $\frac{1}{2}, \frac{3}{2}, \frac{5}{2}, \cdots$, if N is odd. Thus if N is even we obtain singlet, triplet, quintet, $\cdots$ states. For odd N the corresponding spin states are doublet, quartet, sextet, $\cdots$.

---

* E. P. Wigner, *Group Theory*, Academic, New York, 1960, p. 176.

CHAPTER XIV

APPROXIMATION METHODS

XIV.1. General Remarks on Perturbation Theory

In quantum mechanics the number of problems that can be solved exactly are rather few. We have to use approximations, and for this purpose various methods are available. The most important of these is the perturbation theory. This method is based on the fundamental assumption that the total energy H (Hamiltonian) of the system can be separated into two parts.

(a) A part H_0, which is simple. The corresponding Schrödinger equation can be solved exactly. (This is not a necessity but in most problems an exact solution for H_0 does exist.)
(b) A part H', which is small compared to H_0. This is a perturbation on the original system and gives rise to a small correction to it.

A separation of the Hamiltonian into two parts is motivated either by mathematical difficulties or by the nature of a particular physical process where no new information is obtained by an exact treatment, as with Coulomb scattering. At first sight the separation of H does not involve any new physical assumption about the system, but a reasonable physical interpretation is always provided by the nature of the problem.

In principle the knowledge of the Hamiltonian of a dynamical system is sufficient, by means of Schrödinger's equation, to predict all of its most probable behavior. Thus any assumptions on total H, such as separation into two, will automatically affect the state of the system. There is no a priori justification for the separability of an H into two or more parts. However, a solution in the form of a power series in powers of a small parameter is the result of the perturbation theory. The proof of convergence of this series is a formidable task. Despite this, the perturbation theory is considered quite satisfactory even if the series does not converge. In most cases of interest the first approximation leads to acceptable results.

The split of the Hamiltonian is taken over from the classical analogy. Here also one assumes a possible separation into free and interacting parts. The separability of the total energy into two parts is inherent in both classical and quantum theories. We seem to know, in advance, how much of the energy is free and how much remains for interaction.

For a particular problem the method of perturbation theory to be applied will depend on the time behavior of the Hamiltonian. For a time-independent Hamiltonian, for example, one applies "stationary-state perturbation" theory, where the effect of a small perturbation consists of changing the original state of motion of the dynamical system. The "Stark effect" is an example of stationary-state perturbation where an external electric field causes changes in the initial state of the system. For a time-dependent Hamiltonian, where the unperturbed part is time-independent, one is interested in the time variation of a stationary state caused by a time-dependent perturbing part. A third, but less practical method is the so-called perturbation of boundary conditions, which may include either a change in the boundary conditions or a change in the shape of the boundary surface or both. This is especially useful when one has no detailed knowledge of the perturbation or the interaction of the system.

XIV.1.A. Stationary-State Perturbation Theory

We shall assume that (a) the perturbed part of the Hamiltonian has discrete eigenvalues only, and (b) the separations of energy levels are large compared to the changes in them caused by the perturbation. Let the total Hamiltonian be

$$H = H_0 + H', \tag{XIV.1.1}$$

where H' is the small perturbing energy, and where we assume that each eigenvalue E of H lies very close to one and only one eigenvalue E_0 of H_0. Thus for a state $|\Psi\rangle$ we have, approximately,

$$(E - E_0) \cong \langle\Psi|H'|\Psi\rangle. \tag{XIV.1.2}$$

The general eigenvalue equation is

$$H|E\rangle = E|E\rangle \tag{XIV.1.3}$$

or

$$(E - H_0)|E\rangle = H'|E\rangle. \tag{XIV.1.4}$$

The stationary-state perturbation theory deals with the solutions of the eigenvalue equation (*XIV.1.4*). We proceed by assuming that the eigenstate $|E\rangle$ and corresponding energy eigenvalue E can be expanded according to

$$|E\rangle = |E_0\rangle + |E_1\rangle + |E_2\rangle + \cdots, \qquad (XIV.1.5)$$

$$E = E_0 + E_1 + E_2 + \cdots, \qquad (XIV.1.6)$$

where $|E_1\rangle$ and E_1 are first-order quantities, $|E_2\rangle$ and E_2 are second-order quantities, and so on. The nth-order quantities are of the order of $(H')^n$. If we substitute (*XIV.1.5*) and (*XIV.1.6*) in (*XIV.1.4*) and equate the terms of the same order on both sides, we get the set of equations

$$(E_0 - H_0)|E_0\rangle = 0, \qquad (XIV.1.7)$$

$$(E_0 - H_0)|E_1\rangle + E_1|E_0\rangle = H'|E_0\rangle, \qquad (XIV.1.8)$$

$$(E_0 - H_0)|E_2\rangle + E_1|E_1\rangle + E_2|E_0\rangle = H'|E_1\rangle, \qquad (XIV.1.9)$$

$$\cdots.$$

We can use the eigenstates $|E_0\rangle$ of H_0 to set up a representation. If there is a degeneracy we introduce further observables ζ, say. The new representation would then be simultaneous eigenstates of the complete commuting set of observables H_0 and ζ. If $|E_0, \zeta'\rangle$ is a simultaneous eigenstate of the complete commuting set of observables H_0 and ζ, then the scalar product of $|E_0'\rangle$ and $|E_0'', \zeta''\rangle$ is of the form

$$\langle E_0'', \zeta''|E_0'\rangle = \delta_{E'_0E''_0}F(\zeta''), \qquad (XIV.1.10)$$

where $F(\zeta'')$ is some function of the variables ζ''. By using these results and taking the representative of (*XIV.1.8*) in the new representation we obtain

$$(E_0' - E_0'')\langle E_0'', \zeta''|E_1\rangle + E_1\delta_{E'_0E''_0}F(\zeta'') = \sum_{\zeta'} \langle E_0'', \zeta''|H'|E_0', \zeta'\rangle F(\zeta'). \qquad (XIV.1.11)$$

There are two cases to be considered. (a) Let us suppose that $E_0' = E_0''$; in this case (*XIV.1.11*) yields the result

$$E_1F(\zeta'') = \sum_{\zeta''} \langle E_0', \zeta''|H'|E_0', \zeta''\rangle F(\zeta'), \qquad (XIV.1.12)$$

which constitutes a set of linear homogeneous equations for $F(\zeta')$; they are to be used to determine the energy E_1. The possible values of E_1 are just eigenvalues of the matrix

$$H'_{mn} = \langle E_0', \zeta^{(m)}|H'|E_0', \zeta^{(n)}\rangle, \qquad (XIV.1.13)$$

whose rows and columns refer to the same energy E_0'. Each of the eigenvalues of H'_{mn} for E_1 gives, to the first order, an energy level of the perturbed system lying close to the energy level E_0' of the unperturbed system. As an interesting example, let us suppose that the extra variables ζ, in addition to H_0, are just the total angular momenta; then we can label the states by the eigenvalues of J_3. Thus the matrix equation (*XIV.1.12*) becomes

$$E_1F(J_3'') = \sum_{j'_3=-j}^{j} \langle E_0', J_3''|H'|E_0', J_3'\rangle F(J_3'). \qquad (XIV.1.14)$$

Hence the equation determining E_1 is a $(2j + 1)$-dimensional eigenvalue equation,

$$\det [H'_{m''m'} - E_1\delta_{m''m'}] = 0, \qquad (XIV.1.15)$$

where $H'_{m''m'} = \langle E'_0, m''|H'|E'_0, m'\rangle$.

In this way we obtain $2j + 1$ energy eigenvalues E_1 that are close to E'_0 of the unperturbed system. The number $2j + 1$ does not exceed the number of independent states of the unperturbed system belonging to the level E'_0. Hence we see that the energy levels E'_0 and E''_0 that coincided for the unperturbed system H_0 has been separated by the perturbation H'.

Now, knowing $F(\zeta')$ from $(XIV.1.12)$, we can determine to the zeroth order the representative $(XIV.1.10)$ of the stationary states of the perturbed system belonging to energy levels lying close to E'_0.

(b) Let us now suppose that there is only one stationary state of the unperturbed system belonging to each energy level. In this case no extra variables ζ are required; H by itself can fix a representation. Thus for $E'_0 = E''_0$ we have

$$E_1 = \langle E'_0|H'|E'_0\rangle. \qquad (XIV.1.16)$$

There is only one energy level $E'_0 + E_1$ of the perturbed system lying close to any energy level of the unperturbed system, and the change in energy is equal in the first order to the corresponding diagonal element of the perturbing energy H' in the representation for the unperturbed system. Equations $(XIV.1.10)$ and $(XIV.1.11)$ in this case read respectively,

$$\langle E''_0|E'_0\rangle = \delta_{E'_0E''_0} \qquad (XIV.1.17)$$

and

$$(E'_0 - E''_0)\langle E''_0|E_1\rangle + E_1\delta_{E'_0E''_0} = \langle E''_0|H'|E'_0\rangle. \qquad (XIV.1.18)$$

For $E'_0 \neq E''_0$ we have

$$\langle E''_0|E_1\rangle = \frac{\langle E''_0|H'|E'_0\rangle}{E'_0 - E''_0}. \qquad (XIV.1.19)$$

A similar treatment of $(XIV.1.19)$ leads to the energy change

$$E_1 + E_2 = \langle E'_0|H'|E'_0\rangle + \sum_{E_0'' \neq E_0'} \frac{\langle E'_0|H'|E''_0\rangle\langle E''_0|H'|E'_0\rangle}{E'_0 - E''_0}. \qquad (XIV.1.20)$$

XIV.1.B. The Brillouin-Wigner Perturbation Expansion

An improved form of the stationary-state perturbation theory can be based on a solution of Schrödinger's equation $(XIV.1.4)$, where the energy denominators do not depend on the differences of unperturbed energy eigenvalues. It is a definite improvement over the former method.

Let us write Schrödinger's equation (*XIV.1.4*) in the form

$$(E - H_0)|\Psi\rangle = H'|\Psi\rangle, \qquad (XIV.1.21)$$

where the eigenstate $|\Psi\rangle$ corresponds to the eigenvalue E of H. The state vector $|\Psi\rangle$ can be split up as

$$|\Psi\rangle = |\Psi_0\rangle + |\Phi\rangle, \qquad (XIV.1.22)$$

where $|\Psi_0\rangle$ is an eigenstate of H_0 corresponding to the eigenvalue E_0. We shall assume that E_0 does not coincide with the total energy E. The state vector $|\Psi_0\rangle$ is normalized as

$$\langle\Psi_0|\Psi_0\rangle = 1, \qquad (XIV.1.23)$$

and it is orthogonal to $|\Phi\rangle$; that is,

$$\langle\Psi_0|\Phi\rangle = 0. \qquad (XIV.1.24)$$

Hence it follows that the normalization of $|\Psi\rangle$ is given by

$$\langle\Psi_0|\Psi\rangle = 1. \qquad (XIV.1.25)$$

We have seen in Section I.5.B that for every vector normalized according to (*XIV.1.23*) we can form the corresponding projection operators by

$$M = |\Psi_0\rangle\langle\Psi_0| \qquad (XIV.1.26)$$

and

$$P = 1 - M = 1 - |\Psi_0\rangle\langle\Psi_0|. \qquad (XIV.1.27)$$

Subtracting the equations $H_0|\Psi\rangle = (E - H')|\Psi\rangle$ and $H_0|\Psi_0\rangle = E_0|\Psi_0\rangle$ we obtain

$$H_0|\Phi\rangle = (E - H')|\Psi\rangle - E_0|\Psi_0\rangle. \qquad (XIV.1.28)$$

Operating by projection operator M, equation (*XIV.1.28*) yields

$$E_0|\Psi_0\rangle = E|\Psi_0\rangle - MH'|\Psi\rangle.$$

By substituting in (*XIV.1.28*) for $E_0|\Psi_0\rangle$, we obtain

$$(E - H_0)|\Phi\rangle = PH'|\Psi\rangle.$$

Hence, since $E \neq E_0$, we obtain

$$|\Phi\rangle = \frac{1}{E - H_0} PH'|\Psi\rangle. \qquad (XIV.1.29)$$

Thus the Schrödinger equation (*XIV.1.21*) is now transformed into an integral equation,

$$|\Psi\rangle = |\Psi_0\rangle + \frac{1}{E - H_0} PH'|\Psi\rangle, \qquad (XIV.1.30)$$

where

$$E = E_0 + \langle\Psi_0|H'|\Psi\rangle. \qquad (XIV.1.31)$$

So far, everything is exact. If we assume that the difference between perturbed and unperturbed energy $(E - E_0)$ is greater than $\langle\Psi_0|H'|\Psi_0\rangle$, then the perturbation expansion consists of the iteration of the integral equation (*XIV.1.30*). Iteration of (*XIV.1.30*) leads to

$$|\boldsymbol{\Psi}\rangle = |\boldsymbol{\Psi}_0\rangle + |\boldsymbol{\Psi}_1\rangle + |\boldsymbol{\Psi}_2\rangle + \cdots, \tag{XIV.1.32}$$

$$E = E_0 + E_1 + E_2 + \cdots, \tag{XIV.1.33}$$

where

$$|\boldsymbol{\Psi}_1\rangle = \frac{1}{E - H_0} PH'|\boldsymbol{\Psi}_0\rangle, \tag{XIV.1.34}$$

$$|\boldsymbol{\Psi}_2\rangle = \frac{1}{E - H_0} PH' \frac{1}{E - H_0} PH'|\boldsymbol{\Psi}_0\rangle, \tag{XIV.1.35}$$

$$\cdots,$$

and

$$E_1 = \langle\boldsymbol{\Psi}_0|H'|\boldsymbol{\Psi}_0\rangle, \tag{XIV.1.36}$$

$$E_2 = \langle\boldsymbol{\Psi}_0|H' \frac{1}{E - H_0} PH'|\boldsymbol{\Psi}_0\rangle, \tag{XIV.1.37}$$

$$\cdots.$$

The perturbing energy E_1 agrees with previous result (*XIV.1.16*) but higher-order perturbations do not agree.

XIV.2. Examples of Stationary-State Perturbation Theory

XIV.2.A. The Linear Stark Effect

An application of the second-order calculation of the energy can best be illustrated in the Stark effect of the atoms other than hydrogen. (Hydrogen must be given a special treatment because of the degeneracy of levels of the same n and different l.) It consists of a shift of energy levels of an atom in an external electric field. Let this field be in the z direction. The total Hamiltonian for an arbitrary atom is

$$H = \frac{\boldsymbol{p}^2}{2m} + V + H', \qquad H' = e\mathcal{E}\sum_i z_i, \tag{XIV.2.1}$$

where the sum is taken over the electrons. In general,

$$\langle H'\rangle = \langle E_0|H'|E_0\rangle = \int \langle E_0|\boldsymbol{r}\rangle\langle\boldsymbol{r}|H'|\boldsymbol{r}'\rangle\langle\boldsymbol{r}'|E_0\rangle\, d^3\boldsymbol{x}\, d^3\boldsymbol{x}',$$

the average value of interaction energy with respect to field-free states, vanishes. In terms of the eigenfunctions $\psi_0 = \langle\boldsymbol{r}|E_0\rangle$ of the field-free atoms, the average of H' is written as

$$\langle H'\rangle = \int |\psi_0|^2 H'\, d^3\boldsymbol{x}. \tag{XIV.2.2}$$

Because of the linear dependence of H' on the coordinates z_i, the integrand changes sign under a reflection of coordinates and therefore $\langle H'\rangle$ vanishes. However, for a transition between two states ψ_I and ψ_F of opposite parity the matrix element

$$\langle E_F^0|H'|E_I^0\rangle = \int \psi_F^* H' \psi_I \, d^3\boldsymbol{x}, \qquad (XIV.2.3)$$

of H', where ψ_F and ψ_I refer to eigenstates of opposite parity, does not vanish. For hydrogenlike atoms, for example, the wave function, being of the form $f_l(r)Y_{lm}(\theta, \phi)$, implies that the integral (*XIV.2.3*) does not vanish provided that for a fixed m the angular momentum quantum number l changes by ± 1. Hence we see that for hydrogenlike atoms the degeneracy, arising from several l values for a fixed principal quantum number n, can be removed. In this case the eigenfunctions in the presence of the weak external field $\mathcal{E}$ are superpostions of field-free functions with different l values and the effect linear in $\mathcal{E}$; that is, the first-order perturbation energy does not vanish.

The linear Stark effect can most conveniently be treated by expressing the Schrödinger equation in parabolic coordinates, which are defined by

$$x_1 = \sqrt{(\xi\eta)} \cos \zeta, \qquad x_2 = \sqrt{(\xi\eta)} \sin \zeta, \qquad x_3 = \tfrac{1}{2}(\xi - \eta). \qquad (XIV.2.4)$$

Hence we have

$$r = \tfrac{1}{2}(\xi + \eta), \qquad \xi = r + x_3, \qquad \eta = r - x_3, \qquad \zeta = \tan^{-1}\left(\frac{x_2}{x_1}\right). \qquad (XIV.2.5)$$

The line element and volume element in parabolic coordinates are

$$\begin{aligned} ds^2 &= \frac{\eta + \xi}{4\xi}\, d\xi^2 + \frac{\eta + \xi}{4\eta}\, d\eta^2 + \eta\, d\zeta^2, \\ dV &= \tfrac{1}{4}(\xi + \eta)\, d\xi\, d\eta\, d\zeta. \end{aligned} \qquad (XIV.2.6)$$

Hence the Laplacian operator takes the form

$$\nabla^2 = \frac{4}{\xi + \eta}\frac{\partial}{\partial \xi}\left(\xi \frac{\partial}{\partial \xi}\right) + \frac{4}{\xi + \eta}\frac{\partial}{\partial \eta}\left(\eta \frac{\partial}{\partial \eta}\right) + \frac{1}{\xi\eta}\frac{\partial^2}{\partial \zeta^2}.$$

Thus the Schrödinger equation for hydrogen corresponding to the Hamiltonian (*XIV.2.1*) can be written as

$$\left[\frac{\partial}{\partial \zeta}\left(\xi \frac{\partial}{\partial \xi}\right) + \frac{\partial}{\partial \eta}\left(\eta \frac{\partial}{\partial \eta}\right) + \left(\frac{1}{4\eta} + \frac{1}{4\xi}\right)\frac{\partial^2}{\partial \zeta^2} + \frac{me^2 Z}{\hbar^2} - \frac{1}{4}\frac{em\mathcal{E}}{\hbar^2}(\xi^2 - \eta^2) + \frac{m}{2}\frac{E}{\hbar^2}(\xi + \eta)\right]\psi = 0. \qquad (XIV.2.7)$$

By assuming a solution of the form $\psi = f_1(\xi) f_2(\eta) e^{im'\zeta}$ and writing $me^2 Z/\hbar^2 = \kappa_1 + \kappa_2$, the differential equation (*XIV.2.7*) can be separated into two equations

$$\frac{d}{d\xi}\left(\xi\frac{df_1}{d\xi}\right)+\left(\frac{1}{2}\frac{mE}{\hbar^2}\xi+\kappa_1-\frac{m'^2}{4\xi}-\frac{1}{4}\frac{em\mathcal{E}}{\hbar^2}\xi^2\right)f_1=0,$$
$$\frac{d}{d\eta}\left(\eta\frac{df_2}{d\eta}\right)+\left(\frac{1}{2}\frac{mE}{\hbar^2}\eta+\kappa_2-\frac{m'^2}{4\eta}+\frac{1}{4}\frac{em\mathcal{E}}{\hbar^2}\eta^2\right)f_2=0. \tag{XIV.2.8}$$

The two equations differ only in the sign of the last terms. For $\mathcal{E}=0$, the first equation for large ξ behaves like $e^{-(1/2)k\xi}$ and for small ξ like $\xi^{(1/2)m'}$, so its bound-state solutions are of the form

$$f_1 = e^{-(1/2)k\xi}\,\xi^{(1/2)m'}u_1(\xi), \tag{XIV.2.9}$$

where $k=\sqrt{(2mE'/\hbar^2)}$. A similar solution holds for the second equation. Putting $x = k\xi$ and substituting (*XIV.2.9*) in the first equation of (*XIV.2.8*) we obtain

$$x\frac{d^2u_1}{dx^2}+(m'+1-x)\frac{du_1}{dx}+\left(\frac{\kappa_1}{k}-\frac{m'+1}{2}\right)u_1=0.$$

This equation is satisfied by Laguerre functions

$$u_1 = L^{m'}_{n_1+m'}(x), \tag{XIV.2.10}$$

where

$$n_1=\frac{\kappa_1}{k}-\tfrac{1}{2}(m'+1)$$

is a nonnegative integer. In the same way, for $u_2(k\eta)$ we have

$$u_2(k\eta) = L^{m'}_{n_2+m'}(k\eta),$$

with

$$n_2=\frac{\kappa_2}{k}-\tfrac{1}{2}(m'+1).$$

Hence

$$n_1+n_2+m'+1=\frac{1}{k}(\kappa_1+\kappa_2)=Z\sqrt{\left(\frac{me^4}{2E\hbar^2}\right)}=n,$$

where $E'=-E$, leads to the usual formula for the energy levels of hydrogen-like atoms. The normalized eigenfunctions for field-free case are given by

$$\psi^{m'}_{n_1n_2}=\frac{e^{\pm im'\zeta}}{\sqrt{(\pi n)}}\left[\frac{n_1!n_2!k^{2m'+3}}{[(n_1+m')!]^3\,[(n_2+m')!]^3}\right]^{1/2}$$
$$\times\, e^{-(1/2)k(\xi+\eta)}(\xi\eta)^{(1/2)m'}L^{m'}_{n_1+m'}(k\xi)L^{m'}_{n_2+m'}(k\eta). \tag{XIV.2.11}$$

It will be found convenient to treat κ_1 and κ_2 as the eigenvalues in equations (*XIV.2.8*) and record them in the form

$$\kappa_1=\kappa_{10}+\kappa_1^1+\cdots,\qquad f_1=f_{01}+f_1^1+\cdots,$$
$$\kappa_2=\kappa_{20}+\kappa_2^1+\cdots,\qquad f_2=f_{02}+f_2^1+\cdots.$$

Hence it follows* from the first-order perturbation theory that

---

* H. A. Bethe and E. E. Salpeter, *Quantum Mechanics of One- and Two-Electron Systems*, Academic, New York, 1957.

$$\kappa_1^{(1)} = \frac{1}{4}\frac{em\mathcal{E}}{\hbar^2}\int_0^\infty \xi^2 f_1^2\, d\xi$$

$$= \frac{1}{4}\frac{em\mathcal{E}}{k^2\hbar^2}(6n_1^2 + 6n_1m' + m'^2 + 6n_1 + 3m' + 2), \qquad (XIV.2.12)$$

where f_1 is the eigenfunction for field-free atoms. From $(me^2/\hbar^2)Z = \kappa_1 + \kappa_2$ we obtain

$$Z = \frac{\hbar}{e^2}\sqrt{\left(\frac{2E'}{m}\right)}\, n + \frac{3}{4}\frac{\mathcal{E}\hbar^2}{meE'}(n_1 - n_2)n.$$

If we write $Z = ax + b/x^2$ and $x = \sqrt{E'}$, and assume a solution of the form $x = (Z/a) + y$, we obtain, for small y, the result $x = (Z/a) - (ab/Z^2)$ or

$$E = -\frac{Z^2me^2}{2\hbar^2n^2} + \frac{3}{2}\frac{n}{Z}\mathcal{E}\frac{\hbar^2}{em}(n_1 - n_2) \qquad (XIV.2.13)$$

as the energy of the atoms in the field $\mathcal{E}$. The Stark separation of the extreme levels $E(n_1 = 0)$ and $E(n_2 = 0)$ is given by

$$\Delta E = \frac{3}{2}\frac{n}{Z}\frac{\mathcal{E}\hbar^2}{em}(n_1 + n_2).$$

The maximum value of $n_1 + n_2$ is $2(n - 1)$, so

$$E = \frac{3}{Z}\frac{\mathcal{E}\hbar^2}{em}n(n - 1). \qquad (XIV.2.14)$$

Thus the separation of spectral terms in the Stark effect varies as n^2, where n is the principal quantum number.

XIV.2.B. The Quadratic Stark Effect

This is a second-order effect. H can be calculated from

$$\langle E_0'|H'|E_0''\rangle\langle E_0''|H_0'|E_0'\rangle = e^2\mathcal{E}^2\int z'z''\langle E_0'|\boldsymbol{r}\rangle\, d^3\boldsymbol{x}\,\langle \boldsymbol{r}|E_0''\rangle\langle E_0''|\boldsymbol{r}'\rangle\, d^3\boldsymbol{x}'\,\langle \boldsymbol{r}'|E_0'\rangle.$$

Hence

$$\langle E_0'|H'|E_0''\rangle\langle E_0''|H'|E_0'\rangle = e^2\mathcal{E}^2\left|\int z\psi_0^*(\boldsymbol{r}, E_0'')\psi_0(\boldsymbol{r}, E_0')\, d^3\boldsymbol{x}\right|^2$$

$$= e^2\mathcal{E}^2NN'\delta_{mm'}\int_0^\pi \cos\theta\, P_{lm}P_{l'm'}\sin\theta\, d\theta\int_0^\infty R_{ln}R_{l'n'}r^2\, dr$$

$$= |\langle n'l'm'|z|nlm\rangle|^2,$$

where N and N' are normalization factors and the R are radial wave functions. The only components differing from zero come from the selection rules $l' - l = \pm 1$ and $m' = m$. Hence

$$E_2 = e^2\mathcal{E}^2\Sigma\frac{|\langle n'l'm'|z|nlm\rangle|^2}{E_0' - E_0''}, \qquad (XIV.2.15)$$

where the summation is taken over $l' = l \pm 1$, $m' = m$, and n', and where the energies E_0' and E_0'' correspond to lmn and $l'm'n'$, respectively.

We shall not discuss the details of the quadratic Stark effect but it must be mentioned that the quadratic effect refers to a displacement of the field-free lines where the red lines are displaced more than the violet lines. Further, above a critical field strength $\mathcal{E}_c$ the Stark lines disappear; this is called "quenching of the lines."

It is also important to remark that from the potential energy $-V = e\mathcal{E}z - Ze^2/r$ of the electron we can infer that the electric field is capable of ionizing the atom. The potential energy has two minima, one at the atomic center and another at distances which are sufficiently far from the atom. The second minimum occurs in the direction of negative z, where the potential is lower than its value at the atomic center. In between the two minima (potential troughs) there is a potential barrier. There is a finite probability that the electron will make transitions between the two troughs and hence a probability of penetration of the potential barrier. The penetration of the potential barrier leads to an acceleration of the electron away from the atom; therefore an ionization takes place.

XIV.3. Application of Unitary Transformations to Stationary-State Perturbation Theory

We define a unitary operator U by

$$U = \sum_n |E_n\rangle\langle E_n^0|, \qquad (XIV.3.1)$$

where $|E_n\rangle$ and $|E_n^0\rangle$ are the normalized eigenstates of $H(= H_0 + H')$ and H_0, corresponding to the eigenvalues E_n and E_n^0, respectively. The unitary operator U as defined by (*XIV.3.1*) has the property of transforming the state $|E_n^0\rangle$ of the free system into the state $|E_n\rangle$ of the perturbed system. Thus

$$U|E_n^0\rangle = |E_n\rangle. \qquad (XIV.3.2)$$

By using this in the equations $H|E_n\rangle = E_n|E_n\rangle$, we obtain

$$HU|E_n^0\rangle = E_nU|E_n^0\rangle \qquad (XIV.3.3)$$

The boundary condition that for $H' \longrightarrow 0$, the state $|E_n\rangle$ and the corresponding energy E_n must tend to $|E_n^0\rangle$ and E_n^0, respectively, leads to

$$\lim_{H'\to 0} U = \sum_n |E_n^0\rangle\langle E_n^0| = 1.$$

Thus, U can be expanded according to

$$U = 1 + U_1 + U_2 + \cdots . \qquad (XIV.3.4)$$

The matrix elements of U in the representation defined by the state vectors $|E_n^0\rangle$ of the unperturbed system H_0, or

$$U_{rs} = \langle E_r^0|U|E_s^0\rangle = \langle E_r^0|E_s\rangle,$$

are stationary-state transformation functions. Furthermore, from

$$|E_s\rangle = \sum_r |E_r^0\rangle\langle E_r^0|E_s\rangle = \sum_n U_{rs}|E_r^0\rangle \qquad (XIV.3.5)$$

it follows that the U_{rs} are also the expansion coefficients of $|E_s\rangle$.

Now, writing ($XIV.3.3$) in the form

$$(E_n - H_0)U|E_n^0\rangle = H'U|E_n^0\rangle \qquad (XIV.3.6)$$

and using the expansion of E_n,

$$E_n = E_n^0 + E_n^1 + E_n^2 + \cdots,$$

we obtain the representatives of ($XIV.3.6$) in the form

$$(E_n^0 - E_m^0 + E_n^1 + E_n^2 + \cdots)U_{mn} = \sum_s H'_{ms}U_{sn},$$

or

$$(E_n^0 - E_m^0 + E_n^1 + E_n^2 + \cdots)(\delta_{nm} + U_{mn}^1 + U_{mn}^2 + \cdots)$$
$$= \sum_s H'_{ms}(\delta_{sn} + U_{sn}^1 + U_{sn}^2 + \cdots).$$

Hence, equating terms of the same order on both sides, we obtain

$$(E_n^0 - E_m^0)U_{mn}^1 + E_n^1\delta_{mn} = H'_{mn}, \qquad (XIV.3.7)$$

$$(E_n^0 - E_m^0)U_{mn}^2 + E_n^1U_{mn}^1 + E_n^2\delta_{nm} = \sum_s H'_{ms}U'_{sn}, \qquad (XIV.3.8)$$

From ($XIV.3.7$) for $n \neq m$ we get the first-order part of the unitary operator:

$$U'_{mn} = \frac{H'_{mn}}{E_n^0 - E_m^0}. \qquad (XIV.3.9)$$

For $n = m$ we have

$$E_n^1 = H'_{nn}. \qquad (XIV.3.10)$$

Equation ($XIV.3.8$) for $n \neq m$ gives

$$(E_n^0 - E_m^0)U_{mn}^2 + \frac{H'_{nn}H'_{mn}}{E_n^0 - E_m^0} = \sum_{s\neq n} \frac{H'_{ms}H'_{sn}}{E_n^0 - E_s^0}$$

or

$$(E_n^0 - E_m^0)U_{mn}^2 = \sum_{s\neq m,n} \frac{H'_{ms}H'_{sn}}{E_n^0 - E_s^0}.$$

Hence

$$U_{mn}^2 = \sum_{s\neq m,n} \frac{H'_{ms}H'_{sn}}{(E_n^0 - E_m^0)(E_n^0 - E_s^0)}. \qquad (XIV.3.11)$$

For $n = m$, ($XIV.3.8$) yields the equation

$$E_m^1U_{mm}^1 + E_m^2 = \sum_s H'_{ms}U_{sm}^1 = H'_{mm}U_{mm}^1 + \sum_{s\neq m} H'_{ms}U_{sm}^1.$$

Hence

$$E_m^2 = \sum_{s \neq m} H'_{ms} U_{sm}^1 = \sum_{s \neq m} \frac{H'_{ms} H'_{sm}}{E_m^0 - E_s^0}. \tag{XIV.3.12}$$

which agrees with the usual method.

XIV.4. Time-Dependent Perturbation Theory

Time-dependent perturbation theory is concerned with the time variation of the stationary state of the unperturbed system under the action of a time-dependent perturbation. In other words, time-dependent perturbation theory is designed for the formulation of transitions between the stationary states of the unperturbed system.

For the sake of a first orientation we shall assume that H_0 has a discrete spectrum and nondegenerate eigenstates. The perturbing energy H' is time-dependent. We shall use the eigenvalues of a general set of observables ζ to label the states at time t. At the initial time $t = t_0$ the state with energy E_s is $|E_s, t_0\rangle$ and we assume that at $t = t_0$ the system is unperturbed. The apparent conflict with the uncertainty principle arising from the choice of E_s at time t_0 will be clarified when we discuss the boundary conditions.

The Schrödinger equation to be solved is

$$i\hbar \frac{d}{dt} |\zeta', t\rangle = H|\zeta', t\rangle, \tag{XIV.4.1}$$

where

$$H = H_0 + H'(t). \tag{XIV.4.2}$$

Since the $|E_n, t_0\rangle$ form a complete representation, we can express a general state $|\zeta', t\rangle$ as

$$|\zeta', t\rangle = \sum_n |E_n, t_0\rangle\langle E_n, t_0|\zeta', t\rangle. \tag{XIV.4.3}$$

The probability that H_0 has the eigenvalue E_n at time t with respect to the state $|\zeta', t\rangle$ or the probability that the system is in the unperturbed state $|E_n, t_0\rangle$ at time t is

$$\begin{aligned} \langle \zeta', t|\delta_{H_0E_n}|\zeta', t\rangle &= \sum_{n'} \langle \zeta', t|\delta_{H_0E_n}|E_{n'}, t_0\rangle\langle E_{n'}, t_0|\zeta', t\rangle \\ &= |\langle E_n, t_0|\zeta', t\rangle|^2. \end{aligned} \tag{XIV.4.4}$$

This gives us the physical meaning for the expansion coefficients $\langle E_n, t_0|\zeta', t\rangle$.

It will be more convenient to work with the "interaction picture." We introduce the unitary transformation

$$|\zeta', t\rangle = e^{-(it/\hbar)H_0}|I, t\rangle \tag{XIV.4.5}$$

and transform Schrödinger's equation into

$$i\hbar \frac{d}{dt}|I, t\rangle = H_I(t)|I, t\rangle, \qquad (XIV.4.6)$$

where the new interaction energy $H_I(t)$ is given as

$$H_I(t) = e^{(it/\hbar)H_0}H'(t)e^{-(it/\hbar)H_0}. \qquad (XIV.4.7)$$

As before, we may expand the state vector $|I, t\rangle$ of the interaction picture according to

$$|I, t\rangle = \sum_n |E_n, t_0\rangle\langle E_n, t_0|I, t\rangle. \qquad (XIV.4.8)$$

Under a unitary transformation all the algebraic relations remain invariant, so the expansion coefficients $\langle E_n, t_0|I, t\rangle$ have the same physical meaning as $\langle E_n, t|\zeta', t\rangle$:

$$\langle \zeta', t|\delta_{H_0E_n}|\zeta', t\rangle = \langle I, t|\delta_{H_0E_n}|I, t\rangle. \qquad (XIV.4.9)$$

Let us put $a_n(t) = \langle E_n, t_0|I, t\rangle$, and from $(XIV.4.6)$ we can obtain the equations

$$i\hbar \frac{da_n}{dt} = \sum_m H_I^{nm}a_m(t), \qquad (XIV.4.10)$$

where

$$H_I^{nm} = \langle E_n, t_0|H_I|E_m, t_0\rangle. \qquad (XIV.4.11)$$

Equations $(XIV.4.10)$ are a set of infinite number of differential equations defining each a_n in terms of a_m.

The time variation of a_n depends on the perturbing energy $H'(t)$ and on the type of unperturbed system with which it started. This is also seen from the definition of the probability amplitudes a_n. The boundary condition is contained in the statement that the system starts out at a definite unperturbed state $|E_n, t_0\rangle$ at time t_0. The state $|E_n, t_0\rangle$ may be taken as one of the stationary states of an atom. The infinite extent of time prior to the application of the perturbing energy at time t_0 makes it possible to determine the original energy E_n of the system with arbitrarily great precision, so no conflict with the uncertainty principle arises. The time available prior to the disturbance of the stationary state extends from $t = -\infty$ to $t = t_0$.

Let us assume that the particular state we start with is an excited state of the atom, $|E_s, t_0\rangle$. This means that at time $t = t_0$ all the probability amplitudes a_m are zero except a_s, say. If the system is actually in the stationary state $|E_s, t_0\rangle$ with energy E_s, then we can take $|a_s|^2 = 1$. However, if the perturbing energy is switched on slowly (or adiabatically) then the probability amplitudes a_m, where $m \neq s$, for transitions to other states, begin gradually to form. Just after $t = t_0$ the amplitudes a_m, where $m \neq s$, are quite small; accordingly, the probability amplitude for finding the system in the state $|E_s, t_0\rangle$ will start decreasing, but $|a_s|^2$ will remain close to unity. This state of perturbation will continue for some period of time, depending on $H_I(t)$. To see the situation more clearly, let us expand $a_n(t)$ in powers of H_I as

$$a_n(t) = \sum_r a_n^{(r)}(t), \qquad (XIV.4.12)$$

where $a_n^{(r)}(t)$ are of the rth order in H_I.

We use (*XIV.4.7*) and write equation (*XIV.4.10*) as

$$i\hbar \frac{d}{dt} a_n = \sum_m H'_{nm}(t)e^{(i/\hbar)t(E_n - E_m)}a_m(t). \qquad (XIV.4.13)$$

Using the expansion (*XIV.4.12*) we obtain

$$i\hbar \frac{d}{dt} a_n^{(r)} = \sum_m H'_{nm}a_m^{(r)}(t)e^{(i/\hbar)t(E_n - E_m)}. \qquad (XIV.4.14)$$

Equating coefficients of the same order we get

$$i\hbar \frac{d}{dt} a_n^{(0)} = 0,$$

$$i\hbar \frac{d}{dt} a_n^{(r+1)} = \sum_n H'_{nm}(t)a_m^{(r)}(t)e^{(it/\hbar)(E_n - E_m)}, \qquad (XIV.4.15)$$

where $r = 0, 1, 2, \cdots$.

Thus the $a_n^{(0)}$ are constants in time. They specify the initial conditions of the problem. Initially we assumed that all the $a_n^{(0)}$, except $a_n^{(0)}$, where $n \neq s$, are zero, so the system is in a definite stationary state when H' starts perturbing. From (*XIV.4.12*) we have $a_s(t) = a_s^{(0)}(t)$. Therefore, in accordance with the initial conditions, we can put $a_n^{(0)} = \delta_{ns}$. The first-order equation from (*XIV.2.15*) is then

$$i\hbar \frac{d}{dt} a_n^{(1)} = \sum_m H'_{nm}(t)\delta_{ms}e^{(i/\hbar)t(E_n - E_m)}$$

or

$$i\hbar \frac{d}{dt} a_n^{(1)} = H'_{ns}(t)e^{(i/\hbar)t(E_n - E_s)}.$$

We have thus made an estimation of the order of magnitude of the a_n. We may now work in terms of the a_n rather than the $a_n^{(r)}$. If $m \neq s$, then a_m is proportional to H'. By separating out the term referring to a_s we can rewrite (*XIV.4.13*):

$$i\hbar \frac{d}{dt} a_n(t) = H'_{ns}(t)a_s(t)e^{(i/\hbar)t(E_n - E_s)} + \sum_{m \neq s} H'_{nm}(t)a_m(t)e^{(i/\hbar)t(E_n - E_m)}. \quad (XIV.4.16)$$

Hence, to the first order in H', we obtain

$$i\hbar \frac{d}{dt} a_s = H'_{ss}a_s, \qquad (XIV.4.17)$$

which is solved by

$$a_s(t) = \exp\left[-\frac{i}{\hbar}\int_{t_0}^{t} H'_{ss}(t)\,dt\right]. \qquad (XIV.4.18)$$

If H' is independent of time we have

$$a_s(t) = \exp\left[-\frac{i}{\hbar}(t - t_0)H'_{ss}\right]. \qquad (XIV.4.19)$$

Since H'_{ss} is a real function the probability $|a_s(t)|^2$ does not change, so no transition can result from it. But, to a first-order approximation, the term H'_{ss} changes the angular frequency by an amount $(1/\hbar)H'_{ss}$. This is the same as changing the unperturbed energy by H'_{ss}; that is.

$$E = E_0 + H'_{ss}. \qquad (XIV.4.20)$$

XIV.4.A. Sudden Switch-On of a Time-Dependent Perturbing Energy

From the previous discussion, if $n \neq s$, we take $a_m = 0$ and $a_s = 1$ and obtain the equations

$$i\hbar \frac{d}{dt} a_n(t) = H'_{ns} e^{(i/\hbar)t(E_n - E_s)}.$$

This is solved by

$$a_n(t) = -\frac{i}{\hbar}\int_{t_0}^{t} H'_{ns}(t) e^{(i/\hbar)t(E_n - E_s)} dt. \qquad (XIV.4.21)$$

In order to ensure the vanishing of H' before its application, and hence the vanishing of all the a_n except a_s for $n = s$, we choose the initial time from the infinite past and put $t = -\infty$. In this case (*XIV.4.21*) leads to

$$a_n(t) = -\frac{i}{\hbar}\int_{-\infty}^{t} H'_{ns}(t) e^{(i/\hbar)t(E_n - E_s)}\,dt. \qquad (XIV.4.22)$$

Let us now assume that the perturbing energy is independent of time except that it is switched on and off at some small time interval $(0, t)$. Therefore, the first-order probability amplitude at time t is

$$a_n(t) = \frac{H'_{ns}}{E_n - E_s}\left[1 - e^{(i/\hbar)t(E_n - E_s)}\right], \qquad (XIV.4.23)$$

where we use the boundary condition $E_n = E_s$ at time $t = -\infty$. Hence, the probability that the system is at time t in the state n when it was in the state s at $t = -\infty$ is

$$|a_n|^2 = |H'_{ns}|^2 \frac{1 - \cos\left(\dfrac{E_n - E_s}{\hbar}t\right)}{(E_n - E_s)^2}. \qquad (XIV.4.24)$$

The largest contribution to the probability comes from those states foı which $E_n = E_s$—that is, for those states for which the energy is conserved. Thus the conservation of energy, when t is very large (in accordance with the principle of uncertainty), is an automatic consequence of the time-dependent perturbation theory. In general, a large probability results from

$$\frac{E_n - E_s}{\hbar} t = \frac{\Delta E}{\hbar} t \geqq 1$$

or

$$\Delta E \geqq \frac{\hbar}{t}. \qquad (XIV.4.25)$$

We see that for large t the spread ΔE in energy is very small and therefore conservation of energy comes in accordance with the principle of uncertainty. The energy E_n in (*XIV.4.23*) can be regarded as a final-state energy. If we confine ourselves to the case of discrete energies the probability will not be as large as it will be in the case of continuous or nearly continuous final-state energies. This is because the energy spread ΔE in relation (*XIV.4.25*) can be made smaller than the discrete energy spread.

In order to calculate the transition probability per unit time, we must first count the number of possible final states. Let us suppose that the system is contained in a large cube of dimensions L and that the eigenstates $|E_n, t\rangle$ are normalized to unity in the cube. If a group of final states E_n have nearly the same energy as the initial state E_s, we can find a density function for these final states. Let $\boldsymbol{k}$ be the wave number vector. If we assume periodic boundary conditions on the walls of the cube L^3 the $\boldsymbol{k}$ values must satisfy the relations $k_i = (2\pi/L)n_i$, where n_i are positive and negative integers. The number of possible $\boldsymbol{k}$ values is given by

$$\Delta N = \Delta n_1 \Delta n_2 \Delta n_3 = \frac{L^3}{(2\pi)^3} d^3\boldsymbol{k}.$$

Hence

$$\Delta N = n^2\, dn\, d\Omega = \frac{L^3}{(2\pi)^3} k^2\, dk\, d\Omega.$$

We may now define the number of final states per unit volume as

$$\frac{\Delta N}{L^3} = \rho_k\, dk\, d\Omega = \frac{k^2\, dk\, d\Omega}{(2\pi)^3}, \qquad (XIV.4.26)$$

where ρ_k is the density of the final states. Using $E = \hbar^2 k^2/2m$, we can write

$$\rho_E\, dE\, d\Omega = \frac{2mE}{\hbar^2} \frac{dE\, d\Omega}{(2\pi)^3}, \qquad (XIV.4.27)$$

where $\rho_E\, dE$ is the number of final states whose energies lie in the range E, $E + dE$. We shall assume that this density ρ_E of the final states is nearly independent of the energy E.

With these premises we can calculate a transition probability from a state $|E_s, t_0\rangle$ at $t_0 = 0$ with energy E_s to a state $|E, t\rangle$ at time t with energy E. Since we want to measure the energy E we shall not be interested in times t, which are short or of the order of one period $\hbar/\Delta E$, say. In order to be consistent with our assumptions that t must be small enough that the amplitude a_s does not vary much, we must state that the times under consideration are small compared to the lifetime of the initial state, but large enough for relation (*XIV.4.25*) to hold, so a sharp measurement of energy is possible. For large t we can write

$$\frac{1}{t}\,|a_n(t)|^2 = \frac{2\pi}{\hbar}\,|H'_{ns}|^2\delta(E_n - E_s), \qquad (XIV.4.28)$$

where we use the δ function property

$$\delta(x) = \frac{1}{\pi}\lim_{\lambda\to\infty}\frac{1}{\lambda}\frac{1 - \cos x\lambda}{x^2}.$$

For a nearly continuous final-state distribution the transition probability per unit time to one of the final states is obtained by multiplying (*XIV.4.28*) by the number of final states and integrating over the energy of the final states. Thus

$$W = \frac{1}{t}\int |a_n|^2\rho(n)\,dE_n.$$

A definite transition to final states is most favorable when $\rho(n)$ is independent of E_n and when the interaction energy does not vary appreciably over the extent of the final energies. In this case the transition probability per unit time is

$$W_{FO} = \frac{2\pi}{\hbar}\,|H'_{FO}|^2\rho(n), \qquad (XIV.4.29)$$

where the letters O and F refer to initial and final states.

The factor $\delta(E_n - E_s)$ in (*XIV.4.28*) does not designate a degeneracy; it only means that the energy is conserved in the transition and that transitions take place between states of equal unperturbed energy.

Expression (*XIV.4.27*) for the number of final states, using $E = \mathbf{p}^2/2m$, can also be written as

$$\frac{dN}{V} = \frac{4\pi p^2\,dp}{(2\pi\hbar)^3} = \frac{4\pi p^2\,dE}{(2\pi\hbar)^3 v},$$

where we use the relation $dE = v\,dp$, with v and p being the velocity and momentum in the center of mass system of the final-state particles (emitted particle + nucleus). This must be multiplied by the spin multiplicity in the final state. The relevant factor is $(2S_F + 1)(2I_F + 1)$, where $S_F =$ the spin of the emitted particle and $I_F =$ the spin of the final nucleus. Thus the correct formula for the number of final states is

$$\rho_F = \frac{1}{V}\frac{dN}{dE} = \frac{4\pi p^2}{(2\pi\hbar)^3 v}(2S_F + 1)(2I_F + 1). \qquad (XIV.4.30)$$

In the case of the photon emission the multiplicity of states must be ascribed to the two possible states of polarization, so the factor $(2S_F + 1)$ must be replaced by the number two.

Result (*XIV.4.29*) is the fundamental formula of the time-dependent perturbation theory. In many cases H'_{FO} vanishes and we have to proceed to higher approximations. For this we shall apply the method of an integral equation formulation of the time-dependent perturbation theory.

XIV.5. The Integral Equation Formulation of the Time-Dependent Perturbation Theory

The formalism to be developed in the following is applicable to scattering, bound states, and related problems. In all cases we have a total Hamiltonian of the system, including the interaction energy. For simplicity we can take a system consisting of two interacting parts.

The Hamiltonian of the system has the following characteristic properties.

(a) The total Hamiltonian is $H = H_0 + H'$, where H_0 is such that in the absence of H' the two parts of the system would have some similar internal structures and would suffer neither a scattering nor form a bound state.

(b) In a scattering process we would be interested in a transition from one eigenstate of H_0 to another.

(c) This transition would take place under the action of the perturbing energy H'.

(d) For bound states we would be interested in finding the stationary states corresponding to a time-independent total Hamiltonian.

All these problems can, in principle, be formulated in a rather simple way by using the unitary operator

$$U(tt_0) = \int |\zeta', t\rangle \, d\zeta' \, \langle \zeta', t_0|, \qquad (XIV.5.1)$$

where the state vector $|\zeta', t\rangle$ satisfies Schrödinger's equation,

$$i\hbar \frac{d}{dt} |\zeta', t\rangle = H_I(t)|\zeta', t\rangle,$$

in the interaction picture, as in (*XIV.4.5*). The definition (*XIV.5.1*) of $U(tt_0)$ shows that if $t = t_0$, then $U = I$, and that the eigenvalues ζ' of the complete commuting set ζ are the same at times t_0 and t. If ζ' is the energy itself, then the definition (*XIV.5.1*) contains the law of conservation of energy. The integration in (*XIV.5.1*) can also be taken as a discrete summation or both, depending on the nature of the problem.

We can use the eigenstates $|\zeta', t_0\rangle$ of ζ_0 and set up a representation. In this representation the matrix elements of the unitary operator are

$$\langle\zeta', t_0|U(tt_0)|\zeta'', t_0\rangle = \int \langle\zeta', t_0|\zeta'', t\rangle \, d\zeta'' \, \langle\zeta'', t|U(t, t_0)|\zeta'', t_0\rangle$$

$$= \int \langle\zeta', t_0|\xi'', t\rangle \, d\xi'' \, \delta(\xi'' - \zeta'') = \langle\zeta', t_0|\zeta'', t\rangle. \tag{XIV.5.2}$$

A comparison with the previous formulation of the time-dependent theory shows that the transformation functions (*XIV.5.2*) are the probability amplitudes of a transition taking place from the state $|\zeta', t_0\rangle$ to a state $|\zeta'', t\rangle$ during the time interval (t_0, t). In the case of discrete states, the total probability that a transition will take place is

$$P = \int |\langle\zeta', t_0|\zeta'', t\rangle|^2 \, d\zeta'' = \langle\zeta', t_0|\zeta', t_0\rangle = 1.$$

We thus see that the whole problem of calculating transition probabilities can be reduced to the problem of finding the representatives of the unitary operator U.

If we operate on both sides of (*XIV.5.1*) by H_I and integrate from t_0 to t, we obtain the integral equation

$$U(tt_0) = 1 - \frac{i}{\hbar}\int_{t_0}^{t} H_I(t')U(t't_0)\, dt'. \tag{XIV.5.3}$$

The solutions of this integral equation can be found (see Sections I.7.A and I.7.B). To the first order in $H_I(t')$ the iteration method yields

$$U(tt_0) = 1 - \frac{i}{\hbar}\int_{t_0}^{t} H_I(t')\, dt' = 1 + U_1(t). \tag{XIV.5.4}$$

In general, we have

$$U = 1 + U_1 + U_2 + \cdots + U_n + \cdots,$$

where

$$U_n(t) = \frac{1}{n!}\left(\frac{-i}{\hbar}\right)^n \int_{t_0}^{t} \cdots \int_{t_0}^{t} P[H_I(t_1)H_I(t_2) \cdots H_I(t_n)]\, dt_1 dt_2 \cdots dt_n. \tag{XIV.5.5}$$

(See Section 1.7.8.)

If at time t_0 $(= 0)$, H_0 is the only observable forming a complete commuting set by itself, then we can use it for ζ at t_0 and set up a representation, where

$$H_0|E_n, t_0\rangle = E_n|E_n, t_0\rangle.$$

The transition probability to the first order is

$$|\langle E_n|U_1|E_0\rangle|^2 = \frac{1}{\hbar^2}\left|\int_0^t \langle E_n|H_I(t')|E_0\rangle\, dt'\right|^2$$

$$= \frac{1}{\hbar^2}\left|\int_0^t \langle E_n|H'(t')|E_0\rangle e^{-(i/\hbar)(E_n-E_0)t'}\, dt'\right|^2$$

or

$$|U_{FO}^{(1)}|^2 = \frac{1}{\hbar^2}\left|\int_0^t H'_{FO}(t')e^{-(i/\hbar)(E_F-E_0)t'}\, dt'\right|^2, \qquad (XIV.5.6)$$

where we use the letters F and O, in place of discrete index n, to signify final and initial states, respectively. If we assume that H'_{FO} is independent of time during its action from initial time to final time t, then we get

$$|U_{FO}^{(1)}|^2 = \frac{2|H'_{FO}|^2}{(E_F - E_O)^2}\left[1 - \cos\left(\frac{E_F - E_O}{\hbar}t\right)\right]. \qquad (XIV.5.7)$$

Further discussion of this transition probability proceeds as in the previous section. The above formalism is also an illustration of the physical meaning of a transformation function which is a representative of the unitary operator in a certain representation obtained from the eigenstates of ζ at the initial time.

If the representative H'_{FO} vanishes or is small compared to other representatives of H', then it is necessary to calculate higher-order transition probabilities. The second-order transition probability amplitude is, as follows from ($XIV.5.5$), given by

$$U_{FO}^{(2)} = -\frac{1}{\hbar^2}\int_0^t \int_0^{t_1} dt_1 dt_2 \sum_I \left[H'_{FI}H'_{IO}e^{(i/\hbar)(E_F-E_I)t_1}e^{(i/\hbar)(E_I-E_O)t_2}\right],$$

where the letter I implies summation over intermediate states. As before, assuming that H' is independent of time—at least during the time interval (o, t)—the integrals can be carried out and we obtain

$$U_{FO}^{(2)} = \sum_I \frac{H'_{FI}H'_{IO}}{E_I - E_O}\left[\frac{e^{(i/\hbar)t(E_F-E_O)} - 1}{E_F - E_O} - \frac{e^{(i/\hbar)t(E_F-E_I)} - 1}{E_F - E_I}\right]. \qquad (XIV.5.8)$$

The transition for which the probability will increase occurs for $E_F = E_O$ and $E_F = E_I$. The transition $E_O = E_F$ is a statement of conservation of energy since E_O is the energy of the initial state while E_F is the energy of any one of a group of final states. The transition $E_F = E_I$ need not occur. The states E_I are called "intermediate states" over which a summation is taken.

If we assume that only energy-conserving transitions can occur, then the first term in the square brackets in ($XIV.5.8$) must be treated as in the first-order theory. If H' does not produce any transitions in the first order, then $H'_{FO} = o$. In this case the summation in ($XIV.5.8$) need not include the terms $I = F$ and $I = O$. Note that the terms $I = F$ and $I = O$ are not singular.

The second term in the square brackets has a large energy denominator

$E_F - E_I$ (nonconservation of energy in the intermediate states) and is negligible compared to the first term. The result is then

$$U_{FO}^{(2)} = \sum_I \left[\frac{H'_{FI}H'_{IO}}{(E_I - E_O)} \frac{e^{(i/\hbar)t(E_F - E_O)} - 1}{(E_F - E_O)}\right]. \qquad (XIV.5.9)$$

The second factor in (*XIV.5.9*) can be treated as in the first-order theory. Hence the transition probability per unit time is

$$W_{FO} = \frac{1}{t}\int |U_{FO}^{(2)}|^2 \rho_F \, dE_F$$

or

$$W_{FO} = \frac{2\pi}{\hbar}\left|\sum_{I \neq 0} \frac{H'_{FI}H'_{IO}}{E_I - E_O}\right|^2 \rho_F. \qquad (XIV.5.10)$$

In the second-order perturbation theory the transition from the initial state O to the final states F takes place through the intermediate state I. These states exist for a short time, and their energy, in accordance with the uncertainty principle, is not measurable.

In connection with the density of final states ρ_F occurring in (*XIV.5.10*), it is important to note that if the particles have spins the density of states is increased by the multiplicity of spins. This is essentially the case for a particle scattered from a nucleus. This multiplicity depends on the spin orientation. Thus the correct density of final states is obtained by multiplying ρ_F by $(2S + 1)(2I + 1)$, where S is the spin of the emitted particle and I the spin of the nucleus.

XIV.6. Resonance Transitions and the Compound Nucleus

A particle scattered from a nucleus can loose some of its energy by transferring it to the nucleus particles. This results in a redistribution of energy among all the particles of the nucleus and the incident particle forming a "compound nucleus" with the original nucleus. According to Bohr's theory, each of the particles of the compound nucleus will have some energy but not enough energy to escape from the compound nucleus. There is, however, a probability that after a certain time the incident particle may regain the lost energy and escape from the nucleus, leaving it in an excited state. If the escaping particle is of the same kind as the incident one and the initial state of the nucleus is left unaltered, then the process is an "elastic scattering." This is only one special case; the probability of "inelastic collisions"—for example a nucleus left in an excited state or a different particle being emitted—is larger than the probability of elastic collisions. There is also a high probability of emission of radiation.

Nuclear collisions can be described in terms of the compound nucleus as transitions from compound states to the final and initial states:

Incident particle + initial nucleus ⟶ compound nucleus ⟶ final nucleus + emitted particle.

The compound nucleus can conveniently be represented by the intermediate states of the time-dependent perturbation theory. In this way the quasi-stationary states of the compound nucleus may have some interesting consequences. One of these is the so-called "resonance phenomenon." If the energy of the incident particle is such that the total energy of the particle + nucleus is nearly equal to one of the energy levels of the compound nucleus, then the probability of the formation of a compound or an intermediate state increases. If the total energy falls between two resonance levels the probability of compound nucleus formation is smaller.

In the language of perturbation theory, the quantity $|H'_{FO}|^2$ will have some irregular variations, instead of being constant. Near a resonance the transition probability would behave like $1/(E - E_R)^2$, since

$$W_{FO} = \frac{2\pi}{\hbar}\left|\frac{H'_{FI}H'_{IO}}{E_O - E_I}\right|^2 \rho_F = \frac{2\pi}{\hbar}\left|\frac{H'_{FC}H'_{CO}}{E_O - E_C}\right|^2 \rho_F. \qquad (XIV.6.1)$$

Near $E_O = E_C$ (resonance), W_{FO} is very large. At the resonance energy, W_{FO} is infinite. The infinity results from disregarding the short lifetime of the compound state, for formula (*XIV.6.1*) does not take this into account. The correct equations describing the decay of a compound state can be obtained from the integral equation for the unitary operator $U(t)$:

$$U(t) = 1 - \frac{i}{\hbar}\int_0^t H_I(t')\,U(t')\,dt'.$$

There are three possible groups of states.

(a) *The initial states $|E_O\rangle$ with energy E_O refer to the unperturbed states of the particle + nucleus.*

(b) *The final states $|E_F\rangle$ with energy E_F refer to the residual nucleus and the emitted particle.*

(c) *The compound states $|E_C\rangle$ (assumed to be discrete states) with energy E_C refer to the compound nucleus.*

The above groups of states arise, for example, in a radiative capture of neutrons. The energy levels of the initial and final states form a continuous spectrum.

From a group of initial states (O) the experiment will pick out a particular one. We shall assume that no direct transitions from initial states (O) to final states (F) take place. Thus the representatives $H'_{OO'}$, $H'_{FF'}$, H'_{OF} of the interaction energy H' shall be neglected. If we are interested in one level we can assume that there is only one intermediate state in the resonance transition. Under the above assumptions the transition probability amplitudes from one initial state to another, from an initial state to a final state, or from an initial state to a compound state, are respectively given by

$$\begin{aligned} U_{OO'} &= \langle E_O|E_{O'}\rangle - \frac{i}{\hbar} H'_{OC} \int_0^t e^{(i/\hbar)(E_O - E_C)t'} U_{CO'}\, dt', \\ U_{FO'} &= \langle E_F|E_{O'}\rangle - \frac{i}{\hbar} H'_{FC} \int_0^t e^{(i/\hbar)(E_F - E_C)t'} U_{CO'}\, dt', \\ U_{CO'} &= \langle E_C|E_{O'}\rangle - \frac{i}{\hbar} \sum_{O''} H'_{CO''} \int_0^t e^{(i/\hbar)(E_C - E_{O''})t'} U_{O''O'}\, dt' \\ &\quad - \frac{i}{\hbar} \sum_{F'} H'_{CF'} \int_0^t e^{(i/\hbar)(E_C - E_{F'})t'} U_{F'O'}\, dt'. \end{aligned} \qquad (XIV.6.2)$$

In writing the last equation for the transition amplitude we took into consideration the fact that transition from an initial state to a compound state cannot be independent of a certain set of initial and final states, since a compound state amplitude U_{CO} can disintegrate either to the initial state (O) or to the final state (F).

At time $t = 0$ the states O and O' are the same and there are no compound states, so $U_{OO'}(0) = 1$ and $U_{FO'} = U_{CO'} = 0$. From the three-coupled set of integral equations (*XIV.6.2*) we see that we can substitute for $U_{OO'}$ and $U_{FO'}$ in the third equation, from the first and second, and obtain a single integral equation for the compound state probability amplitude $U_{CO'}$. The kernel of the resulting equation involves both first-order and second-order terms in the interaction energy H'. The boundary conditions above imply that the set of equations (*XIV.6.2*) can be replaced by

$$\begin{aligned} U_{OO'} &= \delta_{OO'} - \frac{i}{\hbar} H'_{OC} \int_0^t e^{(i/\hbar)(E_O - E_C)t'} U_{CO'}(t')\, dt', \\ U_{FO'} &= - \frac{i}{\hbar} H'_{FC} \int_0^t e^{(i/\hbar)(E_F - E_C)t'} U_{CO'}(t')\, dt', \\ U_{CO'} &= \frac{i}{\hbar} \sum_{O''} H'_{CO''} \int_0^t e^{(i/\hbar)t'(E_C - E_{O''})} U_{O''O'}(t')\, dt' \\ &\quad - \frac{i}{\hbar} \sum_{F'} H'_{CF'} \int_0^t e^{(i/\hbar)t'(E_C - F_{F'})} U_{F'O'}(t')\, dt'. \end{aligned} \qquad (XIV.6.3)$$

Substituting for $U_{O''O'}$ and $U_{F'O'}$ in the third equation, from the first and second equations, we obtain an integral equation for $U_{CO'}$ in the form

$$a_c(t) = -\frac{\Gamma}{\hbar} \int_0^t a_c(t')\, dt' - \frac{i}{\hbar} H'_{CO} \int_0^t e^{(i/\hbar)t'(E_C - E_O)}\, dt', \qquad (XIV.6.4)$$

where

$$a_c(t) = U_{CO'}(t), \qquad \Gamma = \Gamma_O + \Gamma_F, \tag{XIV.6.5}$$

$$\Gamma_O = \frac{1}{\hbar}\int_0^{t'} \sum_O |H'_{CO}|^2 e^{(i/\hbar)(t'-t'')(E_C-E_O)}\, dt', \tag{XIV.6.6}$$

$$\Gamma_F = \frac{1}{\hbar}\int_0^{t'} \sum_F |H'_{CF}|^2 e^{(i/\hbar)(t'-t'')(E_C-E_F)}\, dt'. \tag{XIV.6.7}$$

For large t'—that is, when E_O is near E_C—we can replace the definitions (*XIV.6.6*) and (*XIV.6.7*) by

$$\Gamma_O = i\sum_O |H'_{CO}|^2 \delta_+(E_C - E_O) e^{-(i/\hbar)t''(E_C-E_O)} \tag{XIV.6.8}$$

and

$$\Gamma_F = i\sum_F |H'_{CF}|^2 \delta_+(E_C - E_F) e^{-(i/\hbar)t''(E_C-E_F)}, \tag{XIV.6.9}$$

where $\delta_+(x)$ is defined by (*III.3.19*). It is clear from the definitions (*XIV.6.8*) and (*XIV.6.9*) that Γ has real and imaginary parts. The real part of Γ is $\frac{1}{2}\hbar$ times the total transition probability per second from state (C) to all other states. The imaginary part of Γ is related to the "self-energy" of the state (C); it will not be discussed in this book.* The real part of Γ is independent of t''.

The integral equation (*XIV.6.4*) is solved by

$$a_c(t) = \frac{iH'_{CO}[e^{-(\Gamma/\hbar)t} - e^{(i/\hbar)(E_C-E_O)t}]}{i(E_C - E_O) + \Gamma}. \tag{XIV.6.10}$$

We introduce a dispersal time τ for the compound state (C) by

$$\Gamma\tau = \tfrac{1}{2}\hbar, \tag{XIV.6.11}$$

where, in accordance with the uncertainty principle and the experimental data on the energy widths, τ will be very small; therefore the term $\exp[-(\Gamma/\hbar)t] = \exp(-t/2\tau)$ can be neglected. In this case the formation of the compound state is proportional to

$$|a_c|^2 = \frac{|H'_{CO}|^2}{(E_C - E_O)^2 + \Gamma^2}, \tag{XIV.6.12}$$

which has the form of a resonance or intensity distribution with an energy width given by the real part of Γ,

$$\Gamma = \pi\sum_O |H'_{CO}|^2 \delta(E_C - E_O) + \pi\sum_F |H'_{CF}|^2 \delta(E_C - E_F), \tag{XIV.6.13}$$

where the imaginary part of Γ is neglected.

Formula (*XIV.6.13*) was first derived by Breit and Wigner.† The maximum

---

* See W. Heitler, *Quantum Theory of Radiation,* Oxford Univ. Press, Oxford, 1954, p. 168.

† G. Breit and E. P. Wigner, *Phys. Rev.,* **49** (1936), 519.

of $|a_c|^2$ occurs at the incident energy $E_O = E_C$, and it is given by

$$|a_c|^2_{\max} = \frac{|H'_{CO}|^2}{\Gamma^2}.$$

Hence the energy width at half maximum is given by

$$\Delta E = 2\Gamma = \gamma_R, \qquad (XIV.6.14)$$

so in terms of energy width γ_R the quantity Γ is defined by

$$\Gamma = \tfrac{1}{2}\gamma_R, \qquad (XIV.6.15)$$

where $(1/\hbar)\gamma_R$ is the disintegration probability per unit time.

XIV.6.A. Transition Rates and Resonance Phenomena

In accordance with formula (*XIV.4.29*) and expression (*XIV.4.27*) for the number of final states, the number N_F of transitions per unit volume per unit time is given by

$$N_F = \frac{1}{\pi\hbar^4}|H'_{FO}|^2\frac{p_F^2}{v_F}(2S_F + 1)(2I_F + 1). \qquad (XIV.6.16)$$

The number N_F can be used to introduce a quantity σ_{OF}, called the "reaction cross-section per nucleus" for processes involving scattering of particles from nuclei. (A general discussion of scattering theory is given in Chapter XVII.) Thus

$$VN_F = n_O v_O \sigma_{OF}, \qquad (XIV.6.17)$$

where

$n_O v_O$ = *the number of incident particles per unit area per second,*
V = *volume of the space.*

With $V = 1$ and an assumed density $n_0 = 1$ per unit volume, we obtain

$$\sigma_{OF} = \frac{1}{\pi\hbar^4}|H'_{OF}|^2\frac{p_F^2}{v_O v_F}(2S_F + 1)(2I_F + 1). \qquad (XIV.6.18)$$

The quantity σ_{OF} has the dimensions of an area and it measures the probability that a reaction initiated by the interaction energy H' will take place.

Now let us assume that in a certain nuclear reaction the probability of the formation of a compound state is a certainty, so $a_c = 1$. The compound state (C) can either return to the initial state or make a transition to a final state. If the decay to the final state results in the emission of a photon, then the probability of transition to the final state per unit volume per unit time, neglecting spin, is

$$\frac{1}{\tau_\gamma} = \frac{1}{\pi\hbar^4}|H'_{FO}|^2\frac{p_\gamma^2}{v_\gamma} = \frac{1}{\pi\hbar^2}|H'_{FO}|^2\frac{\omega^2}{c^2}, \qquad (XIV.6.19)$$

where $p_\gamma = \hbar\omega/c$ and $v_\gamma = c$. In the same way the probability of transition to the initial state per unit volume per unit time is

$$\frac{1}{\tau_O} = \frac{1}{\pi\hbar^4}|H'_{OF}|^2\frac{p_O^2}{v_O} = \frac{m^2}{\pi\hbar^4}|H'_{OF}|^2 v_O, \qquad (XIV.6.20)$$

where $p_O = mv_O$ and $|H_{OF}|^2 = |H_{FO}|^2$.

Using (*XIV.6.11*) we define partial widths by

$$\Gamma_\gamma = \frac{1}{2}\frac{\hbar}{\tau_\gamma}, \qquad \Gamma_O = \frac{1}{2}\frac{\hbar}{\tau_O}. \qquad (XIV.6.21)$$

Hence the total energy width is

$$\Gamma = \frac{1}{2}\frac{\hbar}{\tau} = \frac{1}{2}\left(\frac{1}{\tau_\gamma} + \frac{1}{\tau_O}\right)\hbar$$

or

$$\frac{1}{\tau} = \frac{1}{\tau_\gamma} + \frac{1}{\tau_O}. \qquad (XIV.6.22)$$

If we neglect the growth of the compound state, then the corresponding probability amplitude for the state (C) is

$$a_c = e^{-\Gamma t/\hbar} = e^{-(t/2)(1/\tau_\gamma + 1/\tau_o)}, \qquad (XIV.6.23)$$

where τ_O and τ_γ are the life of the corresponding states against the decay of the compound state. However, the formula that takes into consideration the occupation of the compound state arising from the transition of the initial state is correctly given by (*XIV.6.10*).

In this case the number of nuclear reactions* per second per unit volume is

$$\sigma_{OF} v_O = |a_c|^2 \frac{1}{\tau_F}, \qquad (XIV.6.24)$$

where the reaction takes place in the order *initial state* ⟶ *compound state* ⟶ *final state*. For the reaction where it follows the order *initial state* ⟶ *compound state* ⟶ *initial state*, the number of reactions per second per unit volume is

$$\sigma_{OO} v_O = |a_c|^2 \frac{1}{\tau_O}. \qquad (XIV.6.25)$$

Hence the corresponding cross-sections are

$$\sigma_{OF} = \frac{2\Gamma_F}{\hbar v_O}\frac{|H'_{OF}|^2}{(E_O - E_C)^2 + \Gamma^2}, \qquad (XIV.6.26)$$

$$\sigma_{OO} = \frac{2\Gamma_O}{\hbar v_O}\frac{|H'_{OF}|^2}{(E_O - E_C)^2 + \Gamma^2}. \qquad (XIV.6.27)$$

If the incident particle happens to have a velocity such that it hits the resonance exactly, then from (*XIV.6.20*) we can write

$$\frac{\Gamma_O}{v_O} = \frac{\Gamma_{OR}}{v_R} = \frac{m^2}{2\pi\hbar^3}|H'_{OF}|^2, \qquad (XIV.6.28)$$

* E. Fermi, *Nuclear Physics*, Univ. of Chicago Press, Chicago, 1950, p. 156. Notes compiled by J. Orear, A. H. Resenfeld, and R. A. Schluter.

where v_R is the resonance velocity of the incident particle and Γ_{OR} is the value of the partial width at the resonance velocity v_R. Combining (*XIV.6.27*) and (*XIV.6.28*) we obtain the cross-section σ_{OO} in the form

$$\sigma_{OO} = 4\pi\lambda\!\!\!^{-2}_R \frac{(\Gamma_{OR})^2}{(E_O - E_C)^2 + \Gamma^2}, \qquad (XIV.6.29)$$

where $\lambda\!\!\!^{-}_R = \hbar/mv_R$. Similarly, the Breit-Wigner formula for the cross-section σ_{OF} is

$$\sigma_{OF} = 4\pi\lambda\!\!\!^{-}\lambda\!\!\!^{-}_R \frac{\Gamma_F\Gamma_{OR}}{(E_O - E_C)^2 + \Gamma^2}, \qquad (XIV.6.30)$$

where $\lambda\!\!\!^{-} = \hbar/mv_O$.

In an atomic collision inelastic processes are rare, since the interaction between the incident particle and the individual electrons of the atom is small. Therefore, an incident particle in most cases will pass through the atom without losing any energy, its deflection being produced, essentially, by the average field of the atom (elastic scattering). The cross-sections for emission of radiation (inelastic processes) are small for atomic collisions. However, for nuclear scattering phenomena the interaction between the incident particle and the nucleus is strong, and therefore the former cannot go through the nucleus without transferring some of its energy to nuclear particles. In a short time the incident energy will be shared by the nuclear particles plus the incident particle. After a comparatively long time there will be a probability that one of the nuclear constituents will absorb more energy than the rest of the particles, leading to its escape from the nucleus in a state differing from its initial state. The residual nucleus is left in an excited state. If the escaping particle is of the same kind as the incident one and if the internal state of the nucleus is not changed, then the result is a nuclear elastic process. In contrast to atomic collisions, in nuclear scattering the probability of inelastic processes is much larger than the probability of elastic processes to occur.

In general, every nuclear process must be treated as a many-body phenomenon. In particular, a nuclear collision cannot be described as a stationary state where the energy of the system is sharply defined. The many-body aspect of nuclear collision phenomena leads to a "quasi-stationary state" of a compound nucleus where the energy is not sharply defined. Such a state arises from the finite lifetime of the compound state, which is very large compared to the time required for the incident particle to pass through the nucleus.

The stationary states of a compound nucleus, besides being the cause for elastic, inelastic, and other collisions, are responsible for resonance phenomena. The knowledge of resonances can be utilized to obtain the spacing between neighboring levels of the compound nucleus. The spacing between levels is a function of the mass number A and the excitation energy of the nucleus. Thus the knowledge of spacing is important to the study of nuclear structure.

XIV.6.B. Problems

1. Assume that the only compound nucleus spin states that resonate refer to $S_C = S_A \pm \frac{1}{2}$. By counting the initial parallel and antiparallel spin states, show that the probability that incident particle will form a parallel spin state with the nucleus is $(S_A + 1)/(2S_A + 1)$ and that the incident particle forms a state with antiparallel spins is $S_A/(2S_A + 1)$.

2. Using the results of problem 1, prove that the probability that the incident particle and target nucleus in an unpolarized beam will be found to have the spin S_C of the compound nucleus is

$$g(S_C) = \frac{2S_C + 1}{2(2S_A + 1)}.$$

Hence show that the cross-sections (*XIV.6.29*) and (*XIV.6.30*) must be multiplied by the statistical weight $g(S_C)$ of the compound nucleus spin state.

3. A charged particle moving in a plane normal to the lines of force of a spatially uniform but temporally varying magnetic field B obeys the equation

$$\frac{d^2u}{dt^2} + 2i\omega\frac{du}{dt} + i\frac{d\omega}{dt}u = 0,$$

where

$$u = x_+ \exp\left(-i\int \omega\, dt\right),$$

$$\frac{d^2x_+}{dt^2} + \omega^2 x_+ = 0, \qquad x_+ = x_1 + ix_2,$$

$$\omega = \frac{eB}{2mc} = \tfrac{1}{2}\text{ Larmor frequency.}$$

The probability amplitude a_c for the formation of a compound nucleus obeys the equation

$$\frac{d^2a_c}{dt^2} + 2i\Omega\frac{da_c}{dt} + i\Lambda a_c = 0,$$

where

$$\Omega = -\frac{1}{2}\frac{\Delta E + i\Gamma}{\hbar}, \qquad \Lambda = -\frac{\Delta E\Gamma}{\hbar^2}, \qquad \Delta E = E_C - E_O$$

and the amplitude a_c can be written as

$$a_c = a_+ e^{-i\Omega t},$$

with

$$\frac{d^2a_+}{dt^2} + \Omega^{*2}a_+ = 0, \qquad \Omega^* = -\frac{1}{2}\frac{\Delta E - i\Gamma}{\hbar}, \qquad \Lambda = i(\Omega^2 - \Omega^{*2}).$$

Comment on the oscillators with real and complex frequencies.

4. The amplitude of a classical linear harmonic oscillator with a reaction force

$$F_S = \frac{2e^2}{3c^3}\frac{d^2v}{dt^2}$$

satisfies the equation

$$\frac{d^2x}{dt^2} + \omega_0^2 x + \gamma\frac{dx}{dt} = 0,$$

where

$$\gamma = \frac{2e^2\omega_0^2}{3mc^3}, \qquad \frac{d^2v}{dt^2} = -\omega_0^2 v, \qquad \omega_0 \gg \gamma.$$

Show that the amplitude of the oscillator is given by

$$x = be^{-(1/2)\gamma t},$$

where b satisfies the equation

$$\frac{d^2b}{dt^2} + \nu^2 b = 0,$$

with $\nu^2 = \omega_0^2 - \frac{1}{4}\gamma^2$. The energy of the oscillator averaged over one period is

$$E = \tfrac{1}{2}m(v^2 + \omega_0^2 x^2) = E_0 e^{-\gamma t}.$$

Thus $1/\gamma$ is the lifetime of the oscillator. Therefore the electric vector of the emitted radiation can be taken to be

$$E = E_0 e^{-(1/2)\gamma t} e^{-i\omega_0 t}.$$

It represents a certain intensity distribution

$$I(\omega) = |E(\omega)|^2 = I_0 \frac{\gamma}{2\pi}\frac{1}{(\omega - \omega_0)^2 + \frac{1}{4}\gamma^2},$$

where

$$E = \int_{-\infty}^{\infty} E(\omega) e^{-i\omega t}\, d\omega,$$

$$\int I(\omega)\, d\omega = I_0 = \text{total intensity},$$

$$\gamma = \text{width at half maximum}.$$

5. For a periodic perturbing energy

$$H' = Ae^{-i\omega t} + Be^{i\omega t},$$

show that the transition probability amplitude to the first order is

$$U_{FO}^{(1)} = \frac{A_{FO}}{E_F - E_O + \hbar\omega}\left[e^{-(i/\hbar)(E_F - E_O + \hbar\omega)t} - 1\right] + \frac{A_{OF}^*}{E_F - E_O - \hbar\omega}\left[e^{-(i/\hbar)(E_F - E_O - \hbar\omega)t} - 1\right].$$

Then calculate the corresponding transition probability per unit time. Discuss the cases where $E_F = E_O + \hbar\omega$ and $E_F = E_O - \hbar\omega$.

CHAPTER XV

INTERACTION WITH RADIATION

XV. 1. Einstein Coefficients

The transition of an atom from one state of energy to a state of lower energy leads to emission of electromagnetic radiation. The reverse process of absorption of radiation is the result of an upward transition caused by the action of a radiation field on the atom. For historical reasons and also as a further illustration of Einstein's unfailing judgment in all paths of physics, we shall briefly discuss his theory of spontaneous emission of radiation by a system of atoms. This constitutes one of the first important examples in physics where indeterministic reasoning plays a fundamental role.

Consider two stationary states of an atom, a low state B and an excited state A. Einstein assumed that if the atom is found in the state A, then it has a probability of transition to state B by emitting a photon of frequency

$$\nu_{AB} = \frac{E_A - E_B}{h}.$$

In a large assembly of such atoms the number $N(A)$ of excited atoms that return to state B per unit time is proportional to their number $N(B)$ in the initial state. The resulting radiation will produce a certain probability for the reverse process $B \longrightarrow A$ which represents absorption of a photon of frequency ν_{AB}. The latter probability is proportional to the radiation density of the corresponding frequency. The emitted radiation will influence not only the absorption process, but also the emission process itself—that is, the transition $A \longrightarrow B$. This is called "induced emission," and it is proportional to the radiation density for the frequency ν_{AB}. These assumptions, together with the use of the Maxwell-Boltzmann distribution, gave Planck's formula.

For the calculation of a relation between emission and absorption rates we can proceed in reverse order, by making certain assumptions for a state in thermal equilibrium.

(a) *The relative numbers of atoms belonging to different levels are given by the Maxwell-Boltzmann law,*

$$N(A) = g(A)e^{-E_A/\kappa T}, \tag{XV.1.1}$$

where $g(A)$ is the statistical weight of the level A.

(b) *The radiation density is given by Planck's formula:*

$$\rho\left(\frac{\nu}{c}\right) = \frac{8\pi h}{c^2}\frac{\nu^3}{e^{h\nu/\kappa T} - 1}. \tag{XV.1.2}$$

To these two assumptions we shall further add the "principle of detailed balancing."

(c) *In statistical equilibrium the rates of each elementary process and its inverse are equal.* (See Section XVIII.4.) The "induced" and "spontaneous" emissions together are regarded as one elementary process and the one kind of absorption as its inverse. Now, let $\mathcal{A}(A, B)$ be the probability per unit time of making a spontaneous transition with emission of radiation to each level B of lower energy. The number $N(A)$ of atoms in the excited level will decrease by radiation according to

$$\frac{dN(A)}{dt} = -\left[\sum_B \mathcal{A}(A, B)\right] N(A) \tag{XV.1.3}$$

where the summation is taken over all states of lower energy. If only spontaneous emission occurs, then the system will decay according to

$$N(A) = N_0(A)e^{-t/\tau_A}, \tag{XV.1.4}$$

where τ_A is the mean lifetime of the atom in the state A. In general, τ_A is given by

$$\frac{1}{\tau_A} = \sum_B \mathcal{A}(A, B). \tag{XV.1.5}$$

If the radiation field is assumed to be isotropic and unpolarized and have spectral energy density $\rho(\nu/c)\, d\nu/c$ in the frequency range $d\nu$ at ν, then the calculation of absorption and induced emission rates can be done in a rather simple way. Let C denote an energy level higher than A; then transition from A to C via absorption takes place at a rate

$$N(A)\boldsymbol{\beta}(A, C)\rho\left(\frac{\nu}{c}\right), \tag{XV.1.6}$$

where $\boldsymbol{\beta}(A, C)$ is the probability per unit time of making transition from A to C by absorption of radiation. The emission resulting from transition from C to A as induced by radiation itself takes place at a rate

$$N(C)\boldsymbol{\beta}(C, A)\rho\left(\frac{\nu}{c}\right). \tag{XV.1.7}$$

The probabilities $\mathcal{A}$ and $\boldsymbol{\beta}$ are closely related to the interaction of the atom with radiation field and they are independent of a particular equilibrium state. From the principle of detailed balancing it follows that

$$N(C)\left[\mathfrak{A}(C, A) + \boldsymbol{\beta}(C, A)\rho\left(\frac{\nu}{c}\right)\right] = N(A)\boldsymbol{\beta}(A, C)\rho\left(\frac{\nu}{c}\right). \qquad (XV.1.8)$$

Thus, from (*XV.1.1*), (*XV.1.2*), and (*XV.1.7*), we obtain

$$g(A)\boldsymbol{\beta}(A, C) = g(C)\boldsymbol{\beta}(C, A), \qquad (XV.1.9)$$

$$\mathfrak{A}(C, A) = 8\pi \frac{h\nu^3}{c^2}\boldsymbol{\beta}(C, A). \qquad (XV.1.10)$$

Hence the total rate of the emission process is

$$P_{\text{emission}} = N(C)\mathfrak{A}(C, A)\left[\frac{c^2\rho}{8\pi h\nu^3} + 1\right]. \qquad (XV.1.11)$$

From (*XV.1.8*) it follows that

$$\frac{c^2\rho}{8\pi h\nu^3}\frac{1}{e^{h\nu/\kappa T} - 1} = \bar{n}(\nu)$$

is the average number of photons in the energy range $h\nu$. We may, therefore, write the total emission rate as

$$P_{\text{emission}} = N(C)\mathfrak{A}(C, A)[\bar{n}(\nu) + 1]. \qquad (XV.1.12)$$

This result will be compared with quantum mechanical calculation.

XV.2. General Formulation of the Radiation Problem

The total Hamiltonian of a system of charged particles interacting with the radiation field and between themselves is given by

$$H = H_0 + H', \qquad (XV.2.1)$$

where

$$H_0 = \sum_{i=1}^{n}(c\boldsymbol{\alpha}_i\cdot\boldsymbol{p} + \beta_i m_i c^2) + \sum_{i>j}\frac{e_i e_j}{r_{ij}} + \sum_{s=1}^{\infty}\sum_{\lambda=1}^{2} n_{\lambda s}\hbar\omega_s, \qquad (XV.2.2)$$

$$H' = -\sum_{i=1}^{n} e_i[\boldsymbol{\alpha}_i\cdot\boldsymbol{A}(\boldsymbol{r}_i)], \qquad (XV.2.3)$$

and $\boldsymbol{\alpha}_i$ and β_i, for $i = 1, 2, \cdots, n$, are Dirac matrices corresponding to particles. The last sums in (*XV.2.2*) represent the energy of the radiation field [see (*XI.2.20*)]. The Coulomb energy of the system is represented by the second sum in (*XV.2.2*), where the first sum represents the total relativistic kinetic energy of the particles. We are assuming that the vector potential $\boldsymbol{A}(\boldsymbol{r}_i)$ at the position $\boldsymbol{r}_i$ of the ith particle is an operator satisfying the equation $\boldsymbol{\nabla}\cdot\boldsymbol{A} = 0$. In this case the scalar potential A_4 of the radiation field can be set equal to zero.* In this book it will not be necessary to explain the full construction of the radiation theory; we only need to know some of its direct results. Therefore the discussion based on quantum electrodynamics will be omitted.

The general state of the system will be described by a state vector $|\Psi\rangle$ satisfying Schrodinger's equation:

$$i\hbar \frac{d}{dt}|\Psi\rangle = (H_0 + H')|\Psi\rangle. \qquad (XV.2.4)$$

If the particle field is not quantized, then $|\Psi\rangle$ depends on the coordinates of the particles and the variables used to describe the radiation field. For a system of identical particles the state $|\Psi\rangle$ must be antisymmetric in all particles.

$$H = \sum_i \left\{ \frac{\left[\boldsymbol{p}_i - \frac{e}{c} \boldsymbol{A}(\boldsymbol{r}_i) \right]^2}{2m_i} - \frac{e_i \hbar}{2m_i c} (\boldsymbol{\sigma}_i \cdot \mathfrak{H}) \right\} + \sum_{i>j} \frac{e_i e_j}{r_{ij}}. \qquad (XV.2.5)$$

Hence, neglecting spin, the interaction is given by

$$H' = -\sum_i \left\{ \frac{e_i}{m_i c} [\boldsymbol{p}_i \cdot \boldsymbol{A}(\boldsymbol{r}_i)] - \frac{e_i^2}{2m_i c} \boldsymbol{A}^2(\boldsymbol{r}_i) \right\} \qquad (XV.2.6)$$

For the vector potential $\boldsymbol{A}(\boldsymbol{r})$ we can use an expansion similar to $(XI.2.12)$,

$$A_i = \sum_{s=1}^{\infty} \sum_{\lambda=1}^{2} q_{\lambda s} u_s(\boldsymbol{r}) e_i^{(s)}, \qquad (XV.2.7)$$

where $u_s(\boldsymbol{r})$ are plane waves of the form

$$u_s(\boldsymbol{r}) = \sqrt{(4\pi)} e^{i(\boldsymbol{k}_s \cdot \boldsymbol{r})} e_s.$$

The matrix elements of $q_{\lambda s}$, as follows from $(VII.1.57)$, are given by

$$(q_{\lambda s})_{n+1,n} = \sqrt{\left[\frac{\hbar c^2 (n_{\lambda s} + 1)}{2\omega_s} \right]}. \qquad (XV.2.8)$$

The interaction energy $(XV.2.3)$ for one electron can be written as

$$H' = -e \sum_s \sum_\lambda q_{\lambda s} u_s \boldsymbol{\alpha} \cdot \boldsymbol{e}_\lambda^{(s)}, \qquad (XV.2.9)$$

For a transition of the electron, where only one photon with a definite polarization ($\lambda = 1$ or -1) is emitted or absorbed, the matrix elements of H' are given by

$$\langle a, n_s | H' | b, n_s + 1 \rangle$$

$$= -e \sqrt{\left[\frac{2\pi\hbar^2 c^2 (n_s + 1)}{E_{\gamma s}} \right]} \int \langle \psi_a | [\boldsymbol{\alpha} \cdot \boldsymbol{e}^{(s)} e^{i\boldsymbol{k}_s \cdot \boldsymbol{r}}] | \psi_b \rangle \, d^3\boldsymbol{x}, \qquad (XV.2.10)$$

---

* W. Heitler, *Quantum Theory of Radiation*, Oxford Univ. Press, Oxford, 1954, p. 125.

where the $|\psi\rangle$ are the electron wave functions in a Coulomb potential in initial and final states, and $E_{\gamma s} = \hbar\omega_s$ is the photon energy in mode s. In the nonrelativistic limit we have

$$\langle a, n_s|H'|b, n_s + 1\rangle = -\frac{e}{m}\sqrt{\left[\frac{2\pi\hbar^2(n_s + 1)}{E_{\gamma s}}\right]}\int \psi_a^*[\boldsymbol{e}^{(s)}\cdot\boldsymbol{p}e^{i\boldsymbol{k}_s\cdot\boldsymbol{r}}]\psi_b\, d^3\boldsymbol{x}. \qquad (XV.2.11)$$

In both cases we have $\boldsymbol{k}_s\cdot\boldsymbol{e}^{(s)} = 0$, so the momentum operator commutes with the plane wave. We further note that in formula (*XV.2.11*) the wave functions are normalized in a volume V, so they have the dimensions of $(\text{length})^{-3/2}$.

XV.2.A. Dipole Radiation

The interaction energy between a radiation field and an atom can cause a transition of the unperturbed system from one state of energy to another. This can occur in the form of emission or absorption of radiation from the atom. The atomic energy levels are low compared to the rest mass of the electrons. Therefore, for most purposes a nonrelativistic treatment of the problem is justified. In this case the interaction energy is of the form $H' = -(e/mc)\boldsymbol{p}\cdot\boldsymbol{A}$, where the term proportional to $\boldsymbol{A}^2$ can be neglected, giving rise to transitions in which two quanta are involved.

Let E_O and E_F be any initial and final state energies of the system. In the case of emission of radiation of frequency ω we have, from the conservation of energy, the relation

$$E_O = E_F + \hbar\omega = E_F + E_\gamma.$$

The transition probability per unit time is

$$W_{FO} = \frac{2\pi}{\hbar}|H'_{FO}|^2\rho_F, \qquad (XV.2.12)$$

where H'_{FO} is given by (*XV.2.11*) in the form

$$H'_{FO} = -\frac{e}{m}\sqrt{\left[\frac{2\pi\hbar^2(n_s + 1)}{E_{\gamma s}}\right]}R_{FO}, \qquad (XV.2.13)$$

where

$$R_{FO} = \int \psi_F^*[\boldsymbol{e}^{(s)}\cdot\boldsymbol{p}e^{i\boldsymbol{k}_s\cdot\boldsymbol{r}}]\psi_O\, d^3\boldsymbol{x}. \qquad (XV.2.14)$$

The number of final states consists of the number of radiation oscillators, given by

$$\rho_F\, dE_\gamma = \frac{E_\gamma^2\, dE_\gamma\, d\Omega}{(2\pi\hbar c)^3}. \qquad (XV.2.15)$$

We have assumed that all the light quanta have the same frequency (within

dE_γ), the same direction of propagation (within the solid angle $d\Omega$), and the same polarization. Hence the transition probability per unit time for the emission of a photon of energy $\hbar\omega$ in a direction within $d\Omega$ is given by

$$W_{FO}\,d\Omega = \frac{e^2}{\hbar c}\frac{\omega}{2\pi}\frac{d\Omega}{m^2c^2}|R_{FO}|^2(\bar{n}+1), \qquad (XV.2.16)$$

where we replace n_s in (*XV.2.13*) by the average number $\bar{n}$ of light quanta per radiation oscillator of frequency ω and propagation vector $\boldsymbol{k}$. This is necessary in order to make sure that the emitted radiation is independent of a particular oscillator. *Result* (*XV.2.16*) is of the same form as Einstein's formula (*XV.1.12*).

An elementary application of formula (*XV.2.16*) comes from the following simplifying assumptions.

(a) The dimension of the emitting atom is negligible compared to the wavelength of the radiation. That is, the perturbing energy is constant in the direction of the emission, so it is a constant and changes significantly only over a distance of the order of a wavelength of the light.

(b) If E is the energy of the atom and λ the wavelength of the light, then we shall assume that λ is of the order of $\hbar c/E$. The dimension of the atom, estimated from the potential energy $E = e^2/a$, gives the result $a/\lambda = e^2/\hbar c$, the fine structure constant.

With these assumptions the factor $\exp(i\boldsymbol{k}\cdot\boldsymbol{r})$ is effectively unity in the region where ψ_F and ψ_O are different from zero. Putting $\boldsymbol{p} = m\boldsymbol{v}$ and $\boldsymbol{v}\cdot\boldsymbol{e} = v\cos\theta$, we obtain from (*XV.2.16*) the result

$$W_{FO}\,d\Omega = \frac{e^2}{\hbar c}\frac{\nu}{c^2}\cos^2\theta\,d\Omega|v_{FO}|^2(\bar{n}+1), \qquad (XV.2.17)$$

where

$$|V_{FO}|^2 = V_{1FO}^2 + V_{2FO}^2 + V_{3FO}^2, \qquad \nu = \frac{\omega}{2\pi}.$$

The components of the oscillator velocity $\boldsymbol{V}_{FO}$ satisfy

$$V_{1FO} = -i\omega X_{1FO},$$

so the transition probability becomes

$$W_{FO}\,d\Omega = \frac{e^2}{\hbar c}\frac{\omega^3}{2\pi c^2}\cos^2\theta\,d\Omega|\boldsymbol{X}_{FO}|^2 c(\bar{n}+1). \qquad (XV.2.18)$$

This result can now be compared with Einstein's formula (*XV.1.12*). The first term in (*XV.2.18*), with $\bar{n} = 0$, gives rise to spontaneous emission and is, of course, independent of the intensity of radiation. The second term is proportional to the intensity of the radiation $\bar{n}$ of frequency ω, which was there prior to emission process. This term corresponds to Einstein's induced emission of radiation.

The total intensity of radiation per unit time can be obtained by multiplying (*XV.2.18*) by $\hbar\omega$ and integrating over the angles. Thus if α is the angle between the vector $\boldsymbol{X}$ (the position of the electron with respect to nucleus) and the direction of propagation $\boldsymbol{k}$, then for the spontaneous radiation we obtain

$$\boldsymbol{I}\, d\Omega = \frac{e^2\omega^4}{2\pi c^3} |\boldsymbol{X}_{FO}|^2 \sin^2\alpha \, d\Omega, \qquad (XV.2.19)$$

where

$$d\Omega = \sin\alpha \, d\alpha \, d\beta$$

and $\cos^2\theta$ is replaced by $\sin^2\alpha$. The total intensity follows from (*XV.2.19*) by integrating over all angles (α from 0 to π and β from 0 to 2π), as

$$I = \frac{4e^2}{3c^3}\omega^4 |\boldsymbol{X}_{FO}|^2 \qquad (XV.2.20)$$

in ergs per second per emitting atom. The total transition probability for going from O to F is obtained by dividing (*XV.2.20*) by $\hbar\omega$:

$$A_{FO} = \frac{4}{3}\frac{e^2\omega^3}{\hbar c^3} |\boldsymbol{X}_{FO}|^2, \qquad (XV.2.21)$$

The total probability that the state O is vacated by emission can be obtained by summing over all final states with energy less than that of initial state,

$$B_O = \sum_{E_F < E_O} A_{FO}. \qquad (XV.2.22)$$

This result can be used to define the reciprocal of the mean life of the initial state by

$$\tau_0 = \frac{1}{B_O}, \qquad (XV.2.23)$$

which is of the order of 10^{-9} sec.

XV.2.B. Absorption of Radiation

Light can be absorbed from any of the radiation oscillators. The intensity of a light beam for an initial state with average number of $\bar{n}$ per oscillator is

$$I_0(\omega)\, d\omega = \bar{n}\hbar\omega c\rho_F = \bar{n}\frac{\omega^3}{(2\pi)^3}\frac{\hbar}{c^2}\, d\Omega\, d\omega. \qquad (XV.2.24)$$

In the discussion of absorption transition we multiply the transition matrix element by the number ρ_O of initial states instead of ρ_F, the number of final states used in calculating transition probability for emission process.

The transition probability per unit time, from $\bar{n}$ to $\bar{n} - 1$, is given by

$$W_{FO}\, d\Omega = \frac{e^2}{\hbar c} \frac{\omega}{2\pi} \frac{d\Omega}{m^2c^2} |\boldsymbol{R}_{FO}|^2 \bar{n}. \tag{XV.2.25}$$

Hence the ratio of the emission and absorption probabilities is

$$\frac{P_{\text{emission}}}{P_{\text{absorption}}} = \frac{\bar{n}+1}{\bar{n}}.$$

By repeating the previous calculations we obtain for the absorbed energy per unit time the result

$$I = \frac{e^2}{\hbar c} \frac{4\pi^2\omega}{\hbar c} |\boldsymbol{X}_{FO}|^2 I_0(\omega). \tag{XV.2.26}$$

XV.2.C. Problems

1. If the direction of polarization is resolved into two components, with one $\boldsymbol{e}_1$, perpendicular to $\boldsymbol{X}_{FO}$, then the other one $\boldsymbol{e}_2$ will lie in the plane determined by the propagation vector $\boldsymbol{k}$ and $\boldsymbol{X}_{FO}$ at an angle $(\pi/2) - \alpha$. Show that light of polarization $\boldsymbol{e}_1$ is not emitted, and light of polarization $\boldsymbol{e}_2$ is emitted with an intensity given by (*XV.2.19*).

2. Result (*XV.2.20*) is almost identical with the formula obtained for an oscillator in the classical theory. Compare the assumptions made in deriving classical and quantum mechanical radiation formula.

3. Consider a Hamiltonian for a Z-electron system of the form

$$H = \sum_{i=1}^{Z} \frac{\boldsymbol{p}_i^2}{2m} + V(\boldsymbol{r}_1, \cdots, \boldsymbol{r}_z)$$

and let

$$\boldsymbol{r} = \sum_{i=1}^{Z} \boldsymbol{r}_i, \qquad \boldsymbol{p} = \sum_{i=1}^{Z} \boldsymbol{p}_i. \tag{XV.2.27}$$

By taking the representatives of

$$[r, H] = \frac{i\hbar}{m} \boldsymbol{p},$$

show that

$$\boldsymbol{p}_{FO} = -im\omega_{FO}\boldsymbol{r}_{FO}, \tag{XV.2.28}$$

where

$$\omega_{FO} = \frac{E_O - E_F}{\hbar}.$$

4. By using the results of the problem 3, show that the oscillator strength, defined by

$$f_{FO} = \frac{2m}{\hbar} \omega_{FO} |\boldsymbol{X}_{FO}|^2, \tag{XV.2.29}$$

can be expressed as

$$f_{FO} = -\frac{2i}{\hbar} X_{OF} p_{xFO}.$$

Then prove that

$$\sum_F f_{FO} = \frac{1}{\hbar} [p_x, x]_{OO},$$

where x and p_x are given by (*XV.2.27*), so

$$[x, p_x] = i\hbar \sum_{i,j=1}^{Z} \delta_{ij} = i\hbar Z.$$

Thus

$$\sum_F f_{FO} = Z. \qquad (XV.2.30)$$

5. Prove that if emitted light were polarized in x_2 or x_3 directions then X_{1FO} would not appear in the radiation formula.

6. Derive the transition probability for two-photon emission and show that it is very small compared to one-photon emission.

XV.3. Applications of Radiation Theory

XV.3.A. Angular Momentum Selection Rules

Dipole radiation depends on the representatives of the operator X and therefore angular momentum selection rules can conveniently be formulated in terms of the representatives of x_3 and $x_+ = x_1 + ix_2$, $x_- = x_1 - ix_2$. Thus

$$\langle E_F|x_3|E_O\rangle = \int \langle E_F|\mathbf{r}\rangle\langle \mathbf{r}|E_O\rangle x_3 \, d^3\mathbf{x}$$

$$= \int_0^\infty r^2 \, dr \, R_{n'l'}(r) R_{nl}(r) \int_0^\pi d\theta \int_0^{2\pi} d\phi \, Y_{l'm'}(\theta, \phi) Y_{lm}(\theta, \phi) \cos\theta \sin\theta.$$

It vanishes if $m' \neq m$, so the selection rule for magnetic quantum number is

$$\Delta m = m' - m = 0. \qquad (XV.3.1)$$

If this selection rule is fulfilled, then the integration over θ does not vanish provided the angular momentum obeys the selection rule

$$\Delta l = l' - l = \pm 1. \qquad (XV.3.2)$$

For x_+ and x_- we obtain the selection rule

$$\Delta m = m' - m = \pm 1. \qquad (XV.3.3)$$

Thus in this case the radiation is polarized parallel to the x_1- and x_2-axis. From the θ integration we again obtain the selection rule (*XV.3.2*). All these selection rules are in accord with the general discussion of Section XIII.3.B.

XV.3.B. Parity Selection Rules

From anticommutation of the parity operator with $\boldsymbol{r}$, it follows that $\mathcal{P}$ anticommutes with the electric dipole operator and that the electric moment can have nonvanishing matrix elements only between states of opposite parity.

XV.3.C. Magnetic Dipole and Quadrupole Radiation

If we define the current vector $\boldsymbol{\zeta}$ by $\boldsymbol{\zeta} = (e/m)\boldsymbol{p}$, we may write (*XV.2.13*) in the form

$$H'_{FO} = -\left[\frac{2\pi\hbar^2(n_s+1)}{E_{\gamma s}}\right]^{1/2} \int \psi_F^*[\boldsymbol{e}^{(s)}\cdot\boldsymbol{\zeta}e^{i\boldsymbol{k}_s\cdot\boldsymbol{r}}]\psi_O\, d^3\boldsymbol{x}. \qquad (XV.3.4)$$

If we assume that $\lambda = 1/|k|$ is very much greater than e^2/E, we may then expand the "retardation factor" $e^{i\boldsymbol{k}\cdot\boldsymbol{r}}$:

$$e^{i\boldsymbol{k}\cdot\boldsymbol{r}} = 1 + i\boldsymbol{k}\cdot\boldsymbol{r} - \tfrac{1}{2}(\boldsymbol{k}\cdot\boldsymbol{r})^2 + \cdots.$$

As shown before, the first term of this expansion gives rise to the electric dipole radiation. If dipole transitions do not exist, then we calculate the contribution arising from the term $i\boldsymbol{k}\cdot\boldsymbol{r}$. By using the vector identity

$$(\boldsymbol{e}^{(s)}\cdot\boldsymbol{\zeta})(\boldsymbol{k}\cdot\boldsymbol{r}) = (\boldsymbol{k}\times\boldsymbol{e}^{(s)})\cdot(\boldsymbol{r}\times\boldsymbol{\zeta}) + (\boldsymbol{k}\cdot\boldsymbol{\zeta})(\boldsymbol{e}^{(s)}\cdot\boldsymbol{r}),$$

we may write (*XV.3.4*) in the form

$$H'_{FO} = -\sqrt{\left[\frac{2\pi\hbar^2(n_s+1)}{E_{\gamma s}}\right]}$$

$$\left[i(\boldsymbol{k}_s\times\boldsymbol{e}^{(s)})\cdot\int\psi_F^*(\boldsymbol{r}\times\boldsymbol{\zeta})\psi_0\, d^3\boldsymbol{x} + ek_ie_j^{(s)}\int\psi_F^* x_i x_j\psi_0\, d^3\boldsymbol{x}\right], \qquad (XV.3.5)$$

where the first term on the right is the magnetic dipole term and the second refers to the electric quadrupole term. The intensity of radiation arising from magnetic dipole and electric quadrupole interaction, using (*XV.2.28*) and (*XV.2.12*), can be written as

$$I\, d\Omega = \frac{e^2\omega^4}{2\pi c^2}|[\boldsymbol{X}(\boldsymbol{k}\cdot\boldsymbol{X})]_{FO}|^2 \sin^2\alpha\, d\Omega. \qquad (XV.3.6)$$

This radiation exists only between states of the same parity.

XV.3.D. Nuclear γ Ray Emission

It follows from the above relations that the ratio of dipole and quadrupole radiations are of the order $(a/\lambda)^2$. In nuclear radiations it has been observed that the intensity of dipole and quadrupole radiation are of the same order. From $(R/\lambda)^2$ for 1 Mev γ rays and nuclear radius

$$R = 1.33A^{1/3} \times 10^{-13},$$

one obtains the ratio

$$\left(\frac{R}{\lambda}\right)^2 = \left[\frac{1.33A^{1/3} \times 10^{-13}}{2 \times 10^{-11}}\right]^2 \cong \frac{1}{625},$$

where we take $A = 238$. Thus the quadrupole radiation should be about 625 times weaker than the dipole radiation; thus there is a sharp disagreement with experiment. In general, nuclear dipole radiation is very weak. This can be explained by noting that a system of particles having the same "specific charge" (= charge per unit mass) will not emit any dipole radiation but will emit quadrupole and higher multipole radiation.*

From the above formulation, the dipole and quadrupole transitions for several charges are respectively proportional to

$$\frac{\hbar}{\omega} \int \psi_F^* \sum_i \frac{e_i}{m_i} \nabla_i \psi_O \, d^3\boldsymbol{x}$$

and

$$\frac{i\hbar}{c} \int \psi_F^* \sum_i \frac{e_i}{m_i} (\boldsymbol{k} \cdot \boldsymbol{r}_i) \nabla_i \psi_O \, d^3\boldsymbol{x}.$$

The wave functions ψ_F and ψ_O will depend on the relative coordinates of the particles with respect to the center of gravity. The coordinate of the center of gravity and the relative coordinates are defined by

$$\boldsymbol{R} = \sum_i \frac{m_i \boldsymbol{r}_i}{M}, \qquad M = \sum_i m_i, \qquad \boldsymbol{s}_i = \boldsymbol{r}_i - \boldsymbol{R}. \qquad (XV.3.7)$$

Let x_i, X_i, and η_i be the x components of the vectors $\boldsymbol{r}_i$, $\boldsymbol{R}$, and $\boldsymbol{s}_i$, respectively. Then

$$\frac{\partial \psi_O}{\partial X_i} = \sum_j \frac{\partial \psi_O}{\partial \eta_j} \frac{\partial \eta_j}{\partial x_i} = \frac{\partial \psi_O}{\partial \eta_i} - \frac{m_i}{M} \Sigma \frac{\partial \psi_O}{\partial \eta_j} \qquad (XV.3.8)$$

and

$$\sum_i \frac{e_i}{m_i} \frac{\partial \psi_O}{\partial x_i} = \sum_i \left(\frac{e_i}{m_i} - \frac{\epsilon}{M}\right) \frac{\partial \psi_O}{\partial \eta_i},$$

where $\epsilon = \Sigma e_i$ and $e_i' = e_i - (\epsilon m_i/M)$ is the apparent charge of the particle different from e_i. Neglecting the proton-neutron mass difference, then for a nucleus with mass number A we have $M = mA$ and

$$e_i' = e\left[\frac{1}{2}(1 + \tau_3) - \frac{Z}{A}\right],$$

* H. A. Bethe, *Rev. Mod. Phys.*, **9** (1937), 221.

where τ_3 is the isotopic spin component of the nucleus which is $+1$ for protons and -1 for neutrons. Thus, for dipole radiation we will consider neutrons to have a negative effective charge equal to about half an elementary charge and protons to have a positive effective charge equal to half of their true charge. For a system whose particles have all the same specific charge we have $e = 0$ and therefore for such a system dipole moment would vanish identically. However, quadrupole and magnetic dipole radiations need not be small.

XV.4. Nonrelativistic Calculation of the Lamb Shift

A qualitative discussion of the Lamb shift was given in Section XIII.3. Here we give a nonrelativistic and somewhat phenomenological derivation of the shift, first obtained by Bethe.* According to Dirac's theory the states $2^2S_{1/2}$ and $2^2P_{1/2}$ exactly coincide in energy, the latter being the lower of the two P states. In the absence of external electric fields the S state is metastable, and radiative transition to the ground state $1^2S_{1/2}$ is forbidden by the selection rule $\Delta l = \pm 1$. Actually, contrary to the theory, experiment shows that the $2^2S_{1/2}$ state is higher than the $2^2P_{1/2}$ state by about 1000 Mc. Kemble and Present† and Pasternack‡ have shown that the shift of the $2S$ level cannot be explained by a nuclear interaction.

It was suggested—by Schwinger, Oppenheimer, Weisskopf—that the shift might arise from the interaction of the electron with radiation field. The field theoretical calculations have always led to an infinite value for the shift. Bethe has shown that the infinity arising in the level shift calculation can be associated with an "electromagnetic mass" of a bound as well as of a free electron. He assumed that the observed mass of the electron must include this effect; that is, the infinite mass here must be regarded as the observed mass of the electron and must actually be set equal to it (mass renormalization).

From the remark following formula (*XIV.6.9*), the self-energy of an electron in quantum state n, arising from the emission of virtual photons in intermediate states, can be written as

$$\Delta E_n = \sum_{n'} \frac{|H'_{nn'}|^2}{E_n - E_{n'}}, \qquad (XV.4.1)$$

where $E_{n'} = E_n - E_\gamma$ and $E_\gamma =$ "the virtual photon energy." The transition element $|H'_{nn'}|^2$ is given by

---

* H. A. Bethe, *Phys. Rev.*, **72** (1947), 339.

† E. C. Kemble and R. D. Present, *Phys. Rev.*, **44** (1932), 1031.

‡ S. Pasternack, *Phys. Rev.*, **54** (1938), 1113.

$$-\frac{\hbar}{2\pi} E_\gamma A_{FO} = \frac{2e^2}{3\pi\hbar c^3} \int E_\gamma |V_{FO}|^2 \, dE_\gamma,$$

where $V_{FO} = \omega X_{FO}$.

Integrating over all the possible virtual photon emission we write for the self-energy

$$\Delta E = -\frac{2e^2}{3\pi\hbar c^3} \int_0^K \sum_{n'} \frac{|V_{nn'}|^2}{E_{n'} - E_n + E_\gamma} E_\gamma \, dE_\gamma, \qquad (XV.4.2)$$

where K is a certain upper limit for the virtual photon energy.

For a free electron

$$V_{nn'} = v\delta_{nn'},$$

$$\Delta E_0 = -\frac{2e^2}{3\pi\hbar c^3} \int \frac{v^2 E_\gamma \, dE_\gamma}{E_\gamma}. \qquad (XV.4.3)$$

This represents the change in kinetic energy of the electron for fixed momentum and is due to the addition of the electromagnetic mass of the electron to its *free* (*or bare*) *mass*. This electromagnetic mass, being contained in the experimentally observed electron mass, must be subtracted from (*XV.4.2*) to yield the relevant part of the self-energy.

For the bound electron, from (*XV.2.29*) we may write

$$\sum_{n'} |V_{nn'}|^2 = (V^2)_{nn'}.$$

Hence

$$\Delta W = \Delta E - \Delta E_0 = \frac{2e^2}{3\pi\hbar c^3} \int_0^K dE_\gamma \sum_{n'} \frac{|V_{nn'}|^2 (E_{n'} - E_n)}{E_{n'} - E_n + E_\gamma}. \qquad (XV.4.4)$$

This is to be regarded as the actual shift due to the interaction of the electron with the radiation field.

Integrating over E_γ in (*XV.4.4*) and assuming that K is large compared to all energy differences $E_{n'} - E_n$, we obtain

$$\Delta W = \frac{2e^2}{3\pi\hbar c^3} \sum_{n'} |V_{nn'}|^2 (E_{n'} - E_n) \log\left[\frac{K}{|E_{n'} - E_n|}\right]. \qquad (XV.4.5)$$

If one assumes that $K = mc^2$, then the logarithm in (*XV.4.5*) is very large; it can therefore be regarded as independent of n'. In this case we have to evaluate a sum of the form

$$A = \sum_{n'} |\mathbf{p}_{n'n}|^2 (E_{n'} - E_n). \qquad (XV.4.6)$$

But from

$$\mathbf{p}H - H\mathbf{p} = [\mathbf{p}, H] = -i\hbar\nabla V,$$

we have

$$\langle E_{n'}|(\mathbf{p}H - H\mathbf{p})|E_n\rangle = -i\hbar\delta_{nn'}\nabla V$$

or

$$\boldsymbol{p}_{n'n}(E_{n'} - E_n) = -i\hbar\delta_{nn'}\boldsymbol{\nabla}V. \qquad (XV.4.7)$$

Hence

$$\begin{aligned}(E_n' - E_n)|\boldsymbol{p}_{n'n}|^2 &= -i\hbar\boldsymbol{p}_{nn'}\delta_{nn'}\cdot\boldsymbol{\nabla}V,\\ \sum_{n'}|\boldsymbol{p}_{n'n}|^2(E_{n'} - E_n) &= -i\hbar\boldsymbol{p}_{nn}\cdot\boldsymbol{\nabla}V.\end{aligned} \qquad (XV.4.8)$$

Using (*V.1.25*) we obtain

$$\sum_{n'}|\boldsymbol{p}_{n'n}|^2(E_{n'} - E_n) = -\hbar^2\int\psi_n^*\boldsymbol{\nabla}V\cdot\boldsymbol{\nabla}\psi_n\,d^3\boldsymbol{x}. \qquad (XV.4.9)$$

We use the equation

$$\boldsymbol{\nabla}^2V = 4\pi Ze^2\delta(\boldsymbol{r}) \qquad (XV.4.10)$$

and obtain (*XV.4.9*) in the form

$$\begin{aligned}\sum_{n'}|\boldsymbol{p}_{n'n}|^2(E_{n'} - E_n) &= \tfrac{1}{2}\hbar^2\int|\psi_n|^2\boldsymbol{\nabla}^2V\,d^3\boldsymbol{x}\\ &= 2\pi\hbar^2Ze^2|\psi_n(0)|^2,\end{aligned} \qquad (XV.4.11)$$

where we use the relation $\psi_n = \langle E_n|\boldsymbol{r}\rangle$ and carry out a partial integration canceling the surface integral term. The sum (*XV.4.11*), for any electron with $l \neq 0$, vanishes. For $l = 0$ we have

$$|\psi_n(0)|^2 = \frac{1}{\pi}\left[\frac{Z}{Na}\right]^3, \qquad (XV.4.12)$$

where N is the principal quantum number and a is the Bohr radius. Using (*XV.4.11*) and (*XV.4.12*) in (*XV.4.5*) we obtain

$$\Delta W = \frac{8}{3\pi}\left(\frac{e^2}{\hbar c}\right)^3\frac{Z^4R_y}{N^3}\log\left[\frac{mc^2}{\langle E_{n'} - E_n\rangle}\right], \qquad (XV.4.13)$$

where

$$R_y = \frac{me^4}{2\hbar^2} \qquad (XV.4.14)$$

is the ionization energy of the ground state of hydrogen. The average excitation energy $\langle(E_{n'} - E_n)\rangle$ for the $2S$ state of hydrogen was calculated by Bethe as 17.8 R_y, leading to 7.63 for the logarithm in (*XV.4.13*). The shift comes out as

$$\Delta W = 136\log\left[\frac{mc^2}{\langle(E_{n'} - E_n)\rangle}\right] = 1040\text{ mc}, \qquad (XV.4.15)$$

which is in good agreement with the experimental results.

Another interesting explanation of the Lamb shift was given by Welton.* He pointed out that in a quantized electromagnetic field the lowest energy state does not correspond to a zero field but that there exist zero point oscil-

* T. A. Welton, *Phys. Rev.*, **74** (1948), 1157.

lations. The zero point energy associated with each oscillation is just $\frac{1}{2}\hbar$, so the energy density of the field is determined by

$$\frac{1}{8\pi}(\mathcal{E}^2 + \mathcal{H}^2) = \int \tfrac{1}{2}\hbar\omega \, dN(k),$$

where $dN(\boldsymbol{k}) = (1/4\pi^3)\, d^3\boldsymbol{k}$. Thus the Fourier component of the electric field energy corresponding to wave number $\boldsymbol{k}$ is

$$|\mathcal{E}(\boldsymbol{k})|^2 = \frac{\hbar\omega}{2\pi^2}.$$

The existence of these fluctuating electric fields will induce some rapid variation of position. This leads to an extended picture for the point electron of conventional theory. The attraction at short distances of an extended electron by the nucleus can be expected to be somewhat less than the attraction of a point electron. This means that the state of zero angular momentum will lie higher in energy than other angular momentum states having a finite probability of pushing the electron near the nucleus.

Now let $\delta\boldsymbol{r}$ be the change in the electron's position induced by the fluctuating field. Then the new position of the electron is $\boldsymbol{r} + \delta\boldsymbol{r}$. The average value of $\delta\boldsymbol{r}$ is of course zero, but the average value of $(\delta\boldsymbol{r})^2$ need not be zero. Thus for a bound electron the potential energy is

$$V(\boldsymbol{r} + \delta\boldsymbol{r}) = V(\boldsymbol{r}) + (\delta\boldsymbol{r}\cdot\boldsymbol{\nabla})V(\boldsymbol{r}) + \tfrac{1}{2}(\delta\boldsymbol{r}\cdot\boldsymbol{\nabla})^2V(\boldsymbol{r}) + \cdots. \qquad (XV.4.16)$$

On taking the time average of $(XV.4.16)$, the terms linear in $\delta\boldsymbol{r}$ will average out to zero and in the term

$$(\delta\boldsymbol{r}\cdot\boldsymbol{\nabla})^2V = \left(\delta x_i \frac{\partial}{\partial x_i}\, \delta x_j \frac{\partial}{\partial x_j}\right) V$$

only the diagonal terms,

$$\left[(\delta x_1)^2 \frac{\partial^2}{\partial x_1^2} + (\delta x_2)^2 \frac{\partial^2}{\partial x_2^2} + (\delta x_3)^2 \frac{\partial^2}{\partial x_3^2}\right] V,$$

will contribute. Thus from

$$\langle(\delta x_1)^2\rangle = \langle(\delta x_2)^2\rangle = \langle(\delta x_3)^2\rangle = \tfrac{1}{3}\langle(\delta\boldsymbol{r})^2,$$

we obtain

$$\langle\delta V\rangle = \langle V(\boldsymbol{r} + \delta\boldsymbol{r}) - V(\boldsymbol{r})\rangle = \tfrac{1}{6}\langle(\delta\boldsymbol{r})^2\rangle\boldsymbol{\nabla}^2V.$$

The spread $\delta\boldsymbol{r}$ can be assumed to obey the equations of motion:

$$\frac{d^2}{dt^2}(\delta\boldsymbol{r}) = e\mathcal{E}.$$

Hence for the $\boldsymbol{k}$th component of the forced oscillations we find

$$m\delta\boldsymbol{r}_k = -\frac{e\mathcal{E}(\boldsymbol{k})}{\omega_k^2},$$

so

$$\langle(\delta \boldsymbol{r})^2\rangle = \int \langle(\delta \boldsymbol{r}_k)^2\rangle\, d^3\boldsymbol{k} = \frac{e^2}{m^2}\int \frac{|\mathcal{E}(\boldsymbol{k})|^2}{\omega_k^4}\, d^3\boldsymbol{k}$$
$$= \frac{2}{\pi}\frac{e^2}{\hbar c}\left(\frac{\hbar}{mc}\right)^2 \int_{k_1}^{k_2} \frac{dk}{k},$$

where k_1 and k_2 assure the convergence of the integral. The change of the potential energy is therefore given by

$$\delta V = \frac{1}{3\pi}\frac{e^2}{\hbar c}\left(\frac{\hbar}{mc}\right)^2 \nabla^2 V \log\left(\frac{k_2}{k_1}\right). \tag{XV.4.17}$$

The average value of δV for the state ψ leads to a shift in energy:

$$\delta W = \frac{4}{3}\left(\frac{e^2}{\hbar c}\right)\left(\frac{\hbar}{mc}\right)^2 Ze^2|\psi(0)|^2 \log\left(\frac{k_2}{k_1}\right). \tag{XV.4.18}$$

This statement is of the same form as that obtained by Bethe.

XV.4.A. Problems

1. The retarded potentials of classical electrodynamics are given by

$$A_4 = \int \frac{\rho(\boldsymbol{r}', t')}{R}\, d^3\boldsymbol{x}', \tag{XV.4.19}$$

$$\boldsymbol{A} = \int \frac{\boldsymbol{J}(\boldsymbol{r}', t')}{R}\, d^3\boldsymbol{x}', \tag{XV.4.20}$$

where $R = |\boldsymbol{r} - \boldsymbol{r}'|$ and $t' = t - \frac{R}{c}\cdot$ Assume that charge density ρ and current density $\boldsymbol{J}$ are stationary; that is,

$$\rho(t') = R_e(\rho e^{i\omega t'}) = R_e\left[\rho e^{i\omega t} e^{-i(\omega/c)R}\right]$$

and

$$\boldsymbol{J}(t') = R_e(\boldsymbol{J}e^{i\omega t'}).$$

Then show that the scalar potential can be expanded according to

$$A_4 = \frac{1}{r}\, e^{i(\omega t - kr)}\left[\int \rho P_0\, d^3\boldsymbol{x}' + ik\left(1 - \frac{i}{kr}\right)\int \rho r' P_1\, d^3\boldsymbol{x}'\right.$$
$$\left. - \frac{k^2}{3}\left[\left(1 - \frac{3i}{kr}\right)\int \rho r'^2 P_2\, d^3\boldsymbol{x}' + \frac{1}{2}\int \rho r'^2 P_0\, d^3\boldsymbol{x}'\right] + \cdots\right., \tag{XV.4.21}$$

where

$$k = \frac{\omega}{c},$$

$$\frac{e^{-ikR}}{R} = -ik \sum_{l=0}^{\infty} (2l+1) j_l(kr') h_l(kr) P_l(\cos\alpha). \tag{XV.4.22}$$

The spherical Bessel functions j_l and n_l are defined by

$$j_l(kr) = \sqrt{\left[\frac{\pi}{2kr}\right]} J_{l+1/2}(kr),$$

$$n_l(kr) = \sqrt{\left[\frac{\pi}{2kr}\right]} N_{l+1/2}(kr),$$

$$h_l(kr) = j_l + in_l,$$

and α is the angle between $\boldsymbol{r}$ and $\boldsymbol{r}'$. For a distribution where the total charge is zero, the first term in (*XV.4.21*) vanishes. The second and third terms refer to the electric dipole and electric quadrupole radiations, respectively. The electric dipole and quadrupole moments are defined by

$$\boldsymbol{D} = \int \rho \boldsymbol{r}\, d^3\boldsymbol{x}, \qquad \boldsymbol{Q} = \int \rho \boldsymbol{r}\boldsymbol{r}\, d^3\boldsymbol{x}. \tag{XV.4.23}$$

Compare expansions (*XV.4.21*) and (*IX.1.18*).

2. Using the definitions of the Legendre polynomials, show that

$$\int \rho r' P_1\, d^3\boldsymbol{x}' = \hat{\boldsymbol{r}}\cdot\boldsymbol{D},$$

$$\int \rho r'^2 P_2\, d^3\boldsymbol{x}' = \tfrac{3}{2}\hat{\boldsymbol{r}}\cdot\boldsymbol{Q}\cdot\hat{\boldsymbol{r}} - \tfrac{1}{2}Q_s,$$

$$\int \rho r'^2 P_0\, d^3\boldsymbol{x}' = Q_s,$$

where Q_s is the invariant sum of diagonal terms in $\boldsymbol{Q}$ and $\hat{\boldsymbol{r}}$ is a unit vector in the direction of $\boldsymbol{r}$.

3. For a stationary charge distribution the equation for charge conservation takes the form

$$\nabla\cdot\boldsymbol{J} = -ik\rho,$$

where ρ and $\boldsymbol{J}$ are assumed to vanish outside a finite sphere. For an arbitrary function F, prove that

$$ik \int \rho F\, d^3\boldsymbol{x} = \int \boldsymbol{J}\cdot\nabla F\, d^3\boldsymbol{x}. \tag{XV.4.24}$$

Then show that for $\boldsymbol{F} = \boldsymbol{r}$ and $\boldsymbol{F} = \boldsymbol{r}\boldsymbol{r}$ we obtain

$$\boldsymbol{D} = \frac{1}{ik}\int \boldsymbol{J}\, d^3\boldsymbol{x}, \tag{XV.4.25}$$

$$Q_{ij} = \frac{1}{ik}\int (x_i J_j + x_j J_i)\, d^3\boldsymbol{x}, \tag{XV.4.26}$$

and the vector potential can be expressed as

$$\boldsymbol{A} = \frac{1}{r}e^{i(\omega t - kr)}\left[ik\boldsymbol{D} - ik\left(1 - \frac{i}{kr}\right)\hat{\boldsymbol{r}}\times\mathfrak{m} - \frac{1}{2}k^2\left(1 - \frac{i}{kr}\right)\boldsymbol{r}\cdot\boldsymbol{Q}\right] + \cdots, \tag{XV.4.27}$$

where $\mathfrak{m}$ is the magnetic moment of the electric current distribution:

$$\mathfrak{m} = \tfrac{1}{2} \int (\boldsymbol{r} \times \boldsymbol{J})\, d^3\boldsymbol{x}. \tag{XV.4.28}$$

4. From the expressions for A_4 and $\boldsymbol{A}$ show that the electric and magnetic fields of the field can be written as

$$\mathcal{E} = \frac{1}{r} e^{i(\omega t - kr)} \left[\left(k^2 - \frac{ik}{r} \right) (\boldsymbol{D} - \hat{\boldsymbol{r}} \cdot \boldsymbol{D} \hat{\boldsymbol{r}}) + \frac{2ik}{r} (\hat{\boldsymbol{r}} \cdot \boldsymbol{D}) \hat{\boldsymbol{r}} \right], \tag{XV.4.29}$$

$$\mathcal{H} = \frac{1}{r} e^{i(\omega t - kr)} \left(k^2 - \frac{ik}{r} \right) (\hat{\boldsymbol{r}} \times \boldsymbol{D}). \tag{XV.4.30}$$

Hence show that the time-averaged radiation over large distances is given by

$$P = \frac{1}{4} \frac{c}{4\pi} (\mathcal{E} \times \mathcal{H}^* + \mathcal{E}^* \times \mathcal{H}) = \frac{c}{8\pi} \frac{k^4}{r^2} [\boldsymbol{D}^2 - (\hat{\boldsymbol{r}} \cdot \boldsymbol{D})^2] \hat{\boldsymbol{r}}. \tag{XV.4.31}$$

5. Show from the problem 4 that for transitions in which $\Delta m = 0$ the dipole moment is of the form Dk, directed along the z-axis, and the radiation field is the same as a simple linear oscillator. By comparing with (*IX.1.18*), find the expressions for the corresponding electric and magnetic field vectors. In this case the radiation is linearly polarized with the electric vector in a plane determined by $\boldsymbol{r}$ and $\boldsymbol{D}$. The corresponding intensity in a direction at an angle θ to the z-axis is

$$P = \frac{c}{8\pi} \frac{k^4}{r^2} D^2 \sin^2 \theta\, \hat{\boldsymbol{r}}. \tag{XV.4.32}$$

Hence the total rate of radiation through a large sphere is given by

$$I = \int \boldsymbol{P} \cdot d\boldsymbol{S} = \frac{c}{4} k^4 D^2 \int_0^\pi \sin^3 \theta\, d\theta = \frac{1}{3} \frac{\omega^4 D^2}{c^3}. \tag{XV.4.33}$$

6. Show that for an atom with Z electrons the corresponding moments are

$$\boldsymbol{D} = -e \sum_{i=1}^{Z} \boldsymbol{r}_i, \qquad \boldsymbol{Q} = -e \sum_{i=1}^{Z} \boldsymbol{r}_i \boldsymbol{r}_i,$$

$$\mathfrak{m} = -\frac{e}{2mc} \sum_{i=1}^{Z} (\boldsymbol{L}_i + 2\boldsymbol{S}_i), \tag{XV.4.34}$$

where the $\boldsymbol{S}_i$ are the spins of the electrons.

7. Prove that for transitions $\Delta m = \pm 1$ the dipole moment $\boldsymbol{D}$ is of the form $(1/\sqrt{2}) D(\boldsymbol{e}_1 \pm i\boldsymbol{e}_2)$, where $\boldsymbol{e}_1$ and $\boldsymbol{e}_2$ are unit vectors in x_1 and x_2 directions. In this case $\boldsymbol{D}$ can be written as

$$\boldsymbol{D} = \frac{1}{\sqrt{2}} |D| (\boldsymbol{e}_1 \cos \omega t \mp \boldsymbol{e}_2 \sin \omega t).$$

Thus for $\Delta m = 1$ it rotates in the (x_1, x_2) plane (as viewed from the positive x_3 direction) in the clockwise direction and in the opposite sense for $\Delta m = -1$.

Show that in both cases the intensity in a direction making an angle θ with the x_3 direction is given by

$$\boldsymbol{P} = \frac{ck^4}{8\pi r^2}\frac{1}{2}(1 + \cos^2\theta)\, D^2\hat{\boldsymbol{r}},$$

and that the total intensity over all directions is the same as in (*XV.4.33*).

8. By using the correspondence principle, show that the quantum mechanical forms of the above transitions are as given in the text. Thus the transition probability from a higher state A to a lower state B is

$$\mathcal{A}(A, B) = \frac{4}{3}\frac{\omega^3}{\hbar c^3}\,|\langle A|\boldsymbol{D}|B\rangle|^2. \qquad (XV.4.35)$$

Hence show that the transition probability per unit time for the magnetic dipole radiation is

$$\mathcal{A}_m(A, B) = \frac{4}{3}\frac{\omega^3}{\hbar c^3}\,|\langle A|\mathfrak{m}|B\rangle|^2. \qquad (XV.4.36)$$

CHAPTER XVI

MANY-PARTICLE SYSTEMS

XVI.1. The Hartree-Fock Method

All systems of physical interest are, actually, many-particle systems. A single isolated particle does not correspond to a quantum reality. By a one-particle picture we usually mean a particle interacting with another particle assumed to be at rest. An example is the hydrogen atom, where the assumption of the proton being at rest is a good approximation. In reality there exist mass corrections to the energy level structure of the hydrogen atom, arising from the motion of the proton.

In a many-electron atom, also, we assume that the nucleus is fixed and electrons are moving around it. The electrons are attracted to the nucleus by Coulomb forces, and electrons themselves will repel one another with similar forces.

In practice, for many electron atoms, one aims at a reduction to a system of noninteracting particles. This is zero-order approximation. For weakly interacting particles the next order of approximation is to neglect all three-body and higher-order particle processes and assume instead that only two-body encounters or two-body interactions need be considered. A further approximation is to assume that the various electrons of an atom move approximately as if each were acted on by a central field produced by the average motion of all the other electrons in the atom.

One of the basic features of quantum theory or wave mechanics lies in the fact that it is not closed. The most important mathematical entity of the theory is the Hamiltonian operator. The knowledge of the Hamiltonian via Schrödinger's equation, together with the boundary conditions, determines the solution of a physical problem. In general there exists no special formalism to find the Hamiltonian. For any given physical problem we are guided by the experiment, the symmetries, and above all by intuition, to guess at a reasonable Hamiltonian for which the corresponding Schrödinger's equation possesses solutions. In treating a many-body problem we shall, as we did in the one-particle field, postulate the validity of Schrödinger's equation. The wave function will be assumed to be a function of the coordinates of N particles and also of time t. (In relativistic theory, however, we have to use different time coordinates for different particles.) It is natural to expect that the N-particle Hamiltonian will be a function of $3N$ coordinates and $3N$ momenta of N particles. An N-particle wave function ψ can be used to set up a probability interpretation, thus

$$\psi(1, 2, \cdots, N, t)\, d^3\boldsymbol{x}_1 \cdots d^3\boldsymbol{x}_N$$

is the probability of finding at time t the particle *1* in the volume $d^3\boldsymbol{x}_1$, particle *2* in $d^3\boldsymbol{x}_2$, $\cdots$, and particle N in $d^3\boldsymbol{x}_N$. For noninteracting particles the wave function is just the product of the wave functions of the individual particles. For example, if we neglect the mutual repulsion between the two electrons of an atom, the resulting motion can be described by a wave function which is a product of the individual wave functions of the electrons. The corresponding Hamiltonian can be written as

$$H = \frac{\boldsymbol{p}_1^2}{2m} + \frac{\boldsymbol{p}_2^2}{2m} + V_1(\boldsymbol{r}_1) + V_2(\boldsymbol{r}_2),$$

where $V_1(\boldsymbol{r}_1)$ and $V_2(\boldsymbol{r}_2)$ refer to potential energies of the electrons with respect to the nucleus. However, if interaction between the electrons is not neglected, then the probability of finding one of the electrons at a given region will not be independent of the probability that the other electron is at the same region or in a nearby region. Actually the probability will be smaller if the other electron happens to be near the region in question. In this case there is a correlation between the motions of the electrons and therefore the corresponding Hamiltonian will have to be modified to take this correlation into account. The required extra term in the Hamiltonian, as follows from the first principles, is a function of the coordinates of the particles. To find a consistent approach to the calculation of such an interaction term we shall reconsider the one-particle picture. The average motion of one particle in the presence of other particles can be described by the coupled set of equations

$$i\hbar \frac{\partial}{\partial t}\psi = H\psi, \qquad (XVI.1.1)$$

$$\Box A_\alpha = -\frac{4\pi}{c} J_\alpha, \qquad (XVI.1.2)$$

where

$$J_4 = e|\psi|^2 = \rho, \qquad \boldsymbol{J} = \frac{e\hbar}{2im}(\psi^*\nabla\psi - \psi\nabla\psi^*).$$

For static fields we set $A = 0$ and replace (*XVI.1.2*) by $\nabla^2 A_4 = -4\pi\rho$, so the Hamiltonian can be written as

$$H = \frac{p^2}{2m} + eA_4, \qquad (XVI.1.3)$$

where

$$A_4 = e\int \frac{|\psi(r')|^2}{|r - r''|}\, d^3x'. \qquad (XVI.1.4)$$

Hence

$$H = \frac{p^2}{2m} - e^2 \int \frac{|\psi(r')|^2}{|r - r'|}\, d^3x', \qquad (XVI.1.5)$$

and with $\psi = \psi(r)e^{-(i/\hbar)Et}$ we have

$$E\psi = \left[\frac{p^2}{2m} - e^2 \int \frac{|\psi(r')|^2}{|r - r'|}\, d^3x'\right]\psi. \qquad (XVI.1.6)$$

Thus the average motion of one charge in the presence of others is a non-linear problem. In this case the function ψ must be regarded as a one-particle "reduced probability amplitude." The relativistic form of equation (*XVI.1.6*) is given by

$$\left\{\gamma^\mu\left[p_\mu - \frac{e}{c^2}\int D_F(x - x')J_\mu(x')\, d^4x'\right] + mc\right\}|\psi\rangle = 0, \qquad (XVI.1.7)$$

where $J_\mu(x) = -ie\langle\bar{\psi}|\gamma_\mu|\psi\rangle$ and the $D_F(x - x')$ function satisfies the equation

$$\Box D_F(x - x') = -4\pi\delta(x - x'). \qquad (XVI.1.8)$$

For an N-particle problem we can approximately set up a continuous volume density of electric charge resulting from the particles. Using this charge density we can calculate the corresponding electrostatic potential as a function of position. This is the average field where, in a first approximation, each particle moves independently. Now let us suppose that we do know the motions of the electrons in the average field. In this case we can calculate the corresponding charge density. To keep our assumptions consistent the calculated charge density must be the same as the charge density assumed at the beginning. Such a requirement—the equality of charge densities—characterizes the "self-consistent field method."

In practice one makes an initial guess as to the charge density of a many-particle system, calculates the corresponding potential, and solves Schrödinger's equation to find the final charge density. One then repeats the same calculation with the final charge density, and so on. If these successive approximations approach the initially assumed charge density (or to any one of the calculated densities) then the correct solution of the problem is found. This method was first applied by Hartree and was later generalized by Fock.*

---

* D. R. Hartree, *Proc. Cambridge Philos. Soc.*, **24** (1948), 89.
V. Fock, *Z. Phys.*, **61** (1930), 126.

In the Hartree-Fock approximation one assumes a many-particle Hamiltonian of the form

$$H = \sum_i H_i + \tfrac{1}{2} \sum_{i \neq j} V_{ij}(\boldsymbol{r}_i), \tag{XVI.1.9}$$

where the $\boldsymbol{r}_i$, for $i = 1, 2, 3, \cdots$, are position vectors of the particles in the system, and

$$H_i = \frac{\boldsymbol{p}_i^2}{2m_i} + V(\boldsymbol{r}_i),$$

the $\boldsymbol{p}_i$ being the momenta. Each particle is moving in a field resulting from the sum of the external field $V(\boldsymbol{r}_i)$ plus the field produced by the sum of pairwise interactions of the particles, the second sum in (*XVI.1.9*). The two-body interaction energy V_{ij} is a function of the position vectors $\boldsymbol{r}_i$ and $\boldsymbol{r}_j$ of the ith and jth particles. Hartree's idea was to obtain a reduced interaction in such a way that the ith particle would move in a potential depending only on its own position $\boldsymbol{r}_i$. Such a potential may be called an "effective potential." Therefore the general behavior of all particles must lead to this effective potential, so the resulting field is self-consistent. In this way a many-particle problem can, in principle, be reduced to a one-particle problem.

Consider a system of N particles having a total Hamiltonian H as defined by (*XVI.1.9*). In the self-consistent field approximation, the pair interaction energy $\frac{1}{2} \sum_{i \neq j} V_{ij}$ is constructed as a sum of average pair interactions of the form

$$H_i' = \sum_{j \neq i} \langle \Psi_j | H_{ij} | \Psi_j \rangle, \tag{XVI.1.10}$$

where H_{ij}', for an atomic system, refers to pair interaction energy of the form

$$H_{ij}' = \frac{e^2}{r_{ij}}, \qquad r_{ij} = |\boldsymbol{r}_i - \boldsymbol{r}_j|,$$

and $|\psi_j\rangle$ is a single-particle eigenstate. Thus for H_i' we can write

$$H_i' = \sum_{j \neq i} \int \langle \Psi_j | \boldsymbol{r}' \rangle \, d^3\boldsymbol{x}' \, \langle \boldsymbol{r}' | H_{ij} | \Psi_j \rangle,$$

or, in terms of wave functions, we get

$$H_i' = \sum_{j \neq i} e^2 \int \frac{|\psi_j(\boldsymbol{r}_j')|^2}{|\boldsymbol{r}_i - \boldsymbol{r}_j|} \, d^3\boldsymbol{x}_j. \tag{XVI.1.11}$$

It satisfies the differential equation

$$\nabla^2 H_i' = -4\pi e^2 \sum_{j \neq i} |\Psi_j(\boldsymbol{r}_i)|^2. \tag{XVI.1.12}$$

The state vector $|\Psi_j\rangle$ satisfies a Schrödinger's equation of the form

$$H_j |\Psi_j\rangle = E_j |\Psi_j\rangle, \tag{XVI.1.13}$$

where the Hamiltonian H_j is now defined as

$$H_j = \frac{\boldsymbol{p}_j^2}{2m_j} - \frac{Ze^2}{r_j} + \sum_{i \neq j} e^2 \int \frac{|\psi_{ji}(\boldsymbol{r}_i)|^2}{r_{ij}} \, d^3\boldsymbol{x}_i. \tag{XVI.1.14}$$

The state vector $|\Psi_j\rangle$ is, of course, assumed to be of unit length:

$$\langle \Psi_j | \Psi_j \rangle = \int |\psi_j|^2 \, d^3\boldsymbol{x} = 1. \tag{XVI.1.15}$$

Fock and Slater* have derived the wave equation (*XVI.1.13*) from a variational principle. One postulates

$$\delta \int \langle \Psi | H | \Psi \rangle \, d^3\boldsymbol{x}_i \cdots d^3\boldsymbol{x}_N = 0,$$

subject to the subsidiary conditions $\langle \Psi_i | \Psi_i \rangle = 1$, for $i = 1, 2, \cdots, N$. The N-particle state vector $|\Psi\rangle$ must be defined according to the symmetry principles of identical particles. Thus, for an N-electron system, for example, we have

$$|\Psi\rangle = \sum_P \epsilon_P |\Psi_1\rangle |\Psi_2\rangle \cdots |\Psi_N\rangle,$$

where $\epsilon_P = +1$ for an even and -1 for an odd permutation. The antisymmetrization implied here can be extended to include spin in the case of electrons and isotopic spin and spin in the case of nucleons. The application of Hartree's method (with a number of modifications) to nuclear force problems has recently been proposed by Brueckner.†

XVI.2. The Statistical Description of Many-Particle Systems

For a many-particle system of high density and low temperature a quantum statistical description based on a distribution function, where symmetry or antisymmetry of the wave function plays a basic role, can be used to study many-body phenomena. For example, the electrons in an atom can be regarded, together with the nucleus, as a "bound plasma," in comparison with a free plasma, where the atom is completely stripped of its electrons. By analogy with Liouville's classical distribution function f_N for N particles, we can define a quantum distribution function F_N to describe an electron plasma. Such a distribution function can also be used to describe "ionization and recombination phenomena" in an atomic gas as a process of charge creation and annihilation. The same function can be applied, with appropriate sym-

---

* J. C. Slater, *Phys. Rev.*, **34** (1929), 1293.

† K. A. Brueckner, *Phys. Rev.*, **96** (1954), 508; **97** (1955), 1353; **100** (1955), 36. K. A. Brueckner, R. J. Eden, and N. C. Francis, *Phys. Rev.*, **99** (1955), 76.

metries, to the description of liquid H_e^4 and liquid H_e^3. These two systems are typical quantum liquids that could not possibly be described classically. The formalism to be developed in the following can also be applied to various solid-state problems.

We begin by assuming that the state of a particle system can be identified by the density operator ρ as defined in Section VI.2.A. A quantum distribution function F_N, closely related to Liouville's distribution function f_N, can be defined as a Fourier transform of the function

$$\langle \boldsymbol{r}', t|\rho|\boldsymbol{r}'', t\rangle \qquad (XVI.2.1)$$

with respect to the relative coordinates, where the state vector $|\boldsymbol{r}', t\rangle$ is defined by

$$|\boldsymbol{r}', t\rangle = |\boldsymbol{r}_1', t\rangle|\boldsymbol{r}_2', t\rangle \cdots |\boldsymbol{r}_N', t\rangle.$$

It satisfies Schrödinger's equation

$$i\hbar \frac{d}{dt}|\boldsymbol{r}', t\rangle = H_0|\boldsymbol{r}', t\rangle, \qquad (XVI.2.2)$$

where H_0 is a free N-particle Hamiltonian,

$$H_0 = \sum_{i=1}^{N} \frac{\boldsymbol{p}_i^2}{2m_i}. \qquad (XVI.2.3)$$

The state vector $|\boldsymbol{r}', t\rangle$ is normalized according to

$$\langle \boldsymbol{r}', t|\boldsymbol{r}'', t\rangle = \delta(\boldsymbol{r}' - \boldsymbol{r}''), \qquad (XVI.2.4)$$

where

$$\delta(\boldsymbol{r}' - \boldsymbol{r}'') = \prod_{i=1}^{N} \delta(\boldsymbol{r}_i' - \boldsymbol{r}_i'')$$

and is an eigenstate of the position operator $\boldsymbol{q}$,

$$\boldsymbol{q}|\boldsymbol{r}', t\rangle = \boldsymbol{r}'|\boldsymbol{r}', t\rangle.$$

The quantum distribution function for N particles can now be defined by

$$F_N(\boldsymbol{r}, \boldsymbol{p}, t) = \left[\frac{1}{2\pi\hbar}\right]^{3N} \int \langle \boldsymbol{r}', t|\rho|\boldsymbol{r}'', t\rangle e^{-(i/\hbar)\boldsymbol{p}\cdot\boldsymbol{\lambda}}\, d\boldsymbol{\Gamma}_\lambda, \qquad (XVI.2.5)$$

where $\boldsymbol{r}$ and $\boldsymbol{p}$ represent the $3N$ coordinates and $3N$ momenta of N particles and the vectors $\boldsymbol{\lambda}$ and $\boldsymbol{r}$ are defined as

$$\boldsymbol{\lambda} = \boldsymbol{r}' - \boldsymbol{r}'', \qquad \boldsymbol{r} = \tfrac{1}{2}(\boldsymbol{r}' + \boldsymbol{r}'').$$

The integration is taken over the N-particle space, and the phase factor $\exp[-(i/\hbar)\boldsymbol{p}\cdot\boldsymbol{\lambda}]$ is to be understood as

$$\exp\left[-\frac{i}{\hbar}\sum_{s=1}^{N}(\boldsymbol{p}_s\cdot\boldsymbol{\lambda}_s)\right].$$

Putting $\boldsymbol{\lambda} = \hbar\boldsymbol{\eta}$, the distribution function can finally be defined as

$$F_N(\mathbf{r}, \mathbf{p}, t) = \left(\frac{1}{2\pi}\right)^{3N} \int \langle \mathbf{r} + \tfrac{1}{2}\hbar\boldsymbol{\eta}, t|\rho|\mathbf{r} - \tfrac{1}{2}\hbar\boldsymbol{\eta}, t\rangle e^{-i\mathbf{p}\cdot\boldsymbol{\eta}}\, d\boldsymbol{\Gamma}_\eta. \qquad (XVI.2.6)$$

The complex conjugate of F_N is given by

$$F_N^*(\mathbf{r}, \mathbf{p}, t) = \left(\frac{1}{2\pi}\right)^{3N} \int \langle \mathbf{r} - \tfrac{1}{2}\hbar\boldsymbol{\eta}|\rho|\mathbf{r} + \tfrac{1}{2}\hbar\boldsymbol{\eta}\rangle e^{i\mathbf{p}\cdot\boldsymbol{\eta}}\, d\boldsymbol{\Gamma}_\eta,$$

which with the transformation $\boldsymbol{\eta} \longrightarrow -\boldsymbol{\eta}$ under the integral sign leads to (*XVI.2.6*). Hence $F_N^* = F_N$ and therefore the quantum distribution function is real. However, because $\hbar$ has a finite value, F_N is not necessarily positive. The classical distribution function f_N (*Liouville*) is obtained as $f_N = \lim_{\hbar=0} F_N$, from (*XVI.2.6*). Definition (*XVI.2.6*) of the quantum distribution function F_N was first given by Wigner.* It is, essentially, a probability function and can be used to calculate average values pertaining to the quantum properties of an N-particle system. Its main difference from the classical f_N is that it describes an N-particle system whose members possess wave and particle properties and also obey quantum statistics (Fermi-Dirac or Bose-Einstein).

For a system of particles obeying Bose-Einstein statistics the state vector $|\mathbf{r}', t\rangle$ of the N free particles is expressible as a symmetrical combination of the single particle state vectors $|\mathbf{r}_i', t\rangle$. Thus, a general symmetrical state has the form

$$|\mathbf{r}', t\rangle_s = \sum_P P|\mathbf{r}_a', t\rangle|\mathbf{r}_b', t\rangle \cdots |\mathbf{r}_s', t\rangle, \qquad (XVI.2.7)$$

where $\sum_P$ means the sum over all permutations of P [see (*VI.2.5*)]. For a given total energy E there is only one symmetrical state. Thus for a Bose-Einstein system the representative $\langle \mathbf{r}', t|\rho|\mathbf{r}'', t\rangle$ does not change its sign under the operation of interchange of particles.

For a Fermi-Dirac system of particles we must use an antisymmetrized combination of individual particle state vectors as

$$|\mathbf{r}', t\rangle_A = \det \begin{vmatrix} |\mathbf{r}_{1a}', t\rangle, & |\mathbf{r}_{2a}', t\rangle, & \cdots, & |\mathbf{r}_{Na}', t\rangle \\ |\mathbf{r}_{1b}', t\rangle, & |\mathbf{r}_{2b}', t\rangle, & \cdots, & |\mathbf{r}_{Nb}', t\rangle \\ \cdots, & \cdots, & \cdots, & \cdots \\ \cdots, & \cdots, & \cdots, & \cdots \\ \cdots, & \cdots, & \cdots, & \cdots \\ |\mathbf{r}_{1q}', t\rangle, & |\mathbf{r}_{2q}', t\rangle, & \cdots, & |\mathbf{r}_{Nq}', t\rangle \end{vmatrix}. \qquad (XVI.2.8)$$

In this case the antisymmetrical state $|\mathbf{r}', t\rangle_A$ of the N-particle assembly represents a state where the particle states $a, b, \cdots, q$ are occupied and where

* E. Wigner, *Phys. Rev.*, **40** (1932), 749.
J. Mayal, *Proc. Cambridge Philos. Soc.*, **45** (1949), 95.
J. Irving and R. Zwanzig, *J. Chem. Phys.*, **19** (1951), 1173.
Y. L. Klimentovich and V. P. Silin, *Dokl., Akad. Nauk. SSSR.*, **82** (1952), 361.
J. Bass, *Sci. Rev.*, **3299** (1949), 643.

occupation of any state by each particle is equally likely. The occupation of any of the two states $|\boldsymbol{r}'_a, t\rangle$, $|\boldsymbol{r}'_b, t\rangle$ by any two particles, where $|\boldsymbol{r}'_a, t\rangle$ and $|\boldsymbol{r}'_b, t\rangle$ are the same, does not correspond to a state for the assembly since in this case $|\boldsymbol{r}', t\rangle_A = 0$. We already know that none of these symmetry properties of F_N are possessed by the classical distribution function f_N.

XVI.2.A. The Time Development of the Quantum Distribution Function

In any practical use of F_N we need some method for its actual calculation for a given system. This can be found by using Schrödinger's equation (*XVI.2.2*) and the equation [see (*VI.2.17*)] for the density matrix,

$$i\hbar \frac{d\rho}{dt} = -[\rho, H], \qquad (XVI.2.9)$$

where we assume that the Hamiltonian H for an N-particle system is of the form

$$H = H_0 + H', \qquad H_0 = H_1 + H_2 + \cdots + H_N, \qquad H_i = \frac{\boldsymbol{p}_i^2}{2m_i},$$

for $i = 1, 2, \cdots, N$, and

$$H' = \sum_{i \neq 1}^{N} V(|x_{1s} - x_{is}|). \qquad (XVI.2.10)$$

If we wish, we can also include in H_0 the action of an external field and write

$$H_0 = \sum_{i=1}^{N} \left[\frac{\boldsymbol{p}_i^2}{2m_i} + U(\boldsymbol{r}_i)\right]. \qquad (XVI.2.11)$$

The term $V(|x_{1s} - x_{is}|)$ in H' refers to a centrally symmetric potential and represents the interaction of one particle with each of the remaining ones.

Now, differentiating the distribution function F_N as defined by (*XVI.2.6*) and using equations (*XVI.2.2*) and (*XVI.2.9*), we obtain

$$i\hbar \frac{dF_N}{dt} = \left(\frac{1}{2\pi}\right)^{3N} \Big[\int -\langle \boldsymbol{r} + \tfrac{1}{2}\hbar\boldsymbol{\eta}, t|H_0\rho|\boldsymbol{r} - \tfrac{1}{2}\hbar\boldsymbol{\eta}, t\rangle e^{-i\boldsymbol{\eta}\cdot\boldsymbol{p}}\, d\boldsymbol{\Gamma}_\eta$$
$$+ \int \langle \boldsymbol{r} + \tfrac{1}{2}\hbar\boldsymbol{\eta}, t|\rho H_0|\boldsymbol{r} - \tfrac{1}{2}\hbar\boldsymbol{\eta}, t\rangle e^{-i\boldsymbol{\eta}\cdot\boldsymbol{p}}\, d\boldsymbol{\Gamma}_\eta$$
$$+ \int \langle \boldsymbol{r} + \tfrac{1}{2}\hbar\boldsymbol{\eta}, t|[H, \rho]|\boldsymbol{r} - \tfrac{1}{2}\hbar\boldsymbol{\eta}, t\rangle e^{-i\boldsymbol{\eta}\cdot\boldsymbol{p}}\, d\boldsymbol{\Gamma}_\eta\Big].$$

Hence

$$i\hbar \frac{dF_N}{dt} = \left(\frac{1}{2\pi}\right)^{3N} \int \langle \boldsymbol{r} + \tfrac{1}{2}\hbar\boldsymbol{\eta}, t|[H', \rho]|\boldsymbol{r} - \tfrac{1}{2}\hbar\boldsymbol{\eta}, t\rangle e^{-i\boldsymbol{\eta}\cdot\boldsymbol{p}}\, d\boldsymbol{\Gamma}_\eta. \qquad (XVI.2.12)$$

If we assume that the interaction energy H' is a function of the position operator $\boldsymbol{q}$, then (*XVI.2.12*) can be simplified by inserting in the integration the unit operator,

$$\int |\boldsymbol{r}', t\rangle \, d\boldsymbol{\Gamma}_{r'} \langle \boldsymbol{r}', t| = 1,$$

and we obtain

$$i\hbar \frac{dF_N}{dt} = \left(\frac{1}{2\pi}\right)^{3N} \int \langle \boldsymbol{r} + \tfrac{1}{2}\hbar\boldsymbol{\eta}, t|H'|\boldsymbol{r}', t\rangle \, d\boldsymbol{\Gamma}_{r'} \langle \boldsymbol{r}', t|\rho|\boldsymbol{r} - \tfrac{1}{2}\hbar\boldsymbol{\eta}, t\rangle e^{-i\boldsymbol{\eta}\cdot\boldsymbol{p}} \, d\boldsymbol{\Gamma}_{\eta}$$

$$- \left(\frac{1}{2\pi}\right)^{3N} \int \langle \boldsymbol{r} + \tfrac{1}{2}\hbar\boldsymbol{\eta}, t|\rho|\boldsymbol{r}', t\rangle \, d\boldsymbol{\Gamma}_{r'} \langle \boldsymbol{r}', t|H'|\boldsymbol{r} - \tfrac{1}{2}\hbar\boldsymbol{\eta}, t\rangle e^{-i\boldsymbol{\eta}\cdot\boldsymbol{p}} \, d\boldsymbol{\Gamma}_{\eta}$$

$$= \left(\frac{1}{2\pi}\right)^{3N} \int H'(\boldsymbol{r} + \tfrac{1}{2}\hbar\boldsymbol{\eta}, t)\langle \boldsymbol{r}', t|\rho|\boldsymbol{r} - \tfrac{1}{2}\hbar\boldsymbol{\eta}, t\rangle \delta(\boldsymbol{r} + \tfrac{1}{2}\hbar\boldsymbol{\eta} - \boldsymbol{r}') e^{-i\boldsymbol{\eta}\cdot\boldsymbol{p}} \, d\boldsymbol{\Gamma}_{r'} \, d\boldsymbol{\Gamma}_{\eta}$$

$$- \left(\frac{1}{2\pi}\right)^{3N} \int \mathrm{H}'(\boldsymbol{r} - \tfrac{1}{2}\hbar\boldsymbol{\eta}, t)\langle \boldsymbol{r} + \tfrac{1}{2}\hbar\boldsymbol{\eta}, t|\rho|\boldsymbol{r}', t\rangle \delta(\boldsymbol{r}' + \tfrac{1}{2}\hbar\boldsymbol{\eta} - \boldsymbol{r}) e^{-i\boldsymbol{\eta}\cdot\boldsymbol{p}} \, d\boldsymbol{\Gamma}_{r'} \, d\boldsymbol{\Gamma}_{\eta}.$$

Hence

$$i\hbar \frac{dF_N}{dt} = \left(\frac{1}{2\pi}\right)^{3N} \int [H'(\boldsymbol{r} + \tfrac{1}{2}\hbar\boldsymbol{\eta}) - H'(\boldsymbol{r} - \tfrac{1}{2}\hbar\boldsymbol{\eta})]\langle \boldsymbol{r} + \tfrac{1}{2}\hbar\boldsymbol{\eta}, t|\rho \times |\boldsymbol{r} - \tfrac{1}{2}\hbar\boldsymbol{\eta}, t\rangle e^{-i\boldsymbol{\eta}\cdot\boldsymbol{p}} d\boldsymbol{\Gamma}_{\eta}. \quad (XVI.2.13)$$

Using the definition of F_N by (*XVI.2.6*) we get

$$\langle \boldsymbol{r} + \tfrac{1}{2}\hbar\boldsymbol{\eta}, t|\rho|\boldsymbol{r} - \tfrac{1}{2}\hbar\boldsymbol{\eta}, t\rangle = \int F_N(\boldsymbol{r}, \boldsymbol{p}', t) e^{i\boldsymbol{p}'\cdot\boldsymbol{\eta}} \, d\boldsymbol{\Gamma}_{p'}. \quad (XVI.2.14)$$

Thus the time development of F_N obeys the integrodifferential equation

$$i\hbar \frac{dF_N}{dt} = \left(\frac{1}{2\pi}\right)^{3N} \int [H'(\boldsymbol{r} + \tfrac{1}{2}\hbar\boldsymbol{\eta}) - H'(\boldsymbol{r} - \tfrac{1}{2}\hbar\boldsymbol{\eta})] \times F_N(\boldsymbol{r}, \boldsymbol{p}', t) e^{i\boldsymbol{\eta}\cdot(\boldsymbol{p}'-\boldsymbol{p})} \, d\boldsymbol{\Gamma}_{\eta} \, d\boldsymbol{\Gamma}_{p'}. \quad (XVI.2.15)$$

XVI.2.B. The Classical Limit of the Quantum Distribution Function

We first divide both sides of (*XVI.2.15*) by $\hbar$ and set $\hbar = 0$. Thus, noting that

$$\lim_{\hbar=0} \frac{H'(\boldsymbol{r} + \tfrac{1}{2}\hbar\boldsymbol{\eta}) - H'(\boldsymbol{r} - \tfrac{1}{2}\hbar\boldsymbol{\eta})}{\hbar} = \boldsymbol{\eta}\cdot\boldsymbol{\nabla}H'(\boldsymbol{r}),$$

we obtain

$$\frac{df_N}{dt} = \left(\frac{1}{2\pi}\right)^{3N} \frac{1}{i} \int (\boldsymbol{\eta}\cdot\boldsymbol{\nabla}H') f_N e^{i\boldsymbol{\eta}\cdot(\boldsymbol{p}-\boldsymbol{p}')} \, d\boldsymbol{\Gamma}_{\eta} \, d\boldsymbol{\Gamma}_{p'},$$

where

$$\boldsymbol{\eta}\cdot\boldsymbol{\nabla}H' = \sum_{i=1}^{N} \boldsymbol{\eta}^{(i)}\cdot\boldsymbol{\nabla}_{(i)}H'.$$

The equation for f_N can further be written as

$$\frac{df_N}{dt} = \left(\frac{1}{2\pi}\right)^{3N} \frac{\partial}{\partial \boldsymbol{p}} \cdot \int (\nabla H') f_N e^{i\boldsymbol{\eta}\cdot(\boldsymbol{p}-\boldsymbol{p}')}\, d\boldsymbol{\Gamma}_{\eta}\, d\boldsymbol{\Gamma}_{p'}$$

$$= \frac{\partial}{\partial \boldsymbol{p}} \cdot \int (\nabla H') f_N \delta(\boldsymbol{p}-\boldsymbol{p}')\, d\boldsymbol{\Gamma}_{p'} = \frac{\partial}{\partial \boldsymbol{p}} \cdot [(\nabla H') f_N].$$

Hence, using

$$\frac{df_N}{dt} = \frac{\partial f_N}{\partial t} + \sum_{i=1}^{N} \frac{\boldsymbol{p}_i}{m_i} \cdot \nabla_i f_N,$$

we obtain

$$\frac{\partial f_N}{\partial t} + \sum_{i=1}^{N} \left[\frac{\boldsymbol{p}_i}{m_i} \cdot \nabla_{r_i} f_N - (\nabla_{r_i} H') \cdot \nabla_{p_i} f_N \right] = 0, \qquad (XVI.2.16)$$

which is the Liouville theorem of classical statistical mechanics.

XVI.2.C. The One-Particle Distribution Function

Let us assume that F_N is symmetrical with respect to the interchange of the coordinates $\boldsymbol{r}_1, \boldsymbol{r}_2, \cdots, \boldsymbol{r}_N$ of the N particles. In complete analogy to the classical case, we can define the reduced distribution function for k particles, where $k < N$, by

$$F_k(\boldsymbol{r}_1, \boldsymbol{r}_2, \cdots, \boldsymbol{r}_k, \boldsymbol{p}_1, \boldsymbol{p}_2, \cdots, \boldsymbol{p}_k, t) = \int F_N(\boldsymbol{r}_1, \boldsymbol{r}_2, \cdots, \boldsymbol{r}_N, \boldsymbol{p}_1, \boldsymbol{p}_2, \cdots, \boldsymbol{p}_N, t)\, d\boldsymbol{\Gamma}_{rp}^k, \qquad (XVI.2.17)$$

where

$$d\boldsymbol{\Gamma}_{rp}^k = (d^3\boldsymbol{r}_{k+1} \cdots d^3\boldsymbol{r}_N)(d^3\boldsymbol{p}_{k+1} \cdots d^3\boldsymbol{p}_N).$$

By integrating ($XVI.2.15$) over phase space of the $(N-1)$th particle, we obtain for the one-particle distribution function the result

$$i\hbar \frac{dF_1}{dt} = \left(\frac{1}{2\pi}\right)^3 \int [\Phi(|\boldsymbol{r}_1 - \boldsymbol{r}_2 + \tfrac{1}{2}\hbar\boldsymbol{\eta}|) - \Phi(|\boldsymbol{r}_1 - \boldsymbol{r}_2 - \tfrac{1}{2}\hbar\boldsymbol{\eta}|)] \times F_{12}(\boldsymbol{r}_1, \boldsymbol{r}_2, \boldsymbol{p}_1', \boldsymbol{p}_2, t) e^{i\boldsymbol{\eta}\cdot(\boldsymbol{p}_1'-\boldsymbol{p}_1)}\, d^3\boldsymbol{r}_2 d^3\boldsymbol{p}_2 d^3\boldsymbol{p}_1' d^3\boldsymbol{\eta}, \qquad (XVI.2.18)$$

where F_{12} is the two-particle distribution function and $\Phi = (N-1)V$. In the limit $\hbar = 0$, ($XVI.2.18$) yields the classical equation

$$\frac{df_1}{dt} = \int \nabla_1\Phi \cdot \nabla_{p_1} f_{12}(\boldsymbol{r}_1, \boldsymbol{r}_2, \boldsymbol{p}_1, \boldsymbol{p}_2, t)\, d^3\boldsymbol{r}_2 d^3\boldsymbol{p}_2, \qquad (XVI.2.19)$$

where $-\nabla_1\Phi$ is the average force acting on the particle 1, and Φ is a function of $|\boldsymbol{r}_1 - \boldsymbol{r}_2|$.

In classical transport theory, equation ($XVI.2.19$) can be approximated, under certain assumptions, by the Boltzmann equation:

$$\frac{df}{dt} = \int d^3\boldsymbol{p}_1 \int d\Omega\, |\boldsymbol{p} - \boldsymbol{p}_1| \sigma(|\boldsymbol{p} - \boldsymbol{p}_1|, \theta)(f'f_1' - ff_1), \qquad (XVI.2.20)$$

where $\boldsymbol{p}$ is the relative momentum and the prime and the subscript 1 of the f refer to the momentum variables alone—that is, $f_1 = f(\boldsymbol{r}, \boldsymbol{p}_1, t)$ and $f' = f(\boldsymbol{r}, \boldsymbol{p}', t)$. The four momentum variables $\boldsymbol{p}$, $\boldsymbol{p}_1$, $\boldsymbol{p}'$, $\boldsymbol{p}_1'$ refer to the momenta of the binary collision,*

$$(\boldsymbol{p}, \boldsymbol{p}_1) \longleftrightarrow (\boldsymbol{p}', \boldsymbol{p}_1'), \qquad |\boldsymbol{p} - \boldsymbol{p}_1| = |\boldsymbol{p}' - \boldsymbol{p}_1|,$$

and $\sigma(|\boldsymbol{p} - \boldsymbol{p}_1|, \theta)\, d\Omega =$ the differential cross-section for a collision in the solid angle $d\Omega$ ($= \sin\theta\, d\theta\, d\phi$).

A similar approach can be used to derive a quantum transport equation from (*XVI.2.18*), by truncating the two-particle distribution function F_{12} as a product of the single-particle distribution functions F_1 and F_2 and a pair correlation function g_{12}. The execution of such a laborious task is outside the scope of this book. However, some comments on the use of such a quantum transport equation is in order.

In a many-body system (for example electrons in solids) a perturbing interaction does not lead to a set of stationary states whose energies are sharply defined; instead, it produces a relaxation process. This means that the particles will suffer collisions with one another during a mean free time τ. Classically this leads to replacing the collision term in (*XVI.2.20*) by $-(f - f_0)/\tau$, where $-f/\tau$ describes the removal of particles from some parts of phase space due to collisions, and f_0/τ describes the reappearance of the same particles in some other parts of phase space. The occurrence of the two processes together insures that the initial distribution will tend to equilibrium during a time of the order of τ. The quantum analogue of this procedure was proposed by Karplus and Schwinger† in terms of a density matrix ρ where the interaction Hamiltonian contains a part causing the interparticle collisions and hence making the distribution tend to a thermal equilibrium. In their formalism it is assumed that the change in ρ, as caused by collisions, is of the form

$$i\hbar \left[\frac{d\rho}{dt}\right]_c = [H_1, \rho] = -i\hbar\, \frac{\rho - \rho_0}{\tau},$$

where H_1 is the part of the interaction causing the collisions and ρ_0 is the equilibrium value of ρ. A useful application of this formalism can be found in systems where the influence of relaxation processes upon transitions between various energy states is a dominant and nonclassical feature of the many-particle systems.

---

* S. Chapman and T. G. Cowling, *The Mathematical Theory of Non-Uniform Gases,* Cambridge Univ. Press, Cambridge, 1952.

J. G. Kirkwood and J. Ross, in *International Symposium on Statistical Mechanics,* Edited by I. Prigogine, Interscience, New York, 1957.

† R. Karplus and J. Schwinger, *Phys. Rev.,* 73 (1948), 1020.

In an equivalent but more general approach for the study of relaxation phenomena, the use of the quantum distribution function may be found more realistic, since there can be no ambiguity with regard to a representation of random collisions causing the relaxation process. This procedure has a direct classical analogue; that is, for $\hbar = 0$ we can get a Boltzmann equation.

XVI.2.D. The Quantum Distribution Function of a Harmonic Oscillator

To illustrate the basic difference between classical and quantum distribution functions, we shall solve a related problem. Let us first compare three diffusion type equations:

$$\frac{\partial P}{\partial t} = D\nabla^2 P, \qquad (XVI.2.21)$$

$$\frac{\partial f}{\partial T} = \frac{\kappa}{2m}\nabla_v^2 f, \qquad (XVI.2.22)$$

$$\frac{\partial \psi}{\partial t} = \frac{i\hbar}{2m}\nabla^2 \psi. \qquad (XVI.2.23)$$

These equations are solved by

$$P = \left(\frac{1}{4\pi Dt}\right)^{3/2} e^{-(\mathbf{r}-\mathbf{r}_0)^2/4Dt} \qquad (XVI.2.24)$$

$$f = \left(\frac{m}{2\pi\kappa T}\right)^{3/2} e^{-mv^2/2\kappa T} \qquad (XVI.2.25)$$

$$\psi = \left(\frac{m}{2\pi i\hbar t}\right)^{3/2} e^{i[m(\mathbf{r}-\mathbf{r}_0)^2/2\hbar t]}, \qquad (XVI.2.26)$$

where $P(r, t)\, d^3\mathbf{r}$ is the probability that the particle will find itself between $\mathbf{r}$ and $\mathbf{r} + d\mathbf{r}$ after time t; f is the Maxwellian distribution and ψ represents (*V.5.4*), the probability amplitude of the position operator $\mathbf{q}$ having the value $\mathbf{r}$ at time t if it had the value $\mathbf{r}_0$ at time t $= 0$ (where $\mathbf{q}$ is diagonal).

We can now make a transition from a single-particle quantum path description to a quantum ensemble description by the substitution [comparing (*XVI.2.25*), (*XVI.2.24*), and (*XVI.2.26*)]

$$t = i\hbar\beta, \qquad \beta = \frac{1}{\kappa T}$$

where κ is Boltzmann's constant and T is the temperature of an equilibrium state. We can apply this transformation to the transformation function of a harmonic oscillator [see (*V.5.59*) and (*V.5.60*)] and obtain the density function for a harmonic oscillator in coordinate representation:

$$\rho = \frac{\exp\left[\frac{i}{\hbar}\mathcal{W}(x, x_0, -i\hbar\beta)\right]}{\int_{-\infty}^{\infty}\exp\left[\frac{i}{\hbar}\mathcal{W}(x, x_0, -i\hbar\beta)\right]dx}$$

$$= A\exp\left\{-\frac{m\omega}{4\hbar}\left[(x - x_0)^2\coth\left(\tfrac{1}{2}\beta\hbar\omega\right) + (x + x_0)^2\tanh\left(\tfrac{1}{2}\beta\hbar\omega\right)\right]\right\}, \tag{XVI.2.27}$$

where

$$A = \left[\frac{m\omega}{\pi\hbar}\tanh\left(\tfrac{1}{2}\beta\hbar\omega\right)\right]^{1/2}.$$

From (*XVI.2.6*) and the substitution $x - x_0 = \hbar\eta$ and $\frac{1}{2}(x + x_0) = X$, we obtain

$$F(X, p, t) = \frac{1}{2\pi}A\exp\left[-\frac{m\omega X^2}{\hbar}\tanh\left(\tfrac{1}{2}\beta\hbar\omega\right)\right] \times \int_{-\infty}^{\infty}\exp\left[-\frac{m\omega\hbar}{4}\eta^2\coth\left(\tfrac{1}{2}\beta\hbar\omega\right)\right]\exp(-i\eta p)\,d\eta.$$

Hence

$$F = \frac{1}{\pi\hbar}\tanh\left(\tfrac{1}{2}\beta\hbar\omega\right)\exp\left[-\frac{2E}{\hbar\omega}\tanh\left(\tfrac{1}{2}\beta\hbar\omega\right)\right], \tag{XVI.2.28}$$

where

$$E = \frac{p^2}{2m} + \frac{1}{2}m\omega^2X^2$$

is the energy of the oscillator.

The classical distribution function of a free harmonic oscillator follows by letting $\hbar \longrightarrow 0$ in (*XVI.2.28*):

$$f = \frac{\omega}{2\pi\kappa T}e^{-E/\kappa T} = \left(\frac{1}{2\pi m\kappa T}\right)^{1/2}e^{-p^2/2m\kappa T}\left(\frac{m\omega^2}{2\pi\kappa T}\right)^{1/2}e^{-m\omega^2X^2/2\kappa T}, \tag{XVI.2.29}$$

where f is normalized by $\int f\,dp\,dq = 1$.

As an application of the oscillator quantum distribution function (*XVI.2.28*), we shall derive Planck's formula for the average energy of an oscillator. Thus

$$\langle E\rangle = \int_{-\infty}^{\infty}dx\int_{-\infty}^{\infty}EF\,dp = \tfrac{1}{2}\hbar\omega\coth\left(\tfrac{1}{2}\beta\hbar\omega\right). \tag{XVI.2.30}$$

This result can be rewritten as

$$\langle E\rangle = \tfrac{1}{2}\hbar\omega + \frac{\hbar\omega}{e^{\hbar\omega/\kappa T} - 1}, \tag{XVI.2.31}$$

where the first term refers to zero point oscillation energy.

The form (*XVI.2.30*) of the average energy of a free harmonic oscillator is of some physical as well as historical significance. It was derived by Einstein* for the specific heat of solids. The classical law of Dulong-Petit leads to the same molar specific heat for all monatomic solids. This law is formulated in terms of a classical theory of lattice vibrations. From the equipartition of energy it is found that there are $3N$ (N = Avagadro's number) normal modes in one mole, each with energy κT. Later experiments have demonstrated that the Dulong-Petit law does not hold at low temperatures; κT then becomes less than the spacing of the quantum energy levels and the specific heat begins to depart from the equipartition of energy.

The lattice vibrations of a solid are to be represented by uncoupled quantum harmonic oscillators with energy levels $E_n = [n + \frac{1}{2}]\hbar\omega$. In this case the corresponding average energy of each mode is given by (*XVI.2.30*) instead of κT (corresponding to $\hbar = 0$). However, later studies have shown that the agreement between theory and experiment was more of a qualitative nature, since the expression (*XVI.2.30*) drops off rather steeply and causes a quantitative deviation from experiment. It was found that for solids the uncoupled quantum harmonic oscillators, representing lattice vibrations, ought to have a certain frequency distribution. The correct result was obtained as the average of (*XVI.2.30*) over a given frequency distribution,

$$\overline{E} = \tfrac{1}{2}\hbar \int_0^{\Omega} \omega G(\omega) \coth\left(\tfrac{1}{2}\beta\hbar\omega\right) d\omega,$$

where Ω is the cutoff frequency and $G(\omega)$ is a certain frequency distribution function.

---

* A. Einstein, *Ann. Phys. Leipzig,* **22** (1906), 180, 800.

CHAPTER XVII

THE ELEMENTARY THEORY OF SCATTERING

XVII.1. The Cross-Section for Scattering

Scattering of waves or particles from a force field can be used to obtain information about the nature of the force field, the scattered particle, and the interaction of the two systems. By scattering charged particles from atoms, we can explore the properties of the atoms as highly localized charged nuclei surrounded by planetary electrons. Scattering of electromagnetic waves from charged particles gives information about the interaction of matter and radiation. The scattering of mesons from nucleons is an effective way to probe the interactions of mesons and nucleons and hence to get some information about the nature of nuclear forces, and so on.

Classically a cross-section is defined as the ratio of the amount of energy emitted by the scatterer in a given direction per unit time to the energy flux density of the incident radiation. For example, for the scattering of electromagnetic waves by charged particles the effective differential cross-section is defined by

$$d\sigma = \frac{[dI]\,\text{av}}{[S]\,\text{av}}, \qquad (XVII.1.1)$$

where dI is the energy radiated by the system of charges into the solid angle $d\Omega$ per unit time for an incident wave with the pointing vector S.

In quantum mechanics the cross-section is derivable from the wave function itself. We have a dynamical system consisting of a scattering center and an incident wave which may consist of a beam of localized particles in a pure state; each particle is sufficiently separated from the others that we may neglect interparticle interaction in the beam. The scatterer by itself may have a number of stationary states, and initially it is in one of these states. After the incident particle is scattered it can be left in a different stationary state. This means that the incident wave may induce a transition in the scatterer. We first calculate this transition probability amplitude and show that the cross-section for scattering is proportional to the transition probability.

In a scattering process for any state of motion of the system the particle will spend most of its time at infinity. The probability for such a state of motion and its relation to the scattering cross-section are contained in the wave function of the system. Since the particle spends most of its time at infinity, we shall be interested in the asymptotic behavior of the wave function at large distances from the scattering center. Under these circumstances, the wave function will consist of an incident plane plus an outgoing spherical wave:

$$\psi \cong e^{ikz} + \frac{1}{r} e^{ikr} f(\theta), \tag{XVII.1.2}$$

where e^{ikz} represents a stream of electrons, say, and $k = p/\hbar = mv/\hbar$. At large distances from the scattering center the Hamiltonian of the system tends to a free Hamiltonian, which permits plane wave solutions together with outgoing spherical waves. (For ingoing waves see Section XVIII.3.) The wave e^{ikz} represents a density of electrons of one per unit volume, or

$$|e^{ikz}|^2 = 1,$$

and hence a flow of v electrons across a unit area per unit time. The function $f(\theta)$ has the dimensions of a length. It can be related to the scattering cross-section as follows: the number of electrons in the scattered wave crossing an element of area dS at the point (r, θ, ϕ) is

$$v \frac{dS}{r^2} |f(\theta)|^2$$

per unit time. If the incident beam is such that one electron falls on a unit area per unit time, the number $\sigma(\theta)\, d\Omega$ scattered into a solid angle $d\Omega$ per unit time is equal to

$$|f(\theta)|^2\, d\Omega,$$

and so

$$\sigma(\theta) = |f(\theta)|^2. \tag{XVII.1.3}$$

The numbers of electrons scattered between the angles θ and $d\theta$ is given as

$$\int_0^{2\pi} d\phi |f(\theta)|^2 \sin\theta\, d\theta = 2\pi |f(\theta)|^2 \sin\theta\, d\theta.$$

XVII.1.A. Calculation of the Scattering Cross-Section

We begin by defining a stationary-state Green's operator G_0 by

$$(E - H_0)G_0 = 1. \qquad (XVII.1.4)$$

In order to impose an outgoing wave boundary condition it is sufficient to assume that E has a small positive imaginary part, $i\epsilon$. The Schrödinger equation

$$H|\Psi\rangle = E|\Psi\rangle, \qquad (XVII.1.5)$$

with $H = H_0 + H'$, can be written as

$$(E - H_0)|\Psi\rangle = H'|\Psi\rangle. \qquad (XVII.1.6)$$

Hence, using (*XVII.1.4*), we can derive the integral equation

$$|\Psi\rangle = |\Psi_0\rangle + G_0H'|\Psi\rangle, \qquad (XVII.1.7)$$

where the state vector $|\Psi_0\rangle$ represents the initial state satisfying the equation

$$(E - H_0)|\Psi_0\rangle = 0, \qquad (XVII.1.8)$$

where the energy E can form a continuous spectrum. The size of ϵ is closely related to the spread of the energy of the system; the smaller ϵ is, the sharper the energy. Furthermore, regarding the incident particle as a wave packet approaching the force field or the scatterer, it is important that the size of the packet is not smaller than the range of the force field. The latter also is closely related to the size of ϵ. With these remarks the integral equation (*XVII.1.7*) is well defined and can be used for the discussion of scattering problems.

Let us first consider a conventional discussion of equation (*XVII.1.7*). For this we use Schrödinger's representation and take the representatives of (*XVII.1.4*) to write it as

$$\left(E + \frac{\hbar^2}{2m}\nabla^2\right)G_0(\boldsymbol{r}, \boldsymbol{r}') = \delta(\boldsymbol{r} - \boldsymbol{r}')$$

or

$$(\nabla^2 + k_0^2)G_0 = \frac{2m}{\hbar^2}\delta(\boldsymbol{r} - \boldsymbol{r}'), \qquad (XVII.1.9)$$

where*

$$k_0^2 = \frac{2m}{\hbar^2}E, \qquad G_0(\boldsymbol{r}, \boldsymbol{r}') = \langle\boldsymbol{r}|G_0|\boldsymbol{r}'\rangle.$$

To integrate the equation we use the Fourier representations

---

* In view of the translation invariance of (*XVII.1.9*), Green's function G_0 is a function of the relative coordinates $\mathbf{r} - \mathbf{r}'$.

$$G_0 = \left(\frac{1}{2\pi}\right)^3 \int e^{i\boldsymbol{k}\cdot\boldsymbol{R}} G_0(\boldsymbol{k})\, d^3\boldsymbol{k},$$

$$\delta(\boldsymbol{r} - \boldsymbol{r}') = \left(\frac{1}{2\pi}\right)^3 \int e^{i\boldsymbol{k}\cdot\boldsymbol{R}}\, d^3\boldsymbol{k},$$

and obtain

$$G_0 = \frac{2m}{\hbar^2}\left(\frac{1}{2\pi}\right)^3 \int \frac{e^{i\boldsymbol{k}\cdot\boldsymbol{R}}}{k_0^2 - \boldsymbol{k}^2}\, d^3\boldsymbol{k}, \qquad (XVII.1.10)$$

where

$$R = |\boldsymbol{r} - \boldsymbol{r}'|.$$

Carrying out the angle integrations first, we obtain (*XVII.1.10*) in the form

$$G_0 = -\frac{2m}{\hbar^2}\frac{1}{4\pi^2}\frac{1}{R}\frac{\partial}{\partial R}\int_{-\infty}^{\infty} \frac{e^{ikR}\, dk}{k_0^2 - \boldsymbol{k}^2}. \qquad (XVII.1.11)$$

Because of the small positive imaginary part of k_0 we can write (*XVII.1.11*) as

$$\begin{aligned} G_0 &= \frac{2m}{\hbar^2}\frac{1}{4\pi^2}\frac{1}{R}\frac{\partial}{\partial R}\int_0^{\infty} d\alpha\, d\beta \int_{-\infty}^{\infty} e^{i\alpha(k_0-k)}e^{i\beta(k_0+k)}e^{ikR}\, dk \\ &= \frac{2m}{\hbar^2}\frac{1}{2\pi}\frac{1}{R}\frac{\partial}{\partial R}\int_0^{\infty} d\alpha\, d\beta\, e^{ik_0(\alpha+\beta)}\delta(R + \beta - \alpha) \\ &= \frac{2m}{\hbar^2}\frac{1}{2\pi}\frac{1}{R}\frac{\partial}{\partial R}\int_0^{\infty} d\beta\, e^{ik_0R}e^{2ik_0\beta}, \end{aligned}$$

where in the second line we have to integrate over α first; since both α and β are nonnegative parameters the integration over β first would yield the substitution

$$\beta = \alpha - R,$$

which could become negative. It is easy to see that the method we are employing is equivalent to the usual complex integration. Noting that

$$\int_0^{\infty} d\beta\, e^{2ik_0\beta} = \frac{i}{2k_0},$$

we finally obtain Green's function for the free particle:

$$G_0 = -\frac{2m}{\hbar^2}\frac{1}{4\pi}\frac{1}{R}e^{ik_0R}. \qquad (XVII.1.12)$$

On taking the representatives of equation (*XVII.1.7*) and using (*XVII.1.12*), we get an integral equation for the wave function describing a scattering process:

$$\psi(\boldsymbol{r}) = \psi_0(\boldsymbol{r}) - \frac{2m}{\hbar^2}\frac{1}{4\pi}\int \frac{e^{ik_0R}}{R} H'(\boldsymbol{r}')\psi(\boldsymbol{r}')\, d^3\boldsymbol{x}'. \qquad (XVII.1.13)$$

The second term on the right represents an outgoing wave. For ψ to have the asymptotic form (*XVII.1.2*) we must choose for the incident wave $\psi_0(\boldsymbol{r})$ the form

$$\psi_0(\boldsymbol{r}) = e^{i\boldsymbol{k}_0\cdot\boldsymbol{r}}. \qquad (XVII.1.14)$$

At this point it must be remembered that for Coulomb interaction the incident wave is distorted by the nucleus even at infinity; therefore form (*XVII.1.14*) is not suitable as an incident wave.

If $H'(\boldsymbol{r}')$ decreases faster than $1/r'$, then the contribution to the integral in (*XVII.1.13*) from large values of r' is negligible. In this case we can write, for large r,

$$R = [r^2 + r'^2 - 2rr'\cos\theta]^{1/2} \cong r - \hat{\boldsymbol{r}}\cdot\boldsymbol{r}', \qquad \frac{1}{R} \cong \frac{1}{r},$$

where $\hat{\boldsymbol{r}}$ is a unit vector in the direction of $\boldsymbol{r}$. Putting $\hat{\boldsymbol{r}}k_0 = \boldsymbol{k}_0'$ we obtain

$$\psi(\boldsymbol{r}) \cong e^{i\boldsymbol{k}_0\cdot\boldsymbol{r}} - \frac{1}{4\pi}\frac{2m}{\hbar^2}\frac{e^{ik_0r}}{r}\int e^{-i\boldsymbol{k}'_0\cdot\boldsymbol{r}'}H'(\boldsymbol{r}')\psi(\boldsymbol{r}')\,d^3\boldsymbol{x}'. \qquad (XVII.1.15)$$

This is, of course, exact. In principle the solutions of the integral equation (*XVII.1.15*) correspond to scattering states of the incident particle from the force field H'. The scattering amplitude can be expressed, by iteration of (*XVII.1.15*), as an infinite series. Each term represents a particular physical process in decreasing order of strength. If we neglect all the terms and retain only the first term of the series, then the wave function ψ, as follows from (*XVII.1.15*), is of the form

$$\psi(\boldsymbol{r}) = e^{i\boldsymbol{k}_0\cdot\boldsymbol{r}} + \frac{e^{ik_0r}}{r}f(\theta),$$

where

$$f(\theta) = -\frac{1}{4\pi}\frac{2m}{\hbar^2}\int H'(\boldsymbol{r}')e^{i\boldsymbol{k}_0\cdot\boldsymbol{r}'-i\boldsymbol{k}'_0\cdot\boldsymbol{r}'}d^3\boldsymbol{x}' \qquad (XVII.1.16)$$

is the scattered amplitude.

The above treatment of a scattering process is called the "first Born approximation" and its validity depends on the fulfilment of certain conditions. For a centrally symmetric field $[H'(\boldsymbol{r}') = V(\boldsymbol{r}')]$ $f(\theta)$ can be written as

$$f(\theta) = -\frac{2m}{\hbar^2}\int_0^\infty \frac{\sin Kr}{Kr}V(r)r^2\,dr, \qquad (XVII.1.17)$$

where $K = |\boldsymbol{k}_0 - \boldsymbol{k}_0'|$; for elastic scattering ($|\boldsymbol{k}_0| = |\boldsymbol{k}_0'|$) it can be written as

$$K = 2k_0\sin\frac{\theta}{2} = \frac{4\pi}{\lambda}\sin\frac{1}{2}\theta,$$

where $\lambda = 2\pi/k_0 = h/mv$ and θ is the angle between the initial and final momenta. The intensity scattered into a solid angle element $d\Omega$ around $\boldsymbol{k}_0'$ is

$$dI = \int |f(\theta)|^2\,d\Omega = \int \frac{4m^2}{\hbar^4}\left|\int_0^\infty \frac{\sin Kr}{Kr}V(r)r^2\,dr\right|^2 d\Omega. \qquad (XVII.1.18)$$

For the Coulomb potential energy, or

$$V = \frac{ZZ'e^2}{r},$$

between particles with charges Ze and $Z'e$, the scattered amplitude can be integrated. Thus

$$\begin{aligned} f(\theta) &= -\frac{2m}{\hbar^2}\frac{ZZ'e^2}{K}\int_0^\infty \sin Kr\,dr \\ &= \lim_{\eta\to 0}\left(-\frac{2m}{\hbar^2}\frac{ZZ'e^2}{K}\right)\int_0^\infty \sin Kr\,e^{-\eta r}\,dr = -\frac{2mZZ'e^2}{\hbar^2K^2}, \end{aligned}$$

where $e^{-\eta r}$ with $\eta \geqq 0$ was introduced as a convergence factor. Hence differential scattering cross-section is

$$\sigma(\theta) = |f(\theta)|^2 = \frac{Z'^2Z^2e^4}{16E^2\sin^4\frac{1}{2}\theta}. \qquad (XVII.1.19)$$

This is the well-known Ratherford collision cross-section.

The validity of the Born approximation requires

$$\frac{2m}{\hbar^2}\frac{\lambda ZZ'e^2}{4\pi} \ll 1$$

or

$$\frac{ZZ'e^2}{\hbar v} \ll 1, \qquad (XVII.1.20)$$

so for high-energy scattering the Born approximation can be expected to give good results. For Coulomb scattering of charged particles we have the following special features.

(a) The cross-section is independent of $\hbar$.

(b) The exact quantum mechanical calculation leads to the same result as the one obtained by the use of the first Born approximation.

(c) The classical form of the differential cross-section is the same as (*XVII.1.19*). This might be expected from the absence of $\hbar$ in (*XVII.1.19*).

Because of the infinite range of a Coulomb force, all angular momenta are needed to represent scattering. In this sense the scattering of charged particles from charged scatterers is more like the scattering of wave packets or to a situation where the particlelike aspects tend to be emphasized more, as compared to the wavelike aspects. However, if only a small number of phases or angular momenta are involved, then neither the classical nor the Born scattering can provide a correct description of the scattering process.

XVII.1.B. The Momentum-Space Representation of Scattering

We shall use the notation $|E\rangle$ for a stationary state with energy E and write Schrödinger's equation (*XVII.1.5*) as an integral equation with an outgoing wave boundary condition. We have, from (*XVII.1.5*),

$$|E\rangle = |EI\rangle + \frac{1}{E + i\epsilon - H_0} H'|E\rangle. \qquad (XVII.1.21)$$

It is now easy to obtain momentum-space representation. Thus, taking representatives in momentum-space we get

$$\psi_+(\boldsymbol{p}) = \psi_0(\boldsymbol{p}) + \frac{1}{E + i\epsilon - \dfrac{\boldsymbol{p}^2}{2m}} \langle \boldsymbol{p}|H'|E\rangle,$$

where

$$\psi_+(\boldsymbol{p}) = \langle \boldsymbol{p}|E\rangle, \qquad \psi_0(\boldsymbol{p}) = \langle \boldsymbol{p}|EI\rangle,$$

$$\langle \boldsymbol{p}|H'|E\rangle = \int \langle \boldsymbol{p}|H'|\boldsymbol{p}'\rangle\, d^3\boldsymbol{p}' \psi_+(\boldsymbol{p}').$$

Hence

$$\psi_+(\boldsymbol{p}) = \psi_0(\boldsymbol{p}) + \frac{1}{E + i\epsilon - \dfrac{\boldsymbol{p}^2}{2m}} \int \langle \boldsymbol{p}|H'|\boldsymbol{p}'\rangle \psi_+(\boldsymbol{p}')\, d^3\boldsymbol{p}' \qquad (XVII.1.22)$$

is the required integral equation for a scattering process.

The factor $[E + i\epsilon - (\boldsymbol{p}^2/2m)]^{-1}$ in (*XVII.1.22*) can be written as

$$\frac{2m}{\hbar^2} \frac{1}{k_0^2 - \boldsymbol{k}^2 + i\epsilon},$$

where $k_0^2 = 2mE/\hbar^2$ and $\boldsymbol{k}^2 = \boldsymbol{p}^2/\hbar^2$. The function $(1/2\pi^2)[1/(k_0^2 - \boldsymbol{k}^2)]$ is the Fourier transform of the Green's function $(1/R)e^{ik_0R}$, so the scattered amplitude is the coefficient of $(1/2\pi^2)[1/(k_0^2 - \boldsymbol{k}^2)]$ in the asymptotic limit. In terms of the wave vector $\boldsymbol{k}$, we have

$$\langle \boldsymbol{p}|H'|\boldsymbol{p}'\rangle = \int \langle \boldsymbol{p}|\boldsymbol{r}\rangle\, d^3\boldsymbol{x}\, \langle \boldsymbol{r}|H'|\boldsymbol{p}'\rangle$$

$$= \left(\frac{1}{2\pi\hbar}\right)^3 \int e^{i(\boldsymbol{k}-\boldsymbol{k}')\cdot\boldsymbol{r}} H'(\boldsymbol{r})\, d^3\boldsymbol{x} = \frac{1}{\hbar^3} H'(\boldsymbol{k} - \boldsymbol{k}'),$$

where $H'(\boldsymbol{k} - \boldsymbol{k}')$ is the Fourier transform of $H'(\boldsymbol{r})$. Hence the integral equation (*XVII.1.22*) becomes

$$\psi_+(\boldsymbol{k}) = \psi_0(\boldsymbol{k}) + \frac{2m}{\hbar^2} \frac{1}{k_0^2 - \boldsymbol{k}^2} \int H'(\boldsymbol{k} - \boldsymbol{k}')\psi_+(\boldsymbol{k}')\, d^3\boldsymbol{k}'. \qquad (XVII.1.23)$$

If in the asymptotic limit of $\boldsymbol{k} \longrightarrow 0$, $H'(\boldsymbol{k} - \boldsymbol{k}')$ increases more slowly than

$1/\boldsymbol{k}^2$, then it is nearly independent of $\boldsymbol{k}'$ and can be taken outside the integral over $\boldsymbol{k}'$, so

$$\psi_+ \cong \psi_0 + \frac{2m}{\hbar^2}\frac{H'(\boldsymbol{k}-\boldsymbol{k}')}{k_0^2-\boldsymbol{k}^2}\int \psi_+(\boldsymbol{k}')\, d^3\boldsymbol{k}'. \qquad (XVII.1.24)$$

Hence the scattered amplitude in the first Born approximation is

$$f(\theta) = -2\pi^2\frac{2m}{\hbar^2}H'(\boldsymbol{k}-\boldsymbol{k}')\int \psi_0(\boldsymbol{k}')\, d^3\boldsymbol{k}', \qquad (XVII.1.25)$$

where the incident plane wave $\psi_0(\boldsymbol{k})$ is to be represented by a delta function,

$$\psi_0(\boldsymbol{k}) = \delta(\boldsymbol{k}).$$

Hence

$$f(\theta) = -2\pi^2\frac{2m}{\hbar^2}H'(\boldsymbol{k}-\boldsymbol{k}'). \qquad (XVII.1.26)$$

For Coulomb scattering we have

$$H'(\boldsymbol{k}-\boldsymbol{k}') = \lim_{\eta\to 0}(2\pi)^{-3}\int \frac{ZZ'e^2}{r}e^{i\boldsymbol{r}\cdot(\boldsymbol{k}-\boldsymbol{k}')}e^{-\eta r}\, d^3\boldsymbol{x}$$

$$= \frac{ZZ'e^2}{2\pi^2}\frac{1}{|\boldsymbol{k}-\boldsymbol{k}'|^2},$$

where, from the conservation of energy, we have

$$|\boldsymbol{k}-\boldsymbol{k}'| = 2k\sin\tfrac{1}{2}\theta,$$

and thus, as before,

$$f(\theta) = -\frac{ZZ'e^2}{4E\sin^2\frac{1}{2}\theta}.$$

XVII.2. Partial Waves and Phase Shift

Consider the partial wave expansion ($IV.3.22$) of a plane wave:

$$\psi = e^{i\boldsymbol{k}\cdot\boldsymbol{r}} = \sum_{l=0}^{\infty}\sum_{m=-l}^{l} i^l(2l+1)j_l(kr)P_l(\cos\theta).$$

The case $l = 1$ corresponds to P waves,

$$\psi_1 = A_1\left(\frac{\cos kr}{r} - \frac{\sin kr}{kr^2}\right)\cos\theta,$$

which for small r behaves like $\psi_1 \cong k^2 r\cos\theta$. The quantity $|\psi_1|^2$ has a maximum approximately at $kr = 1$, after which it decreases, so it is not likely that the particle will get much closer to the origin than the distance

$$r_0 \cong \frac{1}{k} = \frac{\lambda}{2\pi}. \qquad (XVII.2.1)$$

Thus P waves or particles of unit angular momentum are not likely to be nearer to the origin than the distance r_0, where their classical angular momentum $pr_0 = \hbar k r_0$ would be of the order of $\hbar$. For the present case of free waves, one can show in a similar way that the minimum distance at which $|\psi|^2$ is large is given by

$$pr_0 \cong \hbar l. \tag{XVII.2.2}$$

In the presence of a strong attractive force, let us write

$$E = \frac{\mathbf{p}^2}{2m} + V$$

and

$$p = \sqrt{2m(E - V)}.$$

Hence the criterion for the minimum probable radius is

$$r_0 \cong \frac{\hbar l}{\sqrt{2m(E - V)}}. \tag{XVII.2.3}$$

If V is large and negative, the wave may be pulled fairly close to the origin despite the repulsive effects of the centrifugal potential $l(l + 1)/r^2$ arising from the presence of an angular momentum.

The P wave is proportional to $\cos\theta$ and asymptotically it is just the sum of ingoing and outgoing spherical waves. Near the origin it has a complex behavior and does not hit the origin exactly as does the S wave, but instead—because of the centrifugal force—it tends to avoid the origin.

In the presence of a force field the radial wave function

$$\chi_l(r) = \frac{1}{r} G_l(r) \tag{XVII.2.4}$$

satisfies the equation

$$\frac{d^2G_l}{dr^2} + \left[\mathbf{k}^2 - \frac{2m}{\hbar^2} V(r) - \frac{l(l+1)}{r^2}\right] G_l = 0. \tag{XVII.2.5}$$

In this case the partial wave expansion of the wave function is given by

$$\psi = \sum_{l=0}^{\infty} A_l P_l(\cos\theta)\chi_l(r). \tag{XVII.2.6}$$

The constants A_l must be chosen in such a way that the wave function ψ shall represent an incident wave and a scattered wave, so (*XVII.2.6*) shall have the asymptotic form

$$\psi \cong e^{i\mathbf{k}\cdot\mathbf{r}} + \frac{1}{r} e^{ikr} f(\theta).$$

In a scattering process the wave function is everywhere finite. We must therefore choose that solution $\chi_l(r)$ of (*XVII.2.5*) which is finite at the origin. For large r the last two terms of (*XVII.2.5*) drop out, and for the asymptotic form we have

$$G_l \cong B_l \sin(kr + \epsilon). \tag{XVII.2.7}$$

To comprehend this better, let us set

$$G_l = u_l(r)e^{ikr}.$$

We obtain

$$\frac{d^2u_l}{dr^2} + 2ik\frac{du_l}{dr} - \left[\frac{2m}{\hbar^2}V + \frac{l(l+1)}{r^2}\right]u_l = 0, \qquad (XVII.2.8)$$

where u_l is a slowly varying function* of r; therefore for large r we have

$$\frac{d^2u_l}{dr^2} \ll k\frac{du_l}{dr},$$

and it can be neglected. We then get

$$2ik \log u_l = \int^r \left[\frac{2m}{\hbar^2}V + \frac{l(l+1)}{r^2}\right] dr.$$

For large r the right side tends to a constant if and only if V tends to zero faster than $1/r$ as $r \longrightarrow \infty$. Thus, for fields which fall to zero faster than the Coulomb field, G_l has the asymptotic form

$$B_l \sin(kr + \epsilon).$$

For χ_l that is finite at the origin, the particular solution will therefore have the form

$$\frac{C_l}{r}\sin(kr - \tfrac{1}{2}l\pi + \delta_l), \qquad (XVII.2.9)$$

where C_l is an arbitrary constant and δ_l is a constant that depends on k and on the potential V. We added $-\frac{1}{2}l\pi$ to ensure the vanishing of δ_l for $V = 0$.

The arbitrary constant C_l can be fixed by defining $\chi_l(r)$ as that bounded solution of the equation that has the asymptotic form

$$\frac{1}{kr}\sin(kr - \tfrac{1}{2}l\pi + \delta_l). \qquad (XVII.2.10)$$

The expression for the scattered wave can be obtained by subtracting the incident plane wave (*IV.3.22*) from the total wave function. The constants A_l in (*XVII.2.6*) must be chosen in such a way that the result of subtraction of the incident plane wave does actually represent a scattered outgoing wave, without the term $(1/r)e^{-ikr}$ in the asymptotic expansion. Thus for all l we must have

$$A_l\chi_l - (2l+1)i^l j_l(kr) = C_l\frac{1}{r}e^{ikr}, \qquad (XVII.2.11)$$

where C_l is some constant. Hence using the asymptotic forms

$$\frac{e^{ik\rho}}{2ikr}[A_le^{i\delta_l} - (2l+1)i^l], \qquad -\frac{e^{-ik\rho}}{2ikr}[A_le^{-i\delta_l} - (2l+1)i^l],$$

---

* N. F. Mott and H. S. W. Massey, *The Theory of Atomic Collisions*, Oxford Univ. Press, Oxford, 1949, p. 23.

where $k\rho = kr - \frac{1}{2}l\pi$, we must choose A_l so the second term vanishes. Thus

$$A_l = (2l + 1)e^{i\delta_l}i^l.$$

Hence the wave function, containing an incident plane wave plus a scattered outgoing wave in the asymptotic limit, is

$$\psi = \sum_{l=0}^{\infty} (2l + 1)i^l e^{i\delta_l}\chi_l(r)P_l(\cos\theta). \qquad (XVII.2.12)$$

This gives the asymptotic form of the scattered wave $(1/r)e^{ikr}f(\theta)$, where

$$f(\theta) = \frac{1}{2ik}\sum_{l=0}^{\infty} (2l + 1)(e^{2i\delta_l} - 1)P_l(\cos\theta). \qquad (XVII.2.13)$$

The form of $f(\theta)$ can be understood by comparing it with a plane wave. For example, if there were no potential there would still be an outgoing wave, which is just the outgoing part of a plane wave. In the presence of a force field the test for the scattered wave is to see whether the outgoing packet has been modified. Hence the asymptotic form of the scattered wave is obtained by subtracting from the actual outgoing wave the outgoing wave that would be present if there were no potential.

From (*XVII.2.13*) the cross-section can now be written as

$$\sigma(\theta) = |f(\theta)|^2 = a^2 + b^2, \qquad (XVII.2.14)$$

where

$$a = \frac{1}{2k}\Sigma(2l + 1)(\cos 2\delta_l - 1)P_l(\cos\theta),$$

$$b = \frac{1}{2k}\Sigma(2l + 1)(\sin 2\delta_l)P_l(\cos\theta). \qquad (XVII.2.15)$$

Once the phase shifts δ_l are known, formula (*XVII.2.14*) gives an expression for the angular-dependent differential cross-section.

The phase shifts δ_l can be obtained by solving Schrödinger's equation. The angular dependence of the differential cross-section arises, in part, from the interference of waves of different l. If, for example, we scattered waves with $l = 0$ only, then there is no angular dependence, and the cross-section is spherically symmetric. With $l = 1$ alone, the cross-section is proportional to $\cos^2\theta$. If both waves are present, then the amplitude $f(\theta)$ is

$$f(\theta) = A + B\cos\theta,$$

and the differential cross-section is

$$\sigma(\theta) = |A|^2 + |B|^2\cos^2\theta + (A^*B + AB^*)\cos\theta. \qquad (XVII.2.16)$$

The interference term arising from the interference of S and P waves is a typical wave representation of the scattered particles.

In the classical limit we are dealing with scattering of particles only; we must, therefore, by including all the l, form a wave packet in such a way that they build up to a maximum at a definite value of θ. This corresponds to a classical orbit in which particles come in with a fixed collision parameter and scatter through a definite angle; this is also the case for Coulomb scattering in both classical and quantum mechanical treatment.

The series in (*XVII.2.14*) is generally convergent, and there are not many cases where it can be summed into a closed expression, except for Coulomb scattering. The total cross-section σ of an atom for the scattering of electrons of a given velocity is defined as the total number of electrons scattered elastically by the atom, per unit time, from a beam of unit intensity (plane wave); that is, one electron crosses a unit area per unit time:

$$\sigma = 2\pi \int_0^\pi \sigma(\theta) \sin\theta \, d\theta = \frac{4\pi}{k^2} \sum_{l=0}^{\infty} (2l+1) \sin^2 \delta_l. \qquad (XVII.2.17)$$

This result means that in the total cross-section the various partial waves do not interfere. It is only in determining the angular distribution through the study of the differential cross-section that they interfere. For Coulomb scattering—because of the infinite range of Coulomb force—the scatterer can, at a given time, scatter all the particles in a beam of unit intensity so the resulting total cross-section is infinite. However, if the nuclear charge is screened by the atomic electrons, then the particle number scattered can be inhibited by cutting off the long Coulomb range. In this case the total cross-section is finite. For, from

$$f(\theta) = -\frac{2mZZ'e^2}{\hbar^2 K} \int_0^\infty \sin Kr \, e^{-ar} \, dr,$$

we obtain

$$f(\theta) = -\frac{2mZZ'e^2}{\hbar^2(a^2 + K^2)}$$

and

$$\sigma_C = 2\pi \int_0^\pi |f(\theta)|^2 \sin\theta \, d\theta = \left(\frac{2mZZ'e^2}{\hbar^2}\right)^2 \frac{\pi}{a^2\left(a^2 + \frac{4m^2v^2}{\hbar^2}\right)}, \qquad (XVII.2.18)$$

where a^{-1} is the screening radius. Putting

$$p_0 = \hbar a,$$

we write (*XVII.2.18*) as

$$\sigma_C = \frac{4\pi m^2 Z^2 Z'^2 e^4}{p_0^2(p_0^2 + 4p^2)}, \qquad (XVII.2.19)$$

where p_0 may be regarded as the momentum at the screening distance.

XVII.2.A. Problems

1. The potential energy of a beam of incident electrons is assumed to be of the form

$$V(r) = -\frac{Ze^2}{r}(1 - e^{-\kappa r})e^{-ar}, \qquad (XVII.2.20)$$

where a is the screening distance and $\kappa = mc/\hbar$. Show that the differential cross-section in the first Born approximation for scattering is given by

$$\sigma(\theta) = \left(\frac{2mZe^2}{\hbar^2}\right)^2 \frac{\kappa^2(\kappa + 2a)^2}{\left(a^2 + \frac{8EM}{\hbar^2}\sin^2\frac{1}{2}\theta\right)^2\left[(a+\kappa)^2 + \frac{8EM}{\hbar^2}\sin^2\frac{1}{2}\theta\right]^2}, \qquad (XVII.2.21)$$

which in the absence of screening becomes

$$\sigma(\theta) = \sigma_c(\theta)\left[\frac{mc^2}{mc^2 + 8E\sin^2\frac{1}{2}\theta}\right]^2. \qquad (XVII.2.22)$$

Comment on the choice of the constant κ as $mc/\hbar$ and the result that (*XVII.2.22*) is independent of $\hbar$.

2. Protons of low energy, as compared to the proton rest mass, are scattered from a nucleus. If Coulomb interaction is neglected, the elastic scattering of the protons can be assumed to be due entirely to nuclear interaction. The Schrödinger equation determining the scattering process is

$$\nabla^2\psi + \frac{2\mu}{\hbar^2}(E - V)\psi = 0, \qquad (XVII.2.23)$$

where

$$V = -[V_R(E) + iV_I(E)] \qquad (XVII.2.24)$$

for $r < R$ and $V = 0$ for $r > R$, and R is the nuclear radius,

$$R = 1.31 \times 10^{-13}A^{1/3}\text{ cm}.$$

Show from (*XVII.2.23*) that the wave function containing the scattering amplitude is given by

$$\psi = \begin{cases} \sum_{l=0}^{\infty}(l+\frac{1}{2})i^l a_l P_l(\cos\alpha)[g_l(k_I r) + h_l(k_I r)], & \text{for } r < R, \\ \sum_{l=0}^{\infty}(l+\frac{1}{2})i^l P_l(\cos\alpha)[g_l(k_0 r) + \eta_l h_l(k_0 r)], & \text{for } r > R, \end{cases} \qquad (XVII.2.25)$$

where $\eta_l = \exp(2i\delta_l)$, $h_l = j_l + in_l$, $g_l = j_l - in_l$, and j_l, n_l are spherical Bessel functions. Show that the asymptotic form of the wave function for large r is

$$\psi = e^{i\mathbf{k}_0\cdot\mathbf{r}} + \frac{1}{r}e^{ik_0 r}f(\alpha),$$

where

$$f(\alpha) = \frac{1}{2ik_0}\sum_{l=0}^{\infty}(2l+1)[\exp(2i\delta_l) - 1]P_l(\cos\alpha),$$

$$k_0^2 = \frac{2\mu E}{\hbar^2}, \qquad k_I^2 = k_0^2 + \frac{2\mu}{\hbar^2}[V_R + iV_I], \qquad \mu = \frac{A}{A+1}M.$$

3. The finiteness of the wave function of problem 2 at the origin and its normalization imply that the coefficients a_l and η_l can be determined by fitting the internal and external wave functions at $r = R$. The radial wave functions to be fitted are

$$rk_IR_{Il}(r), \qquad rk_0R_{0l}(r),$$

where R_{Il} and R_{0l} refer to respective radial parts of ψ. Show that the phase shifts δ_l and the coefficients a_l are related by

$$\eta_l = \frac{z_0j(z_I)h_{l-1}^*(z_0) - z_Ij_{l-1}(z_I)h_l^*(z_0)}{z_Ij_{l-1}(z_I)h_l(z_0) - z_0j_l(z_I)h_{l-1}(z_0)},$$

$$a_l = \frac{1}{z_I}\left[\frac{ie^{-i\delta_l}}{z_0j_l(z_I)h_{l-1}(z_0) - z_Ij_{l-1}(z_I)h_l(z_0)}\right], \qquad (XVII.2.26)$$

where $z_0 = k_0R$ and $z_I = k_IR$. Compare the scattering cross-section for S and P waves with real and complex potentials.

XVII.3. Scattering of Spinless (Identical) Particles and Mott Scattering

As an example for the scattering of spinless particles we consider the scattering of α particles. We shall assume that the energy of the particles is low enough to neglect nuclear scattering. We shall study only the Coulomb scattering of the particles. Mott and Massey illustrate the scattering of spinless particles with a thought experiment, using two parallel screens with apertures. The wave function before collision is just the product of the wave functions of individual particles:

$$\psi_0(\mathbf{r}_1, \mathbf{r}_2, t) = u_I(\mathbf{r}_1, t)u_{II}(\mathbf{r}_2, t).$$

The wave function after collision, $\psi(\mathbf{r}_1, \mathbf{r}_2, t)$, is the probability amplitude for finding the "first" α particle in the volume element dV_I at time t at the point r_1 and the "second" α particle in the volume element dV_{II} at the same time at the point $\mathbf{r}_2$. With this interpretation of the two-particle wave function —that is, the knowledge that the "first" α particle arrived from the aperture I and the "second" α particle arrived from the aperture II—one can, in accordance with the discussion in Section XII.2, calculate the probability of finding the first or the second one of the particles at $(\mathbf{r}_1, dV_I)$ and $(\mathbf{r}_2, dV_{II})$ at time t as the sum of the probabilities:

$$[|\psi(\mathbf{r}_1, \mathbf{r}_2, t)|^2 + |\psi(\mathbf{r}_2, \mathbf{r}_1, t)|^2]\, dV_I\, dV_{II}. \qquad (XVII.3.1)$$

Obviously this method of interpretation of the wave function does not treat α particles as waves (since the knowledge of their distinguishability as "first" and "second" particle destroys the wave behavior of α particles), and hence no interference of probability amplitudes can occur. The correct procedure is to take into consideration the exchange interaction of identical particles. Thus, if $\psi(\mathbf{r}_1, \mathbf{r}_2, t)$ is the wave function of two α particles (spin zero), the interchange of the particles is equivalent to multiplying the wave function by $(-1)^l$, where l is the orbital angular momentum of the relative motion of the two particles. But α particles obey Bose-Einstein statistics, and therefore under interchange of particles the wave function cannot change its sign. Hence a system of two identical particles with zero spin can assume only even angular momentum.

The correct wave function of a two-particle system with zero spin is given by

$$\psi(\mathbf{r}_1, \mathbf{r}_2, t) = A[u_I(\mathbf{r}_1, t)u_{II}(\mathbf{r}_2, t) + u_I(\mathbf{r}_2, t)u_{II}(\mathbf{r}_1, t)]. \qquad (XVII.3.2)$$

The wave function remains symmetrical at all later times.

Initially the two beams do not overlap, and therefore at time $t = 0$ we must have

$$u_I(\mathbf{r}_1)u_{II}(\mathbf{r}_1) = 0, \qquad (XVII.3.3)$$

since u_{II} at $t = 0$ refers only to the points on the right of aperture II. Thus initially the wave function (*XVII.3.2*), using (*XVII.3.3*), yields the probability

$$|\psi_0(\mathbf{r}_1, \mathbf{r}_2)|^2 = |A|^2|u_I(\mathbf{r}_1)u_{II}(\mathbf{r}_2)|^2 + |A|^2|u_I(\mathbf{r}_2)u_{II}(\mathbf{r}_1)|^2, \qquad (XVII.3.4)$$

where $|\psi_0|^2$ is zero unless $\mathbf{r}_1$ is near I and $\mathbf{r}_2$ near II, or vice versa. This means that $|\psi_0|^2$ is not the probability of finding the particle observed at I in the volume element $(\mathbf{r}_1, dV_I)$ and the particle observed at II in the volume element $(\mathbf{r}_2, dV_{II})$, since the latter probability is zero if $\mathbf{r}_2$ is near I. The quantity $|\psi_0|^2\, dV_I\, dV_{II}$ is to be interpreted as the probability that any one of the α particles can be found in any one of the volume elements. If the initial wave function is ψ_0, then the wave function after time t is

$$\Psi = \psi(\mathbf{r}_1, \mathbf{r}_2, t) + \psi(\mathbf{r}_2, \mathbf{r}_1, t). \qquad (XVII.3.5)$$

The probability that a particle is at $(\mathbf{r}_1, dV_I)$ and the other at $(\mathbf{r}_2, dV_{II})$ is $|\Psi|^2\, dV_I\, dV_{II}$

$$= [|\psi(\mathbf{r}_1, \mathbf{r}_2)|^2 + |\psi(\mathbf{r}_2, \mathbf{r}_1)|^2 + \psi(\mathbf{r}_1, \mathbf{r}_2)\psi^*(\mathbf{r}_2, \mathbf{r}_1) + \psi(\mathbf{r}_2, \mathbf{r}_1)\psi^*(\mathbf{r}_1, \mathbf{r}_2)]\, dV_I\, dV_{II}, \qquad (XVII.3.6)$$

where the time coordinate t is suppressed. The use of the symmetrical wave function does not allow us to assign a probability to finding a particular α particle in the volume element dV_I or dV_{II}. However, if we try to see which α particle is observed, the interaction arising from the act of observation will change the interference terms in (*XVII.3.6*) by some unknown and uncontrollable phase factors [see (XII.2.3)]. For example, by using slow $[(2e)^2/\hbar v \gg 1]$ α particles, it is in principle possible to perform an experiment

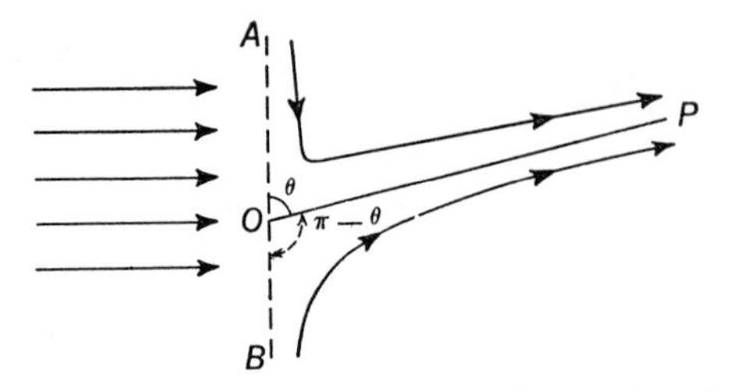

FIG. XVII.1. *Symmetrical scattering of spinless particles.*

where the paths of the wave packets describing the α particles do not overlap at any point. In this case the uncontrollable phases, as in (XII.2.3), will cause the cross-terms in (*XVII.3.6*) to vanish.

Consider now the beam of α particles falling on a slit AB (Fig. 17.1). An α particle may have been deflected through an angle θ from BO or an angle $\pi - \theta$ from AO. The wave equation for the two particles in the center of mass system has the form

$$\nabla^2\psi + \frac{2\mu}{\hbar^2}[E - V(\mathbf{r})]\psi = 0, \qquad (XVII.3.7)$$

where $\mu = \frac{1}{2}m$, $\mathbf{r} = \mathbf{r}_1 - \mathbf{r}_2$, $\mathbf{R} = \frac{1}{2}(\mathbf{r}_1 + \mathbf{r}_2)$, $E = \frac{1}{2}\mu\mathbf{v}^2 = \frac{1}{4}m\mathbf{v}^2$, $V(r)$ = potential energy. The required solution, for a large relative coordinate, must be the sum of a plane incident wave and a scattered spherical wave:

$$\psi \cong e^{ikz} + \frac{1}{r}e^{ikr}f(\theta).$$

If the particles were distinguishable, then the scattering would be described by $|f(\theta)|^2$, and it would be proportional to the probability that the line joining the particles would be deflected by an angle θ. In this case the number of particles scattered along OP would be proportional to

$$|f(\theta)|^2 + |f(\pi - \theta)|^2.$$

This is incorrect, for we must use the symmetrical wave function (*XVII.3.5*) and not the symmetrical probability. In the center of mass system the wave function can be expressed as a product of the center of mass motion and relative motion,

$$\psi(\mathbf{r}_1, \mathbf{r}_2, t) = \psi_C(\mathbf{R})\phi(\mathbf{r}, t), \qquad (XVII.3.8)$$

where, the center of mass being at rest, $\psi_C(\mathbf{R})$ is just a constant factor and ϕ satisfies equation (*XVII.3.7*). The interchange of the particles is equivalent to replacing $\mathbf{r}$ by $-\mathbf{r}$. In polar coordinates, the reflection of coordinates implies replacing θ by $\pi - \theta$. Hence the asymptotic behavior of the scattering beams moving with equal and opposite velocities toward aperture I and II must have the form

$$e^{ikz} + e^{-ikz} + \frac{1}{r}e^{ikr}[f(\theta) + f(\pi - \theta)]. \qquad (XVII.3.9)$$

If each wave for the two beams is normalized to unity in the volumes V_I and V_{II}, then the incident wave

$$e^{ikz} + e^{-ikz} = 2 \cos kz = 2 \cos k(z_1 - z_2)$$

is such that

$$\int |2 \cos kz|^2 \, dV_I \, dV_{II} = 2,$$

representing one particle per unit area in each beam. From (*XVII.3.9*) it follows that the effective cross-section for a collision in which either particle is deflected into the solid angle $d\Omega$ is

$$\sigma(\theta) \, d\Omega = |f(\theta) + f(\pi - \theta)|^2 \, d\Omega. \qquad (XVII.3.10)$$

If one of the particles is initially at rest, then the differential cross-sections $\sigma_L(\Theta)$ and $\sigma_{CM}(\theta)$ in the laboratory and center of mass systems, respectively, are related by

$$\sigma_L(\Theta) \sin \Theta \, d\Theta = \sigma_{CM}(\theta) \sin \theta \, d\theta,$$

where

$$\tan \Theta = \frac{\sin \theta}{b + \cos \theta} = \frac{2 \sin \frac{\theta}{2} \cos \frac{\theta}{2}}{2 \cos^2 \frac{\theta}{2}} = \tan \frac{1}{2} \theta,$$

$$b = \frac{m_2}{m_1} = 1.$$

Hence

$$\Theta = \tfrac{1}{2}\theta$$

and

$$\sigma_L(\Theta) = \sigma_{CM}(2\theta) 4 \cos \theta. \qquad (XVII.3.11)$$

Hence the cross-section for differential scattering is given by

$$\sigma(\Theta) \, d\Omega = |f(2\Theta) + f(\pi - 2\Theta)|^2 4 \cos \Theta \, d\Omega. \qquad (XVII.3.12)$$

For the Coulomb scattering of slow α particles, we use the expression for $f(\Theta)$ and obtain

$$\sigma(\Theta) = \left(\frac{Z^2 e^2}{m v^2}\right)^2 (\operatorname{cosec}^4 \Theta + \sec^4 \Theta + 2\Lambda \operatorname{cosec}^2 \Theta \sec^2 \Theta) 4 \cos \Theta, \qquad (XVII.3.13)$$

where

$$\Lambda = \cos [a \log (\tan^2 \Theta],$$

in which $a = Z^2 e^2 / \hbar v$.

We observe that in Coulomb scattering of identical particles the differential cross-section is not independent of $\hbar$. This is expected, since the concept of Bose-Einstein statistic is only quantum mechanical. It is purely a nonclassical effect.

The ratio of quantum and classical cross-sections

$$\frac{\sigma_q}{\sigma_c} = \frac{\operatorname{cosec}^4 \Theta + \sec^4 \Theta + 2\Lambda \operatorname{cosec}^2 \Theta \sec^2 \Theta}{\operatorname{cosec}^4 \Theta + \sec^4 \Theta}$$

$$= 1 + 2\Lambda \frac{\sin^2 \Theta \cos^2 \Theta}{1 - 2 \sin^2 \Theta \cos^2 \Theta}$$

at $\Theta = 45°$ yields

$$\sigma_q = 2\sigma_c, \qquad (XVII.3.14)$$

so in a quantum treatment twice as many particles will be scattered as under classical theory.

XVII.3.A. Scattering of Particles with Spin $\frac{1}{2}\hbar$

We must use an antisymmetrical wave function to describe a collision. The state before the collision can be defined by

$$|\psi_0\rangle = |u(1)\rangle|v(2)\rangle|a(1)\rangle|b(2)\rangle - |u(2)\rangle|v(1)\rangle|a(2)\rangle|b(1)\rangle, \qquad (XVII.3.15)$$

where $|u\rangle$ and $|v\rangle$ are unit vectors in the two-dimensional spin spaces, referring to the spin states of the two identical particles, and $|a\rangle$ and $|b\rangle$ refer to states other than spin. The state after the collision, neglecting the small relativistic effect due to the possibility that spins may change their average directions, is given by

$$|\boldsymbol{\Psi}\rangle = |u(1)\rangle|v(2)\rangle|\boldsymbol{\Phi}(12)\rangle - |u(2)\rangle|v(1)\rangle|\boldsymbol{\Phi}(21)\rangle, \qquad (XVII.3.16)$$

where $|\boldsymbol{\Phi}(12)\rangle$ is the space part of the wave function. It will be convenient to rearrange (*XVII.3.16*) in such a way that symmetric and antisymmetric spin and space wave functions occur explicitly and write

$$|\boldsymbol{\Psi}\rangle = \tfrac{1}{2}[|u(1)\rangle|v(2)\rangle - |u(2)\rangle|v(1)\rangle]|\boldsymbol{\Phi}_S\rangle + \tfrac{1}{2}[|u(1)\rangle|v(2)\rangle + |u(2)\rangle|v(1)\rangle]|\boldsymbol{\Phi}_A\rangle, \qquad (XVII.3.17)$$

where

$$|\boldsymbol{\Phi}_S\rangle = |\boldsymbol{\Phi}(12)\rangle + |\boldsymbol{\Phi}(21)\rangle, \qquad |\boldsymbol{\Phi}_A\rangle = |\boldsymbol{\Phi}(12)\rangle - |\boldsymbol{\Phi}(21)\rangle.$$

Let the average directions of the two spins be represented by the unit vectors $\boldsymbol{u}$ and $\boldsymbol{v}$ with polar coordinates (θ, ϕ) and (θ', ϕ'), respectively. From (*IX.3.15*) we may write

$$\begin{aligned}
|u(1)\rangle &= \cos\frac{\theta}{2}\,|1\rangle + e^{i\phi}\sin\frac{\theta}{2}\,|-1\rangle \\
|u(2)\rangle &= \cos\frac{\theta}{2}\,|1'\rangle + e^{i\phi}\sin\frac{\theta}{2}\,|-1'\rangle \\
|v(1)\rangle &= \cos\frac{\theta'}{2}\,|1\rangle + e^{i\phi'}\sin\frac{\theta'}{2}\,|-1\rangle \\
|v(2)\rangle &= \cos\frac{\theta'}{2}\,|1'\rangle + e^{i\phi'}\sin\frac{\theta'}{2}\,|-1'\rangle,
\end{aligned} \qquad (XVII.3.18)$$

where $|\pm 1\rangle$ and $|\pm 1'\rangle$ are eigenstates of σ_{1z} and σ_{2z}. Hence

$$\langle\boldsymbol{\Psi}|K|\boldsymbol{\Psi}\rangle = \tfrac{1}{4}(1 - \cos\Theta)\langle\boldsymbol{\Phi}_S|K|\boldsymbol{\Phi}_S\rangle + \tfrac{1}{4}(3 + \cos\Theta)\langle\boldsymbol{\Phi}_A|K|\boldsymbol{\Phi}_A\rangle, \qquad (XVII.3.19)$$

where the operator K is defined by

$$K = \delta(\boldsymbol{r}_1 - \boldsymbol{q}_1)\delta(\boldsymbol{r}_2 - \boldsymbol{q}_2) \qquad (XVII.3.20)$$

and where we use the relation

$$\left|\cos\frac{\theta}{2}\cos\frac{\theta'}{2} + \sin\frac{\theta}{2}\sin\frac{\theta'}{2}\, e^{i(\phi'-\phi)}\right|^2$$

$$= \tfrac{1}{2}[1 + \cos\theta\cos\theta' + \sin\theta\sin\theta'\cos(\phi - \phi')] = \tfrac{1}{2}(1 + \cos\Theta),$$

with Θ = angle between the average directions of the spins, and

$$\cos\Theta = \boldsymbol{u}\cdot\boldsymbol{v} = \cos\theta\cos\theta' + \sin\theta\sin\theta'\cos(\phi - \phi').$$

The expectation value of K with respect to the two-particle state $|\boldsymbol{\Psi}\rangle$ is the probability that one particle is in the volume element dV_I at $\boldsymbol{r}_1$ and the other in the volume element dV_{II} at $\boldsymbol{r}_2$:

$$\langle\boldsymbol{\Psi}|K|\boldsymbol{\Psi}\rangle = \tfrac{1}{4}(1 - \cos\Theta)\int \langle\boldsymbol{\Phi}_S|\boldsymbol{r}_1', \boldsymbol{r}_2'\rangle\, d^3\boldsymbol{x}_1'\, d^3\boldsymbol{x}_2'\, \langle\boldsymbol{r}_1', \boldsymbol{r}_2'|K|\boldsymbol{\Phi}_S\rangle$$
$$+ \tfrac{1}{4}(3 + \cos\Theta)\int \langle\boldsymbol{\Phi}_A|\boldsymbol{r}_1', \boldsymbol{r}_2'\rangle\, d^3\boldsymbol{x}_1'\, d^3\boldsymbol{x}_2'\, \langle\boldsymbol{r}_1', \boldsymbol{r}_2'|K|\boldsymbol{\Phi}_A\rangle = \tfrac{1}{4}(1 - \cos\Theta)P_S$$
$$+ \tfrac{1}{4}(3 + \cos\Theta)P_A, \qquad (XVII.3.21)$$

where

$$P_S = \int \langle\Phi_S|\boldsymbol{r}_1', \boldsymbol{r}_2'\rangle\, d^3\boldsymbol{x}_1'\, d^3\boldsymbol{x}_2'\, \langle\boldsymbol{r}_1', \boldsymbol{r}_2'|K|\Phi_S\rangle$$
$$= \int \langle\boldsymbol{\Phi}_S|\boldsymbol{r}_1', \boldsymbol{r}_2'\rangle\, d^3\boldsymbol{x}_1'\, d^3\boldsymbol{x}_2'\, \delta(\boldsymbol{r}_1 - \boldsymbol{r}_1')\delta(\boldsymbol{r}_2 - \boldsymbol{r}_2')\langle\boldsymbol{r}_1', \boldsymbol{r}_2'|\boldsymbol{\Phi}_S\rangle$$
$$= \langle\boldsymbol{\Phi}_S|\boldsymbol{r}_1, \boldsymbol{r}_2\rangle\langle\boldsymbol{r}_1, \boldsymbol{r}_2|\boldsymbol{\Phi}_S\rangle = |\Phi(12) + \Phi(21)|^2 \qquad (XVII.3.22)$$

and

$$P_A = |\Phi(12) - \Phi(21)|^2. \qquad (XVII.3.23)$$

If Θ is not known—that is, if the two colliding beams are unpolarized—then we must average (*XVII.3.19*) over all the $\cos\Theta$ and obtain

$$\frac{1}{\pi}\int_0^\pi \langle\boldsymbol{\Psi}|K|\boldsymbol{\Psi}\rangle\, d\Theta = \tfrac{1}{4}[P_S + 3P_A]. \qquad (XVII.3.24)$$

The differential cross-section in the center of mass system is

$$\sigma_{CM}(\theta) = \sigma_S(\theta) + 3\sigma_A(\theta), \qquad (XVII.3.25)$$

where

$$\sigma_S(\theta) = |f(2\theta) + f(\pi - 2\theta)|^2 4\cos\theta,$$
$$\sigma_A(\theta) = |f(2\theta) - f(\pi - 2\theta)|^2 4\cos\theta. \qquad (XVII.3.26)$$

If the spins are in the same direction (triplet spin state scattering) then $\cos\theta = 1$, and for singlet spin state $\cos\theta = -1$. The number scattered into a solid angle element $d\Omega$ is, in the triplet state,

$$\langle\boldsymbol{\Psi}|K|\boldsymbol{\Psi}\rangle_T = P_A, \qquad (XVII.3.27)$$

and, in the singlet state,

$$\langle\boldsymbol{\Psi}|K|\boldsymbol{\Psi}\rangle_s = \tfrac{1}{2}(P_A + P_S) = \tfrac{1}{2}[\sigma_S(\theta) + \sigma_A(\theta)]. \qquad (XVII.3.28)$$

We can apply the above results to proton-proton (or electron-electron) scattering where, in addition to Coulomb scattering, protons suffer a nuclear scattering. For a pure Coulomb scattering of protons Mott's formulas (*XVII.3.24*) for singlet and triplet spin states gives the differential cross-sections $\sigma_S(\theta)$ and $\sigma_A(\theta)$, defined by (*XVII.3.26*), and the asymptotic form of the Coulomb wave function* yields

$$\sigma_c(\theta) = \frac{e^4}{M^2v^4}\{\operatorname{cosec}^4\theta + \sec^4\theta - \cos[a \log(\tan^2\theta)] \operatorname{cosec}^2\theta \sec^2\theta\}, \tag{XVII.3.29}$$

where we use (*XVII.3.22*) and

$$P_S = \frac{e^4}{M^2v^4}\left\{\operatorname{cosec}^4\theta + \sec^4\theta + 2\cos\left[\frac{e^2}{\hbar v}\log(\tan^2\theta)\right]\right\}, \tag{XVII.3.30}$$

$$P_A = \frac{e^4}{M^2v^4}\left\{\operatorname{cosec}^4\theta + \sec^4\theta - 2\cos\left[\frac{e^2}{\hbar v}\log(\tan^2\theta)\right]\right\}. \tag{XVII.3.31}$$

However, the angular distribution $\sigma_c(\theta)$ arising from the Coulomb repulsion of protons will determine the scattering so long as the colliding protons do not see each other's nuclear field. We can estimate the closest distance at which the nuclear force will take over from the Coulomb repulsion, by noting that in a head-on collision (with $l = 0$), with a kinetic energy E of the protons, the closest approach can be defined by $E = e^2/r_c$. Thus, for

$$r_c = \frac{e^2}{mc^2}\frac{mc^2}{E} = \frac{e^2}{mc^2}\frac{[\frac{1}{2}\text{mev}]}{E}$$

to be of the order of the range of nuclear forces, E must be of the order of $\frac{1}{2}$ mev.

Finally, we must observe the following points.

(a) From the definitions (*XVII.3.22*) and (*XVII.3.23*), or from (*XVII.3.26*), we see that an interference term $f(2\theta)f^*(\pi - 2\theta) + f^*(2\theta)f(\pi - 2\theta)$ occurs in the cross-section. This term characterizes the exchange interaction. In classical mechanics the particles are distinguishable and the resulting probability is just $\frac{1}{2}(P_A + P_S)$; compare with Figs. XII.5 and XII.6.

(b) If S is the spin in the scattering process, then there exist $(2S + 1)^2$ different spin states; see problems 1, 2, 4 of Section IV.3.B. Of these, $S(2S + 1)$ correspond to states with even spin and $(S + 1)\,(2S + 1)$ to odd spin for half-integral S; the converse holds for integral S.

Using problem 1 of Section XIV.6.B, show that the scattering probabilities of the two particles in even and odd spin states are $S(2S + 1)/(2S + 1)^2$

---

* For the general form of a Coulomb wave function consult Mott and Massey, *Theory of Atomic Collisions*, Oxford Univ. Press, Oxford, 1949.

and $(S+1)(2S+1)/(2S+1)^2$, respectively. Hence the cross-section can be expressed as

$$\sigma(\theta) = \frac{S}{2S+1}\sigma_S(\theta) + \frac{S+1}{2S+1}\sigma_A(\theta) \qquad (XVII.3.32)$$

for half-integral S and as

$$\sigma(\theta) = \frac{S+1}{2S+1}\sigma_S(\theta) + \frac{S}{2S+1}\sigma_A(\theta) \qquad (XVII.3.33)$$

for integral S. The two limiting cases in (*XVII.2.27*) are (a) $e^2/\hbar v \ll 1$, which gives $\sigma(\theta) = (2e^2/Mv^2)^2(1 + 3\cos^2\theta)/\sin^4\theta$, and (b) $e^2/\hbar v \gg 1$, in which the average value of the third term in (*XVII.2.27*) vanishes, yielding the classical formula.

CHAPTER XVIII

THE FORMAL THEORY OF SCATTERING

XVIII.1. The S Matrix

In a scattering process one is interested in a transition from a noninteracting state into another noninteracting state of two colliding systems. In other words, the scattering process is a transition from a state where particles are approaching each other to a state where particles are receding from each other. An elegant formulation of the scattering theory has been given by Lippman and Schwinger and a more general approach is contained in a paper by Gell-Mann and Goldberger.*

The total Hamiltonian $H = H_0 + H'$ is assumed to have a continuous spectrum of eigenvalues. For more general problems a discrete spectrum is superimposed over the continuum spectrum. If $|\zeta t\rangle$ describes the state at time t and $|It\rangle$ the corresponding interaction picture state vector, then we have the equations

$$i\hbar \frac{d}{dt}|\zeta, t\rangle = H|\zeta, t\rangle, \qquad (XVIII.1.1)$$

$$i\hbar \frac{d}{dt}|I, t\rangle = H_I(t)|I, t\rangle \qquad (XVIII.1.2)$$

where

$$|\zeta, t\rangle = e^{-(i/\hbar)tH_0}|I, t\rangle, \qquad (XVIII.1.3)$$

$$H_I(t) = e^{(i/\hbar)tH_0}H'e^{-(i/\hbar)tH_0}, \qquad (XVIII.1.4)$$

so at $t = 0$ we have

$$|\zeta, 0\rangle = |I, 0\rangle.$$

In the absence of interaction the Schrödinger equation can be solved in the form

$$|\zeta_0, t\rangle = |E, t\rangle = e^{-(i/\hbar)tH_0}|E\rangle = e^{-(i/\hbar)tE}|E\rangle, \qquad (XVIII.1.5)$$

---

* A. Lippmann and J. Schwinger, *Phys. Rev.*, **79** (1950), 469.
M. L. Goldberger and M. Gell-Mann, *Phys. Rev.*, **91** (1953), 398.

where $|E\rangle$ is an eigenstate of H_0 with eigenvalue E. We may use the eigenstate $|E\rangle$ of H_0 at the infinite past to set up a representation. The transition from an initial state $|E_0\rangle$ to a final state $|E_F\rangle$ is caused by the interaction H'. From the rate of transition we can determine the differential cross-section. The meaning of the statement of "an initial state $|E_0\rangle$ with energy E_0" was discussed in the formulation of the time-dependent perturbation theory and it will not be elaborated any further at this point.

Consider the unitary operator

$$U(t, t_0) = \int |I,t\rangle\, dI\, \langle I,t_0|, \qquad (XVIII.1.6)$$

such that it can operate on a state $|It_0\rangle$ at time t_0 to produce the state $|I, t\rangle$ at time t,

$$|I, t\rangle = U(t, t_0)|I, t_0\rangle, \qquad (XVIII.1.7)$$

where I labels the state. (It can be taken to be the energy eigen-value of the system.)

The unitary operator $U(t, t_0)$ satisfies the integral equation [see (*I.7.3*)],

$$U(t, t_0) = 1 - \frac{i}{\hbar} \int_{t_0}^{t} \epsilon_+(t, t') H_I(t') U(t', t_0)\, dt', \qquad (XVIII.1.8)$$

which takes account of the direction of flow of time ($t > t_0$). A formal solution of (*XVIII.1.8*), as discussed for the time-dependent orthogonal transformations [see (*I.7.9*)], is given by a time-ordered exponential

$$U(t, t_0) = P \exp\left[-\frac{i}{\hbar} \int_{t_0}^{t} H_I(t')\, dt'\right], \qquad (XVIII.1.9)$$

where the operator P is that defined in Section I.7.

The initially noninteracting parts of the system will be represented by a state vector $|I, -\infty\rangle$. The state $|I, t\rangle$ at a time t is to be obtained from $|I, -\infty\rangle$ by operating with $U(t, t_0)$ on $|I, -\infty\rangle$ at $t_0 = -\infty$. In the limit $t_0 = -\infty$ the operator $U(t, t_0)$ will contain some oscillatory terms. These terms must vanish to insure the existence of the limit of $U(t, t_0)$ for $t_0 \longrightarrow -\infty$. A discussion of this point, in great detail, is given by Gell-Mann and Goldberger, but it is not needed for our present aims. We shall simply set $t_0 = -\infty$ and from (*XVIII.1.8*) we obtain

$$U(t, -\infty) = 1 - \frac{i}{\hbar} \int_{-\infty}^{t} \epsilon_+(t, t') H_I(t') U(t', -\infty)\, dt'. \qquad (XVIII.1.10)$$

A special form of the unitary operator U is the so-called S matrix, which relates states at an infinite past to states at an infinite future. Formally, it can be defined from (*XVIII.1.9*), as

$$S = U(\infty, -\infty) = P \exp\left[-\frac{i}{\hbar} \int_{-\infty}^{\infty} H_I(t')\, dt'\right]. \qquad (XVIII.1.11)$$

Another symbolic definition for a spectrum of continuum eigenstates is

$$S = \int |I, \infty\rangle \, dI \, \langle I, -\infty|, \qquad (XVIII.1.12)$$

where $|I, \infty\rangle$ represents the final state corresponding to interaction and eventual separation of the systems. The state $|I, t\rangle$ at any time t is obtained from the state at infinite past $|I, -\infty\rangle$, by operating on $|I, -\infty\rangle$ with $U(t, -\infty)$:

$$|I, t\rangle = U(t, -\infty)|I, -\infty\rangle. \qquad (XVIII.1.13)$$

Hence

$$|I, \infty\rangle = S|I, -\infty\rangle. \qquad (XVIII.1.14)$$

Furthermore, the unitary operator $U(t, \infty)$, which generates the state $|I, t\rangle$ from the final state $|I, \infty\rangle$, is defined by

$$U(t, \infty) = \int |I, t\rangle \, dI \, \langle I, \infty|. \qquad (XVIII.1.15)$$

Thus

$$|I, t\rangle = U(t, \infty)|I, \infty\rangle. \qquad (XVIII.1.16)$$

From these definitions it follows that

$$U(t, \infty)S = \int |I, t\rangle \, dI \, \langle I, \infty|I', \infty\rangle \, dI' \, \langle I', -\infty|$$

$$= \int |I, t\rangle \, dI \, \langle I, -\infty|.$$

(For bound states the vectors $|I, \infty\rangle$ do not form a complete set, since the $|I, \infty\rangle$ are orthogonal to all bound states.) Hence

$$U(t, \infty)S = U(t, -\infty). \qquad (XVIII.1.17)$$

If we make $t \longrightarrow -\infty$ and noting that $U(-\infty, -\infty) = 1$, we obtain

$$U(-\infty, \infty) = S^{-1} = S^{\dagger}. \qquad (XVIII.1.18)$$

The above procedure is, of course, equivalent to a time-reversal operation.

XVIII.1.A. The Calculation of Scattering Cross-Section

In the representation constructed from the eigenfunctions of H_0 we can form matrix elements (or representatives) of the S matrix and calculate the transition probabilities. However, we must first observe that the final state $|I, \infty\rangle$ must not be regarded as an exact eigenstate of H_0; after the scattering the separation of the two interacting parts implies a localizability of the two free parts of the system. This localization can be described in terms of wave packets formed from a superposition of momentum states. In the center of mass system the two parts of the system can be regarded as a plane wave, so the probability of finding the center of mass in any specified volume, when observation of its position is made, is independent of the location of the volume. But a superposition of momenta enables us to form a wave packet for the description of the center of mass of the two parts of the system. This can represent the final state, without being an exact eigenstate of H_0. We can, however, find a procedure equivalent to a wave packet description of the final state by using an eigenfunction $|E_F\rangle$ of H_0 and by simulating the cessation of interaction, arising from the separation of the component parts of the system, by an adiabatic decrease in the interaction strength as $t \longrightarrow \pm\infty$. This can be achieved by using a function $\exp\,[-(\epsilon/\hbar)|t|]$ where ϵ is a small positive number.

Now let $|E_0\rangle = |I, -\infty\rangle$ be the initial state of the system which is also an eigenstate of H_0. The change in the state caused by the interaction can be described by the operator

$$\boldsymbol{T} = S - 1. \qquad (XVIII.1.19)$$

From the unitary property of S we have

$$\boldsymbol{T}^\dagger\boldsymbol{T} = -(\boldsymbol{T}^\dagger + \boldsymbol{T}). \qquad (XVIII.1.20)$$

The probability that the system will be found in a particular final state differing from the initial one is

$$\boldsymbol{T}_{FO} = \langle E_F|\boldsymbol{T}|E_O\rangle \qquad (XVIII.1.21)$$

From $(XVIII.1.10)$, setting $t = \infty$, we write

$$S = 1 - \frac{i}{\hbar}\int_{-\infty}^{\infty} dt\, H_I(t)U(t, -\infty). \qquad (XVIII.1.22)$$

Hence

$$\boldsymbol{T}_{FO} = -\frac{i}{\hbar}\langle E_F|\int_{-\infty}^{\infty} dt\, H(t)U(t, -\infty)|E_0\rangle. \qquad (XVIII.1.23)$$

To be consistent with the adiabatic switch-off of the interaction we must insert the factor $\exp\,[-(\epsilon/\hbar)|t|]$ and write

$$\boldsymbol{T}_{FO} = -\frac{i}{\hbar}\langle E_F|H'|E_{F^+}\rangle, \qquad (XVIII.1.24)$$

where

$$|E_{F^+}\rangle = \int_{-\infty}^{\infty} dt \exp\left[\frac{it}{\hbar}(E_F - H_0)\right] \exp\left(-\frac{\epsilon}{\hbar}|t|\right)U(t, -\infty)|E_0\rangle. \qquad (XVIII.1.25)$$

In a similar way we have

$$\langle E_F|\boldsymbol{T}^\dagger|E_0\rangle = \frac{i}{\hbar}\langle E_F|H'|E_{F^-}\rangle, \qquad (XVIII.1.26)$$

where

$$|E_{F^-}\rangle = \int_{-\infty}^{\infty} dt \exp\left[\frac{it}{\hbar}(E_F - H_0)\right] \exp\left(-\frac{\epsilon}{\hbar}|t|\right) U(t, \infty)|E_0\rangle. \qquad (XVIII.1.27)$$

To derive an integral equation for $|E_{F^+}\rangle$ we use equation (*XVIII.1.10*). Thus, introducing (*XVIII.1.10*) into the right side of (*XVIII.1.25*), we obtain

$$|E_{F^+}\rangle = \int_{-\infty}^{\infty} dt \exp\left[\frac{it}{\hbar}(E_F - E_0) - \frac{\epsilon}{\hbar}|t|\right]|E_0\rangle$$
$$-\frac{i}{\hbar}\int_0^{\infty} d\tau \exp\left[\frac{i\tau}{\hbar}(E_F - H_0) - \frac{\epsilon}{\hbar}\tau\right]H'|E_{F^+}\rangle,$$

where $\tau = |t - t'|$. Similarly,

$$|E_{F^-}\rangle = \int_{-\infty}^{\infty} dt \exp\left[\frac{it}{\hbar}(E_F - E_0) - \frac{\epsilon}{\hbar}|t|\right]|E_0\rangle$$
$$+\frac{i}{\hbar}\int_0^{\infty} d\tau \exp\left[-\frac{i\tau}{\hbar}(E_F - H_0) - \frac{\epsilon}{\hbar}\tau\right]H'|E_{F^-}\rangle.$$

Carrying out the time integrations we obtain the integral equations

$$|E_{F^\mp}\rangle = 2\pi\hbar\delta(E_F - E_0)|E_0\rangle + \frac{1}{E_F \mp i\epsilon - H_0}H'|E_{F^\mp}\rangle. \qquad (XVIII.1.28)$$

We may introduce the states $|\mp\rangle$ by

$$|E_{F^\mp}\rangle = 2\pi\hbar\delta(E_F - E_0)|\mp\rangle$$

and reduce the integral equations (*XVIII.1.28*) to

$$|\mp\rangle = |E_0\rangle + \frac{1}{E_F \mp i\epsilon - H_0}H'|\mp\rangle. \qquad (XVIII.1.29)$$

These same equations could be obtained by solving the Schrödinger equation

$$(E - H_0)|\zeta_0\rangle = H'|\zeta_0\rangle$$

in the form

$$|\zeta_0, \mp\rangle = |E_0\rangle + \frac{1}{E \mp i\epsilon - H_0}H'|\zeta_0, \mp\rangle,$$

where the total Hamiltonian H is time-independent.

The integral equations (*XVIII.1.29*) provide a time-independent formulation of the scattering theory. The small positive and negative imaginary parts in the denominator serve to select outgoing or incoming scattered waves, respectively.

In terms of the state vectors $|+\rangle$ and $|-\rangle$, the representatives of $\boldsymbol{T}$ can be expressed as

$$\begin{aligned} \boldsymbol{T}_{FO} &= -2\pi i\delta(E_F - E_0)\langle E_F|H'|+\rangle \\ &= -2\pi i\delta(E_F - E_0)\langle -|H'|E_0\rangle. \end{aligned} \qquad (XVIII.1.30)$$

The transition probability is given by

$$W_{FO} = 4\pi^2[\delta(E_F - E_0)]^2|\langle E_F|H'|+\rangle|^2. \qquad (XVIII.1.31)$$

From the definition

$$\delta(E_F - E_0) = \lim_{\epsilon\to 0}\frac{1}{2\pi\hbar}\int_{-\infty}^{\infty} \exp\left[\frac{i}{\hbar}t(E_F - E_O) - \frac{\epsilon}{\hbar}|t|\right]dt,$$

we obtain

$$[\delta(E_F - E_0)]^2 = \frac{1}{2\pi\hbar}\,\delta(E_F - E_0)\int_{-\infty}^{\infty} dt.$$

Hence

$$W_{FO} = \frac{2\pi}{\hbar}\,\delta(E_F - E_0)|\langle E_F|H'|+\rangle|^2 \int_{-\infty}^{\infty} dt. \qquad (XVIII.1.32)$$

This formula shows that the only contributions to the transitions come from the equal energies in the initial and final states. The integral $\int_{-\infty}^{\infty} dt$ represents the total time of effective interaction. The transition probability per unit time is then given by

$$W'_{FO} = \frac{W_{FO}}{\int_{-\infty}^{\infty} dt} = \frac{2\pi}{\hbar}\,\delta(E_F - E_0)|\langle E_F|H'|+\rangle|^2. \qquad (XVIII.1.33)$$

Lippmann and Schwinger gave a second derivation of (*XVIII.1.33*) by evaluating

$$W'_{FO} = \frac{\partial}{\partial t}\,[|\langle E_F|U(t, -\infty)|E_0\rangle|^2]. \qquad (XVIII.1.34)$$

This expresses the increase per unit time of the probability that the system starting in a state $|E_0\rangle$ will be found at time t in a state $|E_F\rangle$. Thus

$$\begin{aligned} W'_{FO} &= \frac{\partial}{\partial t}\,[\langle E_F|U(t, -\infty)|E_0\rangle\langle E_0|U^\dagger(t, -\infty)|E_F\rangle] \\ &= \langle E_F|\,\frac{\partial}{\partial t}\,U(t, -\infty)|E_0\rangle\langle E_0|U^\dagger(t, -\infty)|E_F\rangle \\ &\qquad + \langle E_F|U(t, -\infty)|E_0\rangle\langle E_0|\,\frac{\partial U^\dagger(t, -\infty)}{\partial t}\,|E_F\rangle \\ &= \frac{i}{\hbar}\,\langle E_F|U(t, -\infty)H_I(t)|E_0\rangle\langle E_0|U^\dagger(t, -\infty)|E_F\rangle + \text{complex conjugate}. \end{aligned}$$

Using the definition of $H_I(t)$ we obtain

$$\begin{aligned} W'_{FO} = \frac{1}{\hbar^2}\int_{-\infty}^{t} dt'\,\langle E_0|U^\dagger(t, -\infty)e^{-(it/\hbar)(E_F - H_0)}H'|E_F\rangle \\ \times\,\langle E_F|H'e^{(it'/\hbar)(E_F - H_0)}U(t', -\infty)|E_0\rangle + \text{complex conjugate}. \end{aligned}$$

From (*XVIII.1.25*) and the definition of $|+\rangle$ we obtain

$$\begin{aligned} &\int_{-\infty}^{\infty} dt\, e^{(i/\hbar)t(E_F - H_0) - (\epsilon/\hbar)|t|}U(t, -\infty)|E_0\rangle \\ &\qquad = 2\pi\hbar\delta(E_F - E_0)|+\rangle = \lim_{\epsilon\to 0}\int_{-\infty}^{\infty} e^{(it/\hbar)(E_F - E_0) - (\epsilon/\hbar)|t|}\,dt|+\rangle. \end{aligned}$$

Hence

$$e^{-(i/\hbar)tH_0}U(t, -\infty)|E_0\rangle = e^{-(it/\hbar)E_0}|+\rangle.$$

This is the state vector in Schrödinger's picture. The above results can be combined into

$$W'_{FO} = \frac{1}{\hbar^2} |\langle E_F|H'|+\rangle|^2 \int_{-\infty}^{\infty} dt'\, e^{[i(t-t')/\hbar](E_F-E_0)} + \text{complex conjugate.}$$

We multiply W'_{FO} by the density of the final states ρ_F and integrate over the final energies to obtain the transition probability per unit time in the form

$$W'_{FO} = \frac{2\pi}{\hbar} |\langle E_F|H'|+\rangle|^2 \rho_F. \qquad (XVIII.1.35)$$

The first- and second-order transition probabilities can be obtained by iterating the integral equation for $|+\rangle$ and substituting in (*XVIII.1.35*). Thus, neglecting higher-order transitions in H', we have

$$\underset{}{W_{FO}} = \underset{1}{W_{FO}} + \underset{2}{W_{FO}}, \qquad (XVIII.1.36)$$

where

$$\underset{1}{W_{FO}} = \frac{2\pi}{\hbar} |\langle E_F|H'|E_0\rangle|^2 \rho_F$$

and

$$\underset{2}{W_{FO}} = \frac{2\pi}{\hbar} |\langle E_F|H' \frac{1}{E_F + i\epsilon - H_0} H'|E_0\rangle|^2 \rho_F$$

$$= \frac{2\pi}{\hbar} \left| \sum_I \langle E_F|H'|E_I\rangle\langle E_I| \frac{1}{E_F + i\epsilon - H_0} H'|E_0\rangle \right|^2 \rho_F$$

$$= \frac{2\pi}{\hbar} \left| \sum_I \frac{H'_{FI} H'_{IO}}{E_F - E_I} \right|^2 \rho_F. \qquad (XVIII.1.37)$$

These results were also obtained previously in the time-dependent perturbation theory.

If v is the relative velocity of the colliding systems, then the differential cross-section for the transition $|E_0\rangle \longrightarrow |E_F\rangle$—or the effective area that must be hit by an incident particle in order to be scattered in a unit solid angle about the direction of the final relative momentum—is equal to the transition rate divided by v. Hence the final result is

$$\sigma_{FO} = \frac{2\pi}{\hbar v} |\langle E_F|H'|+\rangle|^2 \rho_F. \qquad (XVIII.1.38)$$

XVIII.2. The S Matrix and the Phase Shift

The relation of the S matrix to the phase shift in a scattering process can, most conveniently, be developed in terms of a Hermitian reaction operator K defined by [see (*I.7.10*)]

$$S = \frac{I - \frac{1}{2}iK}{I + \frac{1}{2}iK}. \qquad (XVIII.2.1)$$

We shall introduce a phase shift operator Δ by the relation

$$\tfrac{1}{2}K = -\tan\Delta \qquad (XVIII.2.2)$$

and obtain the S matrix in the form

$$S = \exp(2i\Delta), \qquad (XVIII.2.3)$$

so

$$\boldsymbol{T} = S - I = 2i\sin\Delta\, e^{i\Delta}. \qquad (XVIII.2.4)$$

The relation of the phase shift operator Δ to the actual phase shift in a scattering process can be found by studying the representatives of K in a given representation.

Let us assume that $U(t, -\infty)$ can be written as

$$U(t, -\infty) = V(t)M, \qquad (XVIII.2.5)$$

where M is a constant operator. Putting $t = \infty$ and $t = -\infty$, and using $U(\infty, -\infty) = S$, $U(-\infty, -\infty) = 1$, we obtain $S = V(\infty)M$ and $1 = V(-\infty)M$. Hence

$$S = \frac{V(\infty)}{V(-\infty)}, \qquad (XVIII.2.6)$$

which suggests the substitutions $V(\infty) = 1 - \tfrac{1}{2}iK$ and $V(-\infty) = 1 + \tfrac{1}{2}iK$. Hence $M = \tfrac{1}{2}(1 + S)$. Then

$$U(t, -\infty) = \tfrac{1}{2}V(t)(1 + S) \qquad (XVIII.2.7)$$

$$U(t, +\infty) = \tfrac{1}{2}V(t)(1 + S^{-1}). \qquad (XVIII.2.8)$$

With these results the integral equations for $U(t, -\infty)$ and $U(t, +\infty)$ become integral equations for $V(t)$. Thus

$$V(t) = V(-\infty) - \frac{i}{\hbar}\int_{-\infty}^{t} H_I(t')V(t')\,dt',$$

$$V(t) = V(\infty) + \frac{i}{\hbar}\int_{t}^{\infty} H_I(t')V(t')\,dt'.$$

By adding these two equations and using $V(-\infty) + V(\infty) = 2$, we get

$$V(t) = 1 - \frac{i}{2\hbar}\int_{-\infty}^{\infty} \eta(t - t')H_I(t')V(t')\,dt', \qquad (XVIII.2.9)$$

where the step function $\eta(t - t')$ is defined by

$$\eta(t - t') = \begin{cases} +1 & \text{if } t > t', \\ -1 & \text{if } t < t'. \end{cases}$$

The expression for K is

$$K = i[V(\infty) - V(-\infty)] = \frac{1}{\hbar}\int_{-\infty}^{\infty} H_I(t)V(t)\,dt. \qquad (XVIII.2.10)$$

The representatives of K are given by

$$K_{FO} = \langle E_F|K|E_O|\rangle = \frac{1}{\hbar}\langle E_F|\int_{-\infty}^{\infty} dt\, e^{(it/\hbar)H_0}H' \times e^{-(it/\hbar)H_0}V(t)|E_O\rangle = \frac{1}{\hbar}\langle E_F|H'|E'\rangle, \qquad (XVIII.2.11)$$

where

$$|E'\rangle = \int_{-\infty}^{\infty} dt \exp\left[\frac{it}{\hbar}(E_F - H_0) - \frac{\epsilon}{\hbar}|t|\right] V(t)|E_O\rangle. \qquad (XVIII.2.12)$$

The equation determining the state $|E'\rangle$ can be obtained by using the integral equation (*XVIII.2.9*) in (*XVIII.2.12*). It yields

$$|E'\rangle = \int_{-\infty}^{\infty} \exp\left[\frac{it}{\hbar}(E_F - H_0) - \frac{\epsilon}{\hbar}|t|\right]|E_O\rangle\, dt - \frac{i}{2\hbar}\int_{-\infty}^{\infty}\int_{-\infty}^{\infty} dt\, dt'\, \eta(t - t')$$
$$\exp\left[\frac{it}{\hbar}(E - H_0) - \frac{\epsilon}{\hbar}|t|\right] \times H_I(t')V(t')|E_O\rangle$$
$$= 2\pi\hbar\delta(E_F - E_O)|E_O\rangle - \frac{i}{2\hbar}\int_{-\infty}^{\infty}\int_{-\infty}^{\infty} dt\, dt'\, \eta(t - t')$$
$$\times \exp\left[\frac{it}{\hbar}(E - H_0) - \frac{\epsilon}{\hbar}|t|\right] \exp\left(\frac{it}{\hbar}H_0\right) H' \exp\left(-\frac{it}{\hbar}H_0\right) V(t')|E_O\rangle.$$

Making the transformations $t = t' + \mu$ and $t' = t'$, and suppressing the factor $\exp\left[-(\epsilon/\hbar)|t|\right]$, we obtain

$$|E'\rangle = 2\pi\hbar\delta(E_F - E_O)|E_O\rangle - \frac{i}{2\hbar}\int_{-\infty}^{\infty} d\mu\, \eta(\mu) \exp\left[\frac{i\mu}{\hbar}(E - H_0)\right]$$
$$\times H'\int_{-\infty}^{\infty} dt' \exp\left[\frac{it'}{\hbar}(E_F - H_0)\right] V(t')|E_O\rangle.$$

From

$$P\left(\frac{1}{E - H_0}\right) = -\frac{i}{2\hbar}\int_{-\infty}^{\infty} d\mu\, \eta(\mu) \exp\left[\frac{i\mu}{\hbar}(E - H_0)\right],$$

we obtain

$$|E'\rangle = 2\pi\hbar\delta(E_F - E_O)|E_O\rangle + P\left(\frac{1}{E - H_0}\right) H'|E'\rangle. \qquad (XVIII.2.13)$$

By writing

$$|E'\rangle = 2\pi\hbar\delta(E_F - E_O)|I\rangle, \qquad (XVIII.2.14)$$

we find that

$$|I\rangle = |E_O\rangle + P\left(\frac{1}{E - H_0}\right) H'|I\rangle. \qquad (XVIII.2.15)$$

Thus from (*XVIII.2.12*) and (*XVIII.2.14*) we get

$$2\pi\hbar\delta(E_F - E_O)|I\rangle = \int_{-\infty}^{\infty} dt \exp\left[\frac{it}{\hbar}(E_F - E_O) - \frac{\epsilon}{\hbar}|t|\right] V(t)|E_O\rangle,$$

which can be written as

$$\int_{-\infty}^{\infty} dt \exp\left[\frac{it}{\hbar}(E_F - E_O) - \frac{\epsilon}{\hbar}|t|\right]|I\rangle$$

$$= \int_{-\infty}^{\infty} dt \exp\left[\frac{it}{\hbar}(E_F - H_0) - \frac{\epsilon}{\hbar}|t|\right]V(t)|E_O\rangle.$$

Hence, the time-independent state vector $|I\rangle$ describes a stationary state according to the relation

$$e^{-(it/\hbar)E_O}|I\rangle = e^{-(it/\hbar)H_0}V(t)|E_O\rangle. \qquad (XVIII.2.16)$$

XVIII.2.A. Eigenvalues of the Reaction Operator

The representatives of the reaction operator K can be expressed as

$$K_{FO} = 2\pi\delta(E_F - E_O)\langle E_F|H'|I\rangle, \qquad (XVIII.2.17)$$

the operator form of which is

$$K = 2\pi\Lambda\mathrm{K}, \qquad (XVIII.2.18)$$

where

$$\Lambda = |E_O\rangle\langle E_F| \qquad (XVIII.2.19)$$

and

$$\langle E_F|H'|I\rangle = \langle E_F|\mathrm{K}|E_O\rangle. \qquad (XVIII.2.20)$$

In a similar way the operator form of the equation for T is

$$\boldsymbol{T} = -2\pi i\Lambda\tau, \qquad (XVIII.2.21)$$

where τ also is defined for states of equal energies and is such that

$$\langle E_F|\tau|E_O\rangle = \langle E_F|H'|+\rangle. \qquad (XVIII.2.22)$$

Now we use the relations (*XVIII.2.2*) and (*XVIII.2.3*), (*VIII.2.18*) and (*XVIII.2.21*) to obtain

$$\kappa = -\frac{1}{\pi}\Lambda^{-1}\tan\Delta \qquad (XVIII.2.23)$$

and

$$\tau = -\frac{1}{\pi}\Lambda^{-1}\sin\Delta\, e^{i\Delta}. \qquad (XVIII.2.24)$$

Let us introduce an operator δ by

$$\tan\Delta = \Lambda\tan\delta,$$

so

$$\sin\Delta e^{i\Delta} = \Lambda\sin\delta\, e^{i\delta}.$$

Hence

$$\boldsymbol{T} = -2\pi i\Lambda\tau = 2i\Lambda\sin\delta\, e^{i\delta} \qquad (XVIII.2.25)$$

and

$$|\boldsymbol{T}_{FO}|^2 = 4[\delta(E_F - E_O)]^2|\langle E_F|\sin\delta\, e^{i\delta}|E_O\rangle|^2$$

$$= \frac{2}{\pi\hbar}|\langle E_F|\sin\delta\, e^{i\delta}|E_O\rangle|^2\delta(E_F - E_O)\int_{-\infty}^{\infty} dt.$$

The transition probability per unit time is

$$W_{FO} = \frac{2}{\pi\hbar} \langle E_F| \sin\delta\, e^{i\delta}\, |E_O\rangle|^2\, \delta(E_F - E_O). \qquad (XVIII.2.26)$$

Using the operator property (*XVIII.1.20*) of the operator $\boldsymbol{T}$ we can write the relation between the matrix elements of τ as

$$4\pi^2 \sum_I \delta(E_F - E_I)\delta(E_I - E_O)\tau_{IF}^*\tau_{IO} = 2\pi i\delta(E_F - E_O)[\tau_{FO} - \tau_{OF}^*].$$

Summing over E_F or E_O and setting $E_O = E_F$, we get

$$4\pi^2 \sum_I \delta(E_I - E_O)|\tau_{IO}|^2 = -4\pi Im(\tau_{OO}).$$

Hence the total rate of transition from the initial state is

$$\sum_{E_F} W_{FO} = -\frac{2}{\hbar} Im(\tau_{OO}). \qquad (XVIII.2.27)$$

We now introduce the eigenstates of the reaction operator K by

$$K|K_A\rangle = K_A|K_A\rangle. \qquad (XVIII.2.28)$$

The vector $|K_A\rangle$ is also an eigenstate of τ, so that

$$\tau|K_A\rangle = \tau_A|K_A\rangle = -\frac{1}{\pi} \sin\delta_A\, e^{i\delta_A}|K_A\rangle$$

and

$$K|K_A\rangle = K_A|K_A\rangle = -\frac{1}{\pi} \tan\delta_A|K_A\rangle.$$

The eigenvalues K_A and τ_A are, therefore, given by

$$K_A = -\frac{1}{\pi} \tan\delta_A, \qquad \tau_A = -\frac{1}{\pi} \sin\delta_A\, e^{i\delta_A}.$$

Introducing the representation in which K is diagonal, the transition probability (*XVIII.2.26*) can be expressed as

$$W_{FO} = \frac{2}{\pi\hbar} |\Sigma \sin\delta_A e^{i\delta_A} f_{FA} f_{AO}^*|^2 \delta(E_P - E_O), \qquad (XVIII.2.29)$$

where $f_{FA} = \langle E_F|K_A\rangle$ is the eigenfunction of K in the representation in which H_0 is diagonal.

Formula (*XVIII.2.27*) yields the result

$$\begin{aligned} \sum_{E_F} W_{FO} &= \frac{2}{\pi\hbar} Im\langle E_O|\sin\delta e^{i\delta}|E_O\rangle = \frac{2}{\pi\hbar} \langle E_O|\sin^2\delta|E_O\rangle \\ &= \frac{2}{\pi\hbar} \sum_A |f_{OA}|^2 \sin^2\delta_A, \end{aligned} \qquad (XVIII.2.30)$$

which is the total probability per unit time for transitions from a particular state. Finally, the sum of the total transition probability per unit time over all initial states of the same energy is expressed by

$$\sum_{E_F E_O} W_{FO} = \frac{2}{\pi\hbar} \sum_{A} \sum_{E_O} |f_{OA}|^2 \sin^2 \delta_A = \frac{2}{\pi\hbar} \sum_{A} \sin^2 \delta_A. \qquad (XVIII.2.31)$$

Obviously, the δ_A are the usual phase shifts, and the functions f_{OA} can be related to spherical harmonics. The eigenfunctions $f_{OA} = \langle E_{FO}|K_A\rangle$ are functions of the vector $\boldsymbol{k}_0[k_0^2 = 2EM/\hbar^2]$ and the representatives K_{FO}, as functions of $\boldsymbol{k}_F$ and $\boldsymbol{k}_0$, are invariant under a simultaneous rotation of $\boldsymbol{k}_F$ and $\boldsymbol{k}_O$. The vectors $\boldsymbol{k}_O$ and $\boldsymbol{k}_F$ are the propagation vectors defining the initial and final states.

Following Lippmann and Schwinger, we put $f_{OA} = CY_{lm}(\hat{\boldsymbol{k}}_0)$ and $A \equiv l, m$; the eigenvalues for K depend only upon the order of the spherical harmonics—that is, $\delta_A = \delta_l$. From the normalization condition we have

$$|C|^2 \int Y^*_{lm}(\hat{\boldsymbol{k}}) Y_{l'm'}(\hat{\boldsymbol{k}}) \rho \, d\Omega = \delta_{ll'}\delta_{mm'},$$

where $\rho \, d\Omega$ is the number of states per unit energy range associated with the motion within the solid angle element $d\Omega$, or

$$\rho = \frac{Vp^2 \, dp}{8\pi^3\hbar^3 \, dE} = \frac{V}{8\pi^3\hbar} \frac{k^2}{v} = \frac{k^2}{8\pi^3\hbar v},$$

where we take V to be a unit volume.

Spherical harmonics normalized in a unit sphere require that

$$|C|^2 = \frac{1}{\rho} = 8\pi^3 \frac{\hbar v}{k^2}.$$

From ($XVIII.2.29$), for the probability per unit time that the particle from the direction $\boldsymbol{k}_O$ is scattered into the solid angle $d\Omega$ around the direction of $\boldsymbol{k}_F$, we have the expression

$$W = \frac{2}{\pi\hbar} \Big| \sum_{l,m} \sin \delta_l \, e^{i\delta_l} |C|^2 Y_{lm}(\hat{\boldsymbol{k}}_F) Y_{lm}(\hat{\boldsymbol{k}}_0) \Big|^2 \rho \, d\Omega. \qquad (XVIII.2.32)$$

Dividing by the relative velocity v of the particles, which measures the flux of incident particles, and using the spherical harmonics addition theorem

$$\sum_{m=-l}^{l} Y_{lm}(\hat{\boldsymbol{k}}_F) Y^*_{lm}(\hat{\boldsymbol{k}}_0) = \frac{2l+1}{4\pi} P_l(\cos\theta),$$

we obtain the differential cross-section for scattering through an angle θ:

$$d\sigma(\theta) = \frac{1}{k^2} \Big| \sum_{l} (2l+1) \sin \delta_l \, e^{i\delta_l} P_l(\cos\theta) \Big|^2 d\Omega, \qquad (XVIII.2.33)$$

where θ is the angle between $\hat{\boldsymbol{k}}_O$ and $\hat{\boldsymbol{k}}_F$.

The total scattering cross-section, according to ($XVIII.2.30$), is

$$\sigma = \frac{2}{\pi \hbar v} \sum_{l,m} \sin^2 \delta_l |C|^2 |Y_{lm}(\hat{\boldsymbol{k}}_0)|^2 = \frac{4\pi}{k^2} \sum_l (2l+1) \sin^2 \delta_l, \qquad (XVIII.2.34)$$

where

$$\sum_{m=-l}^{l} |Y_{lm}(\hat{\boldsymbol{k}}_0)|^2 = \frac{2l+1}{4\pi}.$$

Finally, we note that $S = e^{2i\Delta} = \mathrm{T} + 1$ can be used to study the relation of the phase shift and the potential which is the cause of the phase shift. Because of the Hermitian property of K the phase shifts are real quantities.

A careful study by Bargmann of the relation between the phase shift and scattering potential shows that phase shifts do not determine the energy of bound states. The extent of a possible determination of the scattering potential $V(r)$ by the phase shifts δ_l as functions of energy has been studied by Levinson and also by Bargmann.* Levinson has shown that two potentials which fall off rapidly enough and have the same phase shifts δ_l for all angular momenta are identical, provided they do not give rise to bound states. Thus let V_1 and V_2 be the two potentials and δ_l', δ_l'' the corresponding phase shifts. If

$$\int_0^\infty r|V_i|\,dr,$$

for $i = 1, 2$, is finite [see (*XVIII.5*)] and if for some l

$$V_i(r) + \frac{l(l+1)}{r^2} \geqq 0,$$

where $i = 1, 2$, then $\delta_l' = \delta_l''$ implies that $V_1(r) = V_2(r)$.

For every bounded potential which has the property that for large r it is smaller than C/r^2, where C is a constant, the above inequality is satisfied, for sufficiently large l. Thus if V_1 and V_2 are potentials of this kind and if $\delta_l' = \delta_l''$ for all l, then for a large enough l_0 the inequality holds and we obtain $V_1 = V_2$. This argument is not, of course, sufficient for the construction of a potential from its corresponding phase shifts. In terms of the S matrix, the phase shifts δ_l are related to the eigenvalue of the S matrix by $S(k) = \exp[2i\delta_l(k)]$.

By analytic continuation, the function $S(k)$ may be defined for complex k, and, in particular for imaginary values $k = -i\kappa$, for $\kappa > 0$. It has been observed by Kramers† that the stationary states should be obtained from the zeros of $S(-i\kappa)$. However, as shown by Ma‡ there exist some zeros of $S(k)$

---

* V. Bargmann, *Phys. Rev.*, **75** (1949), 301.
N. Levinson, *Phys. Rev.*, **75** (1949), 1445.
† Quoted by C. Moller, *Kgl. Danske, Vid. Sels. Math-Fys. Medd.*, **24**, No. 19 (1946).
P. A. M. Dirac, *Proc. Roy. Soc. London*, **49** (1937).
‡ S. T. Ma, *Phys. Rev.*, **69** (1946), 668; **71** (1947), 195.
See also D. ter Haar, *Physica*, **12** (1946), 509.

which do not correspond to bound states.* For further discussion of this point see Section *XVIII.6.B*.

XVIII.2.B. Problems

1. Consider the unitary operator

$$U = \Sigma|+\rangle\langle E_O|,$$

where the states $|+\rangle$ and $|E_O\rangle$ are those of (*XVIII.1.29*). By using the definition $U^\dagger U = UU^\dagger = I$ of unitarity, prove that U is not unitary for bound states.

2. Show that the S matrix is unitary for bound states.

XVIII.2.C. Scattering from Two Potentials

An example of scattering under the combined influence of Coulomb and nuclear fields is the low-energy $P - P$ scattering. Another interesting example is the process of "bremsstrahlung." In the case of electron bremsstrahlung the potentials are the Coulomb field of the nucleus and the interaction of the electrons with photons. One of the potentials—the Coulomb—can be treated exactly, and the resulting states can be used to calculate the transition probabilities caused by the interaction between the electron and the radiation field.

Let us consider the integral equation

$$|+\rangle = |E_O\rangle + \frac{1}{E + i\epsilon - H_0} H'|+\rangle, \qquad (XVIII.2.35)$$

where

$$H' = H_1' + H_2' \qquad (XVIII.2.36)$$

and H' is to be treated by perturbation theory. Thus, if $|E_O\rangle$ is the eigenstate of H_0 belonging to energy E_O, then the probability amplitude for transition to another free state (plane wave)$|E_F\rangle$ with energy E_F is given by

$$\begin{aligned} \mathbf{T}_{FO} = \langle E_F|\mathbf{T}|E_O\rangle &= -2\pi i\delta(E_F - E_O)\langle E_F|(H_1' + H_2')|+\rangle \\ &= -2\pi i\delta(E_F - E_O)\langle -|(H_1' + H_2')|E_O\rangle. \end{aligned} \qquad (XVIII.2.37)$$

Let us further introduce a state vector $|F-\rangle$ by

$$|F-\rangle = |E_F\rangle + \frac{1}{E - i\epsilon - H_0} H_1'|F-\rangle \qquad (XVIII.2.38)$$

where the $|F-\rangle$ are solutions of the problem without H_2'. The reasons for the

---

* See R. Jost, *Helv. Phys. Acta.*, **20** (1947), 256.

choice of ingoing wave boundary conditions can be understood, if we solve (*XVIII.2.38*), substitute in

$$\langle E_F|(H_1' + H_2')|+\rangle,$$

and use (*XVIII.2.35*), which leads to

$$\langle E_F|(H_1' + H_2')|+\rangle = \langle F-|H_2'|+\rangle + \langle F-|H_1'|E_O\rangle. \qquad (XVIII.2.39)$$

This interesting result was obtained by Gell-Mann and Goldberger. If H_2' were actually zero, the state $|+\rangle$ in (*XVIII.2.35*) could be replaced by $|F+\rangle$, and (*XVIII.2.39*) could be written as

$$\langle E_F|(H_1' + H_2')|+\rangle = \langle F-|H_2'|F+\rangle + \langle F-|H_1'|E_O\rangle. \qquad (XVIII.2.40)$$

The second term in (*XVIII.2.40*) is the scattering amplitude that would be found, even if H' were zero. In this term the final state contains the ingoing wave boundary condition, and it is the probability amplitude for transition from a state $|E_O\rangle$ to a state $|F-\rangle$, under the action of H_1'. But in the case of bremsstrahlung there is a photon in the final state, while the state arising from the state $|E_O\rangle$ under the influence of H_1' cannot give rise to a photon, since by assumption H_1' is not related to the interaction of the charged particle with the radiation field. This term must, in this case, vanish. The only term contributing to the transition probability is, therefore, the first term in (*XVIII.2.40*).

It must be noted that because of the small imaginary part in the denominators, a state $|+\rangle$ with outgoing wave boundary conditions becomes, under the operation of Hermitian conjugation, a state $|-\rangle$ with ingoing wave boundary condition.

The first term in (*XVIII.2.40*) is invariant with respect to Hermitian conjugation, that is,

$$[\langle F-|H_2'|F+\rangle]^\dagger = \langle F-|H_2'|F+\rangle,$$

and the final state is an incoming state vector contrary to the usual practice of choosing final states. However, the fact that the choice of $|F-\rangle$ for the final state is the correct one will be explained in the next section.

For later reference it will be useful to write the integral equation (*XVIII.2.35*) in different forms. We can introduce an outgoing wave state $|F+\rangle$ as a stationary solution of Schrödinger's equation with the total Hamiltonian $H_O + H_1'$. The Schrödinger equation,

$$(E - H_0 - H')|+\rangle = H_2'|+\rangle,$$

is then solved by

$$|+\rangle = |F+\rangle + \frac{1}{E - H_0 - H_1' + i\epsilon} H_2'|+\rangle, \qquad (XVIII.2.41)$$

where $|F+\rangle$ is an eigenstate of $H_0 + H_1'$ and the original outgoing wave boundary condition is, of course, still maintained.

XVIII.3. Final States in Scattering Problems and Ingoing Waves

In an interesting paper Breit and Bethe have discussed* the outgoing or ingoing wave nature of the final state in the calculation of transition probabilities. This question will arise only if the states in question are not pure plane waves, but are modified by the addition of an ingoing or outgoing wave. In this case the transition probabilities are to be calculated with respect to plane waves modified by the action of a potential.

In the space-time description of scattering (the wave picture) we use stationary-state wave functions, and the time dependence of the process is represented by forming a wave packet. In space-time description of scattering we start with a steady incident beam, part of which is deflected, and from the intensity of the scattered wave we compute the differential cross-section. In a scattering process the size of the incident packet is large compared to the scatterer, and it is a good approximation to represent the incident beam by a plane wave exp (ikz). When the wave enters the force field a scattered wave is produced, and for the stationary-state wave functions $(r \longrightarrow \infty)$ we write

$$\psi \cong \exp(ikz) + \chi(r).$$

A wave packet can be produced by sending a steady beam of incident particles through a collimating slit.

In scattering by a central field the time-independent wave function for $r \longrightarrow \infty$ has the form

$$\psi_k \cong \exp(ikz) + f(\theta)\frac{1}{r}\exp(ikr). \qquad (XVIII.3.1)$$

The last term represents a modification of the plane wave by an outgoing wave. For a time-dependent ψ we form a wave packet which at time $t = 0$ will be supposed to be moving along the z-axis toward the scattering center. The time-dependent wave function is represented by

$$\psi = \int A(\mathbf{k})\langle\mathbf{k}|\mathbf{r}\rangle e^{-(it/\hbar)E}\, d^3\mathbf{k},$$

where

$$E = \frac{\hbar^2k^2}{2m}. \qquad (XVIII.3.2)$$

For $t < 0$ the wave packet has not yet seen the potential, and it behaves

* G. Breit and H. A. Bethe, *Phys. Rev.*, **93** (1954), 888.

as a free packet in space. After the collision there are scattered waves, both ingoing and outgoing (Fig. 18.1). The ingoing waves arise from the interference of the secondary waves (Huygen's principle) with the outgoing waves.

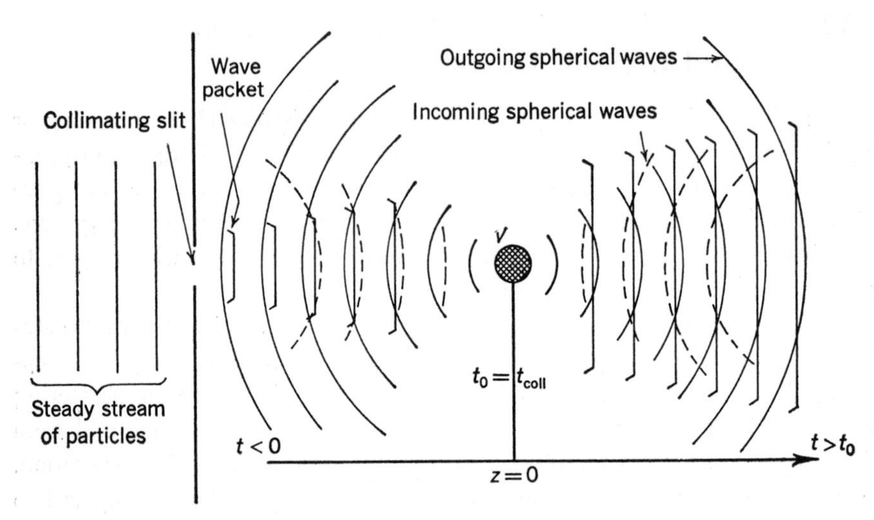

FIG. XVIII.1. *Ingoing and outgoing scattered waves.*

The wave packet (*XVIII.3.1*) consists of two terms: one formed from the superposition of the incident plane waves (to the left of $z = z_0$) $\exp(ikz)$, and the other formed from the outgoing waves $1/r \exp(ikr)$. For $t < 0$ the wave has not yet hit the scatterer, and therefore, there are no scattered waves; that is, for $t < 0$,

$$\int C_k \exp\left(ikr - \frac{it}{\hbar} E\right) d^3\mathbf{k} = 0. \qquad (XVIII.3.3)$$

In the time region $t < 0$, r is the same as z and is negative. Thus for $t < 0$,

$$kr = -kz.$$

This shows that along the z direction, just before $z = 0$ the phases in the packet change in opposite ways. This is the reason for the destructive interference between outgoing wave $1/r \exp(ikr)$ and an ingoing wave. For $t > t_{\text{collision}}$ the signs of r and z are the same, and constructive interference occurs in the same places for both terms (*XVIII.3.1*). If the plane wave is modified by the addition of $(1/r)f(\theta) \exp(-ikr)$, the relative phase relations discussed above would reverse themselves, and the corresponding process would not be the intended one.

Let the total Hamiltonian be $H = H_0 + H'$, where H_0 comprises the kinetic energies of the incident particle plus the scatterer. The Schrödinger equation for H_0 is

$$i\hbar \frac{d}{dt} |E, t\rangle = H_0 |E, t\rangle. \qquad (XVIII.3.4)$$

If we wish, we can represent the state $|E, t\rangle$ by a wave packet. If a plane wave, for example, is incident, the state $|E, t\rangle$ is modified by an interaction energy H':

$$i\hbar \frac{d}{dt} |\zeta', t\rangle = (H_0 + H')|\zeta', t\rangle. \qquad (XVIII.3.5)$$

Let $|E\rangle$ be the time-independent solution of $(XVIII.3.4)$, so

$$|E, S, t\rangle = e^{-(i/\hbar)Et}|E, S\rangle,$$

where the label S enumerates the continuum of possibilities for solutions at a fixed energy E. For example, the waves may have different propagation vectors and spin specifications.

The observables H_0, S, and spin s must form a complete commuting set, so the wave function representing the state $|E, S, s\rangle$ in the Schrödinger picture can be normalized by

$$\int \langle \mathbf{r}|E, S, s\rangle \, dS d\, E \, \langle E, S, s'|\mathbf{r}'\rangle = \delta_{ss'}\delta(\mathbf{r} - \mathbf{r}'). \qquad (XVIII.3.6)$$

In the interaction formulation, equation $(XVIII.3.5)$ can be replaced by the integral equation

$$|I, t\rangle = |I, 0\rangle - \frac{i}{\hbar} \int_0^t H_I(t')|I, t'\rangle \, dt',$$

where

$$|\zeta', t\rangle = e^{-(it/\hbar)H_0}|I, t\rangle, \qquad |\zeta', 0\rangle = |I, 0\rangle = |E, S, s\rangle,$$

and

$$H_I(t) = e^{(it/\hbar)H_0} H' e^{-(it/\hbar)H_0}.$$

It is solved, to the first order in H', by

$$|I, t\rangle = |E, S, s\rangle - \frac{i}{\hbar} \int_0^t H_I(t')|E, S, s\rangle \, dt',$$

which is equivalent to

$$|\zeta', t\rangle = |E, S, s, t\rangle - \frac{i}{\hbar} \int_0^t \exp\left[\frac{i}{\hbar}(t' - t)H_0\right] H'|E, S, s, t'\rangle \, dt' \qquad (XVIII.3.7)$$

Introducing the unit operator

$$\sum_s \int |E, S, s\rangle \, dE \, dS \, \langle E, S, s| = 1,$$

we obtain

$$\psi(\mathbf{r}, S, t) = \psi_0(\mathbf{r}, S, t) - \frac{i}{\hbar} \sum_s \int_0^t dt' \int dE \int dS$$

$$\times \int d^3r' \exp\left[\frac{i}{\hbar}(t - t')E\right] \phi^*_{ES}(\mathbf{r}, s)\phi^*_{ES}(\mathbf{r}', s) H_0 \psi_0(\mathbf{r}', s, ,t) \qquad (XVIII.3.8)$$

where

$$\begin{aligned}\psi(\boldsymbol{r}, S, t) &= \langle \boldsymbol{r}|\zeta', t\rangle,\\ \psi_0(\boldsymbol{r}, S, t) &= \langle \boldsymbol{r}|E, S, s, t\rangle,\\ \phi_{ES}(\boldsymbol{r}, s) &= \langle \boldsymbol{r}|E, S, s\rangle,\\ \langle \boldsymbol{r}'|H'|\boldsymbol{r}\rangle &= H'\delta(\boldsymbol{r} - \boldsymbol{r}').\end{aligned}$$

The completeness relation (*XVIII.3.6*) can be satisfied by having $\phi_{ES}(\boldsymbol{r}, s)$ be asymptotic, at large r, to either (a) plane plus outgoing wave, or (b) plane plus ingoing wave. Either modification of the plane wave gives a complete set of functions.

Neglecting the spin for the present, the distorted plane waves may be represented in the form

$$\chi_k = \sum_l i^l(2l + 1)P_l(\hat{\boldsymbol{k}}\cdot\hat{\boldsymbol{r}})\,\frac{\mathrm{T}_l(kr)}{kr}, \qquad (XVIII.3.9)$$

where, outside the potential,

$$\mathrm{T}_l = (F_l \cos\delta_l + G_l \sin\delta_l)e^{\mp i\delta_l}, \qquad \hat{\boldsymbol{k}}\cdot\hat{\boldsymbol{r}} = \cos\theta.$$

The plus sign corresponds to outgoing waves, and the minus sign to ingoing waves. The functions F_l and G_l are the standard regular and irregular solutions, respectively.

From the addition theorem of spherical harmonics, equation (*XVIII.3.9*) can be written as

$$\chi_k = 4\pi \sum_{l=0}^{\infty}\sum_{m=-l}^{l} Y_{lm}(\hat{\boldsymbol{k}})Y_{lm}^*(\hat{\boldsymbol{r}})\,\frac{\mathrm{T}_l(kr)}{kr}.$$

Multiplying by $Y_{l'm'}(\hat{\boldsymbol{k}})$ and integrating over $d\Omega_k$ (an element of the solid angle around the direction $\hat{\boldsymbol{k}}$), we find that

$$\int \chi_k Y_{lm}^*(\hat{\boldsymbol{k}})\,d\Omega_k = Y_{lm}(\hat{\boldsymbol{r}})\,\frac{\mathrm{T}_l(kr)}{kr}. \qquad (XVIII.3.10)$$

Thus the polar coordinate solutions are related to χ_k by means of a unitary transformation, the coefficients of which are $Y_{lm}^*(\hat{\boldsymbol{k}})\,d\Omega_k$. The unit vectors $\hat{\boldsymbol{k}}$ and $\hat{\boldsymbol{r}}$ are defined by the polar angles. As a consequence of the unitary character of the transformation, the functions $Y_{lm}(\hat{\boldsymbol{r}})[\mathrm{T}_l(kr)/kr]$ form a complete set; so does χ_l. The choice of sign for the δ_l in the factor $\exp(\pm i\delta_l)$ is immaterial because of the unitary nature of the transformation. If we use an outgoing wave modification of the plane wave, then in the region of large kz the ϕ_{ES} contains terms $\exp(ikr)$ coming from $\exp(ikz)$ and also terms $\exp(ikr)$ coming from the outgoing wave.

In (*XVIII.3.7*) the second term represents the first-order effect of H' in the form of a superposition of ϕ_{ES}. We have seen in the S-matrix formulation of the scattering theory that for large times we are led to conservation of energy. For example, an inelastically scattered electron (as in the case of bremsstrahlung) wave in each energy region is represented as a superposition of ϕ_{ES}. As pointed out above, in the direction of $\hat{\boldsymbol{k}}$ each ϕ_{ES} contains two terms with the same phase $\exp(ikr)$, and they both contribute to the wave packet of inelastically scattered particles. The contributions from $\exp(ikz)$ and $1/r \exp(ikr)$ at large r are of the same order, since from the partial wave analysis of $\exp(ikz)$ we know that it contains mainly terms of the forms $1/r \exp(ikr)$ and $1/r \exp(-ikr)$. The reduction of intensity in the primary beam arises from the interference of the outgoing wave parts of $\exp(ikz) + (1/r)f(\theta) \exp(ikr)$ with the unscattered wave packet. Hence in the calculation of an inelastically scattered wave packet, the outgoing wave part of ϕ_{ES} cannot be neglected. This argument of Breit and Bethe shows clearly that the calculation of (*XVIII.3.8*) in terms of distorted plane waves with outgoing wave modification is possible but is not directly interpretable in terms of a differential cross-section.

If, on the other hand, we take ϕ_{ES} as plane waves distorted by "ingoing" wave modification, that is, as

$$\exp(ikz) + 1/r \exp(-ikr)f(\theta),$$

then in the direction of each $\hat{\boldsymbol{k}}$ the phases of the ingoing waves are just opposite to those of the plane wave parts. For the ingoing wave part, one has destructive interference. Then the second term of (*XVIII.3.8*) gives a representation of the inelastically scattered wave packet in terms of undistorted plane waves and is, of course, interpretable in terms of the number of particles. The above argument does not effect the initial state of the system. It is still, asymptotically, a plane wave plus an outgoing wave. But *the final state must be chosen in such a way that at large r it consists of a distortion of a plane wave by an ingoing wave.* All the above considerations in the choice of a final state are closely related to the invariance under time-reversal operation, which for a time-independent wave function consists of a complex conjugation operation.

XVIII.3.A. Problems

1. Prove that the eigenvalues of the S matrix are of the form $e^{2i\lambda}$, where λ is an eigenvalue of the phase-shift operator Δ introduced by (*XVIII.2.2*), where λ is a function of wave vector $\boldsymbol{k}$.

2. Prove that the S matrix commutes with the Hamiltonian, momentum, and angular momentum operators.

3. Show that the basic operators K and τ of the scattering theory are related by

$$\tau = K - i\pi K\Lambda\tau.$$

Hence

$$\tau_{FO} = K_{FO} - i\pi \sum_{E_I} K_{FI}\delta(E_I - E_O)\tau_{IO}.$$

This is called the radiation damping equation.

4. From equations (*XVIII.1.29*) show that the states $|+\rangle$ and $|-\rangle$ are related according to

$$|+\rangle = \mathfrak{J}|-\rangle,$$

where $\mathfrak{J}$ is a time-reversal operator. Show also that asymptotically the wave function contains a plane wave. Discuss the significance of the state $|-\rangle$ in the problem of bremsstrahlung where, after the photon is produced, the charged particle and the nucleus may interact strongly through the long-range Coulomb field. Does this affect the γ-ray spectrum?

5. By using the transformation

$$|+\rangle = \Omega|E_O\rangle,$$

show that the operator Ω satisfies the integral equation

$$\Omega = 1 + \frac{1}{E + i\epsilon - H_0} H'\Omega.$$

Show also that it is solved by

$$\Omega = 1 + \frac{1}{E + i\epsilon - H} H',$$

where $(E + i\epsilon - H)^{-1}$ can be regarded as the Green's operator of Schrödinger's equation.

6. Discuss the physical significance of the scalar product of the states $|+\rangle$ and $|-\rangle$.

XVIII.4. The Principle of Detailed Balancing

In classical statistical mechanics, a collision between any two members of an ensemble in an equilibrium state corresponds to a state where the two members can occupy a part of phase space with initial momenta $\boldsymbol{p}_1$ and $\boldsymbol{p}_2$ and leave that part of phase space, after collision, with momenta $\boldsymbol{p}_1'$ and $\boldsymbol{p}_2'$. The reverse process of entering with momenta $-\boldsymbol{p}_1'$ and $-\boldsymbol{p}_2'$ and leaving with momenta $-\boldsymbol{p}_1$ and $-\boldsymbol{p}_2$ (the time-reversed state) is also possible. In general, the total rate of transfer of members from either portions of phase space where momenta are $\boldsymbol{p}$ or $-\boldsymbol{p}$ to other portions of phase space where momenta are $\boldsymbol{p}'$ and $-\boldsymbol{p}'$ is equal to the transfer rate in the opposite sense. In classical theory this is regarded as a sufficient condition for the entropy to increase and permit the system to reach statistical equilibrium. In statistical mechanics the process is governed by what is called the "principle of detailed balancing."

In quantum mechanics the principle of detailed balancing, for a system in equilibrium, refers to a direct balance between the rates of processes in opposing directions of time. This means that a transition from a state A to a state B can be balanced by a transition from the state B to the state A without the need of an intermediate transition between A and B. We must remember at this point that the transitions in question are determined by transition probability amplitudes (see Chapter XII).

For particles without spin the detailed balancing means that the probability that the collision process,

$$\mathbf{p}_1, \mathbf{p}_2 \longrightarrow \mathbf{p}_1', \mathbf{p}_2',$$

will occur is the same as the probability that the reverse collision,

$$-\mathbf{p}_1', -\mathbf{p}_2' \longrightarrow -\mathbf{p}_1, -\mathbf{p}_2,$$

will occur. For particles with spin we must recall that under time-reversal operation the spins are reversed. In this case the principle of detailed balancing requires equal probability of occurrence of the opposing processes,

$$\mathbf{p}_1, \mathbf{p}_2, \mathbf{s}_1, \mathbf{s}_2 \longrightarrow \mathbf{p}_1', \mathbf{p}_2', \mathbf{s}_1', \mathbf{s}_2'$$

and

$$-\mathbf{p}_1', -\mathbf{p}_2', -\mathbf{s}_1', -\mathbf{s}_2' \longrightarrow -\mathbf{p}_1, -\mathbf{p}_2, -\mathbf{s}_1, -\mathbf{s}_2.$$

A general quantum mechanical derivation of the detailed balancing theorem was given by Coester and also by Watanabe.* Here we give a short derivation of the principle.

We wish to determine in what way a transition from a state A to a state B is related to its reverse transition from B to A. Under a time-reversal operation the transition probability amplitude (*XVIII.1.35*), as follows from (*VI.1.20*) in problem 2 of Section VI.2.A, assumes the form

$$W_{FO} = W_{-O-F}, \qquad (XVIII.4.1)$$

where the right side represents the transition probability amplitude in reverse order. Thus, in accordance with (*VI.1.18*) and (*VI.1.19*), the transition W_{-O-F} contains the states with momenta and spins opposite to those contained in W_{FO}.

Let $d\sigma_{FO}$ be the cross-section for a collision between two particles where the relative velocity of the particles deviates into a solid angle $d\Omega_F$ in a coordinate system where the center of mass is at rest. To incorporate conservation of energy ($E_O = E_F$) we may, equivalently, write the cross-section in the form

$$d\sigma_{FO}\delta(E_F - E_O)\, dE_F$$

---

* F. Coester, *Phys. Rev.*, 84 (1951), 1259.
S. Watanabe, *Phys. Rev.*, 84 (1951), 1008.

which must be equal to [see (*XVIII.1.38*)]

$$\frac{d\Omega_F}{v_O}\frac{\rho_F}{N_{sO}}\left[\sum_{sF,sO}|W_{FO}|^2\right]\delta(E_F - E_O)\,dE_F, \qquad (XVIII.4.2)$$

which for the reversed transition is given by

$$\frac{d\Omega_0}{v_F}\frac{\rho_0}{N_{sF}}\sum_{sF,sO}|W_{-O-F}|^2\,\delta(E_F - E_O)\,dE_O, \qquad (XVIII.4.3)$$

where N_{sO} and N_{sF} are spin degeneracies in states O and F, respectively. The differential cross-section (*XVIII.4.3*) is a function of $-\boldsymbol{p}_1$, $-\boldsymbol{p}_2$, $-\boldsymbol{p}_1'$, $-\boldsymbol{p}_2'$. But (*XVIII.4.3*) does not change under a space reflection, and it is therefore a function of $\boldsymbol{p}_1$, $\boldsymbol{p}_2$, $\boldsymbol{p}_1'$, $\boldsymbol{p}_2'$. Since the sums over spins of the initial and final states in both (*XVIII.4.2*) and (*XVIII.4.3*) are the same, we obtain the detailed balancing theorem:

$$\frac{d\sigma_{FO}}{d\Omega_O}v_O N_{sO}\,\rho_0 = \frac{d\sigma_{OF}}{d\Omega_F}v_F N_{sF}\,\rho_F. \qquad (XVIII.4.4)$$

The detailed balance cannot be established without summations over spins. An interesting example in classical statistical mechanics is Boltzmann's observation that detailed balancing does not hold for collisions between molecules with a nonspherical shape. For quantum theory, when angular momenta, polarizations, or any other intrinsic properties are involved, the principle of detailed balancing will hold only to the first order. However, in general, to insure the increase of entropy of a system it is assumed that the lack of detailed balancing will be made up by other processes.

XVIII.4.A. The Spin of the π Meson

It was suggested by Marshak and by Cheston* that the spin of a π^+ meson may be observed by producing it in a collision process of the type

$$p + p \longrightarrow D + \pi^+$$

and also by the inverse process of π^+ absorption in deuterium. In the above proton-proton reaction we shall assign the symbols O and F to the left and right sides, respectively. Thus in the center of mass system the velocity of the proton is given by $\boldsymbol{v}_0 = 2\boldsymbol{p}/M$, where $\frac{1}{2}M$ is the reduced mass and $\boldsymbol{p}$ refers to the momentum of the proton. The velocity in the final state in center of mass, neglecting deuteron energy, is $\boldsymbol{v}_F = (1/M_{\pi D})\boldsymbol{p}_\pi$, where $\boldsymbol{p}_\pi$ is the momentum of π_+ and $M_{\pi D}$ refers to the reduced mass of the π-D system. From

* R. E. Marshak, *Phys. Rev.*, **82** (1951), 313.
W. B. Cheston, *Phys. Rev.*, **83** (1951), 1118.

$$\rho_0 = p^2 \frac{dp}{dE}, \qquad \rho_F = p_\pi^2 \frac{dp_\pi}{dE_\pi},$$

we get, approximately,

$$\rho_0 = \tfrac{1}{2} pM, \qquad \rho_F = M_\pi p_\pi.$$

Since spin of the proton is $\frac{1}{2}\hbar$, the spin degeneracy is

$$N_{sO} = 2(2s + 1) = 4.$$

If the spin of π is s, then

$$N_{sF} = (2s + 1)(2 \times 1 + 1) = 3(2s + 1)$$

where the spin of the deuteron is $\hbar$. We may now use equation (*XVIII.4.4*) and obtain

$$\frac{d\sigma(pp \longrightarrow \pi^+ D)}{d\Omega} \frac{2p}{M} \frac{pM}{2} 4 = \frac{d\sigma(\pi^+ D \longrightarrow pp)}{d\Omega} \frac{p_\pi}{M_{\pi D}} p_\pi M_{\pi D} 3(2s + 1).$$

Hence the ratio of cross-sections is

$$\frac{\dfrac{d\sigma(\pi^+ D \longrightarrow pp)}{d\Omega}}{\dfrac{d\sigma(pp \longrightarrow \pi^+ D)}{d\Omega}} = \frac{4}{3(2s + 1)} \left[\frac{p}{p_\pi}\right]^2, \qquad (XVIII.4.5)$$

in which the only unknown is the spin degeneracy $(2s + 1)$. For agreement with the experiments carried out at Berkeley* and Columbia† the choice $s = 0$ for the π^+ meson is necessary.

XVIII.4.B. Problems

1. Prove that for the scattering of spinless S waves the representations of the S matrix are symmetrical.
2. Prove that in the scattering of the initially polarized particles time-reversal operation does not yield detailed balancing.
3. To get detailed balancing for the scattering of unpolarized particles, it is necessary to average over the initial spins and to sum over final spins. Does one obtain detailed balancing if the scattered particles are polarized?

XVIII.5. Expansions of Scattering Amplitude

We have seen that the S matrix elements represent the probability amplitudes for the transition from the state $|\boldsymbol{\Psi}(-\infty)\rangle$ at an infinite past to a state

* W. F. Cartwright, C. Richman, M. N. Whitehead, and H. A. Wilcox, *Phys. Rev.*, **91** (1953), 677.

† R. Durbin, H. Loar, and J. Steinberger, *Phys. Rev.*, **83** (1951), 646, 84, 851L.
D. L. Clark, A. Roberts, and R. Wilson, *Phys. Rev.*, **83** (1951), 649L.

$|\boldsymbol{\Psi}(\infty)\rangle$ at an infinite future. According to this description the states $|\boldsymbol{\Psi}(\pm\infty)\rangle$ may consist either of elementary systems not interacting with one another—that is, sufficiently separated from one another—or of their combinations in bound states. Therefore the problem of distinguishing between the initial and final states of noninteracting particles and their bound states is important. This rather complicated problem has been solved by Klein.* Its discussion is not included here, but the interested reader may find it very useful to read Klein's paper.

We further note that in Section XVII.1 only the first Born approximation was used; contributions from higher orders were neglected. The first Born approximation is reliable only for higher energies and for weak potentials. The higher approximations are usually too complicated for practical purposes and for rapid estimates on scattering cross-section. Higher terms in the Born expansion have been investigated by Wu and also by Källen† for various central potentials. In particular, in view of breakdown of a potential description for high-energy phenomena, the Born expansion is not expected to be of any use there; for a low-energy region, higher terms in the Born expansion deserve closer attention. A detailed and rigorous treatment of this problem and also an investigation of the general behavior of the solutions for the scattering integral equation as a function of potential strength parameters have been carried out by Jost and Pais.‡ Here we shall follow an operator technique to reproduce some of the results of Jost and Pais.

We shall begin with the integral equation (*XVII.1.7*) of the scattering theory. Its formal solution can be written down in the form

$$|\boldsymbol{\Psi}\rangle = (1 - G_0H')^{-1}|\boldsymbol{\Psi}_0\rangle, \qquad (XVIII.5.1)$$

where $|\boldsymbol{\Psi}_0\rangle$ represents the initial state of the scattering system of particles. For the scattering process to take place, the operator must have a finite norm (see Section I.5.D). The condition for this can be obtained by extending the definition in Section I.5.D, for finite-dimensional spaces, to continuously infinite-dimensional spaces. Thus, from

$$[\text{norm } (G_0H')]^2 = \int \langle \boldsymbol{r}|(G_0H')^\dagger G_0H'|\boldsymbol{r}\rangle\, d^3\boldsymbol{r},$$

we find that norm (G_0H') must be smaller than or equal to

$$\int_0^\infty r|V(r)|\, dr = \text{constant},$$

where $\langle \boldsymbol{r}|H'|\boldsymbol{r}'\rangle = V(\boldsymbol{r})\delta(\boldsymbol{r} - \boldsymbol{r}')$, and $V(\boldsymbol{r})$ represents the potential energy.

* A. Klein, *Prog. Theor. Phys.*, **14** (1955), 580.
† T. Y. Wu, *Phys. Rev.*, **73** (1948), 934.
G. Källen, *Ark. Fysik,* **2** (1950), 33.
‡ R. Jost and A. Pais, *Phys. Rev.*, **82** (1951), 840.

If we assume the validity of an expansion in powers of the operator

$$K = G_0H' \qquad (XVIII.5.2)$$

from (*XVIII.5.1*) we obtain the result

$$|\Psi\rangle = |\Psi_0\rangle + \sum_{n=1}^{\infty} K_n|\Psi_0\rangle, \qquad (XVIII.5.3)$$

where $K_n = (G_0H')^n$ and $K_1 = K$. The scalar product of (*XVIII.5.3*) with the vector $|\boldsymbol{r}\rangle$ yields the equation

$$\psi(\boldsymbol{r}) = \psi_0(\boldsymbol{r}) + \sum_{n=1}^{\infty} \int K_n(\boldsymbol{r}, \boldsymbol{r}')\psi_0(\boldsymbol{r}')\, d^3\boldsymbol{r}', \qquad (XVIII.5.4)$$

where $K_n(\boldsymbol{r}, \boldsymbol{r}') = \langle \boldsymbol{r}|K_n|\boldsymbol{r}'\rangle$.

From the definition of the operator K_n we have

$$K_n = K_1K_{n-1} = KK_{n-1},$$

so its representatives obey the equation

$$K_n(\boldsymbol{r}, \boldsymbol{r}') = \int K(\boldsymbol{r}, \boldsymbol{r}'')K_{n-1}(\boldsymbol{r}'', \boldsymbol{r}')\, d^3\boldsymbol{r}'', \qquad (XVIII.5.5)$$

where

$$K(\boldsymbol{r}, \boldsymbol{r}') = G_0(\boldsymbol{r} - \boldsymbol{r}')V(\boldsymbol{r}'). \qquad (XVIII.5.6)$$

By substituting from (*XVIII.5.5*) in (*XVIII.5.4*), we can separate out the scattering amplitude $f(\theta)$ as the coefficient of $1/r \exp(ik_0r)$. Thus we obtain

$$f(\theta) = -\frac{1}{4\pi}\sum_{n=1}^{\infty}\frac{2m}{\hbar^2}\int e^{i\boldsymbol{k}_0\cdot\boldsymbol{r}''}V(\boldsymbol{r}')K_{n-1}(\boldsymbol{r}'', \boldsymbol{r}')e^{i\boldsymbol{k}\cdot\boldsymbol{r}'}\, d^3\boldsymbol{r}'\, d^3\boldsymbol{r}'', \qquad (XVIII.5.7)$$

where the vector $\boldsymbol{k}_0$ is in the direction of the position vector $\boldsymbol{r}$ and where we took $\psi_0(\boldsymbol{r}) = e^{i\boldsymbol{k}\cdot\boldsymbol{r}}$ and $|\boldsymbol{k}_0| = |\boldsymbol{k}|$.

We can also work in terms of the momentum eigenstates $|\boldsymbol{p}\rangle$ and obtain from (*XVIII.5.3*) the momentum wave function in the form

$$\phi(\boldsymbol{p}) = \phi_0(\boldsymbol{p}) + \sum_{n=1}^{\infty}\int K_n(\boldsymbol{p}, \boldsymbol{p}')\phi_0(\boldsymbol{p}')\, d^3\boldsymbol{p}', \qquad (XVIII.5.8)$$

where $\phi(\boldsymbol{p}) = \langle \boldsymbol{p}|\Psi\rangle$ and $\phi_0(\boldsymbol{p}) = \langle \boldsymbol{p}|\Psi_0\rangle$ and

$$\begin{aligned} K_n(\boldsymbol{p}, \boldsymbol{p}') &= \langle \boldsymbol{p}|K_n|\boldsymbol{p}'\rangle = \int \langle \boldsymbol{p}|\boldsymbol{r}\rangle\langle \boldsymbol{r}|K_n|\boldsymbol{r}'\rangle\langle \boldsymbol{r}'|\boldsymbol{p}'\rangle\, d^3\boldsymbol{r}\, d^3\boldsymbol{r}' \\ &= \left[\frac{1}{2\pi\hbar}\right]^3\int K_n(\boldsymbol{r}, \boldsymbol{r}')e^{(i/\hbar)(-\boldsymbol{p}\cdot\boldsymbol{r}+\boldsymbol{p}'\cdot\boldsymbol{r}')}\, d^3\boldsymbol{r}\, d^3\boldsymbol{r}'. \end{aligned} \qquad (XVIII.5.9)$$

If we choose ϕ_0 as a plane incident wave—that is, a delta function—then (*XVIII.5.8*) becomes

$$\phi(\boldsymbol{p}) = \delta(\boldsymbol{p}_0 - \boldsymbol{p}) + \sum_{n=1}^{\infty} K_n(\boldsymbol{p}, \boldsymbol{p}_0). \qquad (XVIII.5.10)$$

The kernel of the integral equation in momentum space is

$$K(\mathbf{p}, \mathbf{p}') = \langle \mathbf{p}|K|\mathbf{p}'\rangle = \int \langle \mathbf{p}|G_0|\mathbf{p}''\rangle\langle \mathbf{p}''|H'|\mathbf{p}'\rangle\, d^3\mathbf{p}''. \qquad (XVIII.5.11)$$

It can further be simplified either by direct integration in coordinate space or by using the definition (*XVII.1.4*) of the Green's function and writing

$$\langle \mathbf{p}|G_0|\mathbf{p}''\rangle = \langle \mathbf{p}\left|\frac{1}{E - H_0}\right|\mathbf{p}''\rangle = \frac{\delta(\mathbf{p} - \mathbf{p}'')}{E - \dfrac{\mathbf{p}^2}{2m}} = \frac{2m}{\hbar^2}\frac{\delta(\mathbf{p} - \mathbf{p}'')}{k_0^2 - \mathbf{k}^2 + i\epsilon}.$$

Hence (*XVIII.4.11*) becomes

$$K(\mathbf{p}, \mathbf{p}') = \frac{2m}{\hbar^2}\frac{\langle \mathbf{p}|H'|\mathbf{p}'\rangle}{k_0^2 - \mathbf{k}^2}, \qquad (XVIII.5.12)$$

where $k_0^2 = 2mE/\hbar^2$ and $\mathbf{k}^2 = \mathbf{p}^2/\hbar^2$; the positive imaginary part $i\epsilon$, as before, serves to make the integration over $\mathbf{p}$ well defined, so that the kernel K corresponds to outgoing waves only.

A further useful relation is given by

$$\int K_n(\mathbf{p}, \mathbf{p})\, d^3\mathbf{p} = \int K_n(\mathbf{r}, \mathbf{r})\, d^3\mathbf{r}, \qquad (XVIII.5.13)$$

which follows from

$$\begin{aligned}\int \langle \mathbf{p}|K_n|\mathbf{p}\rangle\, d^3\mathbf{p} &= \int \langle \mathbf{p}|\mathbf{r}\rangle K_n(\mathbf{r}, \mathbf{r}')\langle \mathbf{r}'|\mathbf{p}\rangle\, d^3\mathbf{r}\, d^3\mathbf{r}'\, d^3\mathbf{p}\\ &= \left[\frac{1}{2\pi\hbar}\right]^3 \int e^{-(i/\hbar)\mathbf{p}\cdot\mathbf{r} + (i/\hbar)\mathbf{p}\cdot\mathbf{r}'}\, d^3\mathbf{p}\, d^3\mathbf{r}\, d^3\mathbf{r}'\, K_n(\mathbf{r}, \mathbf{r}')\\ &= \int \delta(\mathbf{r} - \mathbf{r}')K_n(\mathbf{r}, \mathbf{r}')\, d^3\mathbf{r}\, d^3\mathbf{r}' = \int K_n(\mathbf{r}, \mathbf{r})\, d^3\mathbf{r}.\end{aligned}$$

We also have

$$K_{n+1}(\mathbf{p}, \mathbf{p}') = \int K_n(\mathbf{p}, \mathbf{q})K(\mathbf{q}, \mathbf{p}')\, d^3\mathbf{q}. \qquad (XVIII.5.14)$$

The scattering amplitude can easily be obtained from (*XVIII.5.10*) and (*XVIII.5.14*), as in Section XVII.1.B, in the form

$$f(\theta) = -\frac{1}{4\pi}\sum_{n=1}^{\infty}\frac{2m}{\hbar^2}\int \langle \mathbf{p}_0|H'|\mathbf{p}'\rangle K_{n-1}(\mathbf{p}', \mathbf{p})\, d^3\mathbf{p}', \qquad (XVIII.5.15)$$

where $K_0 = \delta(\mathbf{p}' - \mathbf{p})$. We have thus expressed the scattering amplitude as an infinite series in powers of the potential strength.

The expansions (*XVIII.5.7*) and (*XVIII.5.15*) for $f(\theta)$ can readily be obtained from the scattering amplitude operator, defined by

$$f = q[|\boldsymbol{\Psi}\rangle\langle\boldsymbol{\Psi}_0| - |\boldsymbol{\Psi}_0\rangle\langle\boldsymbol{\Psi}_0|], \qquad (XVIII.5.16)$$

where the position operator q, or

$$q = \sqrt{(q_1^2 + q_2^2 + q_3^2)},$$

is defined by (*V.1.1*) with eigenvalue r and eigenstate $|\mathbf{r}\rangle$. The state vectors

$|\Psi\rangle$ and $|\Psi_0\rangle$ are those appearing in the wave equation (*XVII.1.7*). The operator (*XVIII.5.16*) can also be written as

$$f = q[(1 - G_0H')^{-1} - 1]|\Psi_0\rangle\langle\Psi_0|. \qquad (XVIII.5.17)$$

By using the operator f, the differential cross-section can be defined, for large r, as

$$\sigma(\theta) = |\langle r|f|r\rangle|^2. \qquad (XVIII.5.18)$$

XVIII.5.A Expansion in Spherical Harmonics

The expansion of $1/R \exp(ikr)$ in spherical harmonics is given* by

$$\frac{1}{R}\exp(ikr) = \pi \sum_{l=0}^{\infty} \left(l + \frac{1}{2}\right) G_l(r, r')P_l(\cos\theta), \qquad (XVIII.5.19)$$

where θ is the angle between the position vectors $\boldsymbol{r}$ and $\boldsymbol{r}'$ and, for $r' > r$,

$$G_l(r, r') = \frac{1}{\sqrt{(rr')}} J_{l+1/2}(kr)[(-1)^l J_{-l-1/2}(kr') + iJ_{l+1/2}(kr')].$$

For $r > r'$ the function G is defined by interchanging r and r'. Introducing the expansions

$$\psi(\boldsymbol{r}) = \sum_{l=0}^{\infty} \phi_l(r)P_l(\cos\theta), \qquad \psi_0(\boldsymbol{r}) = \sum_{l=0}^{\infty} f_l(r)P_l(\cos\theta)$$

in the wave equation (*XVII.1.13*), we obtain

$$\sum_{l=0}^{\infty} \phi_l(r)P_l(\cos\theta) = \sum_{l=0}^{\infty} f_l(r)P_l(\cos\theta) - \frac{2m}{\hbar^2}\frac{1}{4}\sum_{l,s=0}^{\infty}$$

$$\int \left(l + \frac{1}{2}\right) G_l(r, r')P_l(\cos\omega)H'(r')r'^2\,dr'\phi_s(r')P_s(\cos\theta')\sin\theta'\,d\theta'\,d\phi',$$

where the angle ω between $\boldsymbol{r}$ and $\boldsymbol{r}'$ is given by

$$\cos\omega = \cos\theta\cos\theta' + \sin\theta\sin\theta'\cos(\phi - \phi'),$$

$$P_l(\cos\omega) = \frac{4\pi}{2l+1}\sum_{m=-l}^{l} Y_{lm}^*(\theta', \phi')Y_{lm}(\theta, \phi),$$

$$P_s(\cos\theta') = \sqrt{\left(\frac{4\pi}{2s+1}\right)}\, Y_{s0}(\theta', \phi').$$

Hence, using the orthogonality property (*IV.3.21*) of spherical harmonics and also (*IV.2.27*), we obtain the integral equation

$$\phi_l(r) = f_l(r) - \frac{\pi m}{\hbar^2}\int_0^{\infty} G_l(r, r')V(r')\phi_l(r')r'^2\,dr', \qquad (XVIII.5.20)$$

---

* G. N. Watson, *Theory of Bessel Functions*, Cambridge Univ. Press, Cambridge, 1944, p. 366.

where $f_l(r)$ [see (IV.3.22)] is given by

$$f_l(r) = i^l(2l+1)\sqrt{\left(\frac{\pi}{2kr}\right)}\,J_{l+1/2}(kr).$$

Equation (*XVIII.5.20*) for the radial wave functions was derived by Jost and Pais. It is an equation for partial waves and is therefore suitable only for scattering processes where only a few partial waves are needed for a good estimate of the cross-section. This type of equation is not suitable for central potentials with long tails (like a Coulomb scattering), where a complete set of partial waves is required for a correct calculation of the cross-section. For nuclear interactions (nucleon-nucleon, nucleon-nucleus scattering) where usually—depending on the energy of the incident beam and the final state interaction—the first few partial waves are sufficient to describe the scattering, equation (*XVIII.5.20*) may be found quite useful.

Consider an S state ($l = 0$) scattering and the corresponding integral equation

$$\phi_0 = f_0 - \frac{\pi m}{\hbar^2}\int_0^\infty G_0(r, r')V(r')\phi_0(r')r'^2\,dr',$$

where, since $r > r'$,

$$\begin{aligned}\pi r'^2 G_0(r, r') &= \frac{\pi r'^2}{\sqrt{(rr')}}J_{1/2}(kr')[J_{-1/2}(kr) + iJ_{1/2}(kr)]\\ &= \frac{\pi r'^2}{\sqrt{(rr')}}\sqrt{\left[\frac{2}{\pi kr'}\right]}\sqrt{\left[\frac{2}{\pi kr}\right]}\frac{1}{2i}[e^{ikr'} - e^{-ikr'}]e^{ikr}\\ &= \frac{r'}{ikr}[e^{ik(r+r')} - e^{ik|r-r'|}]\end{aligned}$$

and $f_0 = \sin kr/kr$. Putting $r\phi_0(r) = \phi(r)$ we get

$$\phi(r) = \frac{\sin kr}{k} + e^{ikr}\frac{im}{k\hbar^2}\int_0^\infty g(r, r')V(r')\phi(r')\,dr', \qquad (XVIII.5.21)$$

where

$$g(r, r') = e^{ikr'} - e^{ik|r-r'|-ikr}, \qquad (XVIII.5.22)$$

and the equation contains a boundary condition where $\phi(r) = 0$ for $r = 0$.

The asymptotic form of $\phi(r)$, for large r, is

$$\phi(r) \cong \frac{\sin kr}{k} + e^{ikr}f(\theta), \qquad (XVIII.5.23)$$

where

$$f(\theta) = -\frac{2m}{k\hbar^2}\int_0^\infty \sin kr\,V(r)\phi(r)\,dr \qquad (XVIII.5.24)$$

is the eigenvalue of the $\boldsymbol{T}$ matrix corresponding to zero angular momentum and wave number k. Calculation of the scattering cross-section requires either the use of Born expansion or one of the methods discussed in later sections.

XVIII.5.B. Dispersion of S Waves

We shall consider a collision process where dispersion can play an important role. This type of scattering resembles optical dispersion by a medium containing damped oscillators with various natural frequencies. Nucleon-nucleus and meson-nucleus collisions, as many-body phenomena, are affected by the contributions of dispersive scattering. A simple case refers to the dispersive scattering of S waves. We will discuss this in some detail.

Let us assume that the potential can be prescribed up to an arbitrary parameter a such that $V(r) = 0$ for $r > a$. Therefore the integral equation (*XVIII.5.21*) for S waves becomes

$$\phi(r) = \frac{\sin kr}{k} + e^{ikr} \frac{im}{k\hbar^2} \int_0^a g(r, r')V(r')\phi(r')\,dr'. \qquad (XVIII.5.25)$$

If $r = a$, then $g(r, r')$ becomes $g(a, r') = 2i \sin kr'$, so

$$\phi(a) = \frac{\sin ka}{k} + e^{ika} f(\theta). \qquad (XVIII.5.26)$$

By comparing this with (*XVIII.5.23*) and (*XVIII.5.24*), we see that the scattering amplitude is given by

$$f(\theta) = \left[\phi(a) - \frac{\sin ka}{k}\right] e^{-ika}. \qquad (XVIII.5.27)$$

We note that the wave function outside the potential (that is, for $r > a$) is given by the right side of (*XVIII.5.23*) and equals the wave function given by (*XVIII.5.25*) at the point $r = a$.

Let us assume the existence of the eigenfunctions $u_s(r)$ defined over the interval $0 \leqq r \leqq a$ and also the corresponding eigenvalues k_s as solutions of the homogeneous integral equation

$$u_s(r) = \frac{im}{\hbar^2 k_s} e^{ik_s r} \int_0^a g_s(r, r')V(r')u_s(r')\,dr', \qquad (XVIII.5.28)$$

where k_s will, in general, be complex and a function of k, and where $g_s(r, r')$ is obtained from $g(r, r')$ by replacing k by k_s.

The theory of dispersive scattering of S waves was first worked out by Kapur and Peierls.* Here we shall follow the method of the integral equation which contains all the boundary conditions of the problem. To obtain the differential equations corresponding to the integral equations (*XVIII.5.25*) and (*XVIII.5.28*), we introduce the function $\epsilon(r, r')$ and its differential coefficient by

---

* S. Kapur and R. Peierls, *Proc. Roy. Soc. London, A*, **166** (1938), 277.

$$\epsilon(r - r') = \begin{cases} 1 & \text{for } r > r', \\ -1 & \text{for } r < r', \end{cases}$$

$$\frac{d\epsilon}{dr} = 2\delta(r - r'),$$

and obtain

$$g(r, r') = e^{ikr'} - e^{ik[(r-r')\epsilon(r-r')-r]},$$

$$\frac{dg}{dr} = ik[1 - \epsilon(r - r')]e^{ik[(r-r')\epsilon(r-r')-r]},$$

$$\frac{d^2g}{dr^2} = -2ike^{-ikr}\delta(r - r') - 2ik\frac{dg}{dr}.$$

Hence the corresponding differential equations are

$$\frac{d^2\phi}{dr^2} + \left[k^2 - \frac{2m}{\hbar^2}V(r)\right]\phi = 0, \qquad (XVIII.5.29)$$

$$\frac{d^2u_s}{dr^2} + \left[k_s^2 - \frac{2m}{\hbar^2}V(r)\right]u_s = 0. \qquad (XVIII.5.30)$$

As seen from the integral equations, both ϕ and u_s vanish at the point $r = 0$. From the integral equations we also obtain the boundary conditions:

$$\left[\frac{du_s}{dr}\right]_a = ik_s u_s(a), \qquad (XVIII.5.31)$$

$$\left[\frac{d\phi}{dr}\right]_a = e^{-ika} + ik\phi(a). \qquad (XVIII.5.32)$$

We shall assume that the eigenfunctions $u_s(r)$ constitute a complete set in the interval $0 \leqq r \leqq a$ and expand $\phi(r)$ in the usual way,

$$\phi(r) = \sum_n c_n u_n(r), \qquad (XVIII.5.33)$$

where the boundary condition $\phi(0) = 0$ is satisfied. By multiplying equations (*XVIII.5.29*) and (*XVIII.5.30*) by u_s and ϕ, respectively, and subtracting the resulting expressions, we obtain

$$\frac{d}{dr}\left[u_s\frac{d\phi}{dr} - \phi\frac{du_s}{dr}\right] = (k_s^2 - k^2)u_s\phi.$$

Integrating both sides in $0 \leqq r \leqq a$, we get

$$u_s(a)\left[\frac{d\phi}{dr}\right]_a - \phi(a)\left[\frac{du_s}{dr}\right]_a = (k_s^2 - k^2)C_sN_s, \qquad (XVIII.5.34)$$

where

$$N_s = \int_0^a [u_s(r)]^2\,dr, \qquad \int_0^a |u_s|^2\,dr = 1, \qquad \int_0^a u_s u_s'\,dr = 0,$$

and $k_s^2 \neq k_{s'}^2$. Using the boundary conditions (*XVIII.5.31*) and (*XVIII.5.32*), we obtain

$$C_s = \frac{u_s(a)e^{-ika}}{N_s(k_s^2 - k^2)}. \qquad (XVIII.5.35)$$

Hence

$$\phi(a) = \sum_s \frac{[u_s(a)]^2 e^{-ika}}{N_s(k_s^2 - k^2)}. \qquad (XVIII.5.36)$$

Thus the total cross-section,

$$\sigma = \int |f(\theta)|^2 \, d\Omega = 4\pi |f(\theta)|^2,$$

as follows from (*XVIII.5.36*) and (*XVIII.5.27*), is given by

$$\sigma = \frac{\pi}{k^2} \left| \sum_s \frac{W_s^2 e^{-2ika}}{N_s(E_s - E - \frac{1}{2}i\Gamma_s)} - 2 \sin ka \, e^{-ika} \right|^2, \qquad (XVIII.5.37)$$

where we take

$$k_s^2 = \frac{2m}{\hbar^2}\left(E_s - \frac{1}{2}i\Gamma_s\right), \qquad k^2 = \frac{2m}{\hbar^2} E, \qquad W_s^2 = \frac{k^2\hbar^2}{m}[u_s(a)]^2. \qquad (XVIII.5.38)$$

The use of the boundary condition (*XVIII.5.31*) yields

$$\Gamma_s = |W_s|^2. \qquad (XVIII.5.39)$$

The cross-section is the sum of two terms. The sum in the first term is the characteristic of dispersion theory for a set of oscillators with energy levels E_s and of natural width Γ_s. The second term in (*XVIII.5.37*) represents "potential scattering" due to the finite extension of the potential. If the natural width of the oscillators vanishes, then the scattering cross-section is just

$$\sigma = \frac{4\pi \sin^2 ka}{k^2},$$

so it represents the amplitude scattered from an impenetrable sphere of radius a. For an incident wave with wavelength much larger than the radius a, the potential scattering cross-section reduces to

$$\sigma = 4\pi a^2,$$

which is just the geometrical cross-section.

XVIII.6. Application of Fredholm's Method to Scattering Theory

Fredholm's method* for the solution of integral equations can be applied to an investigation on the validity of a Born approximation in scattering problems and it can also serve for a deeper understanding of scattering proc-

* W. V. Lovitt, *Linear Integral Equations*, Dover, New York, 1950.

esses. In this section we shall develop Fredholm's method in an operator formalism, suitable for application to nonrelativistic as well as to relativistic problems.

Consider a one-dimensional integral equation,

$$u(x) = f(x) + \lambda \int_a^b K(x, x')u(x')\, dx'. \qquad (XVIII.6.1)$$

In Fredholm's method the solutions of this integral equation are expressed as a ratio of two infinite series and, for a well-behaving kernel $K(x, x')$, these solutions are valid for all values of λ. The method consists of replacing the integral over the interval (a, b) by the limit of a finite sum. Thus, putting

$$h = \frac{b-a}{n}, \qquad x'_n = a + nh,$$

for $n = 1, 2, \cdots$, we divide the interval (a, b) into n equal parts. Equation $(XVIII.6.1)$ can now be replaced by the approximate expression

$$u(x) - \lambda h \sum_{i=1}^{n} K(x, x'_i)u(x'_i) = f(x), \qquad (XVIII.6.2)$$

valid for every value of x. Equation $(XVIII.6.2)$ is valid also if we choose $x = x'_1, x'_2, \cdots, x'_n$ and obtain n linear equations,

$$|u\rangle - \lambda h K|u\rangle = |f\rangle, \qquad (XVIII.6.3)$$

where

$$|u\rangle = \begin{bmatrix} u(x_1) \\ u(x_2) \\ \cdot \\ \cdot \\ \cdot \\ u(x_n) \end{bmatrix}, \qquad |f\rangle = \begin{bmatrix} f(x_1) \\ f(x_2) \\ \cdot \\ \cdot \\ \cdot \\ f(x_n) \end{bmatrix},$$

and

$$K = [K_{ij}] = \begin{bmatrix} K(x_1, x_1), & K(x_1, x_2), & \cdots, & K(x_1, x_n) \\ K(x_2, x_1), & K(x_2, x_2), & \cdots, & K(x_2, x_n) \\ \cdots & \cdots & \cdots, & \cdots \\ \cdots & \cdots & \cdots, & \cdots \\ \cdots & \cdots & \cdots, & \cdots \\ K(x_n, x_1), & K(x_n, x_2), & \cdots, & K(x_n, x_n) \end{bmatrix}. \qquad (XVIII.6.4)$$

The existence of solutions for $(XVIII.6.3)$ require that the determinant

$$\Delta = \det (I - \lambda h K) \qquad (XVIII.6.5)$$

be finite. The linear system of equations are solved by

$$u_i = \frac{1}{\Delta} \sum_{j=1}^{n} \Delta_{ij} f_j, \qquad (XVIII.6.6)$$

where Δ_{ij} denotes the first minor of the element in the ith row and jth column of Δ.

The solution of the integral equation is to be obtained by letting n increase indefinitely. Therefore we need to know the limits of Δ and Δ_{ij} as n tends to infinity. From (*XVIII.6.5*) we have

$$\Delta = 1 - \lambda \sum_{i=1}^{n} hK_{ii} + \frac{\lambda^2}{2!} \sum_{i,j}^{n} h^2 \begin{vmatrix} K_{ii} & K_{ij} \\ K_{ji} & K_{jj} \end{vmatrix} + \cdots + (-1)^n h^n \lambda^n \begin{bmatrix} K_{11} & K_{12} & \cdots & K_{1n} \\ K_{21} & K_{22} & \cdots & K_{2n} \\ \cdots & \cdots & \cdots & \\ \cdots & \cdots & \cdots & \\ K_{n1} & K_{n2} & \cdots & K_{nn} \end{bmatrix}. \qquad (XVIII.6.7)$$

Hence, for $n \longrightarrow \infty$, we may, formally, write Fredholm's determinant $D(\lambda)$ in the form

$$D(\lambda) = \lim_{n\to\infty} \Delta = 1 + \sum_{n=1}^{\infty} \frac{(-\lambda)^n}{n!} \int_a^b dx_1 \cdots \int_a^b dx_n \times \begin{bmatrix} K(x_1, x_1), & K(x_1, x_2), & \cdots, & K(x_1, x_n) \\ K(x_2, x_1), & K(x_2, x_2), & \cdots, & K(x_2, x_n) \\ \cdots & \cdots & \cdots & \cdots \\ \cdots & \cdots & \cdots & \cdots \\ K(x_n, x_1), & K(x_n, x_2), & \cdots, & K(x_n, x_n) \end{bmatrix} \qquad (XVIII.6.8)$$

By using theorem 6 of Section I.5.A we can write $D(\lambda)$ in a closed form. Thus, from

$$1 - \lambda K = \exp\,[\log\,(1 - \lambda K)],$$

it follows that

$$D(\lambda) = \exp\,\{\mathrm{tr}\,[\log\,(1 - \lambda K)]\}, \qquad (XVIII.6.9)$$

where now K is an operator in infinite-dimensional space and its trace is defined as

$$\mathrm{tr}\,K = \int \langle 1|K|1\rangle\, d1 = \int K(1, 1)\, d1.$$

The trace operation is defined over the limits of the integration in the integral equation. A point with coordinates x_1, x_2, x_3 in three-dimensional (or four-dimensional) space is represented by a numeral. In this way we are extending Fredholm's one-dimensional determinant to the case of higher-dimensional spaces. The vectors $|1\rangle$, $|2\rangle$, and so on, are to be regarded as the ket vectors of the infinite-dimensional space of the type introduced in the previous chapters. Thus

$$\mathrm{tr}\,K^2 = \int \langle 1|K|2\rangle\langle 2|K|1\rangle\, d1\, d2 = \iint K(1, 2)K(2, 1)\, d1\, d2,$$

where, for example, in three-dimensional space we have

$$K(1, 2) = K(\mathbf{r}_1, \mathbf{r}_2), \qquad d1\, d2 = d^3\mathbf{r}_1\, d^3\mathbf{r}_2.$$

We can, formally, expand the operatoı log $(1 - \lambda K)$ as

$$\log (1 - \lambda K) = -\sum_{n=1}^{\infty} \frac{(\lambda K)^n}{n},$$

and obtain

$$\mathrm{tr}\,[\log (1 - \lambda K)] = -\lambda \int K(1, 1)\, d1 - \tfrac{1}{2}\lambda \iint K(1, 2)K(2, 1) \times d1\, d2 - \tfrac{1}{3}\lambda^3 \int K(1, 2)K(2, 3)K(3, 1)\, d1\, d2\, d3 + \cdots .$$

Hence it is easy to verify that the expansion of (*XVIII.6.9*) yields (*XVIII.6.8*).

In a similar way one can show that the limit of Δ_{ij} as $n \longrightarrow \infty$ is given by

$$\lim_{n\to\infty} \Delta_{ij} = D(1, 2, \lambda) = \langle 1|D^{(1)}|2\rangle,$$

where $D^{(1)}$ is an operator for Fredholm's first minor $D(1, 2; \lambda)$, which is given by

$$D(1, 2; \lambda) = \lambda K(1, 2) - \lambda^2 \int \begin{vmatrix} K(1, 2), & K(1, 2') \\ K(2', 2), & K(2', 2') \end{vmatrix} d2' + \frac{\lambda^3}{2!} \iint \begin{vmatrix} K(1, 2), & K(1, 2'), & K(1, 3') \\ K(2', 2), & K(2', 2'), & K(2', 3') \\ K(3', 2), & K(3', 2'), & K(3', 3') \end{vmatrix} d2'\, d3' + \cdots . \qquad (XVIII.6.10)$$

From (*XVIII.6.8*) and (*XVIII.6.10*) we may easily obtain the relation

$$\lambda \frac{dD(\lambda)}{d\lambda} = -\int D(1, 1; \lambda)\, d1 = -\,\mathrm{tr}\, D^{(1)}. \qquad (XVIII.6.11)$$

Furthermore, by differentiating (*XVIII.6.9*) we get another relation,

$$\frac{dD(\lambda)}{d\lambda} = -\,\mathrm{tr}\,[(1 - \lambda K)^{-1}K]D(\lambda). \qquad (XVIII.6.12)$$

On comparing (*XVIII.6.11*) and (*XVIII.6.12*) we get the operator equations

$$D^{(1)} = \lambda(1 - \lambda K)^{-1}KD(\lambda) = \lambda K(1 - \lambda K)^{-1}D(\lambda) \qquad (XVIII.6.13)$$

for the first minor, so the ratio of $D^{(1)}/D(\lambda)$ is given by

$$\frac{D^{(1)}}{D(\lambda)} = \lambda(1 - \lambda K)^{-1}K = \lambda K(1 - \lambda K)^{-1}. \qquad (XVIII.6.14)$$

We can now use (*XVIII.6.13*) and obtain Fredholm's first and second fundamental relations. From (*XVIII.6.13*) we have the operator equations

$$D^{(1)}(1 - \lambda K) = \lambda KD(\lambda), \qquad (1 - \lambda K)D^{(1)} = \lambda KD(\lambda).$$

Hence, taking the representatives, we get

$$D(1, 2; \lambda) = \lambda K(1, 2)D(\lambda) + \lambda \int K(3, 2)D(1, 3; \lambda)\, d3 \qquad (XVIII.6.15)$$

and

$$D(1, 2; \lambda) = \lambda K(1, 2)D(\lambda) + \lambda \int K(1, 3)D(3, 2; \lambda)\, d3, \qquad (XVIII.6.16)$$

which are Fredholm's first and second fundamental relations, respectively.

Now consider the operator form of a linear inhomogeneous integral equation

$$|u\rangle = |u_0\rangle + \lambda K|u\rangle, \qquad (XVIII.6.17)$$

which can be written as

$$|u\rangle = (1 - \lambda K)^{-1}|u_0\rangle.$$

Operating by λK on both sides, we get

$$\lambda K|u\rangle = \lambda K(1 - \lambda K)^{-1}|u_0\rangle$$

and from (*XVIII.6.17*), we write

$$|u\rangle = |u_0\rangle + \lambda K(1 - \lambda K)^{-1}|u_0\rangle. \qquad (XVIII.6.18)$$

Thus, from (*XVIII.6.14*), it follows that the integral equation (*XVIII.6.17*) is, at least formally, solved by

$$|u\rangle = |u_0\rangle + \frac{D^{(1)}}{D(\lambda)}|u_0\rangle. \qquad (XVIII.6.19)$$

Taking the representatives we obtain the expression

$$u(1) = u_0(1) + \frac{1}{D(\lambda)} \int D(1, 2; \lambda)u_0(2)\, d2 \qquad (XVIII.6.20)$$

as the solution of the actual integral equation, where

$$u(1) = \langle 1|u\rangle, \qquad f(1) = \langle 1|f\rangle, \qquad D(1, 2; \lambda) = \langle 1|D^{(1)}|2\rangle.$$

Finally, let us consider the homogeneous integral equation

$$u(1) = \lambda \int K(1, 2)u(2)\, d2. \qquad (XVIII.6.21)$$

On setting $u_0 = 0$ in (*XVIII.6.20*) we see that for $D(\lambda) \neq 0$ the only solution of (*XVIII.6.21*) is given by $u = 0$. However, if $D(\lambda) = 0$ for a special value of $\lambda = \lambda_0$, then the equation

$$u(1) = \lambda_0 \int K(1, 2)u(2)\, d2$$

has a nonzero solution. This can be seen by putting $\lambda = \lambda_0$ and $D(\lambda_0) = 0$ in (*XVIII.6.14*) and obtaining

$$D(1, 2; \lambda_0) = \lambda_0 \int K(1, 3)D(3, 2; \lambda_0)\, d3. \qquad (XVIII.6.22)$$

If we assume that equation (*XVIII.6.22*) holds for every value of the point 2 and therefore for a fixed value $2 = 2_0$, then we get

$$D(1, 2_0; \lambda_0) = \lambda_0 \int K(1, 3)D(3, 2_0, \lambda_0)\, d3, \qquad (XVIII.6.23)$$

which is just equation (*XVIII.6.21*) with $u(1)$ replaced by $D(1, 2_0; \lambda_0)$. Thus

$$u(1) = D(1, 2_0; \lambda_0) \qquad (XVIII.6.24)$$

is a solution of the homogeneous integral equation corresponding to $\lambda = \lambda_0$ for a fixed point $2 = 2_0$. Here we assume that $D(1, 2; \lambda_0)$ does not vanish for the choice $2 = 2_0$.

Further discussion, especially mathematical justifications of the above summary of Fredholm's method, will not be included here. The interested reader can find satisfactory answers and other details of integral equations in specialized texts.

XVIII.6.A. Expansion of the Scattering Amplitude as a Fredholm Series

The singularity in the kernel of the integral equation (*XVIII.1.7*) does not allow application of Fredholm's method. However, if we iterate it once, then a Fredholm solution for the iterated form of the integral equation does exist.* Thus the integral equation to be solved in terms of a Fredholm series is

$$|\Psi\rangle = (1 + G_0H')|\Psi_0\rangle + \lambda^2 K|\Psi\rangle = |\Phi_0\rangle + \lambda^2 K|\Psi\rangle, \qquad (XVIII.6.25)$$

where

$$|\Phi_0\rangle = (1 + G_0H')|\Psi_0\rangle, \qquad K = \frac{1}{\lambda^2} G_0H'G_0H' \qquad (XVIII.6.26)$$

and λ is the basic parameter of the scattering process (for example potential strength). From the definition (*XVII.1.12*) of the Green's function, it follows that the representative of the kernel operator K is given by

$$K(\boldsymbol{r}, \boldsymbol{r}') = \langle \boldsymbol{r}|K|\boldsymbol{r}'\rangle$$

$$= \frac{1}{\lambda^2} V(\boldsymbol{r}') \left[\frac{2m}{4\pi\hbar^2}\right]^2 \int \frac{e^{ik_0[|\boldsymbol{r} - \boldsymbol{r}''| + |\boldsymbol{r}'' - \boldsymbol{r}'|]}}{|\boldsymbol{r} - \boldsymbol{r}''|\,|\boldsymbol{r}'' - \boldsymbol{r}'|} V(\boldsymbol{r}'')\, d^3\boldsymbol{r}'', \qquad (XVIII.6.27)$$

which has no singularity at $\boldsymbol{r} = \boldsymbol{r}'$. The asymptotic form of $K(\boldsymbol{r}, \boldsymbol{r}')$ for large r is given by

$$K(\boldsymbol{r}, \boldsymbol{r}') \cong -\frac{2m}{4\pi\hbar^2\lambda^2} V(\boldsymbol{r}') \frac{e^{ik_0r}}{r} \int e^{-i\boldsymbol{k}\cdot\boldsymbol{r}''} G_0(\boldsymbol{r}' - \boldsymbol{r}'') V(\boldsymbol{r}'')\, d^3\boldsymbol{r}'', \qquad (XVIII.6.28)$$

where the propagation vector $\boldsymbol{k}$ after scattering is $\boldsymbol{k} = k_0\hat{\boldsymbol{r}}$.

We may now write the Fredholm solution of (*XVIII.6.26*) in the form

$$|\Psi\rangle = |\Phi_0\rangle + \frac{1}{D(\lambda^2, k_0)} D^{(1)}|\Phi_0\rangle, \qquad (XVIII.6.29)$$

where Fredholm's determinant $D(\lambda^2, k_0)$ and the operator of the first minor $D^{(1)}$ are to be formed with respect to the kernel K defined by (*XVIII.6.26*).

---

* N. N. Khuri, *Phys. Rev.*, **107** (1957), 1148.

Hence, by taking the representatives, we obtain the wave function $\psi(\boldsymbol{r})$:

$$\psi(\boldsymbol{r}) = \phi_0(\boldsymbol{r}) + \frac{1}{D(\lambda^2, k_0)} \int D(\boldsymbol{r}, \boldsymbol{r}'; \lambda^2, k_0)\phi_0(\boldsymbol{r}')\, d^3\boldsymbol{r}', \qquad (XVIII.6.30)$$

where

$$\psi(\boldsymbol{r}) = \langle \boldsymbol{r}|\boldsymbol{\Psi}\rangle, \qquad \psi_0(\boldsymbol{r}) = \langle \boldsymbol{r}|\boldsymbol{\Psi}_0\rangle,$$

$$\phi_0(\boldsymbol{r}) = \langle \boldsymbol{r}|\boldsymbol{\Phi}_0\rangle = \psi_0(\boldsymbol{r}) + \int G_0(\boldsymbol{r} - \boldsymbol{r}')V(\boldsymbol{r}')\psi_0(\boldsymbol{r}')\, d^3\boldsymbol{r}', \qquad (XVIII.6.31)$$

$$\psi_0(\boldsymbol{r}) = e^{i\boldsymbol{k}_0\cdot\boldsymbol{r}}.$$

Jost and Pais have shown that the series solution (*XVIII.6.30*) for the wave function, with some restrictions on the potential, converges uniformly and absolutely. Moreover, $\psi(\boldsymbol{r})$ has no singularities for real λ and real k (except possibly at $k = 0$).

The scattered wave is

$$\psi_s(\boldsymbol{r}) = \psi(\boldsymbol{r}) - \psi_0(\boldsymbol{r})$$

$$= \int G_0(\boldsymbol{r} - \boldsymbol{r}')V(\boldsymbol{r}')\psi_0(\boldsymbol{r}')\, d^3\boldsymbol{r}' + \frac{1}{D(\lambda^2, k_0)} \int D(\boldsymbol{r}, \boldsymbol{r}', \lambda^2, k_0)\phi_0(\boldsymbol{r}')\, d^3\boldsymbol{r}'. \qquad (XVIII.6.32)$$

Hence the scattering amplitude as a function of k_0 and momentum transfer $q = |\boldsymbol{k} - \boldsymbol{k}_0|$, [see (*XVII.1.24*), where the scattering amplitude is expressed as a function of $|\boldsymbol{k} - \boldsymbol{k}'|$], is obtained as

$$f(k_0, q) = \lim_{r\to\infty} [re^{-ik_0r}\psi_s(\boldsymbol{r})]. \qquad (XVIII.6.33)$$

To find the asymptotic limit we shall use Fredholm's second fundamental relation (*XVIII.6.16*) and the asymptotic form (XVIII.6.28) of $K(\boldsymbol{r}, \boldsymbol{r}')$. Thus

$$re^{-ik_0r}D(\boldsymbol{r}, \boldsymbol{r}'; \lambda^2, k_0)$$

$$\cong -\frac{2m}{4\pi\hbar^2} V(\boldsymbol{r}')D(\lambda^2, k_0) \int e^{-i\boldsymbol{k}\cdot\boldsymbol{r}_1}G_0(\boldsymbol{r}' - \boldsymbol{r}_1)V(\boldsymbol{r}_1)\, d^3\boldsymbol{r}_1 - \frac{2m}{4\pi\hbar^2}$$

$$\times \int e^{-i\boldsymbol{k}\cdot\boldsymbol{r}_1}G_0(\boldsymbol{r}'' - \boldsymbol{r}_1)V(\boldsymbol{r}_1)V(\boldsymbol{r}'')D(\boldsymbol{r}'', \boldsymbol{r}'; \lambda^2, k_0)\, d^3\boldsymbol{r}_1\, d^3\boldsymbol{r}''.$$

Substituting in (*XVIII.6.32*) and (*XVIII.6.33*), we get

$$f(k_0, q) = -\frac{2m}{4\pi\hbar^2}\bar{V}(q) - \frac{2m}{4\pi\hbar^2}\int e^{-i\boldsymbol{k}\cdot\boldsymbol{r}_1}G_0(\boldsymbol{r}' - \boldsymbol{r}_1)V(\boldsymbol{r}')V(\boldsymbol{r}_1)$$

$$\times \phi_0(\boldsymbol{r}')\, d^3\boldsymbol{r}'\, d^3\boldsymbol{r}_1 - \frac{2m}{4\pi\hbar^2}\frac{1}{D(\lambda^2, k_0)}\int e^{-i\boldsymbol{k}\cdot\boldsymbol{r}_1}G_0(\boldsymbol{r}'' - \boldsymbol{r}_1)$$

$$\times V(\boldsymbol{r}_1)V(\boldsymbol{r}'')D(\boldsymbol{r}'', \boldsymbol{r}'; \lambda^2, k_0)\phi_0(\boldsymbol{r}')\, d^3\boldsymbol{r}'\, d^3\boldsymbol{r}_1\, d^3\boldsymbol{r}'', \qquad (XVIII.6.34)$$

where

$$\bar{V}(q) = \int e^{i(\boldsymbol{k}_0 - \boldsymbol{k})\cdot\boldsymbol{r}}V(\boldsymbol{r})\, d^3\boldsymbol{r},$$

$$|\boldsymbol{q}| = |\boldsymbol{k}_0 - k_0\hat{\boldsymbol{r}}| = k_0\sqrt{[2(1 - \cos\theta)]}. \qquad (XVIII.6.35)$$

This completes the formal expansion of $f(k_0, q)$. It has been proved by Khuri that for a large class of potentials and for a complex k_0 the scattering amplitude is an analytic function of k_0, regular in the complex k_0 plane where $\text{Im}k_0 = \kappa > 0$ and also uniformly bounded in the region $\kappa \geqq 0$. On the real axis, $f(k_0, q)$ has branch points at $k_0 = \pm\frac{1}{2}q$; that is, $\theta = \pm\pi$.

For bound states the discussion of the homogeneous integral equation leads to the result that all zeros of $D(\lambda^2, k_0)$ lie on the positive imaginary axis. The corresponding eigenfunctions are the bound-state wave functions.

XVIII.6.B. Remarks on Dispersion Relations

For a nonrelativistic study of dispersion relations and also for more references to the extensive literature on dispersion relations we refer the reader to the paper by Blankenbecler, Goldberger, Khuri, and Treiman.* The method of dispersion relations avoids any form of series expansion, but is based on the analytic properties of the representatives of the S matrix as a whole. It is found that a relation between real and imaginary parts of the S-matrix elements (dispersion relation) contains the information required for the description of a physical process. We must therefore study the analytic properties of the S matrix elements as a function of energy. The basic mathematical tool for dispersion relations is the Cauchy integral formula for an analytic function $f(z)$. Thus from a typical energy denominator,

$$\frac{1}{E' - E - i\epsilon} = P\frac{1}{E' - E} + i\pi\delta(E' - E),$$

we may, for an analytic function $g(E)$, write

$$g(E) = \frac{1}{i\pi} P \int_{-\infty}^{\infty} \frac{g(E')\, dE'}{E' - E}. \qquad (XVIII.6.36)$$

Hence, taking the real part, we obtain a relation between the real and imaginary parts of $g(E)$:

$$\text{Re}\, g(E) = \frac{1}{\pi} P \int \frac{\text{Im}\, g(E')}{E' - E}\, dE'. \qquad (XVIII.6.37)$$

The function $g(E)$, defined by

$$g(E) = f(k_0, q) + \frac{2m}{4\pi\hbar^2} \overline{V}(q),$$

as shown by Khuri, is analytic everywhere in the E plane except for a branch cut on the real positive axis and poles on the negative real axis. Thus if $R_i(q)$

---

* R. Blankenbecler, M. L. Goldberger, N. N. Khuri, and S. B. Treiman, *Ann. Phys.*, **10** (1960), 62.

are the residues of $g(E)$ at the bound states E_i, then we apply Cauchy's formula,

$$\frac{1}{2\pi i}\int_\Gamma \frac{F(z')}{z'-z}\,dz' = \begin{cases} F(z) & \text{if } z \text{ lies inside } \Gamma, \\ 0 & \text{if } z \text{ lies outside } \Gamma, \end{cases}$$

and obtain, for $E_i < 0$,

$$\int_\Gamma \frac{g(E')\,dE'}{E'-E} = 2\pi i \sum_{i=1}^{N} \frac{R_i(q)}{E_i - E}. \qquad (XVIII.6.38)$$

Because G_0H' and $G_0H'G_0H'$ are real for k_0 on the positive imaginary axis, the residues $R_i(q)$ above are real. Noting the negative imaginary part in energy E, formula (*XVIII.6.38*) yields the dispersion relation

$$\operatorname{Re} f(E, q) = \frac{1}{\pi} P \int_0^\infty \frac{\operatorname{Im} f(E', q)}{E'-E}\,dE' + \sum_{i=0}^{N} \frac{R_i(q)}{E - E_i} - \frac{2m}{\pi\hbar^2}\bar{V}(q), \qquad (XVIII.6.39)$$

where N is the number of bound states for potentials satisfying the condition*

$$\int_0^\infty r|V(r)|\,dr = \text{constant}.$$

Investigations on the forward scattering amplitude f have shown† that its imaginary part is proportional to the total cross-section. This is called the "optical theorem." For a meson-nucleon system it is given by

$$\operatorname{Im} f = \frac{|\boldsymbol{p}|}{4\pi}\,\sigma \qquad (XVIII.6.40)$$

and

$$\frac{d\sigma}{d\Omega} = |f|^2,$$

where $\boldsymbol{p}$ is the momentum of the meson.

---

* V. Bargmann, *Proc. Nat. Acad. Sci. U.S.A.*, **38** (1952), 961.
† R. Karplus and M. A. Ruderman, *Phys. Rev.*, **98** (1955), 771.
M. Goldberger, H. Miyazawa, and R. Oehme, *Phys. Rev.*, **100** (1955), 986.
A. Salam, *Nuovo Cimento*, **3** (1956), 424.
A. Salam and W. Gilbert, *Nuovo Cimento*, **3** (1956), 607.
C. Polkinghorn, *Nuovo Cimento*, **4** (1956), 216.

AUTHOR INDEX

SUBJECT INDEX

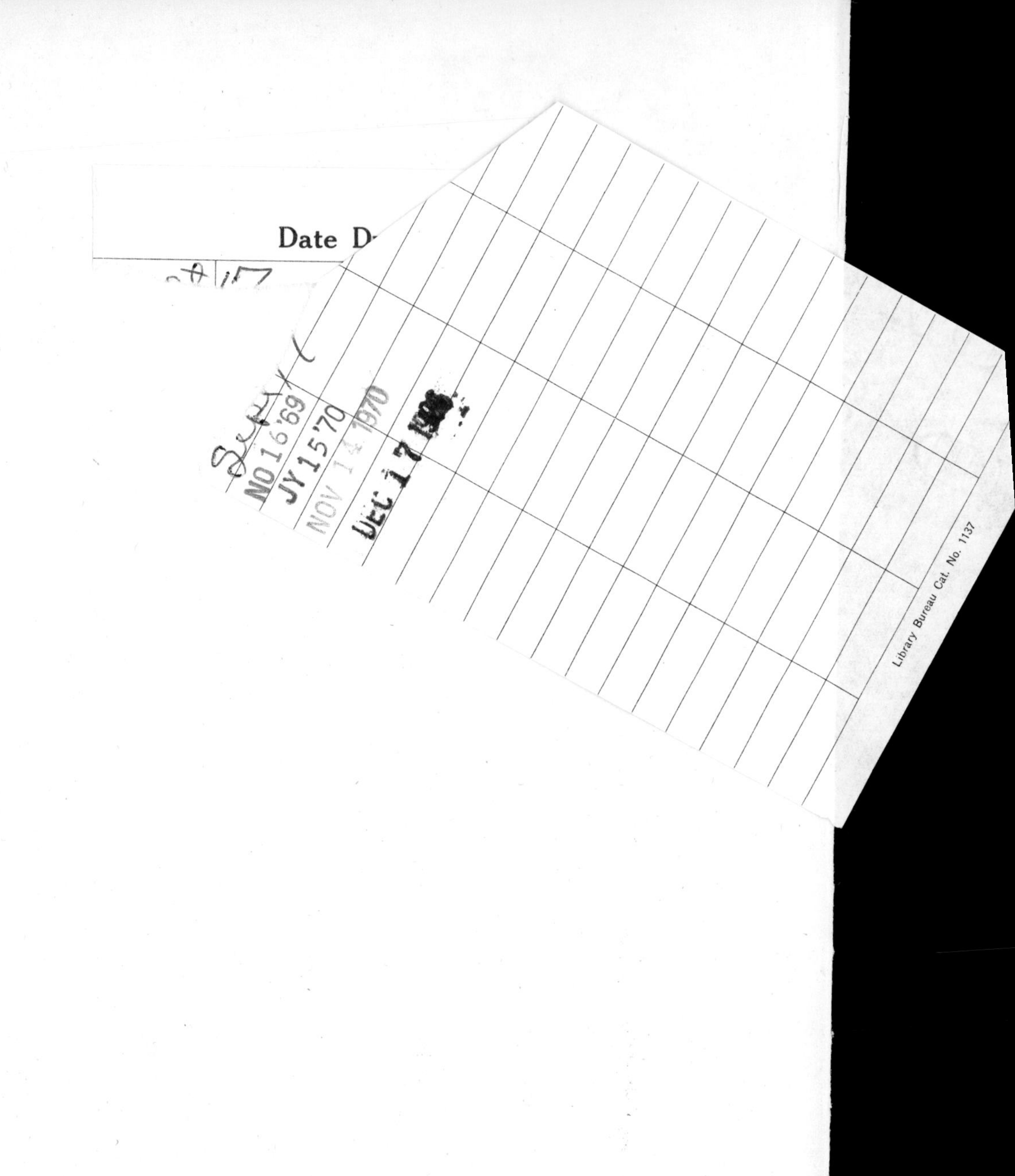
Date D
NO 16 '69
JY 15 '70
NOV 14 1970
Library Bureau Cat. No. 1137